High-resolution Nuclear Magnetic Resonance

High-resolution Nuclear Magnetic Resonance

J. A. POPLE

NATIONAL PHYSICAL LABORATORY
TEDDINGTON, ENGLAND

W. G. SCHNEIDER AND H. J. BERNSTEIN

NATIONAL RESEARCH COUNCIL
OTTAWA, CANADA

McGRAW-HILL BOOK COMPANY, INC.

New York   Toronto   London

1959

HIGH-RESOLUTION NUCLEAR MAGNETIC RESONANCE

VII

50516

THE MAPLE PRESS COMPANY, YORK, PA.

PREFACE

The subject of nuclear magnetic resonance has expanded in a remarkable manner since the first experiments on bulk matter in 1945. Early high-resolution work on liquids indicated that magnetic nuclei could detect small changes in chemical environment and promised a number of important applications in various branches of chemistry and chemical physics. In the last few years this promise has been fulfilled and the rapid development of instrumentation has made nuclear magnetic resonance one of the most powerful tools for investigating chemical problems. It is now widely used by organic chemists to assist in structure determination and by physical and inorganic chemists to investigate such properties as isomerism, tautomeric equilibriums, relaxation processes, reaction rates, and hydrogen bonding. In view of the great current interest in the field, the authors have felt that many chemists and physicists would appreciate a book which gives a fairly full account of the principles underlying high-resolution NMR work, the range of NMR application, and a survey of achievement to date. This book is an attempt to meet this need. Only high-resolution work on liquids and gases is included, and no attempt is made to cover the subject of broad-line nuclear magnetic resonance of solids.

The book is divided into two parts: Part 1 describes the basic principles of the subject and the nature of the apparatus used, and Part 2 surveys the applications to chemical problems. In the theoretical parts, emphasis is laid on those aspects, such as spectral analysis and the interpretation of chemical shifts, which are likely to be important in connection with chemical applications. Although a full study of the subject inevitably requires some detailed quantum-mechanical knowledge, we feel that many of the topics can be appreciated semiquantitatively without it. With this in mind some of the chapters in Part 1 have been written in a more qualitative manner. The reader interested in a general introduction to the subject should read Chap. 1, the first part of Chap. 3 on the magnetic-resonance method, parts of Chap. 4 on apparatus, and Chap. 5 on the principal features of high-resolution spectra. A list of general review articles, together with an extensive bibliography of individual research contributions, is given at the end of the book.

In Part 2 an attempt is made to incorporate most of the high-resolution studies that have been published to the time of writing, although some omissions are unavoidable. A considerable amount of unpublished material from the authors' laboratories has also been included. Inevitably some of the experimental data will rapidly become outdated by new work in the field. A large part of the experimental material described is concerned with the magnetic resonance of protons. To some extent this reflects the interests of the authors, but there is no doubt that protons have been and will continue to be the most important nuclei studied by this technique.

We are indebted to A. A. Bothner-By, H. Finegold, R. E. Glick, M. Karplus, P. C. Lauterbur, S. Meiboom, W. D. Phillips, H. Primas, R. E. Richards, N. Sheppard, G. V. D. Tiers, and J. S. Waugh for sending us copies of unpublished manuscripts. We also wish to thank R. U. Lemieux, H. C. Longuet-Higgins, and R. K. Kullnig for helpful comments on parts of the book; R. Abraham and J. Nicholson for assistance in obtaining spectra; and particularly R. Maillet for invaluable assistance with the illustrations. We are also indebted to Varian Associates and the editors of the following journals for permission to reproduce published material: *The Journal of the American Chemical Society, The Journal of Physical Chemistry, The Journal of Chemical Physics, The Physical Review, Proceedings of the Royal Society (London), Journal of Molecular Spectroscopy, Journal of the Chemical Society (London), Journal of the Physical Society of Japan, Svensk Kemisk Tidskrift, Canadian Journal of Chemistry, Helvetica Physica Acta, Transactions of the Faraday Society,* and *Discussions of the Faraday Society.*

J. A. Pople
W. G. Schneider
H. J. Bernstein

CONTENTS

PART 2. APPLICATIONS

PART 1

PRINCIPLES

CHAPTER 1

INTRODUCTION

In addition to acting as point electrostatic charges, some atomic nuclei possess magnetic moments. This was originally put forward as a hypothesis by Pauli[323] to explain some of the details of hyperfine structure found in optical atomic spectra; it has since been confirmed by a variety of methods. If an external magnetic field is applied to a system of nuclei with magnetic moments, these nuclear magnets will experience torques and will tend to be lined up parallel to the field. Although direct observation of such a lining up is difficult, it is possible, under appropriate conditions, for these magnets to absorb energy from a magnetic field oscillating with a frequency in the radio-frequency region. Such absorption gives rise to what are called nuclear magnetic resonance spectra (often abbreviated to NMR spectra). If the nucleus has no magnetic moment, no magnetic resonance spectrum can be observed. The first successful application of NMR techniques was in connection with molecular-beam experiments,[361] but it was pointed out at an early stage that it should be possible to observe resonance absorption in other forms of matter.[145] Nuclear resonance effects were first detected in bulk matter in 1945 by Purcell, Torrey, and Pound[358] and by Bloch, Hansen, and Packard[53] using such simple materials as solid paraffin and water.

By measuring NMR spectra, we are using a nucleus essentially as a magnetic probe to investigate local magnetic effects inside a molecular system. The local magnetic field near a particular nucleus will depend on its chemical environment and is determined by a number of factors including the polarization of remote parts of the sample, magnetic moments (nuclear and electronic) of neighboring molecules, and intramolecular effects due to other nuclei and electrons in the same molecule. This form of spectroscopy is therefore of potential value in problems involving the investigation of molecular structure and environmental effects, and its application to many diverse branches of chemistry has rapidly followed the development of physical techniques. It is with these applications to molecular problems, particularly in the liquid and gaseous states, that we shall be concerned in this book.

1-1. Magnetic Properties of Nuclei

Nuclear Magnetic Moments. With regard to their magnetic properties, nuclei are best classified in terms of their angular momenta and spin. According to general principles of quantum mechanics, the maximum measurable component of the angular momentum of any system (in particular, a nucleus) must be an integral or half-integral multiple of the modified Planck constant $\hbar$ ($= h/2\pi$). If we write the maximum component as I, I is then the spin quantum number. It is found that the nucleus will have $2I + 1$ distinct states in which the component of angular momentum along any selected direction will have values I, $(I - 1)$, $\ldots$, $(-I + 1)$, $-I$. In the absence of external fields, these states will all have the same energy.

All data on the magnetic properties of nuclei are consistent with the hypothesis that the magnetic moment is zero if $I = 0$ and that, if I is nonvanishing, the moment is always parallel to the angular-momentum vector. Thus, we may define a *maximum observable component of the magnetic moment* μ in terms of which the complete set of observable values are $m\mu/I$, where m, the *magnetic quantum number*, may have the values

$$m = I, I - 1, I - 2, \ldots, -I + 1, -I \tag{1-1}$$

Since the magnetic moment and angular momentum behave as parallel vectors, it is frequently convenient to specify magnetic properties in terms of the ratio γ defined by

$$\mu = \gamma(I\hbar) \tag{1-2}$$

γ will be called the *magnetogyric ratio;* it has the dimensions of radians per gauss second. (The term "gyromagnetic ratio" has more commonly been used in the past, but is less appropriate.)

Another way in which nuclear moments are sometimes measured is in units of the nuclear magneton. This is the magnetic moment which would be ascribed to a proton (which has spin $I = 1/2$) if it could be treated as a spinning spherical particle with all its mass and charge spread uniformly over the surface. This is easily calculated to be $e\hbar/2M_p c$, where M_p is the proton mass, e is the proton charge, and c is the velocity of light. The magnitude of the nuclear magneton is 5.0493×10^{-24} erg/gauss. However, this oversimplified model only gives an order of magnitude for nuclear magnetic moments. The observed magnetic moment for a nucleus of spin I can be expressed in terms of the nuclear magneton by

$$\mu = g \frac{e\hbar}{2M_p c} I \tag{1-3}$$

where g, a nondimensional constant, is referred to as the *nuclear g factor*.[†]

It should be emphasized that all these definitions have been made in terms of maximum observable components of the various vectors. According to quantum mechanics, this is different from the magnitude or length of the vector itself. Thus the magnitude of the angular-momentum vector for a system with spin I is

$$\hbar \sqrt{I(I + 1)} \tag{1-4}$$

and similar modifications will have to be made for other vectors.

A table of nuclei with nonvanishing spins and magnetic moments [as defined by Eq. (1-3)] is given in Appendix A. In the complete table of known nuclear spins there are certain regular features which may be expressed in terms of the charge number Z and the mass number A. These may be summarized as follows:

1. If the mass number A is odd, the nuclear spin I is half integral.

2. If the mass number A and the charge number Z are both even, the spin is zero.

3. If the mass number A is even but the charge number Z is odd, the spin is integral.

Nuclei with spin $I = 0$ have no magnetic resonance spectra. It is important to note that some very commonly occurring nuclei such as C^{12} and O^{16} are in this class. This means that the very large number of organic molecules containing only H, C, and O atoms give only a proton magnetic resonance spectrum free from complications due to spins of the other nuclei (apart from the effects of small concentrations of the isotopes C^{13} and O^{17}).

Nuclear Electric Quadrupole Moments. Another nuclear property which is of some importance in connection with NMR experiments is the electrical quadrupole moment, which is also related to the spin. This is a measure of the nonsphericity of the electric charge distribution within the nucleus, that is, whether it is drawn out into a cigar shape or flattened into a plate form. An important rule for which there is strong theoretical backing[367] is that only nuclei with spins greater than or equal to unity possess electric quadrupole moments. NMR experiments on nuclei with $I = 1/2$ including protons, therefore, are not complicated by direct interactions of the nuclear spin with the electrical environment. Values of the electric quadrupole moment where applicable are also given in the table in Appendix A.

[†] This g factor is in fact the counterpart of the Landé g factor for electrons for which a relation corresponding to Eq. (1-3) may be written. The theoretical electron moment, $e\hbar/2mc$, where m is the electron mass, defines the Bohr magneton; it has the value 9.273×10^{-21} erg/gauss. Thus because of their relative mass, the proton has a magnetic moment that is small compared with the electron's magnetic moment.

1-2. Nuclear Energy Levels in a Magnetic Field

If a nucleus with a magnetic moment is introduced into a uniform magnetic field H_0 in the z direction, its energy (relative to that in zero field) will be given by

$$-\mu_z H_0 \qquad (1\text{-}5)$$

where μ_z is the component of the nuclear moment in the same direction. This interaction energy also applies in a quantum-mechanical treatment, so, for a nucleus of spin I, for which μ_z can have $2I + 1$ distinct values, the energy levels of the various states will become separated and will be

$$-\mu H_0, \ -\frac{I-1}{I}\mu H_0, \ \ldots, \ \frac{I-1}{I}\mu H_0, \ \mu H_0 \qquad (1\text{-}6)$$

These levels are equally spaced, the separation between them being $\mu H_0/I$. This splitting of energy levels in a magnetic field may be referred to as a *nuclear Zeeman splitting*, because it is analogous to the magnetic splitting of electronic levels (Zeeman effect). It is illustrated for a system with $I = 1$ (and consequently with three states) in Fig. 1-1.

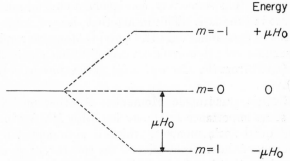

FIG. 1-1. Zeeman splitting of nuclear energy levels in a magnetic field.

The basis of NMR experiments is to induce transitions between these Zeeman levels by the absorption or emission of energy quanta. For a transition between neighboring levels, the frequency ν of the radiation required can be found from the Bohr frequency condition

$$h\nu = \frac{\mu H_0}{I} \qquad (1\text{-}7)$$

or, using the definition of the magnetogyric ratio, Eq. (1-2),

$$\nu = \frac{\gamma H_0}{2\pi} \qquad (1\text{-}8)$$

Thus, this frequency is proportional to the applied field. If we substitute, as typical values, μ for the proton (1.42×10^{-23} erg/gauss) and $H_0 = 10,000$ gauss, we find that the appropriate frequency is 42.6 Mc/sec, which is conveniently produced by rf techniques.

A more detailed consideration of transition probabilities shows that, in general, transitions between neighboring levels are the only ones that can be induced by an oscillating uniform magnetic field. Thus, in Fig. 1-1, transitions may be observed between levels $m = -1$ and $m = 0$, or between $m = 0$ and $m = 1$, but not between $m = -1$ and $m = 1$. We see, therefore, that for a given magnetic field H_0, transitions will be observed only for a characteristic frequency for each species of nucleus, this being proportional to both H_0 and the magnetogyric ratio γ, provided all environmental effects are ignored.

1-3. Magnetic Dipole Interaction

Frequently, the largest single factor modifying the magnetic environment of a nucleus is the field due to magnetic moments of neighboring nuclei in fixed positions. If another nucleus is at a distance R, the magnitude of such a field can be anywhere between $\pm 2\mu/R^3$. For a proton at a distance of 1 A this is a range of 57 gauss. Thus instead of all nuclei experiencing the same uniform magnetic field H_0, different nuclei in a specimen will experience various fields spreading over a range of this order. Consequently, magnetic resonance will occur over a range of frequencies and the spectral line will be broadened.

These considerations are effective, however, only if the nuclei maintain the same orientations relative to one another and to the external field, as in solids. In liquids and gases, where the molecules are rotating and tumbling about rapidly, the magnetic field at any one nucleus due to the others effectively averages out to zero. This is one example of a general phenomenon in resonance experiments in which sufficiently rapid fluctuations of environment show up only as an average. The cause of the magnetic dipole broadening is removed by this averaging, and the resonance signals become much sharper. Consequently, NMR spectroscopy of liquids and gases is in many ways very different from that of solids and generally requires different experimental techniques.

The width of the broad lines observed in solid-state spectra is determined by the relative positions of the nuclei and can be used as a source of information about molecular geometry. There have been a large number of such investigations of molecular crystals. In addition, there can frequently be obtained some information about molecular rotation in crystals, when the magnetic field due to neighboring nuclei is only partially averaged. These topics form a more or less separate subject which has been treated in detail elsewhere, particularly by Andrew.[15] In the present book we shall be concerned only with the NMR spectroscopy of liquids and gases, where magnetic dipole interaction plays a minor role.

1-4. Magnetic Shielding by Electrons

The second environmental effect to be considered is that of the surrounding electrons. If any atom or molecule is placed in a magnetic field, it acquires a diamagnetic moment by virtue of the induced orbital motion of its electrons. These moving electrons constitute effective currents within the molecule and thereby produce a secondary magnetic field which also will act on all the nuclei present. Since the induced currents are proportional to the applied field H_0, the magnitude of this secondary field will also be proportional to H_0. Thus the local magnetic field at the position of a nucleus will be given by

$$H_{\text{local}} = H_0(1 - \sigma) \tag{1-9}$$

where σ is a nondimensional constant independent of H_0 but dependent on the chemical (electronic) environment. The constant σ is called the *screening constant*, because the local field is usually slightly smaller than the applied field. The magnitude of σ varies from about 10^{-5} for protons to values of about 10^{-2} for heavy atoms.

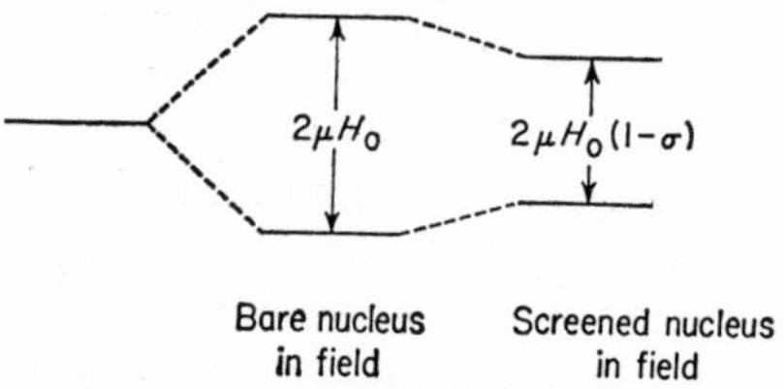

The effect of the screening constant will be to bring the Zeeman levels closer together (Fig. 1-2). As a result, the energy quantum required for a transition between states is smaller, and therefore resonance will occur at a lower frequency. Alternatively, if the experiment is performed by varying the field H_0 until resonance is obtained at a fixed frequency, the applied field will have to have a larger value than would have been the case if the nucleus were unscreened.

Bare nucleus   Screened nucleus
in field   in field

FIG. 1-2. The effect of electronic screening on nuclear Zeeman levels (spin 1/2).

If we examine the NMR spectra of a given species of nucleus in various chemical environments, either in different molecules or in different chemical positions in the same molecule, there will be a corresponding set of different values of the screening constant. As a result, *resonance will occur in a different part of the spectrum for each chemically distinct position.* This displacement of a signal for different chemical environments due to variations in screening constants is referred to as a *chemical shift*. Related effects in metals were observed first by Knight[220] in 1949, and observations of shifts in different chemical compounds were later made by Proctor and Yu[352] for N^{14}, Dickinson[118] for F^{19}, and by Lindström[248] and Thomas[439] for protons. The first spectra with separate lines for chemically different nuclei in the same molecule were obtained for alcohols by Arnold, Dharmatti, and Packard[21] in 1951.

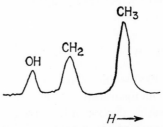

FIG. 1-3. Proton resonance spectrum of liquid ethyl alcohol under low resolution showing distinct signals for methyl, methylene, and hydroxyl protons.

We may consider CH_3CH_2OH, ethyl alcohol, as an example. In this molecule there are three types of proton: the three protons on the methyl group, the two protons on the methylene group, and the one proton on the hydroxyl group. A typical proton magnetic resonance spectrum of liquid ethyl alcohol under conditions of low resolution is given in Fig. 1-3; it clearly shows three separate signals corresponding to the three types of proton. Further, the intensities are approximately in the ratio 3:2:1, allowing immediate identification.

1-5. Electron-coupled Spin Interactions

When a number of liquids were first examined by NMR spectroscopy, it was found that certain substances showed more lines than were required by simple considerations of the number of nonequivalent nuclei.[353,162,177]

FIG. 1-4. Fluorine resonance of $POCl_2F$, showing doublet signal. (Gutowsky, McCall, and Slichter.[166])

An early example is the fluorine resonance of $POCl_2F$, shown in Fig. 1-4. This consists of two lines of equal intensity, although there is only one fluorine atom in the molecule. Other molecules gave symmetrical multiplet signals (triplets, quartets, etc.). A further significant fact about these spectra is that the separations between the components of the multiplet, measured on a frequency scale, are independent of the applied field H_0, instead of being proportional to it as would be the case if the signal arose from different shielding constants. On the basis of several such measurements, it was proposed by Gutowsky, McCall, and Slichter[165] and by Hahn and Maxwell[178] that these multiplets arise from an interaction between neighboring nuclear spins which is proportional to the scalar product

$$I(1) \cdot I(2) \qquad (1\text{-}10)$$

where $I(1)$ and $I(2)$ are the nuclear-spin vectors. Unlike the direct interaction of magnetic dipoles, an energy of this sort does not average to zero when the molecules are rotating, so its effect is still observable in the spectra of liquids. The interpretation of these interactions was first given by Ramsey and Purcell,[368] who showed that they arise from an indirect coupling mechanism via the electrons in the molecule. Thus a nuclear spin tends to orient the spins of electrons nearby, which in turn orient spins of other electrons and consequently spins of other nuclei. The magnitudes of the spin-interaction energies are usually expressed in cycles per second. (This is essentially an energy in units of Planck's constant.) Observed interaction energies vary from about 1,000 cycles/sec to small values at the limit of experimental detection (<1 cycle/sec).

1-6. Application of High-resolution Nuclear Magnetic Resonance Spectroscopy

Continued improvements in experimental techniques have made possible a better resolution of individual nuclear resonance signals and have greatly accelerated applications of the method to a wide variety of problems in the chemical field. There is little doubt that further improvements in instrumental resolution will be forthcoming which will result in obtaining more accurate information and perhaps point the way to new applications.

The term "high-resolution NMR spectroscopy" is now generally applied to nuclear resonance measurements under conditions of resolution such that the chemical shifts of nonequivalent nuclei in the same molecule can be distinguished. Fine-structure splitting of the resonance signals due to spin-spin interaction is also usually observed. Nuclear resonance spectra of most solid samples, on the other hand, give rise to characteristic broad signals due to the direct dipole interaction of nuclear spins; they are referred to as broad-band or wide-line spectra.

A high-resolution NMR spectrum of a molecule with several groups of nuclei exhibits many individual lines (signals) due to the effect of electron screening and spin coupling. To obtain information inherent in such a spectrum, the spectrum must be analyzed in terms of the chemical shifts of individual nuclei and the spin-spin coupling constants between them. The latter provide an important aid in the final assignment of the signals to individual atoms in the molecule. General features of NMR spectra and various methods for arriving at a detailed analysis are outlined in Chaps. 5 and 6.

Information on chemical shifts and spin coupling constants is presently being accumulated for a variety of different molecules. A theoretical interpretation of these quantities may lead to a better understanding of the nature of the electron charge distributions in molecules and chemical bonding. Quantum-mechanical work which has been carried out on these theoretical aspects is described in Chaps. 7 and 8.

It turns out that the time scale involved in NMR measurements makes possible a further application of this method to studies of certain rate processes, including chemical reaction rates. The theory underlying some of these applications is considered in Chap. 10.

Undoubtedly the widest application of NMR spectroscopy at present is in the field of structure determination. The identification of certain atoms or groups in a molecule as well as their position relative to other atoms or groups can frequently be obtained in a very simple and direct manner. Applications of this kind require an accumulation of a catalogue of information on chemical shifts in certain type compounds or classes of compounds. Pertinent data are presented in Chaps. 11 and 12. The present development in NMR spectroscopy closely parallels that which took place in infrared spectroscopy. Following the development of the theory and an accumulation of spectra from which a table of characteristic "group" frequencies could be derived, the infrared spectrometer became an invaluable tool for the chemist. In this connection it may also be worth noting that of all compounds presently known or likely to be synthesized, compounds containing hydrogen comprise a major fraction. This, together with the fact that to date proton magnetic resonance measurements have been carried out more extensively than measurements on other nuclei, in part justifies the emphasis on proton resonance spectroscopy adopted in the present book.

Several other applications are in the fields of isomerism and internal rotation (Chap. 13), conformation analysis (Chap. 14), and tautomerism (Chap. 17). Although the effects observed in these applications have not yet been extensively studied and the theoretical basis is not yet well understood, investigation by proton resonance measurements appears rather promising.

One of the most fruitful applications of proton resonance measurements is in studies of hydrogen bonding, as well as other molecular interactions (Chap. 15). Even rather weak hydrogen bonds can be detected, and for this purpose the NMR method is one of the most sensitive we have to date. The method can also be used to study certain proton-exchange phenomena, as well as dissociation equilibria of acids and bases in aqueous solution (Chap. 18).

Finally, applications of NMR methods to chemical analysis are discussed in Chap. 19. To date the method has not been fully exploited in this direction, partly perhaps because of the relatively higher cost of the equipment involved compared to other instrumental methods. There is no doubt, however, that the method is well suited for certain analytical operations and that it will be more widely used in the future.

CHAPTER 2

PROPERTIES OF MOLECULES IN A MAGNETIC FIELD

2-1. Introduction

The NMR experiment is basically a particular measurement of the behavior of a molecule placed in a magnetic field. It is therefore reasonable to expect the interpretation of such a measurement to be aided by studies of other magnetochemical properties, particularly the magnetic susceptibility. The basic action of a magnetic field on the electrons in a molecule is to induce certain orbital motions or currents and to align electronic spins. These forms of magnetic polarization give rise to effects which show up both in the macroscopic equations of classical electromagnetism and in local internal properties such as those observed by nuclear resonance methods. This chapter, therefore, will be mainly devoted to a discussion of the aspects of magnetic susceptibilities which will later be relevant to the study of nuclear magnetic resonance.

a. Magnetic Susceptibilities. According to the classical electromagnetic equations, the magnetic induction $\mathbf{B}$ and the magnetic field $\mathbf{H}$ in a material are related by

$$\mathbf{B} = \mathbf{H} + 4\pi\mathbf{M} \tag{2-1}$$

where $\mathbf{M}$ is the intensity of magnetization, or magnetic moment per unit volume. For isotropic nonferromagnetic materials, this magnetic moment is proportional to the field $\mathbf{H}$:

$$\mathbf{M} = \chi_v\mathbf{H} \tag{2-2}$$

where χ_v depends only on the nature of the material and is called the *volume magnetic susceptibility.*

The volume susceptibility χ_v may have either sign. If it is positive, that is, if the induced magnetic moment is parallel to the field, the substance is *paramagnetic;* if it is negative, the substance is said to be *diamagnetic.* As a general rule, paramagnetism occurs in substances which have electrons with unpaired spins. Most substances are diamagnetic, and it appears that the fundamental cause of diamagnetism is universal, the total susceptibility of paramagnetic substances being positive only

12

because the electron spin or other contributions more than compensate for the diamagnetic term.

For most materials, the volume susceptibility χ_v is proportional to the density, suggesting that there is a basic susceptibility per molecule. We therefore define a magnetic susceptibility per gram χ and a molar magnetic susceptibility χ_M by

$$\chi_M = M\chi = \frac{M\chi_v}{d} \tag{2-3}$$

where M is the molecular weight and d the density. For diamagnetic substances, χ is usually approximately independent of temperature, whereas in paramagnetic materials it is inversely proportional to temperature.

If magnetic moments and field strengths are both measured in magnetic units, the volume susceptibility χ_v will be dimensionless. Its magnitude is of the order of -10^{-6} for common materials. For paramagnetic substances, χ_v is larger and, of course, of opposite sign.

In crystals of sufficiently low symmetry, the intensity of magnetization **M** may cease to be always parallel to **H**, so that the diamagnetic susceptibilities χ_M and χ_v may have to be replaced by second-rank tensors. These tensors will be specified by the directions of their principal axes and the values of their principal components. The principal components of the molar susceptibility will be written χ_1, χ_2, and χ_3 so that

$$\chi_M = \tfrac{1}{3}(\chi_1 + \chi_2 + \chi_3) \tag{2-4}$$

If the components χ_1, χ_2, and χ_3 are not all equal, the system has a *diamagnetic anisotropy*. If two of the components χ_1 and χ_2 are equal, we shall define the anisotropy as

$$\begin{aligned} \Delta\chi &= \chi_3 - \tfrac{1}{2}(\chi_1 + \chi_2) \\ &= \chi_3 - \chi_1 \end{aligned} \tag{2-5}$$

b. Chemical Equilibria and Reactions in a Magnetic Field. One point which requires consideration before proceeding further is the direct effect of a magnetic field on thermodynamic properties and chemical equilibria. Because rather strong magnetic fields are used to observe nuclear magnetic resonance, it is necessary to investigate to what extent properties such as equilibrium constants may deviate from their values in a normal environment.

We can obtain estimates of the direct effect of a magnetic field by comparing typical magnetic energies with a typical thermal energy. If we consider a substance with molar diamagnetic susceptibility χ_M placed in a magnetic field H, the energy of interaction per mole is $\tfrac{1}{2}\chi_M H^2$. A typical value of χ_M is 10^{-4}, so that a field of 10,000 gauss corresponds to an energy of 5,000 ergs/mole. The thermal energy measured by RT

is of the order of 2.5×10^{10} ergs/mole at room temperature, so magnetic energies have a negligible effect on thermodynamic properties. Even with paramagnetic substances for which χ_M may be larger, magnetic energies are relatively very small except at the lowest temperatures.

Similar considerations apply to the effect of a magnetic field on the rate of a chemical reaction. If the magnetic susceptibility of the transition-state complex is different from that of the reactants, there may, in principle, be a change in the energy of activation. But such changes will again be very small compared with RT, and any alteration in the rate constant is not likely to be large enough to be considered seriously.

2-2. Atomic Diamagnetism

Turning to the electronic interpretation of diamagnetism, we shall first consider the behavior of free atoms in a magnetic field. The theory of this is relatively simple and can be understood on a purely classical basis. In fact, an expression for the atomic susceptibility was obtained by Langevin[231] before the development of a quantum-mechanical theory of atomic structure.

The classical derivation is based on a result due to Larmor[232] on the equivalence of the effects of a magnetic field and a rotating coordinate system. We start with the equation of motion of a moving electron in a magnetic field $\mathbf{H}$ and an electric field $\mathbf{E}$:

$$m \frac{d^2\mathbf{r}}{dt^2} = -\frac{e}{c} \frac{d\mathbf{r}}{dt} \times \mathbf{H} - e\mathbf{E} \qquad (2\text{-}6)$$

The vector $\mathbf{H}$ is a constant, and the electric field $\mathbf{E}$ will be directed away from the center; so if we take the origin at the nucleus, $\mathbf{E}$ is parallel to $\mathbf{r}$.

Now suppose we write down the equation of motion of the electron relative to a system of coordinates rotating with constant angular velocity ω but in the absence of the magnetic field $\mathbf{H}$. Then the equation for the rate of change of $\mathbf{r}$ *relative to the rotating frame* is

$$m \left[\frac{d^2\mathbf{r}}{dt^2} + 2\left(\omega \times \frac{d\mathbf{r}}{dt} \right) + \omega \times (\omega \times \mathbf{r}) \right] = -e\mathbf{E} \qquad (2\text{-}7)$$

For sufficiently small values of ω the third term on the left-hand side of Eq. (2-7) may be neglected. Comparing with Eq. (2-6), we see that, if the field $\mathbf{H}$ is not too large, the equation of motion is identical with that of an electron not in a magnetic field but referred to a coordinate system rotating with angular velocity

$$\omega = \frac{e\mathbf{H}}{2mc} \qquad (2\text{-}8)$$

Now, if the electron is actually moving in such a way that there is no resultant angular velocity in the absence of a magnetic field, then it will appear to have an angular velocity equal to $-\omega$ when referred to the rotating framework. Thus the effect of the magnetic field is to superpose an angular velocity of $e\mathbf{H}/2mc$ on the whole system. In the following chapter we shall see that the nuclear spins behave in a similar manner.

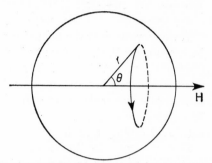

As a consequence of the rotation about the direction of the magnetic field, the electrons will give rise to a magnetic moment. Suppose we consider an electron at distance r from the center making an angle θ

FIG. 2-1. Rotation of electrons about the direction of a magnetic field.

with the direction of the magnetic field $\mathbf{H}$ (Fig. 2-1). The axis of rotation will be parallel to $\mathbf{H}$, and consequently the electron will set up a current in the direction shown of magnitude

$$- \frac{e^2 H}{4\pi mc} \tag{2-9}$$

the negative sign arising because the charge of the electron is $-e$. This current encloses an area $\pi r^2 \sin^2 \theta$ and consequently gives rise to a magnetic moment

$$- \frac{e^2 H r^2 \sin^2 \theta}{4mc^2} \tag{2-10}$$

The direction is opposed to $\mathbf{H}$, so that this mechanism gives rise to diamagnetism. The total moment is found by multiplying Eq. (2-10) by the probability of finding an electron with these values of r and θ and then integrating over space. This gives a total moment

$$- \frac{e^2 H}{6mc^2} \sum_i \overline{r_i^2} \tag{2-11}$$

where $\overline{r_i^2}$ is the mean-square radius of the ith electron. We then have

$$\chi_M = - \frac{Ne^2}{6mc^2} \sum_i \overline{r_i^2} \tag{2-12}$$

for the molar diamagnetic susceptibility.

It should be noted that this formula does not apply if the atom or ion has a free-electron spin or is not in a spherically symmetric state. If it is in a P state, for example, there will be an angular momentum and consequently a magnetic moment even in the absence of a magnetic field.

2-3. Molecular Diamagnetism

If we now consider the behavior of a molecule in a magnetic field, it soon becomes clear that the theory is more complicated. If we examine the electronic currents induced in a molecule with the nuclei held fixed, the resultant magnetic moment may depend on the direction of the applied field. The molecular diamagnetic susceptibility is therefore a tensor which may be anisotropic. In liquids and gases, of course, the molecules turn over rapidly and only the mean value of this tensor is observed.

If we reexamine the classical argument on which the atomic-susceptibility formula is based, it ceases to be applicable for molecules because the electric field which acts on the electrons is no longer spherically symmetric. That is, if we refer the motion of the electrons to a suitably rotating coordinate frame in the presence of a magnetic field, we can no longer say that the equations of motion are the same as for a nonrotating system. This is because the fixed nuclei, other than the one which is used as origin, produce an electric field which varies with rotation about the origin. In a methane molecule with fixed nuclei, for example, we might refer the motion of the electron to a frame rotating about the carbon nucleus with the appropriate frequency, but in such a frame the protons would be moving, so that the equations of motion would not be identical with those for the molecule in the absence of a field.

The condition for the applicability of the classical model is that the electrostatic potential shall be axially symmetric about some line parallel to the magnetic field. This is satisfied for atoms, but the only molecular situation in which the approach is valid is the case of a *linear* molecule in a Σ state with the magnetic field along the molecular axis. The electron cloud will then rotate freely about the axis with an angular velocity $eH/2mc$, and an argument similar to that leading to the atomic formula (2-12) gives

$$\chi_M^{(z)} = -\frac{Ne^2}{4mc^2} \sum_i \overline{x_i^2 + y_i^2} \tag{2-13}$$

where the z direction is parallel to the applied field.

The effect of lack of electrical axial symmetry about the direction of the magnetic field will be to hinder free circulation of this type and consequently reduce the total diamagnetism. In quantum-mechanical terms, this arises because the magnetic field may mix the ground-state wave function with that for some of the excited states. This leads to a lowering of energy corresponding to a lowering of the total diamagnetic susceptibility. Quantitatively the expression (2-13) has to be replaced by the Van Vleck formula[445]

$$\chi_M = -\frac{Ne^2}{4mc^2} \sum_i \overline{x_i^2 + y_i^2} + \frac{Ne^2}{2m^2c^2} \sum_{n(\neq 0)} \frac{|(0|\mathfrak{M}_z|n)|^2}{E_n - E_0} \qquad (2\text{-}14)$$

This expression gives the magnetic susceptibility of the system in the electronic state 0 (which is normally the ground state). The summation $\sum_n$ in the second term is over excited states n, the numerators being the squares of the matrix elements of the electronic angular-momentum component $\mathfrak{M}_z$ and the denominators the excitation energies. It is clear from the form of the equation that this second term is always positive and partly compensates the first. It is sometimes called the "temperature-independent paramagnetic term." In one or two special cases when there are very low-lying excited states, this term may be larger in magnitude than the first, and the material is paramagnetic.

Quantitative calculations of the molar diamagnetic susceptibility according to the Van Vleck formula (2-14) have not been attempted for many molecules. The most elaborate calculation on the hydrogen molecule[470,471] (using the James and Coolidge[207] wave function) gave a value of -3.8×10^{-6}, which may be compared with the experimental value of -4.005×10^{-6} due to Havens.[184] Some theoretical calculations have been made for nitrogen and for methane,[65,80,87] but the results do not agree well with experimental values, largely because of the difficulties in evaluating the second term.

2-4. Experimental and Empirical Studies of Diamagnetic Susceptibilities

Experimental methods of determining diamagnetic susceptibilities of liquids, solutions, and crystals have been described in various standard works.[410] In general the accuracy of these measurements is about 1 per cent in the most favorable cases, but discrepancies of up to 5 per cent are not uncommon. Since liquids vary in the amount of dissolved oxygen (from the air), an appreciable error[132] of up to 1.7 per cent in the measured susceptibility, due to the paramagnetic susceptibility of oxygen, may be encountered. Uncertainty in the values of diamagnetic susceptibilities is reflected, of course, in the estimate of the bulk diamagnetic-susceptibility correction of the measured chemical shifts (Sec. 4-9).

It has been established experimentally that χ_M is very nearly the same for the solid, liquid, and gas phases[371] and is independent of temperature. This is in agreement with the theoretical expectation if there is a susceptibility per molecule independent of environment. In the case of water, for which accurate data are available, a small positive temperature coefficient is observed[24] following the change in hydrogen bonding with temperature.

The simplest hypothesis for the magnetic susceptibility of a mixture of diamagnetic substances is Wiedemann's additivity law, according to which the molar susceptibility of a mixture of two components is given by

$$\chi_{M,\text{mixt}} = x_1\chi_{M_1} + x_2\chi_{M_2} \tag{2-15}$$

where x_1 and x_2 are the mole fractions and χ_{M_1} and χ_{M_2} are the molar susceptibilities of the pure components. There have been numerous investigations of the validity of this law, and in a critical review of existing data, Angus and Tilston[18] conclude that the real magnitude of any small deviations that do occur cannot be separated from experimental errors.

A corresponding relation for volume susceptibilities follows from Eq. (2-15) if we also assume an additivity law for molar volumes. Then

$$\chi_{v,\text{mixt}} = \phi_1\chi_{v_1} + \phi_2\chi_{v_2} \tag{2-16}$$

where ϕ_1 and ϕ_2 are the volume fractions of the components.

a. Pascal Constants. Very often a diamagnetic susceptibility which has not been determined experimentally is required. In such a case it has been common practice to resort to values of atomic and constitutive contributions to calculate the molar diamagnetic susceptibility. Some success can be achieved in this way because χ_M is nearly an additive property. This was recognized very early by Pascal,[321] who arrived at a set of atomic contributions to the molar diamagnetic susceptibility by correlating the existing experimental data. By summing the atomic contributions for the atoms in a particular molecule, the molar diamagnetic susceptibility was calculated, and it agreed fairly well with the observed value. As the data improved, and covered wider varieties of molecules, constitutive corrections were added to the original list of atomic contributions to take account of the deviations from the simple additivity originally proposed. A useful set of the constants and constitutive corrections compiled by Pascal[322] is given in Table 2-1. As pointed out by Ingold,[204] the Pascal constants for Cl, Br, and I are better suited to the calculation of χ_M for aromatic halides than for alkyl compounds. For this reason Ingold proposed an alternative set of values for these halogens which were suitable for alkyl compounds. In Table 2-1 both sets are given. A few constitutive corrections for groups containing one or more Cl or Br atoms are also added. These appreciably reduce most of the discrepancies encountered in using the constants of Table 2-1 for calculating the molar diamagnetic susceptibility of the alkyl halides. Pascal[322] also gives constitutive corrections for tertiary and quaternary C atoms at $\alpha,\beta,\gamma,\delta,\epsilon$ positions relative to a carbonyl group.   An extensive discussion of Pascal's constants is given by Bhatnagar and Mathur,[46] and several reviews have been written by Pacault.[311-313]

TABLE 2-1. PASCAL CONSTANTS[322] FOR THE ELEMENTS ($\times 10^6$)

H	−2.93	F	− 6.4 ⎫		Cl	−17.2 ⎫
C	−6.00	Cl	−19.9 ⎬ Aliphatic	Br	−26.5 ⎬ Aromatic
N (open chain)	−5.55	Br	−30.4		I	−40.5 ⎭
N (ring)	−4.61	I	−44.6 ⎭			
N (monamide)	−1.54					
N (diamide, imide)	−2.11	S	−15.2			
		Se	−23.5			
O (alcohol, ether)	−4.60	B	− 7.3			
		Si	−13.0			
O (aldehyde, ketone)	1.66	P	−10			
O (carboxyl)†	−7.95	As	−21			

Constitutive Corrections for Bonds ($\times 10^6$)

C=C	5.5	N=N	1.85
C≡C	0.8	C=N	8.15
C=C—C=C	10.6	C≡N	0.8

Constitutive Corrections for Rings ($\times 10^6$)

Cyclopropane	3.4	Cyclohexadiene	10.7	Benzene	−1.4
Cyclobutane	1.1	Piperidine	3.6	Pyridine	0.5
Cyclopentane	0	Piperazine	7.5	Triazine	−1.4
Cyclohexane	3.1	Pyrazoline	8.3	Furan	−2.5
Cyclohexene	7.2	Glyoxaline	7.8	Pyrrole	−3.5

Additional Group Corrections for Halogens ($\times 10^6$)

—CH₂Cl	−0.3	—CH₂Br	−1.5
—CHCl₂	−0.6	—CHBr₂	−0.5
—CCl₃	2.5	—CBr₃	10.6

† For both oxygens of the carboxyl group in acids and esters.

b. Diamagnetic Anisotropy.   Molecular diamagnetic anisotropy was first detected in experiments on magnetic birefringence (Cotton-Mouton effect[106]).   The Cotton-Mouton constant is related[230] to the anisotropies of the electric and magnetic susceptibilities and can be used to measure one if the other is known.   For axially symmetric molecules a positive Cotton-Mouton constant indicates that the direction of maximum diamagnetic susceptibility is one of minimum optical polarizability.[40]

Large positive values of the magnetic birefringence of *aromatic* compounds led Raman and Krishnan[362] to the conclusion that these compounds possess pronounced diamagnetic anisotropy.   This is supported by extensive crystal studies.[223-225,256-258,411]   Saturated hydrocarbons and alcohols have small negative Cotton-Mouton constants, and Ramandham[363] calculated that the principal diamagnetic susceptibilities differed by about 10 to 20 per cent. We shall see in later chapters that anisotropies of this order may be of some help in understanding the chemical shifts of proton signals in some magnetically anisotropic molecules.

The large diamagnetic anisotropies of aromatic molecules are due to interatomic electronic ring currents induced by the applied magnetic field. According to the semiclassical theory of Pauling,[325] the mobile π electrons of benzene behave very much like charged particles free to move on a circular wire. If a magnetic field is applied in the direction perpendicular to the plane of the wire loop, diamagnetic circulation will take place, leading to an additional contribution to the susceptibility. If circulation around the ring (of radius a) is assumed to be completely free, the electrons will circulate with the Larmor angular frequency $eH/2mc$, just as they do in atoms. A calculation based on this model[325] gives about -50×10^{-6} for the additional molar susceptibility in the direction perpendicular to the molecular plane, to be compared with the observed value of -54×10^{-6}. This model can be extended to polycyclic aromatic compounds,[325] and its main features are justified by quantum-mechanical theories.[254,255,279,266]

2-5. Molecular Paramagnetism

An atom or molecule has a paramagnetic susceptibility if the induced moment is in the same direction as the applied magnetic field, whereas diamagnetism arises from a moment induced in the opposite direction. Paramagnetism arises in atoms and molecules if one or more electrons have unpaired spins. If a molecule has an unpaired spinning electron, the circulating charge has associated with it a permanent magnetic moment.

A substance containing molecules with permanent magnetic moments has a molar paramagnetic susceptibility which is temperature dependent and, according to Langevin,[231,229] is given by

$$\chi_M = \frac{N\mu^2}{3kT} \qquad (2\text{-}17)$$

There is a distinction between this temperature-dependent paramagnetism of molecules due to permanent magnetic moments and that due to mixing of ground- and excited-state wave functions [Eq. (2-14)] which is independent of temperature and of very much smaller magnitude.

The effective magnetic moment to be used in Eq. (2-17), according to quantum-mechanical theory,[445] is

$$\mu_{\text{eff}} = 2\beta \sqrt{S(S+1)} \qquad (2\text{-}18)$$

where S is the resultant spin (equal to one-half the number of unpaired electrons). Here β is the Bohr magneton, $e\hbar/2mc$. Substitution in Eq. (2-17) gives

$$\chi_M = \frac{4N\beta^2 S(S+1)}{3kT} = \frac{0.496S(S+1)}{T} \tag{2-19}$$

Oxygen, for example, is in a $^3\Sigma$ ground state, so $S = 1$. The molar paramagnetic susceptibility is then calculated to be $3,390 \times 10^{-6}$ by Eq. (2-19). Thus paramagnetic susceptibilities are roughly 100 times larger than diamagnetic susceptibilities. It is not surprising, therefore, that a small amount of air dissolved in liquids can appreciably alter the measured diamagnetic susceptibility (Sec. 2-4). Dissolved oxygen from the air in a sample being investigated for nuclear magnetic absorption can affect the position of the signal in the magnetic field. The presence of paramagnetic ions in a sample also produces local magnetic fields which alter the lifetimes of nuclear spin states and so change the width of the NMR signals (Sec. 9-2).

CHAPTER 3

THEORY OF THE NUCLEAR MAGNETIC
RESONANCE METHOD

3-1. Distribution of Nuclear Spins in a Magnetic Field

As we have seen in the introductory chapter, a uniform static magnetic field H_0 separates the energies of the two spin states (for a nucleus with spin 1/2) by an amount $2\mu H_0$, where μ is the maximum component of the nuclear magnetic moment. If we have a whole assembly of such nuclei in thermal equilibrium at temperature T, the lower of these two states will be more populated. In fact, the ratio of the populations will be given by the Boltzmann factor $\exp(2\mu H_0/kT)$. For nuclei in magnetic fields of the order of 10,000 gauss at room temperature, $2\mu H_0/kT$ is less than 10^{-5}, so that the probabilities of a given nucleus being in the upper or lower state are respectively, to sufficient accuracy,

$$\frac{1}{2}\left(1 - \frac{\mu H_0}{kT}\right) \quad \text{and} \quad \frac{1}{2}\left(1 + \frac{\mu H_0}{kT}\right) \tag{3-1}$$

For nuclei with spin $I = 1/2, 1, 3/2, \ldots$, there are $2I + 1$ equally spaced levels separated by an energy $\mu H_0/IkT$, so that the corresponding probabilities are

$$\frac{1}{2I + 1}\left(1 - \frac{m\mu H_0}{IkT}\right) \tag{3-2}$$

where m takes the values $I, I - 1, \ldots, -I + 1, -I$.

One consequence of the unequal distribution of spins among the various states will be a resultant macroscopic magnetic moment per unit volume in the direction of the applied field H_0. This is a temperature-dependent paramagnetic susceptibility, precisely analogous to the paramagnetic susceptibility due to unpaired electron spins (Sec. 2-5). For nuclei of spin 1/2 the mean value of the component of the nuclear magnetic moment along the direction of the applied field is given by the appropriate weighted average

$$\bar{\mu} = \frac{1}{2}\left(1 + \frac{\mu H_0}{kT}\right)\mu - \frac{1}{2}\left(1 - \frac{\mu H_0}{kT}\right)\mu = \frac{\mu^2 H_0}{kT} \tag{3-3}$$

22

If there are N such nuclei per unit volume, the corresponding volume magnetic susceptibility is

$$\chi_0 = \frac{N\bar{\mu}}{H_0} = \frac{N\mu^2}{kT} \tag{3-4}$$

For protons in water at room temperature this is about 3×10^{-10}, so that this contribution to the magnetic susceptibility is usually masked by electronic diamagnetism which is of the order of 10^{-6}. At low temperatures, however, the nuclear magnetic susceptibility is more important, and it has, in fact, been detected in solid hydrogen.[233]

For nuclei with spin I a similar calculation based on the probabilities (3-1) gives

$$
\begin{aligned}
\chi_0 &= \frac{N}{H_0} \sum_{m=-I}^{I} \frac{1}{2I+1} \left(1 - \frac{m\mu H_0}{IkT}\right) \frac{m\mu}{I} \\
&= \frac{(I+1)N\mu^2}{3IkT}
\end{aligned}
\tag{3-5}
$$

3-2. Spin-lattice Relaxation Time

In addition to the equilibrium distribution of nuclear spins in a magnetic field, we have to consider the rate at which this distribution is approached. As we shall see, this is a very important factor in determining the nature of NMR absorption. Suppose, for example, we have an assembly of nuclear spins (with $I = 1/2$) which is initially not in a magnetic field, so that the populations of the two nuclear spin states are equal. If a steady magnetic field H_0 is then applied to the system, we may inquire how long it takes for the populations to reach their new equilibrium values given by Eq. (3-1). If n_- and n_+ are the number of nuclei per unit volume in the upper and lower states, respectively, we attempt to determine the value of the difference (or excess number per unit volume)

$$n = n_+ - n_- \tag{3-6}$$

as a function of time.

Let $W_{-\rightarrow+}$ and $W_{+\rightarrow-}$ be the probabilities per unit time for a given nucleus to make upward or downward transitions by interaction with

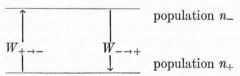

other molecular degrees of freedom. These two probabilities will be slightly different, for in equilibrium the total number of upward transitions per unit time must be equal to the corresponding number of downward transitions.   Thus

$$n_+ W_{+ \to -} = n_- W_{- \to +} \tag{3-7}$$

or, using the equilibrium values of n_+ and n_- from Eq. (3-1),

$$\frac{W_{- \to +}}{W_{+ \to -}} = 1 + \frac{2\mu H_0}{kT} \tag{3-8}$$

Since an upward transition decreases the excess number n by 2 and a downward transition increases it by 2, we have the differential equation

$$\frac{dn}{dt} = 2n_- W_{- \to +} - 2n_+ W_{+ \to -} \tag{3-9}$$

If we write W for the mean of $W_{- \to +}$ and $W_{+ \to -}$, Eq. (3-9) becomes

$$\frac{dn}{dt} = -2W(n - n_{eq}) \tag{3-10}$$

where

$$n_{eq} = \frac{\mu H_0}{kT} (n_+ + n_-) \tag{3-11}$$

and is the equilibrium value of the excess number n.   Thus the rate of approach to equilibrium is proportional to the departure from equilibrium.
    It is usual to define a time T_1 by

$$T_1 = \frac{1}{2W} \tag{3-12}$$

so that the solution of Eq. (3-10) can be written

$$n - n_{eq} = (n - n_{eq})_0 e^{-t/T_1} \tag{3-13}$$

The difference between the excess population and its equilibrium value, therefore, is reduced by a factor e after a time T_1.   This time is a measure of the rate at which the spin system comes into thermal equilibrium with the other degrees of freedom.   It is usually referred to as the *spin-lattice relaxation time.*
    The magnitude of the spin-lattice relaxation time varies considerably with the type of nucleus and the environment.   For protons and other nuclei of spin 1/2, the only way in which the nuclear spin can be coupled with other degrees of freedom is by means of local fluctuating magnetic fields.   Nuclei with higher spin, however, have electric quadrupole moments which can interact with fluctuating electric fields, so that such nuclei usually have smaller values of T_1.   For liquids the value of the spin-lattice relaxation time usually lies between 10^{-2} and 10^2 sec, although in the presence of paramagnetic ions it may be as low as 10^{-4} sec.   In

solids it is frequently larger and may, in extreme cases, be several days. A more detailed discussion of the mechanism of spin-lattice relaxation in liquids and the theoretical interpretation are given in Chap. 9.

a. **Spin Temperature.**   The distribution of spins among the possible states is sometimes discussed in terms of the concept of *spin temperature*. Thus for nuclei with spin 1/2, we may *define* a temperature T_s by the equation

$$\frac{n_+}{n_-} = e^{2\mu H_0/kT_s}$$

$$\approx 1 + \frac{2\mu H_0}{kT_s} \qquad (3\text{-}14)$$

so that T_s is equal to T in thermal equilibrium.   If the excess population $n_+ - n_-$ is less than its equilibrium value, we may say as an alternative that the spin temperature is greater than the lattice temperature.   The process of spin-lattice relaxation then corresponds to the tendency of two thermodynamic assemblies in contact to approach the same temperature. It should be noted, however, that for nuclei of spin greater than 1/2, the concept of spin temperature is less precisely defined; for there will be more than two states, and a unique value of T_s can be obtained only if the ratios of their populations are appropriately related.   If the system can be so polarized that the upper levels are *more* highly populated than the lower ones, it may be said to be at a negative temperature.   Purcell and Pound[357] were able to achieve this with a crystal of lithium fluoride. Abragam and Proctor[1] have thoroughly examined the concept of spin temperature and have shown how it can be extended to small fields.

3-3. Magnetic Resonance Absorption

a. **Classical Treatment.**   Up to this point we have been mainly concerned with the quantum-mechanical stationary-state energy levels of a nucleus in a steady magnetic field H_0.   Some insight into the nature of resonance absorption can be obtained, however, by consideration of the classical motion of a magnetic dipole in a magnetic field.

Since the magnetic moment $\mathbf{\mu}$ and angular momentum $\mathbf{p}$ of a nucleus are related by

$$\mathbf{\mu} = \gamma \mathbf{p} \qquad (3\text{-}15)$$

where γ is the magnetogyric ratio, the classical equation of motion can be written vectorially as

$$\frac{d\mathbf{\mu}}{dt} = \gamma(\mathbf{\mu} \times \mathbf{H}) \qquad (3\text{-}16)$$

where $\mathbf{H}$ is the applied magnetic field.   Now if we rotate the vector $\mathbf{\mu}$

with an angular velocity whose magnitude and direction are given by the vector ω, the expression for the rate of change of μ is

$$\frac{d\mu}{dt} = \omega \times \mu \tag{3-17}$$

Comparing these two equations, we see that the effect of the magnetic field H is exactly equivalent to a rotation with angular velocity

$$\omega = -\gamma H \tag{3-18}$$

Thus if H is a constant field H_0, the magnetic dipole will precess about the direction of H_0 with angular velocity $-\gamma H_0$ (Fig. 3-1). This will apply whatever the direction of μ. The angular velocity of this nuclear precession is usually referred to as the Larmor angular frequency.

If we set up another coordinate system, rotating with the Larmor angular frequency $-\gamma H_0$, then if there were no other magnetic field acting, the magnetic moment vector μ would remain stationary in the new frame. In other words, in the rotating frame, the static magnetic field is effectively reduced to zero. Now suppose another smaller magnetic field H_1

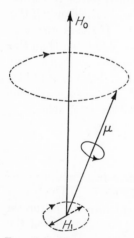

is introduced, a field that is of constant magnitude and perpendicular to the original field H_0 but is rotating about that direction (Fig. 3-1). If the angular velocity of the second field H_1 is different from that of Larmor precession, H_1 will also be rotating in the rotating coordinate system. Its effect will be to exert a torque $\mu \times H_1$ on the nucleus, tending to tip the nuclear moment toward the plane perpendicular to H_0. If the direction of H_1 is moving in the rotating frame, the direction of the torque will vary rapidly, and the only resultant effect will be a slight wobbling perturbation of the steady precessional motion. But if the field H_1 is rotating *at the Larmor frequency itself*, then, in the rotating system, it will behave like a constant field and the torque, being always in the same direction, will cause large oscillations in the angle between μ and the steady field H_0. If we vary the rate of rotation of H_1 through the Larmor frequency, the oscillations will be greatest at the Larmor frequency itself and will show up as a resonance phenomenon.

Fig. 3-1. Precession of magnetic moment μ in a magnetic field H_0.

A similar resonance will occur if H_1 is in a fixed direction but varies sinusoidally with a frequency in the vicinity of the Larmor value. This is because such a variation can be regarded as a superposition of two equal fields rotating with equal angular velocities in opposite directions (the phases being appropriate). The component rotating in the direction opposite to the Larmor precession will have very little effect on the resonance.

b. Quantum-mechanical Treatment. Turning now to the quantum-mechanical description of the resonance phenomenon, we suppose that a nucleus of total spin I is placed in a magnetic field H_0 in the z direction, so that the stationary-state wave functions may be labeled by m, the component of I in the z direction. If, in addition, we have an oscillating magnetic field in the x direction with amplitude $2H_1$ and frequency† ν, there will be an extra term in the Hamiltonian

$$\mathcal{3C}' = 2\mu_x H_1 \cos 2\pi\nu t \qquad (3\text{-}19)$$

Using the relation between the nuclear magnetic moment μ and its spin I, this may also be written

$$\mathcal{3C}' = 2\gamma\hbar H_1 I_x \cos 2\pi\nu t \qquad (3\text{-}20)$$

By the usual transition probability theory,[328] this may give rise to a transition between two states m and m' corresponding to absorption or emission of radiation. The probability for such a transition is

$$P_{mm'} = \gamma^2 H_1{}^2 |(m'|I_x|m)|^2 \delta(\nu_{mm'} - \nu) \qquad (3\text{-}21)$$

where δ is the Dirac δ function, $(m'|I_x|m)$ is the quantum-mechanical matrix element of I_x between states m and m', and $\nu_{mm'}$ is the frequency corresponding to the energy gap between these states, i.e.,

$$h\nu_{mm'} = \frac{|m - m'|\mu H_0}{I} \qquad (3\text{-}22)$$

Now it is well known[328] that the matrix element $(m'|I_x|m)$ vanishes unless $m' = m \pm 1$, so that we immediately derive the selection rule that only transitions in which the quantum number m is changed by ± 1 can occur. (This is no restriction, of course, for nuclei of spin 1/2, for which the only possible values of m are $\pm 1/2$.)

The second point to note about Eq. (3-21) is that it predicts absorption only if the frequency ν exactly coincides with the natural frequency $\nu_{mm'}$. In other words, it corresponds to an infinitely sharp absorption or emission line. In practice, as we shall see below, the lines are broadened by various factors. We therefore introduce a *line-shape function* $g(\nu)$ which is proportional to the absorption at frequency ν and is such that

$$\int_0^\infty g(\nu)\, d\nu = 1 \qquad (3\text{-}23)$$

† This may be regarded as a superposition of two magnetic fields of amplitude H_1 rotating in opposite directions about the z axis.

The causes of broadening cannot be taken into account in the simple theory of an isolated nucleus, but Eq. (3-21) can be modified in a semi-empirical manner in the form

$$P_{mm'} = \gamma^2 H_1{}^2 |(m'|I_x|m)|^2 g(\nu) \tag{3-24}$$

For nuclei of spin 1/2, there is only one value of P:

$$P = \tfrac{1}{4}\gamma^2 H_1{}^2 g(\nu) \tag{3-25}$$

The equivalence of the classical and quantum-mechanical treatments, both leading to a resonance phenomenon at the same frequency, may not be altogether apparent. The complete quantum-mechanical theory of the motion of a magnetic moment in a variable magnetic field was considered by Schwinger[407] and Rabi,[360] using the time-dependent Schrödinger equation. Rabi solved this equation for a nucleus with spin $I = 1/2$ in a steady magnetic field H_0 with another perpendicular magnetic field H_1 rotating about H_0 with angular velocity ω. If θ is the angle the resultant field makes with $\mathbf{H_0}$ (tan $\theta = H_1/H_0$) and if it is sufficiently small, the solution simplifies. If the nucleus is in the state $m = \tfrac{1}{2}$ at time $t = 0$, then it is found that the probability of its being in the state $m = -\tfrac{1}{2}$ at some later time t is

$$\frac{\theta^2}{(1 - \omega_0/\omega)^2 + (\omega_0/\omega)\theta^2} \sin^2 \left\{ \frac{\omega t}{2} \left[\left(1 - \frac{\omega_0}{\omega}\right)^2 + \frac{\omega_0}{\omega}\theta^2 \right]^{\frac{1}{2}} \right\} \tag{3-26}$$

where ω_0 is the Larmor precession angular frequency. This clearly shows the resonance effect as ω is increased through the value ω_0. If $\omega = \omega_0$, the expression (3-26) oscillates between 0 and 1, while if ω is far from ω_0, the probability never becomes large.

c. Line Broadening. As mentioned above, absorption occurs not at one single sharp frequency, but over a range of frequencies giving a broadened line. This broadening is due to a variety of causes some of which we shall consider in this section.

Natural Width Due to Spontaneous Emission. The natural line width of any transition is determined by the finite lifetime of the upper state, because of the possibility of spontaneous emission of radiation. This was investigated by Bloembergen, Purcell, and Pound[59] and found to be quite negligible compared with widths due to other causes.

Width Due to Spin-lattice Relaxation. Of more importance is the finite lifetime of both states because of the possibility of transitions between them being induced by the other molecular degrees of freedom. This is the spin-lattice relaxation process discussed in Sec. 3-2 and is always present. The order of magnitude of the broadening can be estimated from the uncertainty principle

$$\Delta E\, \Delta t \approx \hbar \tag{3-27}$$

Since $\Delta E = h \, \Delta\nu$, Eq. (3-27) implies that the uncertainty in the frequency of absorption is $1/2\pi \, \Delta t$. Thus the line width measured on a frequency scale, owing to spin-lattice relaxation, will be of the order of $1/T_1$.

Spin-lattice relaxation can occur by a variety of mechanisms which will be described in Chap. 9. The most universal mechanism is via the direct interaction of neighboring magnetic dipoles, which varies as the nuclei move relative to one another. In this way energy can be transferred to the spin system from the translational and rotational degrees of freedom.

Additional Magnetic Dipole Broadening. Under certain circumstances, the interaction of magnetic dipoles can lead to a greater broadening than that given by the spin-lattice relaxation. This happens if the nuclei stay in the same relative positions for a long time, as in solids and highly viscous liquids. Under these circumstances one has to treat nuclei as being in a variety of fields because of the local magnetic field due to neighboring dipoles. The magnetic field at a distance of 1 A from a proton, for instance, is of the order of 10 gauss. This will give rise to a broadening of the order of 10^5 cycles/sec, which is substantially larger than normal values of $1/T_1$.

When the width is larger than that due to spin-lattice relaxation, it is convenient to define another characteristic time T_2, smaller than T_1. We may conveniently do this in terms of the maximum value of the line-shape function $g(\nu)$:

$$T_2 = \tfrac{1}{2}[g(\nu)]_{\max} \tag{3-28}$$

The factor $\tfrac{1}{2}$ is introduced to make this consistent with an alternative definition of T_2 to be introduced in Sec. 3-5. Because the interaction between nuclear magnetic moments is the largest cause of broadening in many solids, T_2 is sometimes referred to as the spin-spin relaxation time. The definition (3-28), however, is rather arbitrary if the function $g(\nu)$ is not simple.

In liquids and gases, where the molecules are rotating rapidly, the magnetic fields effectively average out and there remains only spin-lattice relaxation broadening. In these circumstances T_1 and T_2 become approximately equal.

Electric Quadrupole Effects. A further cause of broadening can exist for nuclei with spin $I > 1/2$. As mentioned in Sec. 1-1, these will have electric quadrupole moments which will interact with electric field gradients. This is another mechanism of spin-lattice relaxation and therefore leads to smaller values of T_1. A fuller discussion is given in Chap. 9. In solids, again, the distribution of field gradients can lead to additional broadening (a smaller value of T_2).

Magnetic Field Inhomogeneity Broadening. A further cause of broadening is the variation of the static magnetic field H_0 over the dimensions of the sample. This instrumental limitation means that the observed spectrum will be broadened because it is really a superposition of spectra from molecules in different parts of the sample.

3-4. Saturation

We have seen above that, for nuclei of spin 1/2 in the presence of a static magnetic field in the z direction and an oscillating field of amplitude $2H_1$ and frequency ν in the x direction, the probability per unit time of an induced transition between the two levels is

$$P = \tfrac{1}{4}\gamma^2 H_1^2 g(\nu) \tag{3-29}$$

If the nucleus is initially in the lower state, this expression is a probability of absorption of radiation, while if the nucleus is initially in the upper state, it corresponds to an equal probability of stimulated emission. We have already mentioned the fact that the effect of spontaneous emission is negligible, so the over-all absorption of energy from the oscillating magnetic field is proportional to the product of P and the difference of populations:

$$P(n_+ - n_-) = Pn \tag{3-30}$$

Such an absorption can be measured by various methods to be described in detail in the next chapter.

The tendency of this net absorption of energy will be to reduce the excess population n and so reduce the probability of further absorption. The magnitude of such an effect will increase with the amplitude of the oscillating field and is referred to as *saturation*. It is limited, of course, by the tendency of the spin-lattice relaxation process to restore the excess population to its equilibrium value.

To obtain a quantitative expression for the extent of saturation, we note that, in the absence of the oscillating field, the rate of change of n is determined by the spin-lattice relaxation equation (3-10). This must now be modified by the addition of a further term $-2nP$ to the right-hand side, since each transition induced by the oscillating field reduces n by 2. Thus

$$\frac{dn}{dt} = -\frac{n - n_{eq}}{T_1} - 2nP \tag{3-31}$$

This may be rewritten

$$\frac{dn}{dt} = \frac{1 + 2PT_1}{T_1}\left(n - \frac{n_{eq}}{1 + 2PT_1}\right) \tag{3-32}$$

According to Eq. (3-32), n approaches a new steady value

$$\frac{n_{eq}}{1 + \tfrac{1}{2}\gamma^2 H_1^2 T_1 g(\nu)} \tag{3-33}$$

at a rate for which the characteristic time is

$$\frac{T_1}{1 + \frac{1}{2}\gamma^2 H_1^2 T_1 g(\nu)} \tag{3-34}$$

If the value of H_1 is large, the value of n given by (3-33) may be much less than its equilibrium value, and the corresponding net absorption of energy will be reduced. The greatest degree of saturation occurs at the maximum value of $g(\nu)$, where absorption is reduced by a factor

$$(1 + \gamma^2 H_1^2 T_1 T_2)^{-1} \tag{3-35}$$

This is frequently called the *saturation factor*. If we substitute typical values for liquids $T_1 = T_2 = 1$ sec, $\gamma = 10^4$ gauss^{-1} sec^{-1}, Eq. (3-35) becomes $(1 + 10^8 H_1^2)^{-1}$, so that saturation becomes appreciable when $H_1 \approx 10^{-4}$ gauss.

In addition to reducing the over-all magnitude of the absorption, saturation will distort the signal; for according to Eq. (3-34), the reduction is proportional to $g(\nu)$. Since the reduction is greatest for the maximum value of $g(\nu)$, there will be an apparent increase in half width—a saturation broadening. If the spectrum consists of a number of lines, it is possible that the lines may have different relaxation times, and so may be affected nonuniformly by saturation. This was demonstrated for the proton spectrum of 2-bromo-5-chlorothiophene by Anderson[11] (Fig. 4-6). Considerations of this sort make it advisable to avoid saturation effects if possible by employing sufficiently small rf fields.

Another experimental feature which is characteristic of saturation conditions is the appearance of multiple-quantum transitions. This is a transition which is forbidden by the first-order selection rules but occurs at a higher order with the absorption of two or more quanta. Evidence for this was also found by Anderson.[11] A striking example was given by Kaplan and Meiboom,[213] who found a signal in ethyl alcohol under saturation conditions which was halfway between the methyl and methylene resonances. In this transition two quanta are absorbed, simultaneously turning over the spins of a methyl and a methylene proton. This phenomenon has not yet been widely exploited in spectral interpretation. A simplified theory is given by Kaplan and Meiboom,[213] based on the general treatment of Bloch.[52]

3-5. The Bloch Formulation

In his original formulation of the behavior of nuclear magnetic moments in variable magnetic fields, Bloch[49] used a set of macroscopic or phenomenological equations for the variation of the components of the total nuclear magnetic moment per unit volume. Although these equations are introduced in the first place as postulates, it is found that their solutions reproduce many of the properties of nuclear resonance experiments. They have the further advantage of being suitable for the discussion of various time-dependent phenomena and transient effects, as we shall see in Secs. 3-6 and 3-7. For a discussion of detailed conditions under which they are strictly valid, the reader may consult papers by Wangsness and Bloch[454] and Bloch.[52]

Suppose we write

$$\mathbf{M} = (M_x, M_y, M_z) \tag{3-36}$$

for the resultant magnetic moment per unit volume of an assembly of identical nuclei, with magnetogyric ratio γ. We have already written down the equation of motion of a single magnetic moment in a magnetic field $\mathbf{H}$ [Eq. (3-16)]. By addition of such equations for all nuclei we should deduce that the macroscopic moment $\mathbf{M}$ satisfies a similar equation

$$\frac{d\mathbf{M}}{dt} = \gamma(\mathbf{M} \times \mathbf{H}) \tag{3-37}$$

Consider first the problem of a set of nuclei of spin 1/2 in a steady magnetic field $\mathbf{H}_0$ in the z direction. Then the z component of $\mathbf{M} \times \mathbf{H}$ will vanish and the three components of Eq. (3-37) will be

$$\frac{dM_x}{dt} = \omega_0 M_y \tag{3-38}$$

$$\frac{dM_y}{dt} = -\omega_0 M_x \tag{3-39}$$

$$\frac{dM_z}{dt} = 0 \tag{3-40}$$

where $\omega_0 = \gamma H_0$ and is the angular frequency of Larmor precession. The solution of these equations predicts that the total moment $\mathbf{M}$ will precess about the z direction with the Larmor frequency.

The equations in this form, however, do not allow for the relaxation effects we have already discussed, so they have to be modified by the addition of appropriate damping terms. We have already seen that M_z does not remain constant but approaches its equilibrium value M_0. If there are N nuclei per unit volume, each with spin 1/2, this is

$$M_0 = \frac{N\mu^2 H_0}{kT} = \chi_0 H_0 \tag{3-41}$$

The rate of approach is governed by the spin-lattice relaxation equation

$$\frac{dM_z}{dt} = -\frac{M_z - M_0}{T_1} \tag{3-42}$$

We may also expect a similar equation to hold if the nuclear spins I are greater than 1/2, M_0 then being obtained from Eqs. (3-5) and (3-41).

The equations for the x and y components also must be modified. According to the solution of Eqs. (3-38) and (3-39), the component perpendicular to $\mathbf{H}_0$ rotates about the z axis with the Larmor frequency. However, because of fluctuations and relaxation effects, the individual nuclei will get out of phase, and the components M_x and M_y will decay to zero. Bloch assumed that this decay proceeded in a way that could be represented by a term similar to that representing spin-lattice relaxation, but involving a different time T_2. Thus the x and y equations are

$$\frac{dM_x}{dt} = \omega_0 M_y - \frac{M_x}{T_2} \tag{3-43}$$

$$\frac{dM_y}{dt} = -\omega_0 M_x - \frac{M_y}{T_2} \tag{3-44}$$

In this formulation, T_2 defined in this way is referred to as the *transverse relaxation time*. We shall discuss the relation of the two definitions of T_2 below. Correspondingly the spin-lattice relaxation time T_1 is also called the *longitudinal relaxation time*.

It may not be clear at first why different relaxation times are introduced in the longitudinal and transverse directions. Some insight into this may be obtained if we consider a specimen in which the relative positions (but not directions) of the nuclear spins are held fixed or move only a little, as in a solid at low temperature, for example. The spin-lattice relaxation time T_1 is then very large, and M_z would change only slowly. There will still be a rapid decay of M_x and M_y, however, if we think about the effects of local fields due to neighboring nuclei. If the range of such local fields is δH, the nuclei will be precessing at angular frequencies which cover a range $\gamma(\delta H)$. As a result, different nuclei will get out of phase in a time $1/\gamma(\delta H)$ and the amplitude of M_x or M_y will decay in a time $T_2 \approx 1/\gamma(\delta H)$. This corresponds with our previous discussion of the broadening due to local magnetic fields (Sec. 3-3). The exact equivalence between the two definitions of T_2 will become apparent when we discuss solutions of the phenomenological equations.

These considerations apply when the magnetic field fluctuations due to lattice or molecular motion are slow. We may also consider the other extreme, where molecular rotation and diffusion are taking place rapidly, as in liquids. The local magnetic field then changes rapidly from one value to another and the above arguments do not apply. Indeed, if the local field changes many times during a single rotation of the dipole in its precession with angular frequency ω_0, the mechanism of decay of M_x and M_y will be just the same as it would be for a nonprecessing system. In fact it will be identical with the mechanism of spin-lattice relaxation which makes M_z approach its equilibrium value. T_1 and T_2 will then be identical. We may put this in quantitative terms if we introduce a *correlation time* τ_c which is a measure of the time of fluctuations of the local environment. Thus τ_c is characteristic of the time of rotation of a molecule or the time of diffusion into a neighboring position. Then we may say that if the fluctuations are so rapid that

$$\omega_0 \tau_c \ll 1 \qquad (3\text{-}45)$$

the mechanism of decay of all components M_x, M_y, and M_z becomes identical and $T_1 = T_2$.

For most liquids, τ_c is roughly the time of rotation of a molecule and is generally of the order of 10^{-10} sec. (For polar liquids, for example, we may take it to be the Debye characteristic time in the theory of dielectric relaxation.) The frequency ω_0 is about 10^8 radians/sec for values of H_0 typical of those used in NMR experiments, so that the condition (3-45) is usually satisfied.

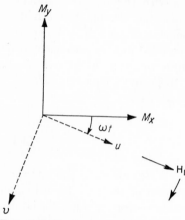

FIG. 3-2. Transverse components of the magnetic moment referred to fixed axes (full lines) and axes rotating with the rf field (dashed lines). The static magnetic field is normal to and upward from the plane of the paper.

So far, we have only considered nuclei in the fixed field H_0 along the z direction. The Bloch equations follow if we add the components of $\gamma(\mathbf{M} \times \mathbf{H}_1)$. Here $\mathbf{H}_1$ is a field perpendicular to $\mathbf{H}_0$ rotating with angular frequency ω (in the negative sense) with components

$$(H_1)_x = H_1 \cos \omega t \qquad (3\text{-}46)$$
$$(H_1)_y = -H_1 \sin \omega t \qquad (3\text{-}47)$$

Thus the complete equations are

$$\frac{dM_x}{dt} = \gamma(M_y H_0 + M_z H_1 \sin \omega t) - \frac{M_x}{T_2} \qquad (3\text{-}48)$$

$$\frac{dM_y}{dt} = \gamma(M_z H_1 \cos \omega t - M_x H_0) - \frac{M_y}{T_2} \qquad (3\text{-}49)$$

$$\frac{dM_z}{dt} = \gamma(-M_x H_1 \sin \omega t - M_y H_1 \cos \omega t) - \frac{M_z - M_0}{T_1} \qquad (3\text{-}50)$$

a. The Bloch Equations for Rotating Axes. The Bloch equations (3-48) to (3-50) take a simpler form if, instead of being referred to fixed axes x, y, and z, they are referred to a set of axes rotating with the applied rf field $\mathbf{H}_1$. This means that we define a new set of axes rotating with angular velocity $-\omega$ about the z axis. Then we define u and v as the components of $\mathbf{M}$ along and perpendicular to the direction of $\mathbf{H}_1$. They are often called the in-phase and out-of-phase components of $\mathbf{M}$; they are shown in Fig. 3-2. The relations between the components are

$$M_x = u \cos \omega t - v \sin \omega t \tag{3-51}$$
$$M_y = -u \sin \omega t - v \cos \omega t \tag{3-52}$$

or, in reverse,

$$u = M_x \cos \omega t - M_y \sin \omega t \tag{3-53}$$
$$v = -M_x \sin \omega t - M_y \cos \omega t \tag{3-54}$$

If we substitute Eqs. (3-51) and (3-52) in the Bloch equations, we obtain a new set for the three components u, v, and M_z referred to rotating axes.

$$\frac{du}{dt} + \frac{u}{T_2} + (\omega_0 - \omega)v = 0 \tag{3-55}$$

$$\frac{dv}{dt} + \frac{v}{T_2} - (\omega_0 - \omega)u + \gamma H_1 M_z = 0 \tag{3-56}$$

$$\frac{dM_z}{dt} + \frac{M_z - M_0}{T_1} - \gamma H_1 v = 0 \tag{3-57}$$

These are now a set of coupled linear differential equations with constant coefficients and are easily solved.

b. Steady-state Solution of the Bloch Equations. To discuss the magnetic resonance absorption experiment, we need the steady-state solution of the Bloch equations in which M_z is constant and the transverse components rotate with the applied rf field $\mathbf{H}_1$. This solution is easily obtained from Eqs. (3-55) to (3-57) by putting all time derivatives equal to zero. Then we obtain

$$u = M_0 \frac{\gamma H_1 T_2{}^2(\omega_0 - \omega)}{1 + T_2{}^2(\omega_0 - \omega)^2 + \gamma^2 H_1{}^2 T_1 T_2} \tag{3-58}$$

$$v = -M_0 \frac{\gamma H_1 T_2}{1 + T_2{}^2(\omega_0 - \omega)^2 + \gamma^2 H_1{}^2 T_1 T_2} \tag{3-59}$$

$$M_z = M_0 \frac{1 + T_2{}^2(\omega_0 - \omega)^2}{1 + T_2{}^2(\omega_0 - \omega)^2 + \gamma^2 H_1{}^2 T_1 T_2} \tag{3-60}$$

The solution for the transverse components may be reconverted to the components relative to fixed axes

$$M_x = \frac{1}{2} M_0 \gamma T_2 \frac{T_2(\omega_0 - \omega)2H_1 \cos \omega t + 2H_1 \sin \omega t}{1 + T_2{}^2(\omega_0 - \omega)^2 + \gamma^2 H_1{}^2 T_1 T_2} \tag{3-61}$$

$$M_y = \frac{1}{2} M_0 \gamma T_2 \frac{2H_1 \cos \omega t - T_2(\omega_0 - \omega)2H_1 \sin \omega t}{1 + T_2{}^2(\omega_0 - \omega)^2 + \gamma^2 H_1{}^2 T_1 T_2} \tag{3-62}$$

All these solutions apply only for a rotating field $\mathbf{H}_1$. It is clear that, if the angular frequency ω is far from the natural frequency ω_0, the magnetic moments induced perpendicularly to the steady field are small. If, therefore, we have a linear oscillating magnetic field

$$H_x = 2H_1 \cos \omega t \tag{3-63}$$
$$H_y = 0 \tag{3-64}$$

where ω is close to ω_0, it can be decomposed into equal and opposite rotating fields. One of them will be rotating in the same direction as the Larmor precession, so that $\omega - \omega_0$ will be small and the resonance effects predicted by Eqs. (3-61) and (3-62) will be large. The effects of the other component rotating in the opposite direction will be given by replacing $\omega - \omega_0$ by $\omega + \omega_0$ and will be negligibly small. The solutions (3-60) to (3-62) therefore apply also to the case of the linear oscillating field.

The effect of the linear field (3-63) is sometimes described in terms of susceptibilities χ' and χ'', often referred to as Bloch susceptibilities. Thus the field $2H_1 \cos \omega t$ produces an in-phase intensity of magnetization equal to $2\chi' H_1 \cos \omega t$ and an out-of-phase part $2\chi'' H_1 \sin \omega t$. Since $M_0 = \chi_0 H_0$,

$$\chi' = \frac{1}{2} \chi_0 \omega_0 \frac{T_2{}^2(\omega_0 - \omega)}{1 + T_2{}^2(\omega_0 - \omega)^2 + \gamma^2 H_1{}^2 T_1 T_2} \tag{3-65}$$

$$\chi'' = \frac{1}{2} \chi_0 \omega_0 \frac{T_2}{1 + T_2{}^2(\omega_0 - \omega)^2 + \gamma^2 H_1{}^2 T_1 T_2} \tag{3-66}$$

If we examine the expression for M_x in Eq. (3-61), that is, the component in the direction of the oscillating linear field, we see there is a term proportional to $\sin \omega t$. This is out of phase with the applied oscillating field. The rate of absorption of energy per unit volume is $-M_x \, dH_x/dt$, which contains a term proportional to $\cos \omega t \sin \omega t$ that averages to zero and a term proportional to $\sin^2 \omega t$ that averages to $\frac{1}{2}$. The mean rate of absorption of energy per unit volume is therefore

$$\frac{\omega \gamma H_1{}^2 M_0 T_2}{1 + T_2{}^2(\omega_0 - \omega)^2 + \gamma^2 H_1{}^2 T_1 T_2} \tag{3-67}$$

which clearly rises to a maximum when ω is in the neighborhood of the Larmor precession frequency ω_0. This rate of absorption is proportional to the Bloch susceptibility χ''.

If the oscillating magnetic field is small, so that

$$H_1 \ll \frac{1}{\gamma \sqrt{T_1 T_2}} \tag{3-68}$$

the rate of absorption of energy becomes

$$\frac{\omega \gamma H_1{}^2 M_0 T_2}{1 + T_2{}^2(\omega_0 - \omega)^2} \tag{3-69}$$

Equation (3-69) gives the form of the line-shape function $g(\nu)$ introduced in Sec. 3-3†

$$g(\nu) = \frac{2T_2}{1 + 4\pi^2 T_2^2 (\nu_0 - \nu)^2} \tag{3-70}$$

Equation (3-70) describes a Lorentzian curve which is proportional to the Bloch susceptibility function χ'' shown plotted in Fig. 3-3a. The peak value is given by

$$[g(\nu)]_{\text{max}} = 2T_2 \tag{3-71}$$

This is consistent with our previous definition of T_2. In practice, line shapes are not always well approximated by the Lorentz-type curve. This, of course, represents a limitation of the original phenomenological equations.

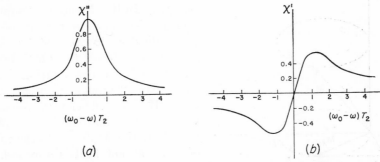

FIG. 3-3. (a) Absorption and (b) dispersion shapes predicted by the Bloch equations.[49]

By a suitable modification of the experimental apparatus, it is also possible to observe the component of M_x which is in phase with the applied rf field. For small values of H_1 this gives a susceptibility χ' which is proportional to

$$\frac{\nu_0 - \nu}{1 + 4\pi^2 T_2^2 (\nu_0 - \nu)^2} \tag{3-72}$$

This is illustrated in Fig. 3-3b. The two extreme values occur at frequencies which are $1/2\pi T_2$ on either side of ν_0.

Returning to the complete expression (3-67), we may note that, at the resonant frequency, the denominator becomes $1 + \gamma^2 H_1^2 T_1 T_2$ and corresponds exactly with the saturation factor derived previously from the quantum-mechanical treatment.

c. Nuclear-induction and Slow-passage Experiments. Another result which follows from the general solution of the Bloch equations (3-48) to (3-50) is that an oscillating magnetic moment is also induced in the y direc-

† In the numerator of Eq. (3-69) ω may be approximated by ω_0.

tion, perpendicular to both the static field H_0 and the oscillating field $2H_1 \cos \omega t$. Thus an electromotive force will be induced in a coil with axis along the y direction, having components both in and out of phase with the applied field. This closely related effect was termed nuclear induction by Bloch and was first detected in the original experiments of Bloch, Hansen, and Packard.[54]

Rather more insight into the nature of induction experiments can be obtained from a study of the magnetic-moment components u and v referred to rotating axes. For given ω and ω_0 these have the steady forms (3-58) and (3-59). In practice, the experiment is carried out by varying the field H_0 for a fixed frequency. For the steady-state solutions to apply, the rate of change of H_0 must be slow. If it is slow enough for Eqs. (3-58) and (3-59) to apply, conditions are said to be those of *slow passage*. In the absence of saturation (small H_1), the component of **M** perpendicular to the static field (sometimes referred to as $\mathbf{M}_{xy}$) traces out a circle in the rotating frame which passes through the origin (Fig. 3-4). If H_0 is well below the resonant value, u and v both vanish and **M** is parallel to the field $\mathbf{H}_0$. As the value of the resonant field is approached, the vector $\mathbf{M}_{xy}$ approaches the point P around the circle, returning to zero on the other side. Either the u or v components of this vector can be observed in the induction circuit as the field sweeps through the resonant value in this manner. The experimental details will be described in Chap. 4.

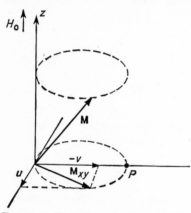

FIG. 3-4. Variation of the magnetization vector in the rotating frame of reference when H_0 is increased slowly through the resonance value.

We now turn to a consideration of the signal strength. By Faraday's law the voltage induced in the receiver coil is proportional to the rate of change of the moment induced in the y direction:

$$V = -K \frac{dM_y}{dt} \tag{3-73}$$

where K is a constant depending on the coil geometry and the sample filling factor. The moment M_y may be rewritten in terms of the Bloch susceptibilities as

$$M_y = 2H_1(\chi'' \cos \omega t - \chi' \sin \omega t)$$

so that
$$V = 2K\omega H_1(\chi'' \sin \omega t + \chi' \cos \omega t) \tag{3-74}$$

From Eq. (3-74) it is evident that the induced emf of the out-of-phase component (v mode) is proportional to $\omega H_1 \chi''$ and that of the in-phase component (u mode) to $\omega H_1 \chi'$. From Eqs. (3-66) and (3-65) the observed signal for the v mode is proportional to

$$\frac{\omega \chi_0 H_0 \gamma H_1 T_2}{1 + T_2^2(\omega_0 - \omega)^2 + (\gamma H_1)^2 T_1 T_2} \qquad (3\text{-}75)$$

and that of the u mode to

$$\frac{\omega \chi_0 H_0 \gamma H_1 T_2^2(\omega_0 - \omega)}{1 + T_2^2(\omega_0 - \omega)^2 + (\gamma H_1)^2 T_1 T_2} \qquad (3\text{-}76)$$

Under optimum conditions, that is, $(\gamma H_1)^2 T_1 T_2 = 1$, the peak voltage of the *absorption* signal is, from Eq. (3-75),

$$V \propto \omega_0 \chi_0 H_0 \left(\frac{T_2}{T_1}\right)^{1/2} \qquad (3\text{-}77)$$

or, employing Eq. (3-5),

$$V \propto N \frac{I+1}{I} \frac{\mu^2}{T} \omega_0 H_0 \left(\frac{T_2}{T_1}\right)^{1/2} \qquad (3\text{-}78)$$

For a given experimental arrangement at constant temperature and for $T_1 = T_2$, it is apparent that, at a given frequency, the signal strength (peak intensity) is proportional to

$$N(I+1)\mu\omega_0^2 \qquad (3\text{-}79)$$

and for a given field, to

$$N \frac{I+1}{I^2} \mu^3 H_0^2 \qquad (3\text{-}80)$$

Several features of these equations are important in the practical determination of intensities, particularly for quantitative analysis (Chap. 19). It is important to know how the intensities measured by areas under absorption signals compare with those obtained from peak heights and how they depend on relaxation times and the rf field H_1. By integration of Eq. (3-75), the area under the absorption signal is

$$A_a \propto \frac{\chi_0 H_1}{(1 + \gamma^2 H_1^2 T_1 T_2)^{1/2}} \qquad (3\text{-}80a)$$

whereas the corresponding peak height is

$$S_{a,\text{max}} \propto \frac{\chi_0 H_1 T_2}{1 + \gamma^2 H_1^2 T_1 T_2} \qquad (3\text{-}80b)$$

For low rf fields, therefore, peak-height comparisons are valid only for identical T_2.

It is sometimes useful to use the dispersion signal (u mode) for which the frequency dependence is given by Eq. (3-76). This has turning points when

$$\omega_0 - \omega = \pm \frac{(1 + \gamma^2 H_1^2 T_1 T_2)^{\frac{1}{2}}}{T_2} \qquad (3\text{-}80c)$$

when the signal amplitude is

$$S_{d,\max} \propto \frac{\chi_0 H_1 T_2}{(1 + \gamma^2 H_1^2 T_1 T_2)^{\frac{1}{2}}} \qquad (3\text{-}80d)$$

It is of interest to note by comparison of Eqs. (3-80b) and (3-80d) that the maximum dispersion signal, unlike the absorption signal, does not diminish to zero as H_1 is increased indefinitely. The area under either half of the dispersion signal is infinite, but a simple result follows if the integration is carried out as far as the turning value (3-80c). One then finds

$$A_{d,\text{partial}} \propto \chi_0 H_1 \qquad (3\text{-}80e)$$

which is completely independent of both relaxation times T_1 and T_2. All these measures of intensity are proportional to the susceptibility χ_0 [Eq. (3-5)] and consequently to the number of nuclei present.

3-6. Phenomena Dependent on Sweep Rate

If the frequency is held constant and the field H_0 is varied rather more rapidly, the slow-passage solution of the Bloch equations discussed in the last section is no longer adequate to describe the results. If the rate of change of H_0 is fast enough, the signal changes its shape and shows a series of characteristic oscillations, or "wiggles," in the tail after passing resonance. This phenomenon was first observed by Bloembergen, Purcell, and Pound,[59] who also gave a qualitative explanation. As we have already seen, the effect of the rf field H_1 near the resonance condition is to turn the vector **M** representing the magnetic moment per unit volume away from its equilibrium value parallel to the strong field H_0. Under the slow-passage conditions, **M** will return to the equilibrium value according to the adiabatic solution after H_0 has passed the resonance value. If the variation of H_0 is rapid, however, the moment will not be able to follow it, and **M** will still be left in a nonequilibrium direction after H_0 has passed so far beyond the resonance value that the rf field is no longer able to exert any effective torque. Under these circumstances the magnetization vector will simply precess in the field H_0 until the transverse components eventually decay in a time of the order of the transverse relaxation time T_2. During this period, the magnetic moment vector **M** and the rf field H_1 will be rotating about the direction of H_0 at different rates, so that they will alternately go in and out of phase. The absorption signal, which measures the out-of-phase component, will therefore show a series of damped oscillations after passage through resonance.

An approximate expression for the spacing of the wiggles can be obtained[57] in terms of the rate of change of the strong field H_0. Suppose that H_0 is a linear function of time and that the rate of change of the corresponding Larmor angular velocity is a; then

$$a = |\gamma| \frac{dH_0}{dt} \qquad (3\text{-}81)$$

Then at a time t after passing the resonance value, the angular velocities of the rf field H_1 and the Larmor precession will differ by at. The phase angle between H_1 and the transverse component of M is then $\frac{1}{2}at^2$ by integration. Including a factor $\exp(-t/T_2)$ to allow for the decay of the transverse component by relaxation, we deduce that the signal shape is proportional to

$$e^{-t/T_2} \cos \frac{1}{2}at^2 \qquad (3\text{-}82)$$

or, in angular-frequency units,

$$e^{-\Delta\omega/aT_2} \cos \frac{\frac{1}{2}(\Delta\omega)^2}{a} \qquad (3\text{-}83)$$

where $\Delta\omega$ is the separation between the instantaneous Larmor angular frequency and the fixed frequency. Under conditions where the decay of wiggles is relatively slow, the separation between two maxima far down the tail will be approximately

$$\delta(\Delta\omega) = \frac{2\pi a}{\omega} \qquad (3\text{-}84)$$

and is inversely proportional to the distance from resonance.

These results are approximate only and do not take adequate account of the effect of the rf field while the system is still near resonance. A more satisfactory treatment based on the Bloch equations was given by Jacobsohn and Wangsness[206] for nonsaturation conditions. They found that, if a is sufficiently large (rapid passage), asymptotic solutions similar to Eqs. (3-82) and (3-83) were valid, but that for smaller a, the wiggles were not as prominent, and did not appear at all if $a \leq \frac{1}{4}T_2^{-2}$. A series of calculated line shapes obtained by Jacobsohn and Wangsness[206] for a series of values of $a^{1/2}T_2$ are shown in Fig. 3-5.

Under suitable conditions, the decay of the wiggles may be used to measure the relaxation time T_2 according to Eq. (3-83). However, this is possible only if the line widths are determined by relaxation rather than inhomogeneity of the magnetic field. The decay of signals in inhomogeneous fields has been discussed in a number of papers by Gabillard.[139-141]

If the slow-passage spectrum consists of two signals rather than one, there may be interference between the wiggles from the two tails if the whole resonance region is traversed sufficiently rapidly. Beats due to this effect were observed by Bené, Denis, and Extermann.[35] More recently it has been used to obtain separations within a spin multiplet by Glick and Bothner-By[143] and by Reilly.[379] This work is discussed further in Sec. 4-7.

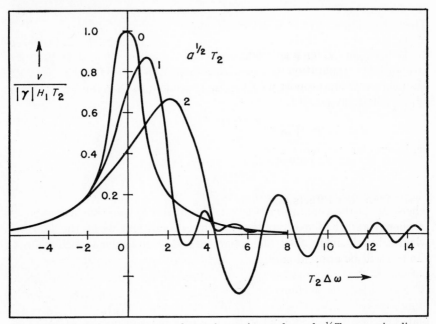

FIG. 3-5. Out-of-phase resonance shapes for various values of $a^{1/2}T_2$, assuming linear sweep. (Jacobsohn and Wangsness.[206])

The formation of these "wiggle beats" can be illustrated by the interference between the tails of two equally intense signals separated by an energy J, measured in cycles per second. If, following Eq. (3-82), it is assumed that the two signals to be superposed are

$$V_1(t) = V_0 e^{-t/T_2} \cos \tfrac{1}{2} a t^2$$
$$V_2(t) = V_0 e^{-(t-t_0)/T_2} \cos \tfrac{1}{2} a (t - t_0)^2 \qquad (3\text{-}85)$$

the time t_0 between the two resonant frequencies is

$$t_0 = \frac{2\pi J}{a} \qquad (3\text{-}86)$$

If t_0 is small compared to the relaxation time T_2, the combined signal can be written

$$V(t) = V_1(t) + V_2(t) = 2V_0 e^{-t/T_2} \cos(\tfrac{1}{2}at^2 - \tfrac{1}{2}att_0 + \tfrac{1}{4}at_0^2)$$
$$\cos(\tfrac{1}{2}att_0 - \tfrac{1}{4}at_0^2) \quad (3\text{-}87)$$

In this expression the first cosine factor represents increasingly rapid oscillations as for a single signal and the second factor represents a modulating factor leading to beats, the time between maxima being

$$\frac{2\pi}{at_0} = \frac{1}{J} \quad (3\text{-}88)$$

Reilly[379] has given a general formula for a multiplet of n equally spaced signals, the separation between neighbors being J cycles/sec and the intensities being proportional to the corresponding binomial coefficients. For sufficiently small t_0, he finds

$$V(t) = 2^{n-1}V_0 e^{-t/T_2} \cos[\tfrac{1}{2}at^2 - (n-1)\pi Jt] \cos^{n-1}\pi Jt \quad (3\text{-}89)$$

so that the period between beat maxima is still $1/J$.

3-7. Transient Effects and Spin Echoes

Up to this point we have been concerned with the application of a continuous rf magnetic field H_1 to a sample in a uniform magnetic field H_0. In such an experiment there is set up a steady state in which the tendency of the rf field to equalize the population of the Zeeman levels (and so demagnetize the system) is balanced against the tendency of thermal motions to restore the Boltzmann distribution. Rather different phenomena of a transient nature are observed if the rf field is changed discontinuously. Useful experiments of this sort are possible because electronic response times are short compared with the time of decay T_2 of a Larmor precession.

Torrey[442] made a detailed study of solutions of the Bloch equations if the system starts with the magnetization vector along the direction of the static field H_0 and the rf field is suddenly switched on. The approach to the steady-state solution is oscillatory in character.

Hahn[175,176] has developed an important method based on electronic pulses of the field H_1 which aims at observing the nuclear-induction signals after the rf field is cut off. From a theoretical point of view, this is rather simpler than the situation considered by Torrey[442] for after removing the field H_1, the nuclear magnetization vector precesses only in the static field H_0, and the Bloch equations take a simpler form.

a. Free Induction Decay. Hahn first examined the response of a system to a single rf pulse.[175] We have already seen that the effect of the rotating field $\mathbf{H}_1$ at the resonance frequency is to tip the magnetization vector $\mathbf{M}$ away from its equilibrium direction parallel to the static field $\mathbf{H}_0$. If the field $\mathbf{H}_1$ is switched on for a finite period and then switched off again, the vector $\mathbf{M}$ will have its direction changed by an amount depending on the length of the pulse and will subsequently precess about $\mathbf{H}_0$ with the Larmor frequency until components perpendicular to $\mathbf{H}_0$ decay by relaxation or other means. The induction signal produced in this *off* period is a *free induction decay*, originally discussed by Bloch.[49]

If the amplitude of the rf field is H_1, the effect of the field on the magnetization vector $\mathbf{M}$ is to rotate it away from the z direction (the direction of the static field) with an angular velocity γH_1 (Sec. 3-3). If the amplitude H_1 is fairly large and the duration of the pulse t_w is short, relaxation effects during the *on* period will be negligible and the total effect will be to rotate $\mathbf{M}$ through an angle $\gamma H_1 t_w$. If H_1 and t_w are so chosen that

$$\gamma H_1 t_w = \tfrac{1}{2}\pi \tag{3-90}$$

the vector $\mathbf{M}$ will be turned into the xy plane. Such pulses are referred to as 90° pulses. Pulses for which $\gamma H_1 t_w = \pi$ are 180° pulses and would have the effect of completely reversing the direction of $\mathbf{M}$. The effects of 90° pulses are best understood in terms of the coordinate frame rotating with the frequency of the pulse (Fig. 3-2). Then, immediately after the pulse, the vector $\mathbf{M}$ will be entirely in the v direction. This applies only if the pulse is short enough, when the effect will be less sensitive to any deviation from the exact resonance frequency.

If the magnetic field $\mathbf{H}_0$ were perfectly homogeneous, the behavior of the magnetic moment vector $\mathbf{M}$ after the end of the pulse will be governed by the relaxation processes previously discussed. Thus the component in the plane perpendicular to $\mathbf{H}_0$ will precess about the z axis with the Larmor frequency while its amplitude decays exponentially, being proportional to $\exp(-t/T_2)$. Meanwhile the z component, having been reduced to zero, will recover to its equilibrium value (in a time of the order of the spin-lattice relaxation time T_1). If we measure the component v by an induction method, therefore, we should get a signal decaying at a rate $\exp(-t/T_2)$.

If the inhomogeneity of the static field $\mathbf{H}_0$ is not negligible, however, decay is more rapid. This can be illustrated pictorially in terms of a series of diagrams representing the positions of the vectors $\mathbf{M}$ in various parts of the specimen at various times in the decay process. The effect of magnetic field inhomogeneity will be a distribution of Larmor precession frequencies ω_0 rather than a single value. We shall suppose the specimen divided up into a number of regions each of which possesses a nuclear magnetization vector **M** and examine the motion of these vectors in a frame of reference which is rotating with an angular velocity which is equal to the mean Larmor precession. Hahn[176] has called these individual vectors *spin isochromats*.

The effect of a 90° pulse will be to turn all the spin vectors into the xy plane perpendicular to the static field. If we choose axes x^* and y^* in the rotating frame, so that the applied rf pulse is in the x^* directon, then at the end of the pulse all the spin isochromats will be parallel to the y^* axis (Fig. 3-6b). But since these have different precession frequencies (being in different fields H_0), some will rotate faster than the reference

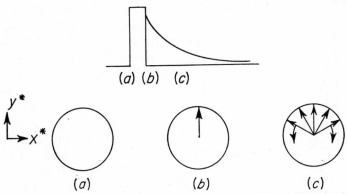

FIG. 3-6. Behavior of spin isochromats during free induction decay (a) at beginning of pulse, (b) at end of pulse, and (c) during decay.

frame and some slower. In the reference frame the effect will be a fanning out of the individual vectors as indicated in Fig. 3-6c. Since the induction coil can detect only the vector sum of these moments, there will be a decay of the observed signal.

To get a quantitative expression for the decay rate, we consider one of the magnetization vectors of Fig. 3-6c corresponding to a region where the Larmor precession frequency exceeds its mean value by $\Delta\omega_0$. Measuring the time t from the end of the pulse (Fig. 3-6b), this vector will have its magnitude reduced by a factor $\exp(-t/T_2)$ and its direction will make an angle $(\Delta\omega_0)t$ with the mean vector. The total resultant will therefore be proportional to

$$e^{-t/T_2} \int_{-\infty}^{\infty} g(\Delta\omega_0) \cos(\Delta\omega_0)t \, d(\Delta\omega_0) \tag{3-91}$$

where $g(\Delta\omega_0) \, d(\Delta\omega_0)$ is the probability of a particular spin vector having its frequency deviation in the range $\Delta\omega_0$ to $\Delta\omega_0 + d(\Delta\omega_0)$. Hahn[175] assumed an explicit form for $g(\Delta\omega_0)$:

$$g(\Delta\omega_0) = \frac{2T_2^*}{1 + (\Delta\omega_0)^2 T_2^{*2}} \tag{3-92}$$

so that T_2^* is a time characterizing the width of the spectrum due to field inhomogeneity. In fact

$$T_2^* = \frac{2}{(\Delta\omega_0)_{\frac{1}{2}}} \tag{3-93}$$

where $(\Delta\omega_0)_{\frac{1}{2}}$ is the total width at half maximum of the function (3-92). Integration of Eq. (3-91) then gives a function that is proportional to $\exp(-t/T_m)$, where

$$\frac{1}{T_m} = \frac{1}{T_2} + \frac{1}{T_2^*} \tag{3-94}$$

Hahn[175] made use of this formula to study the variation of T_2 for protons in aqueous solutions of ferric ions. Two decay signals obtained at different concentrations are illustrated in Fig. 3-7.

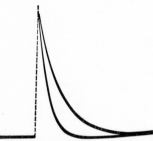

FIG. 3-7. Reproduction of double exposure of oscilloscope trace showing free induction decay of protons in aqueous solutions of $Fe(NO_3)_3$ at different concentrations. (Hahn.[175]) The longer decay corresponds to 2×10^{19} Fe^{3+}/cm^3 and the shorter to 9×10^{19} Fe^{3+}/cm^3, causing values of T_2 of 0.0018 and 0.0004 sec, respectively. Pulse time $t_w \approx$ 100 μsec.

b. Spin Echoes. Except for systems in which the relaxation times are very short, the signal in a free induction decay is dominated by the field inhomogeneity leading to the fanning out of the individual vectors in the xy plane. An important step in eliminating the effects of this artificial decay was made by Hahn[176] when he discovered the existence of *spin echoes*. He found that the application of a second pulse at a time τ after the first was followed by an echo pulse at time 2τ, even though the signal had decayed to zero during the intervening period. Hahn gave a theory of the response of a nuclear system to two or three pulses of equal duration, particularly for 90° pulses. Later Carr and Purcell[86] developed the use of a combination of 90 and 180° pulses, for which the explanation of the effect is qualitatively rather simpler.

The response of the spin isochromats to successive 90 and 180° pulses can be illustrated by the series of diagrams shown in Fig. 3-8. As in Fig. 3-6, these show the behavior of the various vectors in a frame rotating with the Larmor precession frequency corresponding to the mean value of the static field. The various steps are as follows:

(A) Initially the system is in thermal equilibrium and all the spin vectors are lined up in the z direction parallel to the static field.

(B) During the application of the first pulse, the vectors are tipped away from the z direction toward the y' direction in the rotating frame by the rf field in the x' direction.

(C) At the end of the 90° pulse the moments are all in the equatorial plane in the y' direction. If the pulse duration t_w is sufficiently short, there will have been no relaxation or fanning out due to field inhomogeneities.

(D) After the field H_1 is switched off, free induction decay takes place and the individual vectors in the $x'y'$ plane fan out.

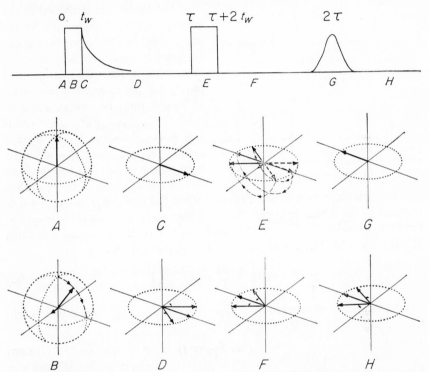

Fig. 3-8. The formation of an echo after successive 90 and 180° pulses. (From Carr and Purcell.[86])

(E) After a time τ a second 180° pulse is applied, lasting for a period $2t_w$. This turns the whole fanned system of vectors through 180° about the x' axis.

(F) After the second pulse, each individual vector continues to move in the rotating frame in the same direction as before. Now, however, this fanning motion will lead to a closing up of the vectors.

(G) At time 2τ, the set of vectors in the $x'y'$ plane will be completely reclustered, leading to a strong resultant moment in the negative y' direction. This will lead to a signal in the detector coil and is the "echo."

(H) After the echo, the vectors again fan out and a normal decay is observed.

It is clear from these diagrams that the shape of the echo, like the shape of the free induction decay, depends on the rate of fanning out of the individual vectors. The width of the echo will be less in an inhomo-

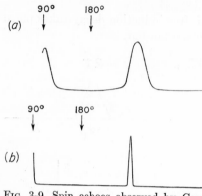

geneous field. Examples of echoes observed by Carr and Purcell[86] are shown in Fig. 3-9.

If the molecules remained in the same part of the magnetic field, the above qualitative description would be accurate and the amplitude of the echo would be determined purely by the relaxation processes. It would then be proportional to exp $(-2\tau/T_2)$. But, in liquids and gases, diffusion is not always negligible, and some loss of coher-

FIG. 3-9. Spin echoes observed by Carr and Purcell[86] (a) in a very homogeneous field and (b) in a less homogeneous field.

ence at the echo time results from the fact that some of the spin vec-

tors change their rate of fanning out when the molecules move to a new position in the inhomogeneous field. This can be investigated quantitatively by random-walk methods and related to the diffusion constant. Hahn[176] showed that the amplitude then depended on τ as

$$\exp\left[-\frac{2\tau}{T_2} - k\frac{(2\tau)^3}{3}\right] \tag{3-95}$$

The theoretical calculation of k was later modified by Carr and Purcell, who obtained for the 90–180° echo

$$k = \tfrac{1}{4}\gamma^2 G^2 D \tag{3-96}$$

where D is the diffusion constant and G is the mean value of the magnetic field gradient $(dH_0/dl)_{\text{av}}$. The main part of the decay will be dominated by the diffusion mechanism, therefore, if

$$\frac{12}{\gamma^2 G^2 D} \ll T_2^3 \tag{3-97}$$

A general theory of the Bloch equations with diffusion terms has been given by Torrey.[443]

Although the qualitative explanation is rather simpler for 90–180° pulse sequence, similar phenomena are observed for other pulses. Hahn[176] employed a pair of 90° pulses in his original experiments. In fact, he found the appropriate solution of the Bloch equations for two equal pulses of arbitrary duration and showed that the dependence on the time between pulses was given by an expression of the type (3-95).

One way in which a sequence of two 90° pulses differs from the 90–180° sequence is in the appearance of a decay signal after the second pulse. This is because, after a time τ, the moment in the z direction has been partially reestablished by the spin-lattice relaxation mechanism. The recovery function will be

$$1 - e^{-\tau/T_1} \tag{3-98}$$

so that the application of a second 90° pulse will lead to a decay the amplitude of which is less than that of the first decay by this factor. For a 180° second pulse, however, this recovery moment in the z direction will be turned through to the negative z direction and will not then possess any component in the xy plane.

The echo experiments can be extended to a larger number of pulses. Hahn[176] gave a detailed account of the several echoes in response to a third pulse. More general methods for any sequence of pulses have been developed by Das and Roy[110] and by Jaynes[209] and Bloom.[61]

Further complications arise if nuclei with different resonance frequencies are involved and if there is an indirect spin coupling interaction between them. The decay of the spin-echo amplitude as a function of the time between pulses τ is then no longer given by the simple form (3-95) but also contains certain periodic terms. Hahn[176] first observed this effect for ethanol, and similar measurements were used by McNeil, Slichter, and Gutowsky[278] and by Hahn and Maxwell[177,179] to get information about the indirect spin coupling constants. We shall not describe the theory in detail, however, because similar information has since been obtained by the steady-state methods.

CHAPTER 4

EXPERIMENTAL METHODS

In the preceding chapter the theory and phenomenological description of NMR absorption has been outlined.   We turn now to the experimental problem of observing nuclear resonance signals and measuring the NMR spectra of liquids and gases.   A variety of experimental methods has been devised to observe resonance signals; the continued improvement and development of the methods has made possible the field of high-resolution NMR spectroscopy.

4-1. The Nuclear Magnetic Resonance Experiment

The simplest experiment and arrangement for observing NMR absorption may be illustrated by means of the schematic diagram in Fig. 4-1. A sample containing nuclei which possess a magnetic moment is placed between the poles of a magnet of magnetic field strength H_0.   The magnetic moments of the nuclei in the sample tend to orient in the direction of the field, giving rise to a resultant macroscopic magnetic moment. The effect of the magnetic field, as shown in Secs. 3-3 and 3-5, is to cause a precession of the macroscopic moment about the direction of the field with an angular frequency γH_0.   If now a small coil T, connected to an rf signal generator, is wound around the sample so that the axis of the coil is at right angles to the direction of the applied field, there is introduced a small alternating magnetic field of strength H_1 which rotates about the H_0 direction with the particular radio frequency used (Fig. 3-1).   The field H_1 tends to tilt the direction of the moment away from the H_0 direction as the radio frequency is increased close to the precession frequency; at the resonant frequency, transitions are induced between the nuclear Zeeman levels.   These transitions correspond to some of the nuclear magnets changing their orientation in the field.   The energy absorbed in this process produces a drop in rf voltage in the tuned circuit containing the transmitter coil; the voltage drop may be detected, amplified, and fed into the vertical deflection plates of an oscilloscope. In practice, the radio frequency of the signal generator is fixed and the applied field H_0 is varied near the value at which resonance occurs.   This is accomplished by mounting, on the pole faces of the magnet, coils which can be used to sweep the field with an amplitude of a few gauss at some low frequency (about 50 cycles/sec).   The same sweep signal can be fed into the horizontal deflection plates of an oscilloscope, and the recurring absorption signal is displayed on the screen.

In 1946, NMR absorption was first detected, independently, by two groups of workers.   Purcell, Torrey, and Pound[358] observed changes in the sample coil (Fig. 4-1) when resonance was obtained in the sample,

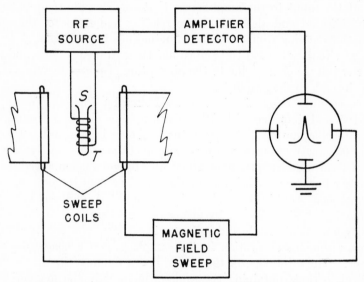

FIG. 4-1. Schematic diagram of apparatus for the NMR experiment. S = sample tube, T = rf coil.

while Bloch, Hansen, and Packard[53,54] investigated the signal induced in a receiver coil wound around the sample but at right angles to a second (transmitter) coil.   Both methods were applied immediately to accurate measurement of nuclear magnetic moments.   In the course of this work, it was found that the value obtained for a particular nucleus depended slightly on the chemical compound chosen.   As described in Sec. 1-4, this displacement of the frequency at which resonance occurred at fixed magnetic field (or the displacement of field at fixed frequency) was observed in metals and for the nuclei N^{14} and F^{19} and protons in various compounds.   High-resolution NMR spectroscopy originated when "internal" chemical shifts were discovered in ethyl alcohol; the shifts gave rise to three separate signals for the chemically different protons. The NMR techniques which enable internal chemical shifts to be resolved, and also the accompanying fine structure (Sec. 1-5), belong to the field of high-resolution NMR spectroscopy.   The present chapter will be primarily concerned with the description of high-resolution methods and apparatus.

4-2. Single-coil Method (Bridge Method)

In the arrangement shown in Fig. 4-1 the signal voltage induced across the tuned circuit is very small, and difficulties are encountered in obtaining a sufficiently high signal-to-noise ratio. In order to reduce the rf level at the input to the amplifier so that considerable rf amplification can be effected and also reduce the relative magnitude of the output fluctuations arising from amplitude fluctuations in the signal generator, a bridge circuit was used to balance out the extraneous noise and allow only the voltage change due to the absorption of power by the nuclei to come through to the amplifier.

A successful bridge circuit was used first by Purcell, Torrey, and Pound[358] and improved by Bloembergen, Purcell, and Pound.[59] A schematic diagram of their apparatus is shown in Fig. 4-2. The field (ca. 7,000 gauss) was provided by a permanent magnet. A signal generator of fixed radio frequency of about 30 Mc/sec was employed, so that the magnet was near the value of the resonant field for protons. The field was then swept in this region with an amplitude of about 15 gauss at a frequency of 30 cycles/sec by means of the sweep coils at the poles of the magnet. The sample and coil were in one arm of a balanced bridge, so that resonance absorption in the sample caused a change in bridge balance. The other arm of the bridge had a dummy circuit which was identical to that containing the sample, but not in the magnetic field. The resonance unbalanced the bridge and gave rise to an absorption signal (Fig. 3-3a), a dispersion signal (Fig. 3-3b), or a mixture of the two according to the amplitude and phase balance of the bridge. Either phase or amplitude unbalance could be obtained as desired, yielding in the first case the dispersion curve and in the second case the absorption curve. The details concerning optimum adjustment and characteristic values for resistances, condensers, and coils may be found in the papers of Bloembergen, Purcell, and Pound[59] and Bloembergen.[57]

For detecting weak signals, a narrow-band amplifier and balanced mixer were used after the rf amplifier and detector. This combination is usually referred to as a "lock-in," or phase-sensitive, amplifier. A detailed description of a lock-in amplifier is given by Dicke.[117] It should be pointed out that the output of the lock-in amplifier in the case of amplitude unbalance gives the derivative of the absorption curve, which resembles qualitatively Fig. 3-3b, whereas for phase unbalance the derivative of the dispersion curve is obtained, i.e., a large peak flanked symmetrically by two minima.

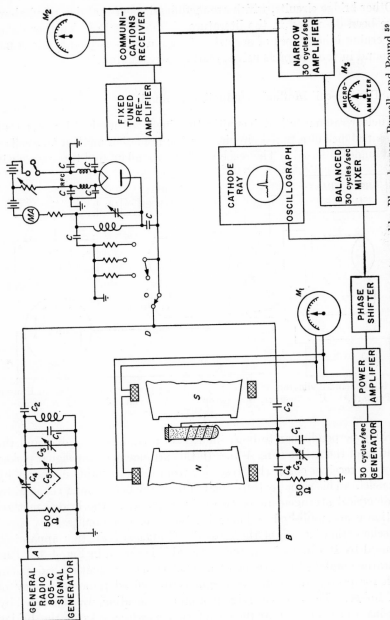

FIG. 4-2. Schematic diagram of the single-coil bridge spectrometer used by Bloembergen, Purcell, and Pound.[59]

Other bridge circuits, which are modifications of that described above, have been described in the literature.[318,442,8,150,455,440,77] Further details concerning other types of spectrometers and various modifications may be found in the comprehensive treatment by Andrew.[15]

4-3. Double-coil Methods (Induction Method)

Nuclear resonance is detected in the single-coil method by changes in the impedance of a tuned circuit. In the induction method two coils at right angles are used. The receiver coil is wound around the sample with

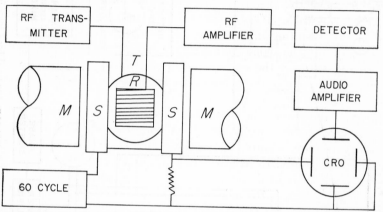

FIG. 4-3. Schematic diagram of the double-coil spectrometer used by Bloch, Hansen, and Packard.[54] M = magnet, S = sweep coils, T = transmitter coil, R = receiver coil.

its axis y perpendicular to both the axis of a transmitter coil x and the direction of the field z (Fig. 4-3). In this arrangement the signal picked up by the receiver coil is that resulting from the absorption of energy by the nuclei. This signal is thus isolated from the background rf signal by a geometrical arrangement of two coils, whereas in the bridge method isolation is accomplished by balancing two electrical circuits.

A schematic diagram of the crossed-coil nuclear-induction apparatus, first used by Bloch, Hansen, and Packard,[54] is shown in Fig. 4-3. This apparatus employed a permanent magnet of field strength 1,826 gauss, which for proton resonance corresponds to a fixed radio frequency of 7.76 Mc/sec. The resonance signal, after amplification, was displayed by sweeping the field at a frequency of 60 cycles/sec. As in the bridge method, for detection of weak signals a narrow-band amplifier and balanced mixer may be used after the rf-amplifier–detector system, that is, a lock-in amplifier.

From Sec. 3-5c we recall that the driving field H_1 is $\pi/2$ out of phase with the signal to be observed. Further, since H_1 is very much larger than the weak signal to be detected,[54] the coupling between transmitter and receiver coils must be small. This is accomplished by having the axes of the two coils almost at right angles to each other. Under these conditions, the residual coupling effect of H_1, called leakage, serves as a source of carrier signal, but as mentioned above, it is $\pi/2$ out of phase with the signal to be detected. If the leakage is denoted by a large vector and the resonance signal by a small vector at right angles to it, it is readily seen that variations in the signal cause variations in amplitude of the vector sum which are quadratic in the signal (a small effect). However, if the phase of the leakage is changed by $\pi/2$ so that the vectors are collinear, variations of signal amplitude appear linearly in the vector sum, and the resulting amplitude modulation is readily detected. Under these conditions the signal displayed will be the absorption mode v [Eq. (3-59)] and will have the shape shown in Fig. 3-3a. Alternatively, by a suitable adjustment of the phase of the leakage, the dispersion mode u is obtained [Eq. (3-58) and Fig. 3-3b].

In order to achieve the desired phase shift of the leakage, a rather ingenious device was introduced.[54] A paddle, which is a semicircular sheet of conductor mounted on a spindle lying along the axis of the transmitter coil, was used to regulate the magnitude of the leakage, or more precisely, the amount of component of the leakage which is $\pi/2$ out of phase. The action of the paddle can be understood by reference to Fig. 4-4. In Fig. 4-4a the transmitter coil is shown with the flux roughly parallel to its axis. Because of the symmetry of the flux about this axis, there is no linkage with any coil whose plane passes through the axis. The paddle is placed at one end of the coil as in Fig. 4-4b, so that the currents induced in it prevent the flux from passing through the sheet and indeed direct it at right angles to the axis of the coil as shown. In Fig. 4-4c the linkage of a coil in the axial plane will be reversed from that in Fig. 4-4b because the flux is now directed in the opposite direction. By rotation of the spindle, either positive or negative flux linkage with the receiver coil may be obtained. In this way the relative amount of in- and out-of-phase component can be varied. The paddle alone is not sufficient for complete control of the rectified signal, since any eddy currents produced in the paddle itself by the flux of the transmitter coil also generate a flux out of phase by $\pi/2$ (flux in quadrature). An additional control was introduced by Packard[315] and Levinthal.[245] An adjustable condenser with resistance network fed an rf voltage from the transmitter coil to the receiver coil in order to compensate for the voltage produced by the quadrature flux.

Just as the bridge is not completely balanced in the bridge method, the coils are never completely balanced in the induction method. An intentional unbalance (leakage) is achieved by first balancing the coils to a high degree and then setting an intentional phase or amplitude unbalance. This is accomplished in the induction head or probe. The nuclear induction head used by Bloch, Hansen, and Packard (illustrating the orthogonality of the receiver and transmitter coils as well as the

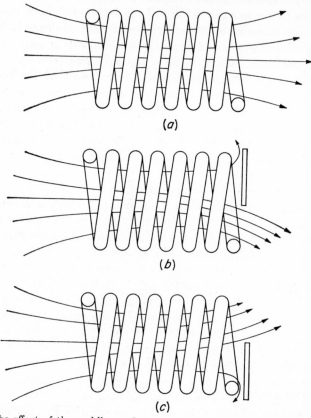

FIG. 4-4. The effect of the paddle on the transmitter coil flux. (Bloch, Hansen, and Packard.[54])

paddle arrangement for selecting the absorption or dispersion mode) is shown in Fig. 4-5.

A modified induction head used by Weaver[457] has the special feature that individual u- and v-mode controls were introduced. Gross decoupling between the receiver and transmitter coils was accomplished by having the axes of the coils perpendicular. Additional adjustment was obtained by tilting one of two transmitter coils with respect to the axis of the receiver coil by means of a differential screw. This relative movement of the two halves of the transmitter coil tilts the rf field, and thereby complete balancing of the quadrature voltage of the rf leakage induced in the receiver coil is achieved.   This is the v-mode balance, and at complete balance the residual leakage due to the in-phase voltage induced in the receiver coil is small but must be canceled.   This is done by a u-mode control consisting of an inductance loop and a series resistance.

A further modification of the induction head used by Bloch, Hansen, and Packard[54] is due to Packard.[315]   Here the transmitter and receiver coils are fixed in position and tuned by means of small ceramic trimmer condensers.   The leakage voltage is reduced to zero by adjusting the paddle and a u-mode control.   The u-mode control is a phase shifter which cancels the leakage, which is $\pi/2$ out of phase with respect to the

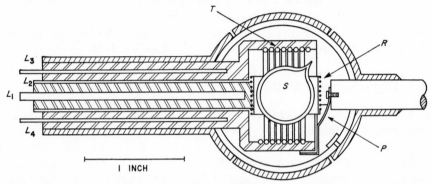

Fig. 4-5. Induction head used by Bloch, Hansen, and Packard.[54] S = sample; R = receiver coil; T = transmitter coil; P = paddle; L_1, L_2 = leads to R; L_3, L_4 = leads to T.

rf field.   When zero balance is obtained, either u or v mode can be obtained by changing the setting of the corresponding control.   Other induction heads used for high-resolution spectroscopy are described in Sec. 4-5b.

Apart from the advantage of being able to find the sign of the nuclear magnetic moment,[49] there seems to be little to choose between single- and double-coil methods.   For work at different temperatures, however, the single-coil methods, because of their greater simplicity of construction and adjustment, are somewhat more convenient.

4-4. Pulse Methods

Torrey[442] and Hahn[176] have investigated NMR signals when the rf field is applied not continuously, but in the form of pulses.   Torrey's method is concerned with the transient decaying oscillations of the signal during the time the pulses are applied (Sec. 3-7), whereas the method of Hahn is concerned with the transient behavior in the *off* time between pulses. In the *off* period the bridge circuit is not essential and the straightforward single-coil arrangement of Fig. 4-1 may be used. In the *off* period the single coil acts as a receiver, and in the *on* period it acts as a transmitter. When intense rf pulses are used, a bridge circuit is employed to prevent overloading of the receiver during the *on* periods.

In the precession and spin-echo experiments of Hahn[176] (Sec. 3-7), the response to a pulse or series of pulses is displayed directly on an oscilloscope. The simplest echo experiment is to observe the signal (at time 2τ) in response to a pair of pulses at times 0 and τ. For purposes of interpretation, it is necessary to find the amplitude of the echo as a function of τ. This is conveniently done by taking a multiple-exposure photograph of the echoes obtained for a series of values of τ each successively increased by a small amount. The "echo envelope" obtained in this way gives the amplitude as a function of τ. The use of these spin-echo methods in the determination of relaxation times is discussed in Sec. 4-10.

4-5. High-resolution Methods

a. **General Requirements.** All high-resolution spectrometers commonly used are modifications of the bridge type (Sec. 4-2) or the induction type (Sec. 4-3). In order to obtain resolution of the order of 1 part in 10^7 or better, a magnetic field of high homogeneity is required. The time stability of the magnetic field and of the rf transmitter must be of high order. The receiver should introduce as little noise as possible so that a high signal-to-noise ratio is obtainable, and the rate of change of the magnetic field (sweep rate) must be sufficiently low that conditions of slow passage (Sec. 3-5) through resonance are established. Further, the sweep rate should be low enough that transient effects (Sec. 3-6) are reduced as much as possible consistent with low enough rf power that saturation is avoided. The rf transmitter, usually of the Meacham crystal-bridge type,[280] has stability of 1 part in 10^9. A receiver preamplifier of the Wallman type[453] is satisfactory. The necessary sweep fields produced in the auxiliary bias coils are derived from a saw-tooth signal generator of the "boot-strap" variety, the output of which is practically linear, and the sweep rate can readily be varied over the ranges required. However, the most demanding requirements for high-resolution NMR measurements are high homogeneity and time stability of the magnetic field. Since high homogeneity over the sample volume enclosed by the rf coils is required, better resolution can be obtained with smaller samples. The effective homogeneity in the magnetic field can be further improved by spinning the sample (Sec. 4-6).

Magnets. Both permanent and electromagnets have been used to supply the main magnetic field in high-resolution spectrometers. Under optimum conditions, resolution corresponding to a homogeneity of 1 part in 10^8 has been achieved with spectrometers employing either type of magnet. It may be of some interest to consider briefly the relative merits and disadvantages of permanent and electromagnets. In order to achieve resolution with an electromagnet comparable to that obtained with a permanent magnet, a feedback stabilizer is necessary. This device averages out fast fluctuations due to current variations or reluctance changes, whereas the stabilizer used in conjunction with a permanent magnet[348] reduces the effects of stray fields and temperature variations. Stabilizers will be discussed in more detail in Sec. 4-5b. Since the signal intensity depends on $H_0{}^2$ (Sec. 3-5), it is desirable to obtain as high a static magnetic field strength as possible. A field strength up to 7,000 gauss can be realized in practice with a permanent magnet, whereas electromagnets can be readily operated at fields up to 13,000 gauss or higher. This represents a significant enhancement in signal strength obtainable with an electromagnet. Further, the field strength of an electromagnet may be varied over a considerable range and still have high field uniformity, whereas the field strength of a permanent magnet is fixed. The fields of both electro- and permanent magnets vary with the temperature. The temperature dependence of the field of the permanent magnet is larger,[170] however, than that of an electromagnet. Both types of magnet require compensation of field inhomogeneities by shimming. In the case of permanent magnets the fringing fields which lead to high radial field gradients can be compensated over the pole faces of the magnet by a circularly symmetrical distribution of current-carrying coils. With electromagnets the shimming has been mechanical in nature and essentially changes the alignment of the pole faces with respect to one another. It is claimed[154,156] that permanent magnets are cheaper and simpler to construct and do not require the extra field stabilization used with an electromagnet to obtain comparable field homogeneity. The construction of permanent magnets has been described by Sanford[394] and in the literature on high-resolution spectrometers.[170,19,20,351,159,164,249] It is apparent, however, that, while both types of magnet can be used in high-resolution spectrometers, each has certain advantages and disadvantages. The particular choice of one or the other will depend among other things on the intended application.

In operating an electromagnet it is not possible to obtain the best uniformity of field by merely turning up the current to give the resonant field strength. Precycling is required. This is accomplished in a variety of ways, but usually the magnet is taken up to a higher current than is necessary to observe a desired resonance, and the current is then reduced until resonance is obtained. The best field homogeneity obtained by cycling and positioning the sample in the field is usually tested by observing the transient decay of a rapid-passage signal (Sec. 3-6).   The longer the transient signal ("ringing") persists, the more homogeneous is the field over the sample.

Sweep Rate and Saturation.   The necessary sweep fields are produced in auxiliary bias coils (Helmholtz coils) by currents which also energize the horizontal deflection plates of a cathode-ray oscilloscope.   The currents are derived from a saw-tooth signal generator with linear output.

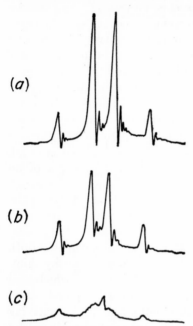

(*a*)

(*b*)

(*c*)

Fig. 4-6. NMR spectra of 2-bromo-5-chlorothiophene: (*a*) at low rf power, (*b*) with rf field increased by a factor of about 3.4 with corresponding decrease in amplifier gain, and (*c*) with rf field increased by another factor of 3.4.   The spacing between the extreme peaks is $\frac{1}{3}$ ppm; the sweep rate is approximately 5 cycles/sec/min.   (Anderson.[11])

The conditions which must be fulfilled for the observation of unsaturated slow-passage resonance are intimately connected with the line width of the observed resonance line.   The time spent in traversing a single resonance line must be greater than the inverse of the line width (in units of circular frequency); the sweep rate must accordingly be reduced in proportion to the square of the line width.[19] Since proton magnetic resonances in liquids have line widths of the order of 0.1 cycle/sec, the sweep rate should be less than about 2×10^{-5} gauss/sec. Furthermore, the sweep must be slow enough that the transient effects (Sec. 3-6) of rapid passage are at a minimum.

In order to avoid saturation effects in the case of narrow lines in slow passage, the amplitude of the irradiating field H_1 should be less than $\Delta\omega/|\gamma|$ (Sec. 3-4).   The very large effect that high values of H_1 can have on the appearance of the NMR spectrum[11] may be seen in Fig. 4-6.   For larger values of H_1 it is possible to avoid the effects of saturation by increasing the sweep rate, provided that the accompanying wiggles are not too serious.

b. High-resolution Spectrometers.   In the remainder of this section some high-resolution spectrometers are described only wherein they differ from the conventional bridge or induction types outlined in Secs. 4-2 and 4-3.   For purposes of this description, spectrometers which can resolve internal chemical shifts of protons are considered to be of the high-

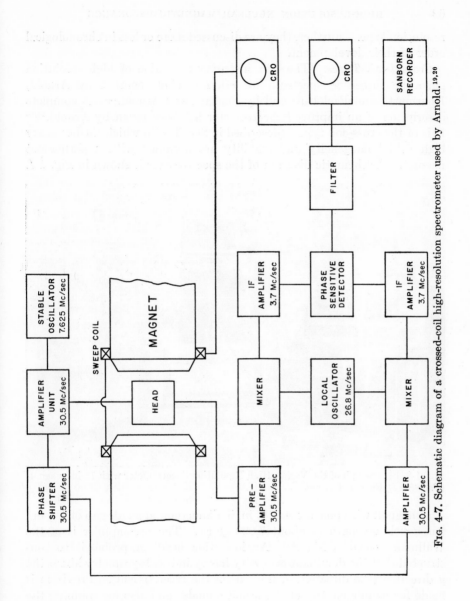

FIG. 4-7. Schematic diagram of a crossed-coil high-resolution spectrometer used by Arnold.[19,20]

resolution type.   Further, they are discussed more or less in chronological order of their development.

Crossed-coil Types.   The first instrument capable of high resolution gave the three-line spectrum for ethyl alcohol reported by Arnold, Dharmatti, and Packard[21] and by Packard and Arnold.[317]   A complete description of an improved spectrometer has been given by Arnold.[19,20] It is of the cross-coil type[54] (described in Sec. 4-3) in which the necessary high field homogeneity and stability are obtained with a permanent magnet.   A schematic diagram of the spectrometer is shown in Fig. 4-7.

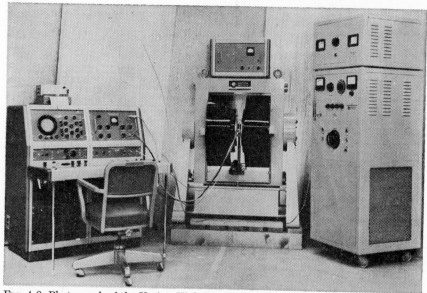

Fig. 4-8. Photograph of the Varian High Resolution Spectrometer with 12-in. magnet. (*Courtesy of Varian Associates.*)

The magnet, with pole faces $12\frac{1}{2}$ in. in diameter and an air gap of $1\frac{1}{2}$ in., has a field strength of about 7,000 gauss.   The preamplifier is of the Wallman cascode design.[453]   An induction head, or probe, is so constructed that the dominant geometry has cylindrical symmetry about the y direction (the direction of the axis of the receiver coil).   Provision is made for paddle control of the u and v modes and also for spinning the sample holder by means of an air-turbine rotor.   The resolution achieved with this spectrometer is about 1 part in 10^8.

High-resolution spectrometers are commercially available from Varian Associates, Palo Alto, California.   They are of the cross-coil type and use an electromagnet with a stabilized power supply.   The magnet may be operated at fields up to about 14,200 gauss.   For proton measurements, rf units can be obtained at 30, 40, or 60 Mc/sec; for fluorine, at

30, 40, or 55 Mc/sec. For resonance measurements of other nuclei, appropriate rf units are available.

The general features of the Varian spectrometer resemble those of the Arnold spectrometer shown schematically in Fig. 4-7. A photograph of the Varian spectrometer is reproduced in Fig. 4-8. The induction head

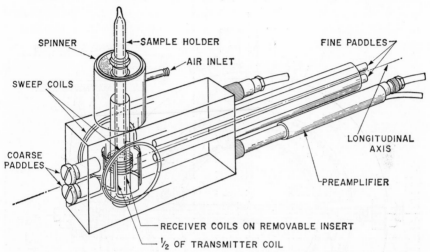

FIG. 4-9. Schematic diagram of the Varian probe assembly. (*Courtesy of Varian Associates.*)

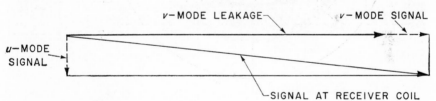

FIG. 4-10. Suppression of the u-mode component of the magnetization vector by adding a large amount of leakage in phase with the v-mode component. (*Courtesy of Varian Associates.*)

or probe, shown in Fig. 4-9, includes the sweep coils, u- and v-mode controls, preamplifier, and tuning condenser. An air-turbine arrangement for sample spinning is also shown. The probe can accommodate various sizes of receiver-coil inserts into which sample tubes up to 15 mm o.d. can be placed. With an intentional amount of leakage, the receiver coil is tuned to maximum output by means of the tuning condenser. The u- and v-mode paddles can then be adjusted until practically perfect balance is obtained, corresponding to zero leakage. The u- or v-mode signal may then be observed by introducing the desired amount of u- or v-mode leakage (Fig. 4-10). The instrument is also supplied with a field stabilizer as an accessory to all Varian 12-in. magnet systems. Two special coils are placed over the pole caps of the magnet. The small residual field changes induce voltages in one of the coils; the voltages are integrated and amplified. The output from this circuit is then fed into the second coil in such a manner as to cancel the original fluctuations. Stabilizer circuits have been briefly described by Lloyd[252] and Dicke.[117]

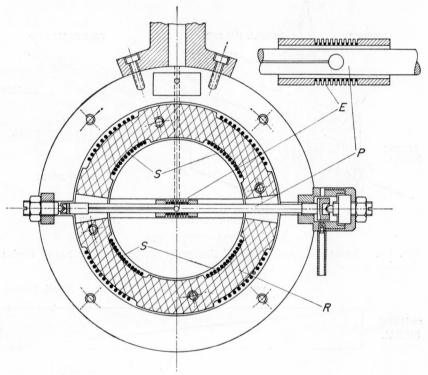

FIG. 4-11. Induction-head section. E = receiver coil, S = transmitter coils, R = Plexiglass ring, P = glass sample holder. (Primas and Gunthard.[349])

Sample sizes from a fraction of one cubic centimeter to 5 cc can be used, and the resolution obtained with the smaller samples is about 1 in 10^8.

A second high-resolution spectrometer is available commercially from Trüb, Täuber and Co., Zurich, Switzerland. It is modeled essentially after that described by Primas and Gunthard.[348,349] The instrument is of the cross-coil type with a permanent magnet of field strength 6,000 gauss and a homogeneity of 1 part in 10^7. Higher field homogeneity can be obtained by the use of special current shims on the magnet pole faces.[350] Field stability has been achieved by stabilization[351] of the permanent magnet against the influence of stray fields from the surroundings and variations due to temperature. To eliminate both slow and fast field variations, voltage changes detected by a receiver coil in the field are amplified and used to drive an integrating feedback system which compensates the field changes to a high degree. The signal generator has over-all stability of 1 in 10^9 and is of the modified Clapp-Gouriet type.[93,146] The induction head is shown in cross section in Fig. 4-11. Unlike other induction heads employed in double-coil spectrometers, paddles are not used to control the leakage. Four transmitter coils wound on a Plexiglass ring are so arranged that the rf field is approxi-

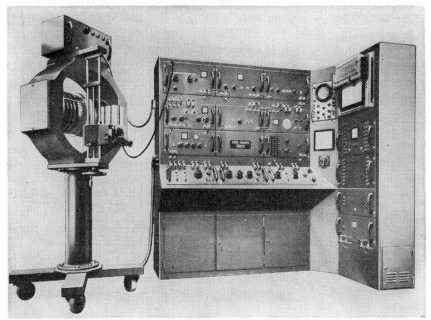

FIG. 4-12. High-resolution NMR spectrometer. (*Courtesy of Trüb, Täuber and Co.*)

mately at right angles to the receiver-coil axis. Nearly exact orthogonality is obtained by slightly turning the Plexiglass ring with respect to the receiver coil. In contrast to the usual methods, the leakage is balanced well below the signal voltage, first by rotation of the Plexiglass ring and then electronically by a bridge arrangement. A circuit diagram of the combined cascode preamplifier and electronic leakage compensator is given by Primas and Gunthard.[349] Since the leakage is practically entirely balanced out, the resonance signals due to absorption and dispersion are obtained by means of a phase-sensitive detector. A photograph of the spectrometer is shown in Fig. 4-12.

The sample holder, which can be set spinning by air jets, is a 3-mm glass rod with a spherical cavity from 1 to 2.5 mm in diameter. The sample is introduced into the cavity through a capillary opening of 0.1 mm diameter. Resolution of 1 part in 10^8 is achieved.

A double-coil spectrometer and electromagnet have been described by Batdorf.[31] The radio frequency was 30 Mc/sec, and the Varian Associates induction head was used. With spinning of the sample, effective resolution of about 1 in 10^7 was achieved.

A modified spectrometer with high stability has been described by Baker and Burd.[28] A Varian electromagnet is stabilized by a feedback loop which uses the error signal from a secondary nuclear resonance probe to control the oscillator driving frequency. Field fluctuations thus produce such frequency variations as to preserve the resonance condition for both short and long times. The same oscillator is used for the measurement probe, and thus the resonance condition is also preserved in the sample being measured. This method of stabilization has an advantage over the method used in the Varian spectrometer in that drift is essentially eliminated.

Single-coil Types. The high-resolution spectrometers mentioned above are all of the double-coil type. The first high-resolution spectrometers of the conventional bridge type were constructed by Gutowsky and Hoffman.[159] The field was modulated, and the radio frequency was kept constant. The resonance lines from two samples were displayed simultaneously on a dual oscilloscope or alternately on a single-beam oscilloscope by manual switching of the samples. A permanent magnet of 2 in. gap with 6-in.-diameter pole faces was used. The field strength was 6,365 gauss. A modification of this spectrometer was described by Gutowsky, McCall, McGarvey, and Meyer.[164] In a later model due to Gutowsky, Meyer, and McClure[170] a permanent magnet of field strength 4,180 gauss was used. The spectrometer was basically of the standard rf-bridge type which was modified to the null T-type bridge due to Tuttle.[444] The spectrometer operated at fixed frequency, the steady field being modulated by a saw-tooth low-frequency signal generator. The resonance shift was obtained from the calibrated field-biasing current. A block diagram is given in Fig. 4-13. The probe contained a split coil. The unknown and reference compounds were placed in separate sample tubes in the two parts of the split rf coil in the sample bridge. Thus the resonance shifts of the two samples were measured in slightly different applied fields, and a certain degree of accuracy was sacrificed even though sample and reference were interchanged for averaging. Small samples of the order of 0.003 cm^3 were used without spinning, and the resolution obtained was about 1 in 10^7.

Another high-resolution spectrometer with single-coil and double-T bridge has been described by Lindström and Bhar.[249] A permanent magnet (3,285 gauss) with a 38-mm gap was used.　With a spinning sample the resolution attained was about 1 in 10^7.

A high-resolution spectrometer using a thermostatically controlled permanent magnet (field 7,000 gauss) has been employed by Richards.[382] The homogeneity of the field was trimmed with printed-circuit coils due to Golay.[143b]　The probe was of the single-coil type, and a twin-T bridge

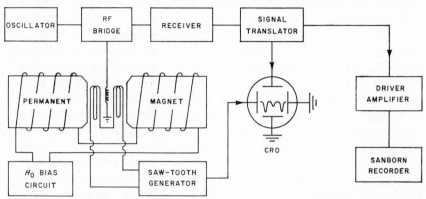

FIG. 4-13. Block diagram of single-coil bridge spectrometer used by Gutowsky and coworkers.[156]

circuit was used.　The bridge was followed by a simple tuned rf amplifier followed by diode detection.　Resolution of 1 in 10^8 was achieved.

4-6. Experimental Techniques

a. The Sample.　The optimum size and shape of sample to be used for high-resolution NMR measurements generally involves a compromise among a number of factors.　The most important limiting factor is the homogeneity of the magnetic field.　For optimum resolution the applied field must be homogeneous over the entire volume of sample within the region of the rf measuring coil of the probe.　In practice, since available magnetic fields always have some degree of inhomogeneity, this optimum condition is more nearly approached by reducing the sample volume. The extent to which the sample volume can be reduced is in turn limited by the signal strength required for observation and depends on the signal-to-noise ratio of the particular receiving and recording equipment used. A suitable compromise among these limiting factors must therefore be established for a particular set of conditions.　It should be noted, however, that although the integrated signal intensity is reduced with smaller sample volumes, the signal amplitude is usually not reduced to the same degree, since the greater field homogeneity over the smaller sample gives rise to sharper signals.   Sample volumes of the order of 0.003 to 0.01 cm³ have been successfully used in some measurements[170,348,249] of proton signals.   Depending on the degree of dilution of the particular nuclear species being measured, sample volumes up to 0.5 cm³, and sometimes larger, may be necessary to obtain an adequate signal strength.

For any given nuclear species the intensity of the resonance-absorption signal is given by Eqs. (3-79) and (3-80).   Assuming equal number of nuclei, the relative signal amplitudes, or *relative sensitivity*, of different magnetic nuclei can be calculated.   These are shown in the fourth and fifth columns of the Table of Nuclear Properties, Appendix A, relative to unit value for the proton.   The resonant frequency ω_0 for each nucleus is taken as that for a fixed magnetic field of 10 kilogauss.   It can be seen from the table that protons give rise to relatively strong signals compared with those of other nuclei.   For most other nuclei (except F^{19} and H^3) considerably larger samples would be required to produce a signal strength comparable to that of the proton.   But in fact the larger sample leads to greater signal broadening due to field inhomogeneity and to a loss in resolution.   However, nature has provided a partial compensation in that the chemical shifts and spin-spin coupling constants for such nuclei are found to be considerably larger than those for protons, so that the conditions for high resolution are somewhat less demanding.   The foregoing considerations will of course only apply for conditions of rf power sufficiently low to avoid saturation.   For nuclei with spin $I > 1$ further complications may arise if T_2 is substantially reduced by quadrupole relaxation (cf. Secs. 5-4 and 9-2).

For high-resolution NMR measurements on any given compound, the sample may be in the form of the pure liquid or the compound may be dissolved in a suitable solvent.   The solvent, if used, must be so selected that its resonance signals will not obscure the signals of the compound being measured.   For proton measurements, solvents such as CCl_4, CS_2, and deuterated compounds are frequently useful.   Samples with high viscosity may cause signal broadening, which may be overcome by solvent dilution or by increasing the temperature of the sample.   Frequently, solid compounds with relatively high melting points are not sufficiently soluble to give adequate resonance signals.   This situation can usually be dealt with by heating the sample to increase the solubility or by melting the pure compound.   Alternatively, a larger sample volume of solution can be used to yield the necessary signal strength, if a slight loss in resolution can be tolerated.   This is also necessary when the effect of solvent dilution is to be studied explicitly, and very dilute solutions are to be measured.   With presently available equipment, and if the signal is reasonably sharp, dilutions down to less than ½ mole per cent can be measured for proton signals of samples in cylindrical tubes approximately 5 to 8 mm o.d.   If the signal arises from more than one equivalent proton, correspondingly smaller concentrations can be measured.

Compounds which are sufficiently volatile can also be measured in the gaseous state.   In order to obtain adequate signal strength, gas pressures in excess of one atmosphere are generally required.   Cylindrical glass sample tubes, 3 mm i.d. and 5 mm o.d., can be safely used at pressures up to 20 atm.   Gases whose critical temperature is above room temperature require heating of the sample to take the vapor above the saturation point.

For routine measurements of NMR spectra it is common practice to employ cylindrical glass sample tubes, although spherical sample tubes have been used by some workers.[54,349]   A spherical sample shape more nearly reproduces the ideal Lorentzian cavity, and no shape correction (Sec. 4-9) of the measured results is necessary.   An acceptable cylindrical sample, on the other hand, must have dimensions such that the ratio of diameter to length approximates that of an "infinite" cylinder in relation to the rf measuring coil.   If the sample diameter is only slightly less than that of the rf coil, the length should be at least five times as great.[120]   It is not always possible to maintain this ratio in practice, particularly when large-diameter sample tubes are used.   This is not a serious situation, and ordinarily the error introduced by sample dimensions is within the experimental accuracy.

It will be apparent from the above discussion that for a comparable "filling" factor of a given rf coil, a smaller total sample volume is required for a spherical sample tube than for one which is cylindrical, since in the latter a large proportion of the sample is outside the field of the coil. This is an important consideration when only small quantities of sample are available.

b. Sample Spinning.   As mentioned previously, one of the limiting factors in high-resolution measurements is the inhomogeneity of the applied magnetic field.   It was pointed out by Bloch[51] that the effective homogeneity of the field can be improved in a rather simple way by providing a motion of the substance within the sample under investigation. Assume that the external field varies over the sample by an amount ΔH and that a given molecule participates in the macroscopic motion of the substance such that during each time interval t it is exposed once to the range of variation ΔH of the magnetic field.   As the motion is made more rapid, i.e., the interval t is made shorter, a nucleus in a molecule reacts as if it were exposed to the average value of the field.   This effect will become appreciable when

$$t \approx \frac{1}{\gamma \, \Delta H} \tag{4-1}$$

Thus for protons, if ΔH is of the order of 10^{-3} gauss, t is of the order of $\frac{1}{4}$ sec, which corresponds to speeds readily attainable by mechanical motion of the sample. The effect of such motion on the resonance signal, first demonstrated by Anderson and Arnold,[12] is rather striking. It was found that spinning a spherical sample of water ($\frac{3}{16}$ in. in diameter) about an axis y coincident with the axis of the receiver coil reduced the half width of the resonance signal by a factor of 17 and increased the peak amplitude by a factor of 7. The field was a 7,000-gauss permanent magnet with a homogeneity over the sample volume of about 10^{-3} gauss. The line narrowing was observed at rotational speeds† in excess of 10 rps, in approximate agreement with Eq. (4-1). It should be noted that spinning of the sample in the above manner effects an averaging of the field around coaxial circles about the y axis, but does not average the field along this axis. No simple mechanical means of accomplishing the latter has yet been devised.

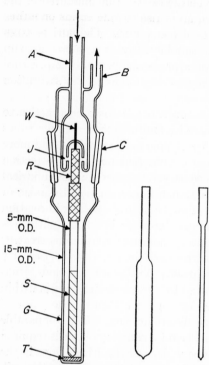

FIG. 4-14. Spinner for use with sample tubes of varying size. A = glass inlet tube terminating in a head with five tangential holes J, serving as air jets. R = machined nylon rotor cap which fits snugly over sample tube. W = 40-mil tungsten wire centered on rotor cap; it is inserted in a hole in the glass head which serves as the upper bearing. S = glass sample tube (5-mm-o.d. size shown; designs for larger and smaller tubes shown at right). A small glass tip, centered in a lathe, is attached to the bottom of the tube. This forms the lower bearing on the Teflon disk T. The glass tube G, 15 mm o.d., is aligned by the ground joint C (No. 29/42). B is an air outlet.

Air-jet-driven devices provide a simple means of sample spinning. The spinning arrangement of the Varian probe (Fig. 4-9) is designed for use with 5-mm-o.d. glass sample tubes. Frequently it is necessary to employ larger- or smaller-diameter sample tubes. The device illustrated in Fig. 4-14, when used with the 15-mm Varian probe insert, permits spinning of sample tubes up to 12 mm o.d. in size. With the smaller-diameter tubes, the filling factor with respect to the

† According to the analysis given by Kaplan,[211a] a periodic rotation is generally more effective than random rotation in producing line narrowing.

larger measuring coil may be somewhat inferior, but in practice this is usually not a serious consideration.

Under certain conditions of field inhomogeneity, the spinning sample causes an amplitude modulation which gives rise to side bands on either side of the resonance signal. The displacement of the side band relative to the resonance signal is equal to the frequency of rotation of the sample, which is in the audio-frequency range. Increasing the rate of spinning causes the side-band signals to become weaker and to move further out to the wings, thus providing a simple means of identifying spurious signals of this type. An analysis of spinning-sample modulation effects has been given by Williams and Gutowsky[465] and by Halbach.[180]

c. Sample-temperature Control. In NMR measurements it is frequently necessary to alter the temperature of the sample being measured. Generally speaking, single-coil NMR spectrometers permit a rather simple arrangement for sample-temperature variation. Since no critical adjustments of the measuring probe are necessary and since such probes can be designed to be simple and rugged, the temperature of the whole probe assembly can be varied by means of a suitable cryostat. Gutowsky, Meyer, and McClure[170] have described a cryostat for this purpose that permits the sample temperature to be varied from $-190°C$ up to approximately $225°C$. The same authors have described another arrangement in which the measuring coil together with the sample was mounted in a U-shaped copper block to which a copper rod was attached. The rod was electrically but not thermally insulated from the copper block. In this manner the temperature of the sample could be varied in the range -30 to $-120°C$ by varying the depth of immersion of the rod in liquid nitrogen. More elaborate cryostats that permit measurements in the range from -196 to $327°C$ have been described by Mulay.[293] No provision was made for sample spinning in any of the above devices, although modifications to include this function should be possible.

With NMR spectrometers of the crossed-coil type, altering the temperature of the entire probe assembly is impractical, owing to its more complicated construction and the need for proper balancing. Control devices for maintaining sample temperature are thus confined to the space within the receiver-coil assembly. Some economy of space is effected by constructing the latter in the form of a small, thin-walled Dewar tube, the receiving coil being wound on the outside of the inner glass wall of the tube. The sample is then preheated or precooled to the desired temperature before it is inserted in the Dewar tube for measurement. Although adequate for certain types of measurement where sample spinning is not essential, this arrangement has a number of obvious limitations. A more satisfactory device, illustrated in Fig. 4-15, has been developed by Shoolery and Roberts[424] for measurements above room temperature. The receiver coil is wound on a glass tube suspended in a small Dewar tube (approximately 18 mm o.d.) by means of a ground joint at its upper end. The Dewar tube fits inside the standard probe assembly of the spectrometer and permits attachment of a spinning head

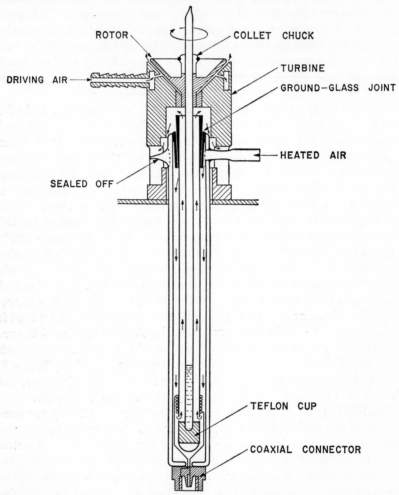

Fig. 4-15. Temperature control device for high-temperature measurements with the Varian NMR spectrometer. (Shoolery and Roberts.[424])

of the type shown in Fig. 4-9. Sample tubes up to 5 mm o.d. can be used. Provision is made for streaming air of controlled temperature down the outside of the receiver coil, around its lower end, and up along the spinning sample tube. Temperatures are measured by inserting a small thermocouple in the air stream above the receiving coil. The device can be used for measurements up to 170°C.   Higher temperatures up to 300°C are possible if special epoxy resins are used in the assembly. The apparatus is, however, not well suited for low-temperature measurements.   An improved device available commercially from Varian Associates permits controlled temperature variation of the sample over the range −60 to 200°C.

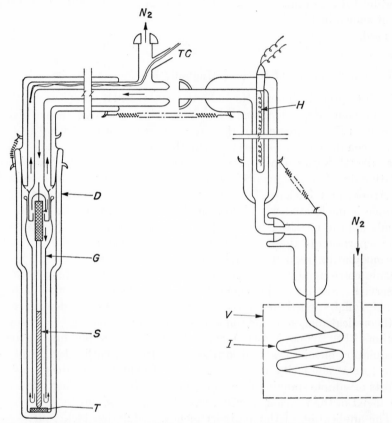

Fig. 4-16. Sample temperature control device for low- and high-temperature measurements. S = sample tube, G = thin-walled glass tube, T = Teflon bearing, D = Dewar tube, TC = thermocouple, H = heater, I = copper coil, V = refrigerant container.

An alternative device,[402] which has been used in the authors' laboratory for NMR measurements with a Varian spectrometer over a temperature range of −150 to 300°C, is shown in Fig. 4-16.   It is designed for use with the 15-mm receiver-coil insert, and hence it is interchangeable with the spinning device for room-temperature operation illustrated in Fig. 4-14.   Essentially, the sample-spinning arrangement of the latter has been built into a Dewar jacket as shown.   In addition a thin-walled glass tube, which is aligned by means of a ground joint on the spinning head, extends to the bottom of the Dewar and directs the incoming gas (which also spins the sample) along the entire length of the sample tube to maintain a uniform temperature.   In operation, a controlled stream of dry nitrogen gas is passed through a liquid-nitrogen heat exchanger or a heating tube to obtain the desired temperature.   As with the arrangement shown in Fig. 4-15, only sample tubes of 5 mm o.d. or smaller can be used.

4-7. Measurements of Nuclear Magnetic Resonance Spectra

To interpret the information inherent in the NMR spectrum requires a measurement of relative separations, or spacing, of the component signals, as well as a measurement of their relative intensities.   Several methods have been developed for carrying out these measurements.

a. Signal Separations.   The most convenient method of measuring relative signal displacements in a spectrum is the side-band technique due to Arnold and Packard.[22]   When the magnetic field impressed on the sample is modulated with a low-amplitude audio-frequency signal, side bands appear on either side of the resonance signals in the spectrum. The separation of these side bands from the resonance signal is equal to the modulating frequency.   When the amplitude of the latter is increased, signals corresponding to overtones of the impressed frequency can be observed.   Similar modulation effects can be produced by modulation of the rf signal applied to the transmitter coils of the crossed-coil probe.[19] A theoretical analysis of field-modulation effects has been given by several authors.[427,82]   There is a close parallel with the corresponding frequency modulation of microwave absorption lines treated earlier by Karplus.[214] The formal similarity of the present field-modulation effects and the effects of sample spinning which may give rise to the spinning side bands, discussed in the previous section, have been pointed out.[12,465]

The application of the audio-frequency-modulation technique is illustrated in Fig. 4-17.   The proton resonance spectrum of acetic acid shown in (a) consists of two signals: A, due to the OH proton, and B, with three times the intensity of A, due to the three protons of the methyl group. When a modulating frequency of 105 cycles/sec is used, the spectrum appears as in Fig. 4-17b.   The side bands belonging to each signal, from which they are separated in frequency by 105 cycles/sec, are labeled A' and B'.   As the modulating frequency is progressively increased, the side-band signals move further out from the fundamentals, until eventually the B' signal can be made to superimpose exactly on the A signal (and the A' on the B signal).   The value of the modulating frequency is then a

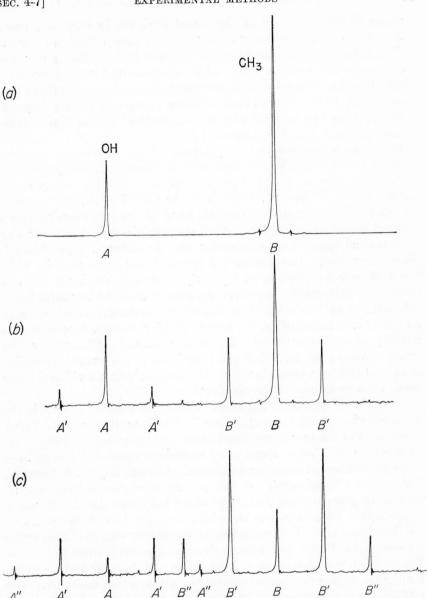

FIG. 4-17. Proton resonance spectrum of acetic acid, showing effect of field modulation. (a) Without modulation. (b) Modulating frequency 105 cycles/sec. (c) Same as (b) but with higher amplitude of the modulating signal. The spectra were recorded at a fixed frequency of 40 Mc/sec; the separation between the hydroxyl- and methyl-group signals is 388 cycles/sec.

measure of the separation of the A and B signals in frequency units. With suitably sharp resonance signals and a favorable signal-to-noise ratio, measurements of this kind can be made to an accuracy of about 1 cycle/sec or better. A stable audio oscillator is therefore essential. As illustrated in Fig. 4-17c, when the amplitude of the modulating signal is increased, the intensity of the side bands increases and the side bands of higher order become more pronounced, but the intensity of the fundamental signals A and B is diminished.

The above simple method is applicable to spectra whose signals are moderately well separated. If the spectrum consists of a group of closely spaced lines, the method is more difficult to apply because of signal distortion. It is then necessary to make use of a suitable external reference signal (Sec. 4-8). The side band of the latter can be superimposed in turn on each of the resolved signals of the spectrum, permitting their mutual separation to be measured. An alternative procedure is often convenient. The spectrum is recorded on a chart recorder while the field is being modulated by a signal of suitable amplitude and frequency. All signal separations can then be obtained by simple linear interpolation on the chart. Assuming the chart recorder is equipped with a synchronous motor drive, the success of this procedure depends on the stability of the magnetic field, the sweep rate, and the linearity of the sweep. When possible, however, it is desirable to confirm the separation of at least two prominent signals in the spectrum with the aid of the side bands from an external reference signal.

A procedure for measuring small separations between signals is the so-called wiggle-beat method, which is based on the transient-decay phenomena of the resonance signal under rapid-passage conditions. As discussed in Sec. 3-6, a single sharp resonance signal is followed by a series of exponential decaying oscillations, or wiggles. When, however, the resonance signal consists of two or more closely spaced components with constant separation, the wiggles of the individual signals will be out of phase and will give rise to the wiggle beats.[35] It was shown in Sec. 3-6 that, if the mutual separation of the component signals is J, in cycles per second, the time between successive beat maxima is equal to $1/J$ sec. The method has been employed by Glick and Bothner-By[143] and by Reilly[379] to measure the signal separations within a spin multiplet. The measurement is independent of sweep speed and sweep linearity, and signal separations of closely spaced lines can be measured with an accuracy of the order of ± 0.1 cycle/sec. In some cases the method can be used when the individual multiplet lines are not sufficiently well resolved to measure J directly. Figure 4-18, reproduced from the work of Reilly,[379] shows the transient-decay pattern for a single sharp signal

(Fig. 4-18a) and for a signal having a triplet structure, the equal separation of the component signals being 1.48 cycles/sec (Fig. 4-18b).

The wiggle-beat method is well suited for measuring the separation of the equally spaced spin-multiplet components of a resonance signal when the latter is well separated from other signals in the spectrum. Furthermore, the contour of the decay signals in a spectrum is frequently a useful indication of whether the spectrum is resolvable into closely spaced multiplets. A further application is in connection with the side-band technique, described above, in which the decay contours can be used as a criterion of exact superposition of the side-band signal on another signal being measured. Thus exact superposition of two sharp signals produces

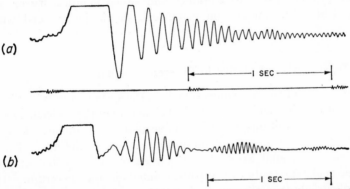

FIG. 4-18. Transient-decay pattern of NMR signals. Simultaneously recorded timing signals are shown with the upper trace. (a) Decay pattern (wiggles) arising from the single sharp signal of the CF_3 group in CF_3COOH. (b) Decay pattern showing wiggle beats from the triplet signal of the CF_3 group in CF_3CF_2COOH. (Reilly.[379])

the decay pattern similar to that of Fig. 4-18a, whereas small deviation from exact superposition introduces wiggle beats into the decay pattern.

b. Signal Intensities. The relative intensity of individual signals in the NMR spectrum is required for the analysis of the spectrum and for the ultimate assignment of signals to individual nuclei in the molecule. Also, if the signals in the spectrum are well separated, the intensities are a direct measure of the relative number of nuclei contributing to the signals. This is of considerable importance in chemical-structure identification and quantitative analysis (Chap. 19).

Intensities can be estimated either by area measurements or measurements of peak heights. The theoretical dependence of these quantities on the rf field H_1 and the relaxation times have already been considered in Sec. 3-5. For low rf power (no saturation), area measurements are most reliable, because a comparison of peak heights is satisfactory only if all signals have the same width (same T_2). At higher values of H_1, which may be required for weak signals, the area comparison becomes dependent on T_1 and T_2 [Eq. (3-80a)]. This is still preferable to peak measurements; for the area tends to a finite limit as H_1 tends to infinity, whereas the peak intensity tends to zero [Eq. (3-80b)].

Areas can be measured by any of the usual methods in spectroscopy. At present, however, these measurements cannot be carried out to the same accuracy as can measurements of signal separations; for broadened signals or with poor signal-to-noise ratio the measurement error may be of the order of 10 per cent or more, although it is rather less for strong sharp signals. In recording the spectrum for intensity measurements, precautions must be taken to avoid transient-decay signals, as well as possible distortion due to amplifier and sweep nonlinearity or drift of the applied field. Saturation conditions should be avoided wherever possible.

4-8. Measurements Relative to Reference Signals

The position of the resonance signals in the spectrum provides information about the electronic and chemical structure of the molecule, and also, under certain conditions, about the molecular environment. In practice it is not possible to measure the absolute value of the applied field for each resonance signal with an accuracy comparable to the small differences of field represented by separate signals in the spectrum. Thus if the applied field is of the order of 10,000 gauss, for protons the value of the field for individual resonance signals may differ, in a typical case, by 10 milligauss, or 1 ppm. Small differences of this order can be accurately measured, however, by the methods of Sec. 4-7, and since ordinarily only the field difference for two resonance signals is of interest, a knowledge of the absolute value of the individual fields is not essential.

When the differences in the resonant fields,† or signal separations, of the signals due to different nuclei of the same molecule are desired, the methods of the previous section can be applied, and the signal separations can be expressed relative to any one signal in the spectrum arbitrarily chosen as a reference. However, if the resonant fields of signals in different molecules, or of the same molecule in different environments, are to be compared, it is necessary to measure all signals relative to a common reference signal. A convenient reference signal is one which is sharp and well separated from other signals in the spectrum. A number of liquid compounds which yield suitable reference signals are given in Sec. 5-1.

a. **Internal Reference Signals.** The reference signal must of course be displayed simultaneously with the spectrum of the compound being measured. The separation of the individual signals in the NMR spec-

† This of course implies that the resonant frequency is held fixed.

trum relative to the reference signal is then measured by the side-band technique (Sec. 4-7). For some purposes it is sufficient to add a small amount of the reference liquid to the sample. If a solution is being measured, the solvent itself may provide a suitable reference signal. The use of an internal reference signal has the advantage that no bulk-susceptibility corrections (Sec. 4-9) are necessary. These procedures are satisfactory only when specific solvent and solution effects (Sec. 5-3) are unimportant.

   b. **External Reference Signals.** An alternative procedure which is usually preferable is to have the reference compound enclosed in a separate compartment in the sample tube. A simple method of doing this is to seal the reference liquid in a small, thin capillary tube, which is then added to the sample to be measured. Various modifications of this arrangement have been employed by some investigators. Shoolery and Alder[421] have used a thin glass membrane across a 5-mm-o.d. Pyrex-tube sample holder. The reference liquid was sealed in the lower compartment, and the liquid to be measured occupied the space above the membrane. Both compartments must extend into the region of the measuring coil. Coaxial-sample-tube arrangements have been used by Zimmerman and Foster[474] and by Morin, Paulett, and Hobbs,[290] the reference liquid being introduced in the annulus between two glass tubes.

   Coaxial-tube arrangements can be employed for their intended purpose only when the sample tube is rotated. In the absence of rotation the liquid in the annulus gives rise to a broad resonance signal with two peaks, owing to the fact that the field experienced by the molecules in the annulus is not uniform. The separation of the two peaks ΔH relative to the applied field H_0 is given by [290,381]

$$\frac{\Delta H}{H_0} = 4\pi \left[(\chi_1 - \chi_2)\frac{a^2}{r^2} + (\chi_2 - \chi_3)\frac{b^2}{r^2} \right] \tag{4-2}$$

where χ_1, χ_2, and χ_3 are the volume susceptibilities of the liquid in the inner glass tube, the glass tube, and the annular liquid, respectively. The radius r refers to the mean radius of the annular liquid, and a and b are the inner and outer radii of the inner glass tube. The application of Eq. (4-2) has been suggested by Reilly, McConnell, and Meisenheimer[381] as a method of measuring diamagnetic susceptibilities. This requires a knowledge of the tube geometry and the susceptibility of the glass and the inner liquid. Measurement of the separation of the two peaks of the resonance signal then permits evaluation of χ_3. The procedure can be simplified if the inner glass tube is substituted by a solid glass rod, in which case the first term in Eq. (4-2) drops out.

   Rotation of the coaxial system about its axis averages the field experienced by the annular liquid, resulting in a single sharp signal which appears midway between the two peaks of the signal observed for the static system. An analysis of coaxial sample tubes has been given by Zimmerman and Foster.[474] It was shown that, when the system is rotated, the average field acting on the sample in the inner tube and in the annulus is identical. According to the analysis given, imperfections in the glass tubing of the assembly may lead to a slight signal broadening, and a tilt of one tube relative to the other may cause a slight signal shift.[474] Detailed experimental tests of these effects have not yet been carried out. For accurate measurements the use of a rotating coaxial system was recommended, the component glass tubes being free of imperfections. Ground-glass tubes for this purpose are commercially available.†

4-9. Bulk-susceptibility Corrections

When an external reference is used, a correction involving the difference between the bulk diamagnetic susceptibilities of the reference compound and the sample must be applied. This is necessitated by the fact that, in the cylindrically shaped containers, the actual fields experienced by individual nuclei will depend on the magnetic polarization near the surface.

The total volume of the cylindrical sample may be divided into two regions by defining a sphere around any given molecule within the sample large enough to be of macroscopic dimensions but small compared with the size of the sample. If the sample is placed in a uniform magnetic field H_0, the field experienced by a nucleus at the center of the sphere is made up of three parts:

1. The external field H_0
2. The field due to induced magnetism in the region between the small sphere and the sample boundary
3. The field due to induced magnetism in the inner sphere

The bulk-susceptibility effect arises from (2) and must be allowed for before genuine comparisons can be made of (3), which includes local intra- and intermolecular contributions. The material in the intermediate region can be treated as a continuum, with a polarization of $\chi_v H_0$ per unit volume, where χ_v is the volume magnetic susceptibility. This polarization can be replaced by an imaginary distribution of magnetic poles on the surface of the sphere and on the outer surface of the cylinder. The distribution on the sphere gives a field $(4\pi/3)\chi_v H_0$, and that on the outer surface gives $-\alpha\chi_v H_0$, where α is a numerical factor depending on the shape of the specimen. (These are the magnitudes of the fields parallel to H_0, it being noted that χ_v is negative for diamagnetic

† Wilmad Glass Company, Landisville, N.J.

substances.)   The field acting on the molecule in the inner sphere, therefore, is

$$H_0 \left[1 + \left(\frac{4\pi}{3} - \alpha \right) \chi_v \right] \tag{4-3}$$

For a spherical sample, $\alpha = 4\pi/3$.   For a cylinder of length large compared with the radius, $\alpha = 2\pi$ and the field in the sphere is then

$$H_{\text{sphere}} = H_0 \left(1 - \frac{2\pi}{3} \chi_v \right) \tag{4-4}$$

The effect of the polarization in the cylinder, then, is equivalent to a contribution $(2\pi/3)\chi_v$ to the screening constant.

Suppose one measures the difference between the total screening for a sample and a reference substance contained in separate long cylindrical tubes.   The chemical shift δ, which is defined as the difference in screening constants, is given by

$$\delta = \sigma - \sigma_r = \frac{H - H_r}{H_r} \tag{4-5}$$

where H and H_r are the resonant fields for the sample and reference, respectively.   (See also Sec. 5-1.)   Substitution from Eq. (4-4) in Eq. (4-5) gives

$$\begin{aligned} \delta_{\text{sphere}} &= \frac{H - H_r}{H_r} + \frac{2\pi}{3} \left(\chi_{v,\text{ref}} - \chi_v \right) \\ &= \delta_{\text{obs}} + \frac{2\pi}{3} \left(\chi_{v,\text{ref}} - \chi_v \right) \end{aligned} \tag{4-6}$$

Experimentally, the chemical shift is often measured by employing an *external* reference substance in a spinning coaxial-sample-tube arrangement.   Under these conditions, and also when the reference material is enclosed in a capillary within the sample tube, Eq. (4-6) can be used to correct the observed chemical shift for the difference in the bulk susceptibility of sample and reference.   If the reference compound is an *internal* standard, that is, the sample and reference are in solution, the bulk susceptibilities are the same and are equal to the susceptibility of the solution.   The second term on the right-hand side of Eq. (4-6) is therefore zero, and the observed value of the chemical shift in the cylindrical-sample arrangement is the same as that which would be observed for spherical samples.   In the case of solutions of varying concentration, measured with respect to an external reference standard, the volume susceptibility required is weighted according to the volume fractions [Eq. (2-16)].   Some susceptibility data are given in Appendix C.

The application of the bulk-susceptibility correction is particularly important for proton resonance measurements, where the chemical shifts are small. The bulk susceptibilities are best obtained from molar susceptibilities, which may have to be estimated (from Pascal's constants, for example) if experimental data are not available. When measurements are carried out over an appreciable temperature range, account must also be taken of the variation of χ_v and $\chi_{v,\text{ref}}$ due to thermal expansion.

If the diameter of the cylinder is not small compared with the length, the factor $2\pi/3$ in Eq. (4-4) must be modified. Dickinson[120] investigated proton resonance signals in tubes of varying length with a given diameter and found that the shift was almost independent of length if the ratio of length to diameter exceeded about four.

It should be emphasized that not all medium effects are allowed for in the bulk-susceptibility correction. In addition there will be effects from molecules in the immediate environment of the one under investigation. These features will be elaborated in Chaps. 15 and 16.

4-10. Measurement of Relaxation Times

a. Continuous-excitation Methods. While the various pulse methods are generally preferred for accurate relaxation-time measurements, several continuous-wave excitation methods which can be conveniently used with conventional NMR spectrometers have been developed. Here we shall consider briefly three such methods for evaluating the spin-lattice relaxation time T_1. Each of these methods has certain limitations, but under favorable conditions each is capable of yielding reliable results. Some modifications of the individual methods can be made to suit particular applications. Two of the methods, the so-called direct method and the progressive-saturation method, were developed by Bloembergen, Purcell, and Pound in their early studies of relaxation times.[59]

Direct Method. This method has the advantage of simplicity. It can be used with most NMR spectrometers, but it is limited to relaxation times of the order of magnitude of 1 sec, or somewhat greater. The resonance signal is first observed at a small rf field H_1. The value of H_1 is then increased to produce saturation (Sec. 3-4) and then suddenly reduced to a small value. Under these conditions the observed recovery of the signal follows the exponential law $1 - e^{-t/T_1}$, thus permitting T_1 to be determined. To make quantitative measurements, the oscilloscope trace can be photographed with a motion-picture camera operating at a known frame speed; the film can then be analyzed to determine the time constant of recovery.

Progressive-saturation Method. The progressive-saturation method complements the direct method because it is applicable to smaller values of T_1, for which the direct method cannot be employed. It will be recalled (Sec. 3-5) that the signal amplitude depends on the maximum value of the Bloch susceptibility χ'', which in turn is related to the saturation factor $(1 + \gamma^2 H_1^2 T_1 T_2)^{-1}$ [Eq. (3-35)]. Under certain conditions the variation of the signal amplitude as the field H_1 is progressively increased is found to be directly proportional to the saturation factor, thus permitting an evaluation of T_1 from a knowledge of H_1 and T_2. The method is most easily employed as a relative method for comparing T_1 values of different substances (whose resonance signals have similar shapes, i.e., similar T_2), or of the same substance at different temperatures. If a substance whose T_1 value has been measured by some other method is available, it may be used for calibration. However to obtain absolute values of T_1, the constant of proportionality between the output voltage of the signal generator and the magnitude of H_1 acting on the sample must be known. This constant can be estimated from the Q and geometry of the sample coil; if the estimate is carefully made, an accuracy of the order of 10 to 20 per cent may be realized. When employed as a relative method, the accuracy may be expected to be considerably better. A detailed analysis of the method may be found in references 59 and 15.

Reversal-of-polarization Method. This method, which was developed by Drain[124] and which has been employed by a number of investigators,[98,90,13,300] makes use of the Bloch nuclear-induction arrangement. Under conditions of adiabatic rapid passage through resonance, defined by

$$\frac{dH_0}{dt} \ll |\gamma| H_1^2 \qquad (4\text{-}7)$$

the presence of the relatively large H_1 field completely reverses the nuclear magnetization vector **M** from the parallel position to the antiparallel position with respect to the direction of **H**$_0$ (reversal of magnetic polarization). If the **H**$_0$ field is symmetrically modulated by a sinusoidal (or triangular) sweep and if the time spent in resonance is short compared with T_1, then at equilibrium the signal on the return trace will be equal in amplitude but inverted from that on the forward trace. The amplitude of the signals, which depends on the time below and above resonance and hence on the audio-sweep frequency, is proportional to the value M_1 of the magnetization at every passage and is given by

$$M_1 = M_0 \frac{1 - e^{-t/T_1}}{1 + e^{-t/T_1}} \qquad (4\text{-}8)$$

where M_0 is the equilibrium value of M_z in the field **H**$_0$ [cf. Eq. (3-41)] and $2t$ is the period of the sweep. Thus from the observed amplitudes at two different sweep frequencies, T_1 can be evaluated directly. For optimum precision, one of the two sweep periods should be of the order T_1, the other several times greater.[90]

A useful modification of the above method makes use of unequal intervals of time above and below resonance obtained by sweeping the field asymmetrically. This is simply achieved by varying the main field so that the signal is no longer centered on the screen of the oscilloscope. The behavior of the nuclear magnetization under these conditions is illustrated schematically in Fig. 4-19, where T_1 is assumed to be of the

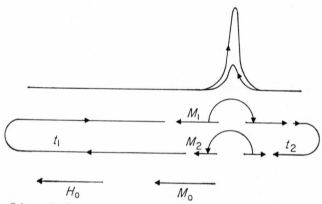

FIG. 4-19. Schematic diagram showing the behavior of the nuclear magnetization during one cycle of the sweep. M_0 is the equilibrium value of the nuclear magnetization in the steady field H_0. (Drain.[124])

order of magnitude of the sweep period $(t_1 + t_2)$, with $t_2 < t_1$. Accordingly, as illustrated in the figure, the amplitude of the signal on the return sweep is less than that on the forward sweep. The relative amplitudes of the signals are proportional to

$$M_1 = M_0 \frac{1 + e^{-(t_1+t_2)/T_1} - 2e^{-t_1/T_1}}{1 - e^{-(t_1+t_2)/T_1}} \tag{4-9}$$

$$M_2 = M_0 \frac{-1 - e^{-(t_1+t_2)/T_1} + 2e^{-t_2/T_1}}{1 - e^{-(t_1+t_2)/T_1}} \tag{4-10}$$

In practice it is convenient to so adjust t_2 that the amplitude on the reverse trace is zero. Equation (4-10) then yields

$$e^{-t_2/T_1} = \tfrac{1}{2}[1 + e^{-(t_1+t_2)/T_1}] \tag{4-11}$$

Hence from the known sweep period and the position of the signal on the oscilloscope trace, T_1 can be evaluated. By varying the sweep frequency, values of T_1 in the range 10^{-2} sec to the longest observable times can be measured.[90]   The method is not suitable for substances having more than one signal in the NMR spectrum unless the signals are well separated.[300]

   b. Pulse Methods.   Spin-echo techniques have been successfully applied to the measurement of relaxation times, particularly those that are too short for direct methods. Hahn[176] first developed several methods for measuring T_1 and T_2 from echoes due to 90° pulses. Some improvements were later incorporated by Carr and Purcell,[86] who also used combinations of 90 and 180° pulses.

   Transverse Relaxation Time T_2.   As described in Sec. 3-7, if two 90° pulses (that is, turning the spins through 90°) are applied at times 0 and τ, an echo will appear at time 2τ.   The amplitude of the echo is

$$\exp\left[-\frac{2\tau}{T_2} - k\frac{(2\tau)^3}{3} \right] \tag{4-12}$$

where k is proportional to the self-diffusion constant of the material. Under conditions where the decay is not dominated by diffusion, therefore, T_2 can be obtained from the shape of the echo envelope.

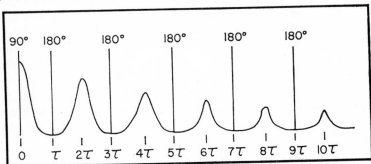

FIG. 4-20. Diagram showing the pulse sequence and resulting echoes used by Carr and Purcell[86] for measuring T_2.

   An ingenious method of eliminating the effects of diffusion was developed by Carr and Purcell.[86]   Their method was to apply a 90° pulse followed by a 180° pulse at time τ.   This again leads to an echo at time 2τ, as explained in detail in Sec. 3-7.   A further 180° pulse is then applied at time 3τ.   By extension of the diagrams in Fig. 3-8 it is clear that this leads to a rephasing of the spin vectors at 4τ, leading to another echo. This process is then repeated at 5τ, 6τ, and so on.   The whole sequence is illustrated in Fig. 4-20.   Carr and Purcell were able to show that the decay of the echo in this sequence was proportional to $\exp\left(-t/T_2\right)$, the effect of diffusion being negligible if the time between pulses τ is small enough.

   Longitudinal Relaxation Time T_1.   Hahn[176] developed a method of measuring the spin-lattice relaxation time T_1 by using a sequence of three

90° pulses. If the pulses are applied at times 0, τ, and T, there will be the usual echo at time 2τ and a set of several echoes after the third pulse. In particular there will be one at time $T + \tau$ which Hahn called a *stimulated echo.* He showed that the decay of this echo was governed by T_1 and that its amplitude was proportional to $\exp(-T/T'_m)$. Here T'_m is given by

$$\frac{1}{T'_m} = \frac{1}{T_1} + k\tau^2 \tag{4-13}$$

and k is again proportional to the diffusion constant. The effective relaxation time T'_m can be found by displaying the stimulated echo as an envelope; T_1 can then be obtained by comparing T'_m for a series of values of τ.

Another pulse method for measuring T_1 has been proposed by Carr and Purcell.[86] It is *initiated* by a 180° pulse, which has the effect of reversing the spin and directing it oppositely to the static field. If left to itself, the magnetization vector would recover to its original position in a time of the order of T_1, remaining all the time in the z direction. Consequently no tail is observed following the 180° pulse. A 90° pulse is then applied at a subsequent time τ. If τ is small compared with T_1, the 90° pulse operates on a magnetic moment of nearly maximum amplitude (although not in the equilibrium direction) and a free induction tail is observed. If τ is large, the moment will have recovered its equilibrium value and again a tail will be observed. For intermediate τ, however, the tails will have a smaller amplitude; for the z component of the moment will be recovering through values near zero. In fact the tail will vanish if τ has the value

$$\tau_{\text{null}} = T_1 \ln 2 \tag{4-14}$$

This relation can then be used to find T_1. The method has the advantage that it is independent of the effects of diffusion and field inhomogeneity. However, it is important to ensure that the time between successive *sequences* of pulses in the experiment is long compared with T_1, so that the nuclei can return to their equilibrium distribution.

CHAPTER 5

GENERAL FEATURES OF NUCLEAR MAGNETIC
RESONANCE SPECTRA

5-1. The Chemical Shift

The most important single parameter to be derived from the NMR spectrum is the chemical shift. Since the NMR signals of nuclei of different elements in a fixed magnetic field normally occur in very different regions of the spectrum, we are ordinarily concerned only with chemical shifts between nuclei of the same element. For example, as pointed out in Sec. 1-4, hydrogen atoms of the same molecule which are not chemically equivalent will experience a different diamagnetic electron screening in a magnetic field and give rise to separate resonance signals. The six hydrogen atoms in ethyl alcohol give rise to three signals (Fig. 1-3): one for protons of the methyl group, one for the protons of the methylene group, and one for the proton of the hydroxyl group. The mutual separations of the three signals is a measure of the chemical shifts between the three distinct groups. Experimentally these separations are measured by the methods discussed in Secs. 4-7 and 4-8 and may be expressed either in units of magnetic field or in frequency units. The two systems of units are readily converted by the equation for the resonance condition, $\nu = \gamma H/2\pi$, from which it is also apparent that the magnitude of the chemical shift is directly proportional to the applied field. When chemical-shift values are expressed in either of the above units, it is also necessary to specify either the magnetic field or the resonant frequency used in the measurements. It is more convenient, therefore, to express chemical shifts in terms of a nondimensional unit defined by

$$\delta = \frac{H - H_r}{H_r} \tag{5-1}$$

where H is the resonant field of the signal being measured at a fixed frequency and H_r the corresponding resonant field for a second proton signal chosen as the reference signal.†

† Instead of the definition (5-1) for δ, the alternative definition $(H_r - H)/H_r$ is preferred by some authors, e.g., ref. 286.

87

The separation of the signals is most readily obtained in frequency units by employing the side-band technique described in Sec. 4-7. The frequency difference obtained in this manner is $\nu - \nu_r$, which corresponds to $H - H_r$ in Eq. (5-1), and δ is obtained by dividing by the *fixed* resonant frequency.† As an example of the orders of magnitude involved, the signal separation $\Delta\nu$ of the methylene protons in ethyl alcohol with reference to the protons of the methyl group, when measured in frequency units at a fixed resonant frequency of 40 Mc/sec, is 98.0 cycles/sec. The chemical shift δ is then 2.45×10^{-6}, or 2.45 ppm (parts per million). Knowing the resonant frequency or the applied field, chemical-shift data expressed in this way are readily converted to the laboratory units of cycles per second or milligauss. Thus, for the above conditions, the applied field for protons at a resonant frequency of 40 Mc/sec is 9,395 gauss, so that the corresponding measure of the signal separation in field units is 23.0 milligauss.

From the discussion of Sec. 1-3 it also follows that δ can be defined in terms of the screening constants σ. If σ and σ_r are respectively the screening constant of the proton to be measured and that of the reference proton, then

$$\delta = \sigma - \sigma_r \tag{5-2}$$

Accordingly, a positive value of δ corresponds to higher electronic screening than for the reference protons.

When two or more nuclei in a given molecule have identical screening constants and give rise to identical chemical shifts, they are said to be *equivalent*.‡ Such nuclei normally also occupy chemically equivalent positions in the molecule. Thus the three protons of the methyl group in ethyl alcohol form a set of equivalent nuclei, and the two protons of the methylene group form another distinct set. The basic classification of the proton resonance spectrum of a given molecule can be made in terms of the number of equivalent sets of protons giving rise to the observed signals and the number of protons in each set. The number of protons giving rise to each signal can be derived from the relative intensities when the chemical shifts are large. If the structure of the compound is known, it is usually a simple matter to determine which nuclei are equivalent by inspection of the chemical formula, or from symmetry considerations (Sec. 6-2).

† It is desirable to reserve the symbol δ for chemical shifts in dimensionless units and not use it for the shift $\Delta\nu = \nu - \nu_r$, expressed in cycles per second. To convert this shift to the δ units, it is permissible to divide by the fixed radio frequency ν_0 rather than ν or ν_r, since the magnitude of any of these frequencies is very large relative to $\Delta\nu$.

‡ The nuclei in an equivalent set may or may not have identical spin coupling with all other magnetic nuclei in the molecule (Sec. 6-2).

The simplest type of NMR spectrum is obtained from molecules which contain only one species of magnetic nuclei, all of which are equivalent. Such compounds give a spectrum consisting only of a single sharp line, with no fine structure. Compounds of this type are therefore particularly well suited as reference compounds in chemical-shift measurements according to the methods described in Sec. 4-8. In Fig. 5-1 the proton chemical shifts of a number of molecules, each having all protons equivalent, are shown on a common scale relative to the signal of cyclohexane.† The values shown refer to the pure liquids at room temperature.

The chemical shifts of a series of compounds, which give rise to relatively simple proton resonance spectra and which are particularly significant in connection with the theory of proton chemical shifts discussed

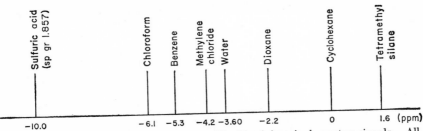

Fig. 5-1. Observed chemical shifts of some liquids giving single proton signals. All shifts are arbitrarily referred to the cyclohexane signal and were measured at room temperature relative to an external reference.

in Chap. 7, are collected in Table 5-1. All the compounds listed were measured[402] as gases at temperatures well above the saturation point and at pressures varying from 5 to 20 atm. The signals of some of the compounds listed exhibit a fine-structure splitting, the origin of which will be discussed in the following section.

The sign of the chemical-shift values shown in Fig. 5-1 and in Table 5-1 indicates whether the proton signal appears at higher or lower applied field than that of the reference signal. The following arbitrary sign convention, which follows from Eq. (5-1), is adopted throughout this book. When the resonance signal of the proton being measured occurs at *higher* field than that of the reference proton signal, that is, $H > H_r$, the chemical shift is *positive*. It will be appreciated that such a sign convention is quite arbitrary and is not independent of the particular reference substance chosen. A further convention is adopted in connection with displaying actual NMR spectra, or chemical-shift data on a common

† Strictly speaking, chloroform does not belong to this class, because chlorine nuclei possess magnetic moments. However, the observed signal is sharp for reasons discussed in Chap. 10.

scale, as in Fig. 5-1. This is that the *direction of increasing applied field* in such spectra or diagrams *is from left to right.*

Figure 5-2 shows some representative chemical-shift data for F^{19}, C^{13}, and N^{14} nuclear resonance signals in a variety of compounds.[159,192,236,194] In each case a single resonance signal was observed.† The C^{13} resonances were measured with the carbon isotope present in its natural abundance (1.108 per cent). The particular C^{13} nucleus measured in each compound of carbon is indicated. It is worth noting in this connection that the

TABLE 5-1. CHEMICAL SHIFTS OF SIMPLE GASEOUS COMPOUNDS[402]

Compound	Relative chemical shifts in	
	Cycles/sec †	Ppm
H_2	−168	−4.20
CH_4	0	0
NH_3	2	0.05
H_2O	− 24	−0.60
SiH_4	−120	−3.00
PH_3	− 59	−1.48
H_2S	− 3	−0.08
HCl	18	0.45
HBr	174	4.35
HI	530	13.25
C_2H_6	− 30	−0.75
C_2H_4	−207	−5.18
C_2H_2	− 54	−1.35
C_6H_6	−285	−7.13

† At a fixed measuring frequency of 40 Mc/sec.

screening constant depends only on the electronic structure and is therefore the same for all isotopic species of an element. Thus the chemical shifts δ, in parts per million, for a particular nucleus in different compounds measured from the same reference are the same as for the corresponding isotopic compounds measured from the isotopically substituted reference. This has been confirmed experimentally[192,352] for N^{14} and N^{15} compounds.

It will be apparent, by comparison with Fig. 5-1, that in general the chemical shifts of the three nuclei shown in Fig. 5-2 are more than an order of magnitude larger than proton chemical shifts. This is also the case for the chemical shifts of P^{31} resonances[163] and O^{17} resonances.[458] Bulk diamagnetic susceptibility corrections are accordingly unimportant. Because the resonance signals of different nuclei occur in widely separated

† Although ordinarily the F^{19} resonance in liquid HF may be expected to give rise to a doublet signal, this is not observed because of proton exchange (Sec. 5-4).

"regions" of the over-all NMR spectral range, chemical shifts of any one species of magnetic nucleus can be measured quite independently of other magnetic nuclei present in the molecule. Sometimes important

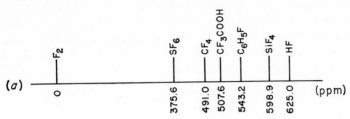

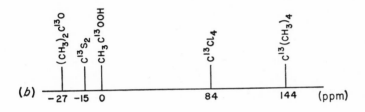

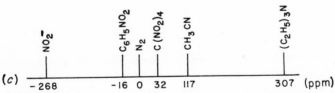

FIG. 5-2. Representative chemical shifts in various compounds for (a) F[19], ref. 159; (b) C[13], refs. 236 and 194; and (c) N[14], ref. 192.

structural information can be gained by measuring the NMR spectra of more than one species of nuclei in the same molecule.

5-2. Fine Structure Due to Spin-Spin Coupling

As mentioned in the previous section, the simplest possible NMR spectrum, consisting of but one signal, is obtained when all the magnetic nuclei in a molecule are equivalent. The theoretical reasons for this are dealt with in Chap. 6. For molecules having two different sets of equivalent nuclei, the spectrum may become considerably more complex, since in addition to the two distinguishable signals now possible, each of these signals may be split into further components due to spin-spin interaction between nonequivalent nuclei. As discussed in Sec. 1-5, this interaction occurs by way of the bonding electrons. In the simplest case of two nonequivalent nuclei, bonded by a covalent bond such as in the molecule HD, the interaction may be described in the following manner.[368] The interaction of one nucleus with the electron of its atom will make the electron spin lie more frequently antiparallel than parallel to the nuclear spin. But the two electron spins in the covalent bond must be antiparallel to each other, so that the electron spin of the other atom will tend to lie more frequently parallel to the spin of the first nucleus. However, the electron of the second atom interacts magnetically with the nucleus of this atom, and consequently the spin of the second nucleus tends to be antiparallel to that of the first. The combination of these coupling effects therefore provides a spin interaction between the two nuclei. The interaction energy has been shown[165,177] to be of the form $J_{12}\mathbf{I}(1) \cdot \mathbf{I}(2)$ (Sec. 1-5) and to be independent of temperature[166] and of the applied field.[166,359,389] The spin coupling constant J_{12} has the dimensions of energy and is usually expressed in cycles per second. The fact that the interaction is independent of applied field can be qualitatively understood if the magnetic fields responsible for the interaction are regarded as arising within the molecule itself.† A more detailed discussion of the origin of spin-spin interaction will be given in Chap. 8.

In the molecule HD, which has two magnetically different (nonequivalent) nuclei, the number of fine-structure components of the proton resonance signal to be expected from spin-spin interaction with the deuteron, which has $I = 1$, is three. This corresponds to the three possible spin states of the deuteron $(2I + 1)$. In other words, because of the electron-coupled spin-spin interaction, the proton spin can "see" the three individual orientations of the deuteron spin. Similarly, the deuteron resonance signal would be expected to be a doublet, corresponding to the two possible spin states of the proton, which has $I = 1/2$. These predicted patterns have been observed experimentally[85,469] for gaseous HD. The proton resonance signals consisted of three equally spaced components of equal intensity. The corresponding deuteron spectrum had two components of equal intensity and the same spacing as that observed for the proton signals. From the measured separation of the component signals the interaction constant J_{HD} was found to be 43 cycles/sec.

Experimental measurements of the fine structure in the spectra of

† The earlier interpretation of the fine-structure components proposed by Andrew[16] on the basis of restricted rotation of molecules can be ruled out, since the splitting is independent of temperature and is identical in the liquid and vapor phase.

a variety of more complex molecules[165,166,162] have shown that electron-coupled spin-spin interaction between members of an equivalent group of nuclei does not give rise to multiplet splitting.† Examples of such systems are the hydrogen or fluorine nuclei in freely rotating CH_3 or CF_3 groups (Sec. 6-2). A simple illustration is provided by the PF_3 molecule, in which both species of nuclei have spin $I = 1/2$. Since the three fluorine nuclei are equivalent, the multiplet splitting of the fluorine signal will arise only from spin-spin interaction with the phosphorus nucleus. It will appear as a doublet because the P^{31} nucleus has two spin states. A schematic reproduction of the observed fluorine spectrum[166] is shown in Fig. 5-3a. We consider next the P^{31} signal, which will be split because of spin-spin interaction with the three equivalent fluorine nuclei. The

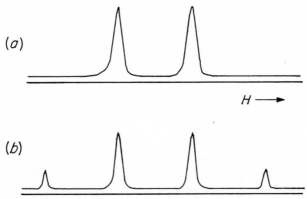

FIG. 5-3. Nuclear resonance spectra of PF_3. (a) F^{19} resonance (schematic). (b) P^{31} resonance (schematic). (Gutowsky, McCall, and Slichter.[166])

energy of the P^{31} transition will depend only on the sum of the spin components of the three fluorine nuclei ΣI_z. Since $I_z = \pm 1/2$, this sum can take the values $3/2$, $1/2$, $-1/2$, $-3/2$, and the phosphorus signal will accordingly be split into a quartet[166] (Fig. 5-3b). This result can be illustrated more precisely if we write down all the possible combinations of spin states for the three fluorine nuclei, as in Table 5-2. Here α and β refer to the two possible spin states ($\pm 1/2$) any one fluorine nucleus can assume. The four resultant values of ΣI_z are seen to have statistical weights 1, 3, 3, 1, two of them being triply degenerate. Thus, as shown in Fig. 5-3b, the P^{31} NMR spectrum has four equally spaced signals whose intensities are in the ratio 1:3:3:1. (See also Sec. 6-4.)

These simple formulations are readily extended to other groups of equivalent nuclei. Thus two equivalent nuclei have three resultant spin states with statistical weights 1:2:1 and give rise to a triplet in the reso-

† Exceptions to this general behavior may occur. This topic is discussed more fully in Chap. 6.

nance signal of a neighboring nucleus with which they interact. Similarly, an equivalent set of four nuclei gives rise to a quintet for the resonance signal of a neighboring nucleus, and the relative intensities of the component signals are in the ratio $1:4:6:4:1$. In the general case for a set of n_A equivalent nuclei of type A interacting with n_X equivalent nuclei of type X, the A signal has $2n_X I_X + 1$ components and the X signal has $2n_A I_A + 1$ components. The relative intensities of each group of signals are in the ratio of the corresponding binomial coefficients. The A and X nuclei may belong to different species, or they may be of the

TABLE 5-2. SPIN STATES OF GROUP OF THREE EQUIVALENT FLUORINE NUCLEI

Fluorine nucleus			I_z	Statistical weight
1	2	3		
α	α	α	$3/2$	1
α	α	β		
α	β	α	$1/2$	3
β	α	α		
α	β	β		
β	α	β	$-1/2$	3
β	β	α		
β	β	β	$-3/2$	1

same species if the chemical shift between their resonance signals is large. In Fig. 5-4 the proton resonance spectra of $CHCl_2CH_2Cl$ and CH_3CH_2Cl are shown.† In the first compound there are three protons, two of which are equivalent. Interaction of the latter produces a triplet splitting on the signal of the proton bonded to the first carbon atom. This signal occurs at lower field. The second signal, which has twice the intensity of the first and which arises from the pair of equivalent protons, is split into a doublet by spin interaction with the single proton on the first carbon atom in the molecule. In ethyl chloride there are two sets of equivalent nuclei, those of the methyl group and those of the methylene group. The signal of the methylene group, which appears at a lower field, is split into a quartet by the three equivalent protons in the methyl group, whereas the signal of the methyl group is a triplet resulting from the spin-spin interaction with the two equivalent protons in the methylene group. The spacing of the individual components in the two signals is identical and has the value $J = 7.5$ cycles/sec. The observed chemical shift between the signals of the methylene protons and the methyl protons is 2.01 ppm.

A more complicated spectrum is obtained with ethyl alcohol, in which

† Again couplings between protons and chlorine nuclei do not affect these spectra.

there are three sets of nonequivalent protons. In addition to the equivalent sets on the methyl and methylene groups, there is a nonequivalent proton in the hydroxyl group. In pure dry alcohol the signal of the latter is split into a triplet by the protons of the methylene group, as is also the methyl signal. But the signal of the methylene-group protons will in turn be split by *both* the protons of the methyl group and the proton of the hydroxyl group. In principle this could lead to eight separate components; in practice they may not be resolved under moderate resolution. Under high resolution, it turns out that the spectrum is rather more complicated (Sec. 6-8).

In complex spectra involving several groups of equivalent nuclei separated by large chemical shifts, it is frequently possible to gain

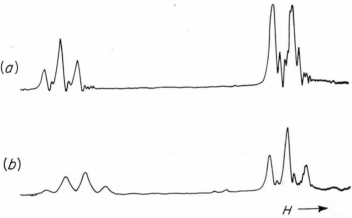

Fig. 5-4. The proton magnetic resonance spectrum of (a) $CHCl_2CH_2Cl$ and (b) CH_3CH_2Cl under moderate resolution.

valuable information by first recording the spectrum under conditions of lower resolution so that the spin coupling fine structure is not resolved. From the relative intensities of the signals obtained in this way information can be gained about the number of equivalent protons giving rise to each signal. When the fine-structure components are resolved under higher resolution, information can then be obtained about the relationship and ultimate assignment of the different proton groups. It may also be noted here that experience has shown that the electron-coupled spin-spin interaction usually attenuates rather rapidly with the number of chemical bonds separating the two nuclei in question.[169,392,27] Thus while the coupling constant between the protons of the methyl group and those of the methylene group is of the order of 7 cycles/sec, no fine-structure splitting on the signal of the hydroxyl-group proton by the methyl protons can ordinarily be detected.

The above simple rules for predicting the number, as well as relative intensities, of fine-structure components are strictly applicable only when the chemical shift (measured in frequency units) is large compared with the value of the coupling constant J. This will always be the case when the two interacting nuclei are of different elements, since for a given applied field their resonant frequencies are widely separated. However, for interacting nonequivalent nuclei of the same species the simple rules may break down and a more complicated spectrum may be obtained. This will occur when the chemical shift (expressed in frequency units) is approximately of the same order of magnitude as the coupling constant J. The spectrum may then exhibit a larger number of signals than would be predicted by the simple rules; individual multiplets become merged in a general mixed group of signals which may have few features of regularity either in the relative ordering of the signals or in their relative intensities. An interesting example of a spectrum of this type is the F^{19} spectrum of the molecule ClF_3, whose structure[81,428] is shown in Fig. 5-5. It is apparent from the structure that the fluorine atom F_1 is unique, being joined to the chlorine atom by a bond shorter than the bonds of the equivalent pair labeled F_2. We may therefore expect to find a measurable chemical shift between F_1 and the two F_2 nuclei. Since F^{19} has a spin $I = 1/2$, on the basis of the above simple rules for multiplet splitting we would predict that the F_1 signal would be a triplet and the second signal would be a doublet, giving a total of five components. In the observed spectrum[291] (Fig. 5-6a) obtained at a fixed measuring frequency of 10 Mc/sec, eight lines are clearly visible. The relative intensities of the lines no longer exhibit a simple pattern. A general enhancement in intensity toward the center of the spectrum and a diminution toward the wings are apparent. The greater number of signals results from the fact that some of the spin states, which are degenerate when the relative chemical shift is large (Table 5-2), now become split because of induced mixing of states by the magnetic field. This situation also leads to the anomalous intensities observed. Under these conditions it is no longer possible to measure the chemical shift or the J values directly, or to arrive at an assignment of the signals to individual fluorine atoms by a simple inspection of the spectrum. A more complete discussion of spectra of this kind, together with methods of analysis, is presented in Chap. 6.

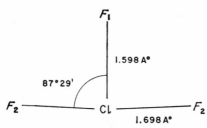

FIG. 5-5. Structure of ClF_3.   (Smith.[428])

As mentioned previously, chemical shifts are field dependent, whereas the separation of the spin-spin components is not. Hence the ratio of the chemical shift to the coupling constant can be altered by varying the

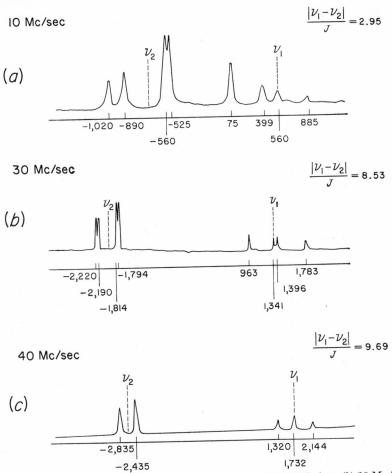

FIG. 5-6. F^{19} spectrum of ClF_3 at measuring frequency of (a) 10 Mc/sec, (b) 30 Mc/sec, and (c) 40 Mc/sec. All spectra were taken at $-60°C$. Signal shifts are shown in cycles per second relative to the reference signal of SF_6. Here $\nu_1 - \nu_2$ is the chemical shift (in cycles per second) between F_1 and F_2. (Muetterties and Phillips.[291])

applied field in the measurements. If the applied field is increased (and thus also the resonant frequency), the spectrum shown in Fig. 5-6b is obtained. This was recorded at a resonant frequency of 30 Mc/sec. A partial regrouping of the spectrum somewhat resembling a doublet and a triplet is apparent. This is even more evident when the spectrum is recorded at 40 Mc/sec (Fig. 5-6c), where the relative intensities of the spin components now more nearly resemble those to be expected for a system with large chemical shift. From this spectrum it is also now apparent that the doublet signal, which occurs at lower field, is to be assigned to the two F_2 nuclei and the triplet signal at higher field to the F_1 nucleus. It should be noted that, because of the limited range of magnetic fields available in practice, it is not always possible to obtain simplification of a complex spectrum to the same extent as that illustrated in Fig. 5-6. In any given case the determining factor will be the ratio of the chemical shift to the J coupling constant.

It follows from the above discussion that, in general, NMR spectra can be roughly classified into two categories, those involving large chemical shifts and those involving small chemical shifts of the order of the J coupling constants. In describing individual spectra it is convenient to use a systematic notation for these two classes. We shall use the symbols A, B, . . . for nonequivalent nuclei of the same species whose relative chemical shifts are of the same order of magnitude as the spin coupling constant between them. The symbols X, Y, . . . will be used for another such set whose signals are not close to those of the set A, B, ... The nuclei in the set X, Y, . . . may or may not be of the same species as those in the set A, B, ... Equivalent nuclei are described by the same symbol, and the number of equivalent nuclei in any given set is indicated by a subscript. Thus the complete spectrum of PF_3 or NH_3 would be referred to as an AX_3 spectrum, and the proton spectrum of $CHCl_2CH_2Cl$ as an AX_2 spectrum. However, the spectrum of ClF_3 recorded at 10 Mc/sec would be described as an AB_2 spectrum (or, alternatively, as XY_2). When the spectrum involves three nonequivalent groups of nuclei, it frequently happens that there is a small chemical shift between two of the groups and the signals of the third are well separated from the other two. Such a spectrum for three nonequivalent nuclei is termed an ABX spectrum. In pyridine, for example, the α-proton signals are well separated from those of the β and γ protons, the latter appearing close together in the spectrum. The NMR spectrum can then be approximately characterized as an AB_2X_2 spectrum.

5-3. Temperature, Solvent, and Other Medium Effects

Consideration must be given to several other effects which may modify the observed NMR spectra in certain cases. Usually such effects will involve an alteration of the chemical shift, and in some instances the structure of the spin-multiplet components.

Accurate measurements of the chemical shift require the measurement of the separation of a given signal relative to some convenient reference signal.   In order that the final chemical-shift values be independent of the medium in which they are measured, it is necessary to correct for the bulk diamagnetic susceptibility of the sample being measured according to the methods outlined in Secs. 4-8 and 4-9.   This correction is of importance mainly for proton resonance measurements.   When measurements are made over a wide temperature range, the variation of the bulk susceptibility of the medium with temperature, owing to density changes, must be taken into account.

Molecular association will alter the proton chemical shift relative to its value for the isolated molecule.   In some cases these effects may be very large and may drastically alter the relative chemical shifts.   This is very pronounced for the resonance signals of hydrogen atoms which can take part in hydrogen bonding, either among molecules of the compound being measured or with solvent molecules.   Association shifts of this kind, a fuller account of which is given in Chap. 15, can in practice be readily detected by varying the temperature or the concentration. Increasing temperature or increasing dilution causes an increasing dissociation of the molecular complexes and gives rise to an observable shift of the resonance signal.   Obviously, for these reasons, associated liquids, unless the temperature or concentration is held sufficiently constant, are not very suitable as reference liquids (Sec. 4-8) in NMR measurements.

A further specific-medium effect occurs with aromatic solvents.   This is due to the fact that aromatic molecules, such as benzene, possess an anomalous diamagnetic susceptibility.   In terms of a simple model, the aromatic ring with its mobile π electrons may be regarded as a circular loop of wire in which a circulating current is induced in a magnetic field (Sec. 2-5).   The circulating current gives rise to a secondary magnetic field which acts on a proton of a neighboring molecule.   Hence a proton in close proximity to the aromatic molecule will suffer a shift of the resonance signal (cf. Sec. 16-2).   The magnitude of this shift will be a function of the concentration, since the effective secondary magnetic field depends on the "mean" distance of approach of the solute molecules and solvent molecules.   Effects of this kind must be taken into account in accurate chemical-shift measurements.   Thus the proton resonance signal of acetone diluted in benzene is displaced by about 0.6 ppm from its position in pure acetone.[71]

Specific-medium effects are also observed in the fluorine resonances of certain molecules, such as benzotrifluoride and 1,2-dibromotetrafluoroethane, when diluted with solvents, particularly those containing large halogen atoms.   Under these conditions the resonance is shifted to lower field by several parts per million.[133a,143a]

5-4. Time-averaging Effects

The NMR spectrum may be modified also if the molecules being measured are taking part in various rate processes. An example of such a process is the phenomenon of proton exchange between different chemical positions. If this exchange is sufficiently rapid, a coalescence of some signals will be observed. This is a manifestation of the uncertainty principle, which may be written in the form

$$\tau \, \Delta\nu \approx \frac{1}{2\pi} \tag{5-3}$$

where $\Delta\nu$ is the separation of the corresponding resonance lines and τ is the smallest time for which the two separate states can be distinguished.

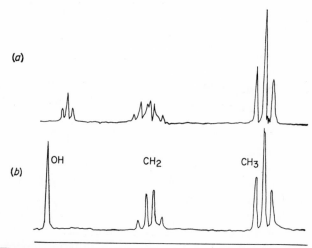

FIG. 5-7. The proton resonance spectrum of ethyl alcohol. (a) Pure dry alcohol. (b) Alcohol to which a small amount of hydrochloric acid has been added. (Arnold.[20])

Thus when the exchange is sufficiently rapid, the lifetimes of the states will become less than this critical value, and the signals cannot be separated. This collapse of signals is illustrated in Fig. 5-7 for the ethyl alcohol spectrum. In pure dry alcohol, as discussed in Sec. 5-2, the proton signal of the OH group is a triplet resulting from spin-spin interaction with the protons of the CH_2 group. It was found[20] that the addition of a small amount of hydrochloric acid to the alcohol causes the OH triplet signal to collapse to a single sharp signal (Fig. 5-7b). The spin-spin interaction with the protons of the methylene group also disappears, so that the signal of the latter group is reduced to a quartet. The interpretation is that the addition of acid causes rapid exchange of the hydroxyl-group protons between neighboring molecules. This exchange is sufficiently rapid to "average out" the electron environment of the proton and the spin interactions of the neighboring methylene-group protons (Sec. 10-2). Rapid proton exchange is also observed in aqueous solutions of mineral acids and bases (Chap. 18).

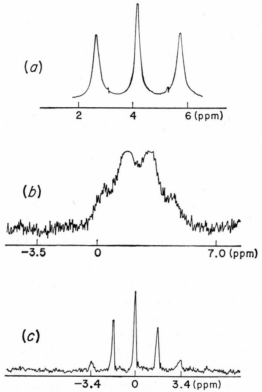

FIG. 5-8. The proton spectrum of $N^{14}H_3$ and the N^{14} spectrum in $N^{14}H_3$ and $N^{14}H_4^+$ ion. (a) H^1 spectrum in $N^{14}H_3$. (Ogg and Ray.[309]) (b) N^{14} spectrum in $N^{14}H_3$. (c) N^{14} spectrum in $N^{14}H_4^+$ ion. (Ogg and Ray.[308])

Generally speaking, the coalescence of signals under certain conditions is a strong indication that some averaging process is taking place. This may involve an intramolecular rearrangement or a hindered rotation. An example of this is found in dimethylformamide (Sec. 13-3). This is a planar molecule, and the two methyl groups bonded to nitrogen are also in the molecular plane. At ordinary temperatures there is a hindered rotation about the carbon-nitrogen bond. Since the two methyl groups on the nitrogen atom are not symmetrically disposed relative to the carbonyl group in the molecule, two methyl signals corresponding to two distinguishable chemical shifts are observed.[155,330] However if the temperature is raised, rotation about the carbon-nitrogen bond can take place sufficiently rapidly to average out the two different environments of the methyl groups, and a single sharp signal is obtained.

It frequently happens that, when a proton is bonded to a nitrogen atom, the proton signals are broadened. In extreme cases the signal is barely detectable. This is due to the fact that the nitrogen nucleus has a quadrupole moment which gives rise to a strong relaxation mechanism if the electron-charge distribution around it is sufficiently asymmetric.† An example of this occurs in the NMR spectrum of pyrrole, where, under ordinary conditions of measurement, the proton signal arising from the NH group is so broad that it is barely detectable above the background noise level. A further interesting example is provided by $N^{14}H_3$. The proton resonance spectrum[309] of pure dry ammonia, shown in Fig. 5-8a, consists of three equally spaced lines due to the spin-spin splitting of N^{14}, which has $I = 1$. The signals are relatively broad. (The broadening of the outer lines relative to that of the central line is discussed in Sec. 10-3.) The N^{14} spectrum (Fig. 5-8b) consists of four components,[308] owing to spin-spin splitting by the three equivalent protons. These are broadened by the nitrogen quadrupole relaxation. However, the spectrum of N^{14} in the $N^{14}H_4{}^+$ ion gives rise to a sharp-line spectrum consisting of five components in the intensity ratio $1:4:6:4:1$, as would be expected from four equivalent protons.[308] These signals are sharp because the N^{14} quadrupole coupling energy is reduced and the relaxation time increased as a result of the small field gradient at the N^{14} nucleus due to the high symmetry of the tetrahedral charge distribution.

Broadening of the signal due to quadrupole coupling can sometimes be removed by double-irradiation experiments[63] (Sec. 10-3). This is frequently a useful technique for confirming an expected signal from a proton attached to nitrogen, when this cannot otherwise be observed. On the other hand, if a broad signal is observed in a proton spectrum and it is known that there is a nitrogen atom in the molecule, this in itself furnishes valuable information in connection with arriving at an assignment of the spectrum.

† A more detailed discussion of this effect is presented in Sec. 10-3.

CHAPTER 6

ANALYSIS OF NUCLEAR MAGNETIC
RESONANCE SPECTRA

6-1. Quantum-mechanical Formulation of Nuclear Spin States and Transitions

In this chapter we shall be concerned with the quantum-mechanical theory of the frequencies and intensities of the lines in an NMR spectrum in terms of the chemical shifts and spin coupling constants. Some of the simpler features have already been outlined in the previous chapter. In many spectra the effects of chemical shift and spin coupling give rise to a complex pattern of lines resulting from the merging of individual multiplets, which then have few features of regularity. One is then faced with the problem of interpreting such a band system, assigning each line to a definite transition, and finally extracting numerical values for the chemical shifts and spin coupling constants. The basic theoretical steps required for the detailed analysis of such spectra were developed by Gutowsky, McCall, and Slichter,[166] Hahn and Maxwell,[179] McConnell, McLean, and Reilly,[273] and others.[29,467,10]

To calculate the energies and intensities of the transitions that may be observed in an NMR spectrum of a group of interacting nuclei, it is necessary to find the energies and stationary-state wave functions for the system in the absence of the rf field. This oscillating field then causes transitions between the states, and the corresponding transition probabilities can be found by perturbation methods closely analogous to those used in the theory of optical transitions. Intensities calculated by using first-order perturbation theory will of course only apply to intensities observed below the saturation power level. We shall approach the problem of spectral analysis by calculating some theoretical spectra for certain simple characteristic groupings of nuclei, and then indicating by some appropriate examples how observed spectra can be completely analyzed with the aid of such calculations.

a. Spin Wave Functions. As mentioned in Chap. 1, each nucleus has a spin vector $\mathbf{I}$ which is such that the angular momentum is $\hbar\mathbf{I}$ and the magnetic moment $\gamma\hbar\mathbf{I}$, γ being the nuclear magnetogyric ratio.

From the general properties of angular momentum in quantum mechanics,[416] it follows that there is a spin quantum number I (which may take integral or half-integral values) so that the nucleus may have $2I + 1$ independent states.

In this chapter we shall be mainly concerned with the analysis of spectra arising from nuclei with spin $I = 1/2$. For each isolated nucleus then there will be two independent states. The degeneracy of these two states is removed by the application of a magnetic field, and we may conveniently express all wave functions for the spin in terms of the two stationary-state functions for the nucleus in a magnetic field in the z direction. In these states the z component of the spin I_z will have a definite value of $\pm 1/2$. We write α for the wave function of the state in which I_z is $1/2$ and β for the function when it is $-1/2$. Using these two functions as a basis, all three components of I will be represented by 2×2 matrices, that for I_z being diagonal. These are the well-known Pauli[416] matrices†

$$I_x = \tfrac{1}{2} \begin{pmatrix} 0 & 1 \\ 1 & 0 \end{pmatrix} \qquad I_y = \tfrac{1}{2} \begin{pmatrix} 0 & i \\ -i & 0 \end{pmatrix} \qquad I_z = \tfrac{1}{2} \begin{pmatrix} 1 & 0 \\ 0 & -1 \end{pmatrix} \quad (6\text{-}1)$$

Next consider the form of Hamiltonian to be used. If the direction of the strong magnetic field H is the *negative* z direction, the energy of a nucleus in this field will be $\gamma \hbar H I_z$, measured in ergs if H is measured in gauss. Ergs are inconvenient units for measurement, and throughout this chapter all energies, and consequently all Hamiltonian matrix elements, will be given in cycles per second. With this unit, the interaction becomes $\gamma H I_z / 2\pi$. For a set of nuclei with magnetogyric ratios γ_i and acted on by fields H_i, the Hamiltonian will be

$$\mathcal{H}^{(0)} = (2\pi)^{-1} \sum_i \gamma_i H_i I_z(i) \qquad (6\text{-}2)$$

γ_i will depend only on the species of nucleus and H_i will differ from the external field H_0 because of electronic screening. Thus we write

$$H_i = H_0(1 - \sigma_i) \qquad (6\text{-}3)$$

where σ_i is the appropriate screening constant. Because the theoretical presentation is simpler, we shall discuss the set of energy levels when the external field H_0 is held constant, although, as we have already seen, the experiment is usually performed by varying H_0 to get resonance at a fixed frequency.

† The convention used for any operator P is that $(\alpha|P|\alpha)$, $(\alpha|P|\beta)$, $(\beta|P|\alpha)$, and $(\beta|P|\beta)$ are respectively the top-left, top-right, bottom-left, and bottom-right elements in the matrix.

The indirect spin coupling may be represented by a Hamiltonian involving the scalar products of the spin vectors of all pairs of magnetic nuclei:

$$\mathcal{3C}^{(1)} = \sum_{i<j} J_{ij}\mathbf{I}(i) \cdot \mathbf{I}(j) \tag{6-4}$$

Again the constants J_{ij} are measured in cycles per second. For the present this is to be regarded as an empirical Hamiltonian which has been successful when used to analyze spectra. The justification for this form and the theory of the origin of the coupling constants J_{ij} will be dealt with in Chap. 8.

If the rate of rotation of the molecules is rapid enough for the dipole-dipole interaction to be neglected, the quantum-mechanical problem is based on the complete Hamiltonian

$$\mathcal{3C} = \mathcal{3C}^{(0)} + \mathcal{3C}^{(1)} \tag{6-5}$$

If the system contains p nuclei (all with spin 1/2), there will be a total of 2^p possible states. The simplest set of functions describing this many-spin system would be the 2^p *basic product functions* such as

$$\psi_n = \alpha(1)\beta(2)\alpha(3) \cdot \cdot \cdot \beta(p) \tag{6-6}$$

This product will usually be shortened to $\alpha\beta\alpha \cdot \cdot \cdot \beta$, it being implied that the rth symbol applies to the rth nucleus. If the nuclei were actually independent, these products would themselves be stationary-state wave functions in the presence of the external magnetic field. However, the spin-interaction Hamiltonian $\mathcal{3C}^{(1)}$ may cause mixing between different product functions. In mathematical terms, the Hamiltonian $\mathcal{3C}^{(0)}$ will have only diagonal matrix elements with respect to the functions ψ_n, whereas $\mathcal{3C}^{(1)}$ may also have off-diagonal elements. Since the various basic product functions ψ_n are all orthogonal to one another, the correct stationary-state wave functions are the linear combinations of these products which diagonalize the matrix of the complete Hamiltonian $\mathcal{3C}$. The corresponding energies are solutions of the secular equation

$$|\mathcal{3C}_{mn} - E\delta_{mn}| = 0 \tag{6-7}$$

where $\delta_{mn} = 1$ if $m = n$, and is zero otherwise.

This secular equation is of order 2^p, but it can be factorized into a number of equations of lower order if we classify the basic functions according to the expectation value of the total spin component in the z direction,

$$F_z = \sum_i I_z(i) \tag{6-8}$$

All the product functions ψ_n are eigenfunctions of this operator, that is, each corresponds to a definite value of F_z. For two nuclei, for example, $\alpha\alpha$ is an eigenfunction of F_z corresponding to the eigenvalue 1 and $\alpha\beta$ is another corresponding to zero. This classification is important because it is possible to show that *there are no off-diagonal matrix elements of the Hamiltonian between basic product functions corresponding to different values of F_z.* To prove this we show that the operator F_z commutes with the Hamiltonian $\mathfrak{IC}$. $I_z(1)$ is a typical term of F_z and it clearly commutes with all the terms in the external-field Hamiltonian $\mathfrak{IC}^{(0)}$. Also we can show that

$$[I_z(1) + I_z(2)][\mathbf{I}(1) \cdot \mathbf{I}(2)] - [\mathbf{I}(1) \cdot \mathbf{I}(2)][I_z(1) + I_z(2)] = 0 \quad (6\text{-}9)$$

if we write the scalar product in full:

$$\mathbf{I}(1) \cdot \mathbf{I}(2) = I_x(1)I_x(2) + I_y(1)I_y(2) + I_z(1)I_z(2) \quad (6\text{-}10)$$

and use the well-known commutation rules

$$I_x(1)I_y(1) - I_y(1)I_x(1) = -iI_z(1) \cdots \quad (6\text{-}11)$$

It follows that F_z also commutes with $\mathfrak{IC}^{(1)}$ and consequently with the total Hamiltonian $\mathfrak{IC}$. Then if ψ_m and ψ_n are basic product functions with different values of F_z, $(F_z)_m$, and $(F_z)_n$, we can write the matrix elements of $\mathfrak{IC}F_z$ and $F_z\mathfrak{IC}$ in the form

$$(\psi_m|\mathfrak{IC}F_z|\psi_n) = (F_z)_n(\psi_m|\mathfrak{IC}|\psi_n)$$
$$(\psi_m|F_z\mathfrak{IC}|\psi_n) = (F_z)_m(\psi_m|\mathfrak{IC}|\psi_n) \quad (6\text{-}12)$$

But the left-hand sides of these two equations must be equal, so it follows that

$$(\psi_m|\mathfrak{IC}|\psi_n) = 0 \quad (6\text{-}13)$$

This important result means that the complete determinantal equation (6-7) factorizes into $p + 1$ separate equations corresponding to all the possible values of F_z. In the simple example of two nuclei, of the four possible basic product functions, $\alpha\alpha$ and $\beta\beta$ do not mix with any others and are therefore stationary-state wave functions for the complete Hamiltonian $\mathfrak{IC}$. The remaining functions $\alpha\beta$ and $\beta\alpha$, on the other hand, both correspond to $F_z = 0$ and may be mixed together.

Further factorization of the secular equation can be carried out to a high degree of approximation if more than one species of nucleus (i.e., of different elements) is involved. If the nuclear species are X, Y, . . . , the total spin component F_z is made up from contributions from each type:

$$F_z = F_z(X) + F_z(Y) + \cdots \quad (6\text{-}14)$$

The basic product functions are eigenfunctions of $F_z(X)$, $F_z(Y)$, . . . , and to a good approximation mixing occurs only between product functions which correspond to the same values of *each of* $F_z(X)$, $F_z(Y)$, ... This follows because the magnitude of the off-diagonal element between functions with different $F_z(X)$, $F_z(Y)$, . . . will be of the order of a spin coupling constant (usually less than 500 cycles/sec) and will be much smaller than the difference between the corresponding diagonal elements which will be dominated by the difference between the resonant frequencies (usually several megacycles per second). Thus for two nuclei of different species, mixing between $\alpha\beta$ and $\beta\alpha$ will be negligible, and all the functions $\alpha\alpha$, $\alpha\beta$, $\beta\alpha$, and $\beta\beta$ will be stationary-state functions. Exactly similar arguments apply to nuclei of the same species with chemical shifts large compared with spin coupling constants. We shall make use of this sort of simplification when setting up a classification of spectra later in this chapter.

b. Matrix Elements of the Hamiltonian. The next step is to evaluate the matrix elements of the total Hamiltonian between basic product functions corresponding to the same value of F_z. We shall deal with diagonal and off-diagonal elements separately.

Diagonal Elements. Since each basic product function ψ_m is itself an eigenfunction of each term in the external-field Hamiltonian, the diagonal matrix elements of $\mathfrak{IC}^{(0)}$ are simply obtained by replacing $I_z(i)$ in $\mathfrak{IC}^{(0)}$ by $\pm 1/2$ according as the corresponding spin function is α or β. For two nuclei, for example, the diagonal element of $\mathfrak{IC}^{(0)}$ for the function $\alpha(1)\beta(2)$, or $\alpha\beta$, is $(4\pi)^{-1}(\gamma_1 H_1 - \gamma_2 H_2)$ from Eq. (6-2).

To find the diagonal matrix element of the spin coupling Hamiltonian $\mathfrak{IC}^{(1)}$, we may consider a typical term, say, $J_{12}\mathbf{I}(1) \cdot \mathbf{I}(2)$. Integration over the remaining spins then gives unity, and the matrix element of this term depends only on whether the spin functions associated with nuclei 1 and 2 in ψ_m are $\alpha\alpha$, $\alpha\beta$, $\beta\alpha$, or $\beta\beta$. The remaining integration can be carried out by writing $\mathbf{I}(1) \cdot \mathbf{I}(2)$ in the full form (6-10) and then using the appropriate components of the Pauli matrices (6-1). Thus

$$[\alpha\alpha|J_{12}\mathbf{I}(1) \cdot \mathbf{I}(2)|\alpha\alpha]$$
$$= J_{12}[(\alpha|I_x|\alpha)^2 + (\alpha|I_y|\alpha)^2 + (\alpha|I_z|\alpha)^2] = \tfrac{1}{4}J_{12} \quad (6\text{-}15)$$
$$[\alpha\beta|J_{12}\mathbf{I}(1) \cdot \mathbf{I}(2)|\alpha\beta]$$
$$= J_{12}[(\alpha|I_x|\alpha)(\beta|I_x|\beta) + (\alpha|I_y|\alpha)(\beta|I_y|\beta) + (\alpha|I_z|\alpha)(\beta|I_z|\beta)]$$
$$= -\tfrac{1}{4}J_{12} \quad (6\text{-}16)$$

Corresponding expansions for $\beta\alpha$ and $\beta\beta$ give $-\tfrac{1}{4}J_{12}$ and $\tfrac{1}{4}J_{12}$, respectively. Adding similar expressions for all terms in $\mathfrak{IC}^{(1)}$, we obtain for the diagonal matrix element

$$(\psi_m|\mathfrak{IC}^{(1)}|\psi_m) = \tfrac{1}{4} \sum_{i<j} J_{ij}T_{ij} \quad (6\text{-}17)$$

where $T_{ij} = 1$ or -1 according as spins i and j are parallel or antiparallel in ψ_m. Thus, for a typical three-spin system,

$$(\alpha\beta\alpha|\mathcal{3C}^{(1)}|\alpha\beta\alpha) = \tfrac{1}{4}(-J_{12} + J_{13} - J_{23}) \tag{6-18}$$

Off-diagonal Elements. Since the basic product functions are themselves eigenfunctions of the Hamiltonian representing interaction with the external field, there are no off-diagonal matrix elements of $\mathcal{3C}^{(0)}$ between basic product functions. There will, however, be off-diagonal elements of $\mathcal{3C}^{(1)}$ which may be evaluated by a method similar to that used for diagonal elements. Consider the matrix element of the particular term $J_{12}\mathbf{I}(1) \cdot \mathbf{I}(2)$ between two different basic product functions ψ_m and ψ_n. Then the matrix element will be zero unless the spin functions for all nuclei other than 1 and 2 are identical in ψ_m and ψ_n. Further, since we are only concerned with elements between functions with the same total spin component F_z, the only possibility to be considered is that ψ_m and ψ_n differ by the interchange of $\alpha(1)\beta(2)$ for $\beta(1)\alpha(2)$. The matrix element is then given by

$$[\alpha\beta|J_{12}\mathbf{I}(1) \cdot \mathbf{I}(2)|\beta\alpha]$$
$$= J_{12}[(\alpha|I_x|\beta)(\beta|I_x|\alpha) + (\alpha|I_y|\beta)(\beta|I_y|\alpha) + (\alpha|I_z|\beta)(\beta|I_z|\alpha)]$$
$$= \tfrac{1}{2}J_{12} \tag{6-19}$$

Combining all the terms in $\mathcal{3C}^{(1)}$, we have the following expression:

$$(\psi_m|\mathcal{3C}^{(1)}|\psi_n) = \tfrac{1}{2}UJ_{ij} \qquad m \neq n \tag{6-20}$$

where $U = 1$ if ψ_m differs from ψ_n by one interchange of spins i and j and is zero otherwise. For example

$$(\alpha\beta\alpha\beta|\mathcal{3C}^{(1)}|\beta\alpha\alpha\beta) = \tfrac{1}{2}J_{12}$$
$$(\alpha\beta\alpha\beta|\mathcal{3C}^{(1)}|\beta\alpha\beta\alpha) = 0 \tag{6-21}$$

c. Determination of Stationary-state Wave Functions. Having found all the matrix elements of the Hamiltonian $\mathcal{3C}_{mn}$ and solved the secular equation (6-7) to obtain the eigenvalues E_q, the corresponding stationary-state wave functions can be found as linear combinations of the basic product functions

$$\Phi_q = \sum_m a_{qm}\psi_m \qquad q = 1, 2, \ldots, 2^p \tag{6-22}$$

where the coefficients a_m satisfy the set of linear equations

$$\sum_n \mathcal{3C}_{mn}a_{qn} = E_q a_{qm} \tag{6-23}$$

This determines the relative values of the coefficients. Their absolute values are fixed by the condition that the wave function (6-22) should be normalized.   This means that the coefficients a_{qm} must also satisfy

$$\sum_m a^*_{qm} a_{qm} = 1 \qquad (6\text{-}24)$$

d. Selection Rules and Intensities of Transitions.   Having obtained a complete set of stationary-state wave functions for the Hamiltonian $\mathcal{H}$, we may next examine the probabilities of a transition being induced by the rf field in the x direction.   This problem has already been dealt with for a single isolated nucleus of spin $\frac{1}{2}$ in Sec. 3-3, where it was shown that the transition probability between states m and m' is given by

$$P_{mm'} = \gamma^2 H_1{}^2 |(m'|I_x|m)|^2 g(\nu) \qquad (6\text{-}25)$$

where the amplitude of the rf field is $2H_1$ and its frequency is ν. $g(\nu)$ is a shape factor incorporating various broadening effects.

We now have to deal with the problem of transitions between states of a set of coupled nuclei, for which the perturbing Hamiltonian is (expressed in ergs)

$$\mathcal{H}' = -2H_1 M_x \cos 2\pi \nu t \qquad (6\text{-}26)$$

where M_x is the component of the nuclear moment in the x direction:

$$M_x = \hbar \sum_i \gamma_i I_x(i) \qquad (6\text{-}27)$$

The stationary-state wave functions are given by Eqs. (6-22).   Under conditions where all signals are well resolved we may discuss the total integrated intensity of each transition without any ambiguity.   For a single nucleus, the integrated intensity is given by Eq. (6-25) with $g(\nu)$ replaced by unity.   Then, for the many-nuclei problem, it is clear that the intensity of the signal arising from the transition $q \to q'$ will be proportional to the square of the modulus of the corresponding matrix element of the nuclear-moment component M_x.   This is

$$\hbar^2 \left| \left[q \left| \sum_i \gamma_i I_x(i) \right| q' \right] \right|^2 \qquad (6\text{-}28)$$

Two important selection rules can be deduced immediately.   The operator $I_x(i)$ will have a matrix element only between two basic products which differ only in the spin of nucleus i.   In a three-nuclei system, for example, $I_x(1)$ would have a nonvanishing element between $\alpha\alpha\beta$ and $\beta\alpha\beta$.   As a result, the total matrix element in Eq. (6-28) will be nonvanishing only between states which have values of the total spin component F_z differing by ± 1.   We may write this selection rule

$$\Delta F_z = \pm 1 \qquad (6\text{-}29)$$

Secondly, if several species of nuclei are involved, we know that both the states q and q' correspond to definite values of the separate spin components of each species $F_z(X)$, $F_z(Y)$, . . . to a high approximation. It follows that, for the matrix element of a typical term of Eq. (6-27) to be nonzero, the states q and q' must differ by ± 1 in *only one* of $F_z(X)$, $F_z(Y)$, ... If $F_z(X)$ is the one that changes, we may call the transition an X transition. Only those terms involving X nuclei in Eq. (6-27) then contribute, and the relative intensity of any X transition will then be proportional to

$$\left| \left[q \left| \sum_{i}^{X} I_x(i) \right| q' \right] \right|^2 \tag{6-30}$$

where $\sum\limits_{i}^{X}$ indicates summation only over those nuclei of type X.

6-2. Symmetry Properties

As with many other molecular properties, further reduction of the quantum-mechanical problem is possible if the molecule possesses elements of symmetry. This simplification was first utilized by McConnell, McLean, and Reilly.[273] A more extensive treatment has been published by Wilson.[467]

a. Sets of Equivalent Nuclei. A set of nuclei will be said to be equivalent if each nucleus of the set has the same electronic environment. It follows that all nuclei of an equivalent set have the same shielding constant σ. Clearly, in a symmetrical molecule, equivalent nuclei are those which can be interchanged by the application of symmetry operations such as rotations and reflections. Straightforward examples are the four protons of methane and the six protons of benzene. The spin coupling constants between nuclei within an equivalent set or between nuclei of two or more different equivalent sets may or may not be all equal. Thus in methane all pairs are identically related, whereas in benzene there are three possible proton coupling constants (between protons in ortho, meta, and para positions). In $H_2C{=}CF_2$, for example, the two hydrogen atoms form one equivalent set and the two fluorine atoms another, but the spin coupling constants between hydrogen and fluorine atoms are in general different for cis and trans positions.

It is convenient to extend the definition of equivalence to a set of nuclei which have the same environment when averaged over a suitable period of time even though they may differ at a particular instant. As mentioned in Sec. 5-4, screening constants should be taken as time averages if fluctuation is sufficiently rapid. This effective equivalence is particularly important in molecules where internal rotation about single bonds may occur. The three protons of the methyl group in a molecule such as CH_3CH_2Cl, for example, are not equivalent in any one configuration, but will become so by virtue of rapid rotation about the CC single bond. From the point of view of nuclear magnetic resonance, therefore, this set of nuclei can be treated as having threefold symmetry.

Let us begin by considering the spin wave functions for a molecule which contains only one group of equivalent nuclei. Then we could, as before, take as a set of basic functions the simple products and classify them according to their total spin component F_z. These basic products will not always belong to irreducible representations of the symmetry group, however. For example, in a set of two equivalent nuclei, the symmetry operation which interchanges them will transform the product function $\alpha(1)\beta(2)$ into $\beta(1)\alpha(2)$. It is always possible, however, to construct a new set of basic functions which do belong to irreducible representations by taking certain linear combinations of the simple products. Such a set will be called *basic symmetry functions*. For the set of two nuclei (Table 6-1) the functions $\alpha\alpha$ and $\beta\beta$ are already sym-

TABLE 6-1. BASIC SYMMETRY FUNCTIONS FOR TWO EQUIVALENT NUCLEI

Spin function	Spin component F_z	Designation
$\alpha\alpha$	1	s_1
$(\alpha\beta + \beta\alpha)/\sqrt{2}$	0	s_0
$(\alpha\beta - \beta\alpha)/\sqrt{2}$	0	a_0
$\beta\beta$	-1	s_{-1}

metrical under interchange and need no modification, but the pair $\alpha\beta$ and $\beta\alpha$ must be replaced by $(\alpha\beta + \beta\alpha)/\sqrt{2}$ and $(\alpha\beta - \beta\alpha)/\sqrt{2}$, which are respectively symmetrical and antisymmetrical. The factor $\sqrt{2}$ is included so that all the new basic functions are normalized. They may be designated by the symbol s or a for symmetrical or antisymmetrical and by their value of F_z as a suffix.

We may proceed in a similar manner with a set of three equivalent nuclei. An example would be CH_3Br, where the bromine nuclear moment can be treated as noninteracting for the purpose of interpreting transitions. The Hamiltonian for the three-proton system is formally identical with that for three protons at the vertices of an equilateral triangle, so we may classify wave functions according to the irreducible representations of the symmetry group C_{3v}. Alternatively, it would be possible to use the representations of the permutation group on three symbols, but for clearer pictorial value, we will use the space group. The total spin component F_z can take values $3/2, 1/2, -1/2, -3/2$. Corresponding to

$F_z = 3/2$, there is only the basic product function $\alpha\alpha\alpha$, which already belongs to the completely symmetrical irreducible representation A_1. It may therefore be designated $(A_1)_{3/2}$. For $F_z = 1/2$ there are three basic product functions $\alpha\alpha\beta$, $\alpha\beta\alpha$, and $\beta\alpha\alpha$. It is well known that three functions of this sort can be replaced by linear combinations belonging to the symmetrical representation A_1 and the doubly degenerate representation E. (The problem is formally identical to the transformation between localized equivalent orbitals and molecular orbitals[244] or the formation of symmetry coordinates in vibrational analysis.[468]) The A_1 combination, which we may refer to as $(A_1)_{1/2}$, is $(\alpha\alpha\beta + \alpha\beta\alpha + \beta\alpha\alpha)/\sqrt{3}$, and the E combinations may be taken as $(\alpha\alpha\beta + \alpha\beta\alpha - 2\beta\alpha\alpha)/\sqrt{6}$ and $(\alpha\alpha\beta - \alpha\beta\alpha)/\sqrt{2}$, although other choices are possible. The other functions with $F_z = -1/2, -3/2$ can be dealt with in a similar manner. The complete set of basic symmetry functions for three nuclei is tabulated in Table 6-2.

TABLE 6-2. BASIC SYMMETRY FUNCTIONS FOR THREE EQUIVALENT NUCLEI

Spin function	Spin component F_z	Designation in C_{3v} symmetry
$\alpha\alpha\alpha$	3/2	$(A_1)_{3/2}$
$(\alpha\alpha\beta + \alpha\beta\alpha + \beta\alpha\alpha)/\sqrt{3}$	1/2	$(A_1)_{1/2}$
$(\alpha\alpha\beta + \alpha\beta\alpha - 2\beta\alpha\alpha)/\sqrt{6}$ $(\alpha\alpha\beta - \alpha\beta\alpha)/\sqrt{2}$	1/2	$E_{1/2}$
$(\beta\beta\alpha + \beta\alpha\beta + \alpha\beta\beta)/\sqrt{3}$	-1/2	$(A_1)_{-1/2}$
$(\beta\beta\alpha + \beta\alpha\beta - 2\alpha\beta\beta)/\sqrt{6}$ $(\beta\beta\alpha - \beta\alpha\beta)/\sqrt{2}$	-1/2	$E_{-1/2}$
$\beta\beta\beta$	-3/2	$(A_1)_{-3/2}$

In a similar way, basic symmetry functions can be constructed for a set of four equivalent nuclei. With four nuclei, however, various molecular symmetries are possible with various relations between the spin coupling constants. In the tetrahedral molecules CH_4 and CF_4, for example, all the spin coupling constants are equal and the functions may be classified according to the representations of the tetrahedral group T_d. If the four nuclei are at the corners of a square, however, there will be two different spin coupling coefficients, and the wave functions can be classified according to the symmetries of the group D_{4h}. A possible set of such functions is given by McConnell, McLean, and Reilly.[273] A third possibility of lower symmetry is a rectangular configuration, as with the four protons in ethylene, where there are three different spin coupling constants. Here the appropriate symmetry group is D_{2h}. In both the square and rectangular configurations, there is an element of arbitrariness in the choice of basic symmetry functions, for there may be more than one function of given symmetry and given F_z.

Basic symmetry functions can also be constructed if other magnetic nuclei are present. For example, in a molecule such as CH_2FX, where X is an atom with a nonmagnetic nucleus, the spin functions for the two equivalent hydrogens and the fluorine could be classified according to their behavior under the operation of reflection in the plane bisecting the proton positions. The fluorine function is symmetric, so a complete set of eight basic symmetry functions can be obtained by combining α and β for the fluorine with the four basic functions for the two protons given in Table 6-1. Thus there will be three functions corresponding to $F_z = 1/2$, for example, which are (writing the fluorine function first) $\alpha(\alpha\beta + \beta\alpha)/\sqrt{2}$ (symmetrical), $\alpha(\alpha\beta - \beta\alpha)/\sqrt{2}$ (antisymmetrical), and $\beta\alpha\alpha$ (symmetrical). Other examples of the construction of basic symmetry functions will be given later in the chapter when we deal with the spectra of specific groupings.

b. Mixing and Selection Rules. The value of using basic symmetry functions rather than the simple products of Sec. 6-1 is that they enable us to reduce the order of the secular determinants to be solved and to formulate further selection rules.

The factorization of the secular equation arises because there are no matrix elements of the Hamiltonian between functions belonging to different irreducible representations. This is because the Hamiltonian is totally symmetric with respect to permutations of equivalent nuclei. As a result we can divide the basic functions into classes according to their values of F_z and their symmetries, and then it is only necessary to evaluate the submatrices of functions in one such class. For two and three equivalent nuclei, for which basic symmetry functions are given in Tables 6-1 and 6-2, this reduces the complete matrix to a set of 1×1 matrices. In other words, for these cases, the basic symmetry functions are themselves stationary-state functions.

The x component of the nuclear moment [Eq. (6-27)] is also a totally symmetric operator with respect to permutations, so that it will have no matrix elements between functions of different symmetry. As a result *transitions between states of different symmetry will be forbidden.* This important selection rule leads to a considerable reduction in the number of lines observed in the spectrum of a symmetrical molecule.

6-3. Summary of Rules for Calculating Spectra

It may be helpful at this stage to summarize the method for calculating a spectrum from the complete Hamiltonian which has been developed in the previous two sections.   The complete calculation may be divided up into a number of steps:

1. Use is made of a complete set of basic symmetry functions as appropriate linear combinations of basic product functions $\psi_n = \alpha\beta\alpha$ . . . .

2. The matrix elements of the Hamiltonian $\mathcal{3C}^{(0)}$ representing interaction with the external field between basic product functions are

$$(\psi_m|\mathcal{3C}^{(0)}|\psi_m) = \frac{1}{2\pi} \sum_i \gamma_i H_i[I_z(i)]_m \qquad (6\text{-}31)$$

where $[I_z(i)]_m$ is $1/2$ if nucleus i has α spin in ψ_m and $-1/2$ if it has β spin. Matrix elements of $\mathcal{3C}^{(0)}$ between different product functions vanish.

3. The matrix elements of the spin-coupling Hamiltonian $\mathcal{3C}^{(1)}$ between product functions are

$$(\psi_m|\mathcal{3C}^{(1)}|\psi_m) = \frac{1}{4} \sum_{i<j} J_{ij}T_{ij} \qquad (6\text{-}32)$$

$$(\psi_m|\mathcal{3C}^{(1)}|\psi_n) = \frac{1}{2}UJ_{ij} \qquad m \neq n \qquad (6\text{-}33)$$

where $T_{ij} = 1$ or -1, depending on whether spins i and j are parallel or antiparallel in ψ_m, and $U = 1$ if ψ_m differs from ψ_n by an interchange of spins i and j and is zero otherwise.   Matrix elements between linear combinations of basic products are evaluated by expansion.

4. The order of the complete secular equation can be reduced by using the rule that no mixing occurs between functions with different values of the total spin component F_z.

5. Further reduction can be made in the case of a symmetrical molecule, since no mixing occurs between functions of different symmetry.

6. If several species of nuclei X, Y, . . . are present, step (4) leads to a further simplification because, to a high approximation, no mixing occurs between functions which differ in any of the total spin components $F_z(X)$, $F_z(Y)$, ...   The same rule can be applied when there are several sets of nuclei of the same species if the chemical shift between them is large compared with the spin coupling constants.   (This arises because mixing is negligible if the difference between diagonal matrix elements of $\mathcal{3C}$ is large compared with the corresponding off-diagonal elements.)

7. Energies and wave functions can then be calculated by diagonalization of the submatrices of the total Hamiltonian.

8. The number of possible transitions is limited by the selection rule

$$\Delta F_z = \pm 1 \qquad (6\text{-}34)$$

which applies for sufficiently small rf fields.

9. For symmetrical molecules, transitions can occur only between functions of the same symmetry.

10. Under the conditions discussed in step (6), transitions are allowed

(to a high approximation) only between functions which differ by ± 1 in only one of $F_z(X)$, $F_z(Y)$, ... This also applies to sets of nuclei with chemical shifts large compared with spin coupling constants.

11. Finally, the relative intensities of the remaining transitions which are not forbidden by the selection rules can be found from the squares of the matrix elements of the total x component of the nuclear moment.

The simplifications that arise from rules (6) and (10) for nuclei of different species or nuclei with chemical shifts large compared with spin coupling constants make the spectra of such systems easier to interpret. The notation that will be used to distinguish them from the more complex general spectra has already been explained in Sec. 5-2.

In the next few sections we shall derive theoretical spectra for small groups of nuclei with various symmetries, using the procedure summarized above. In Sec. 6-4 we shall examine the conditions under which simple first-order spectra (consisting of simple groups of multiplets as described in Sec. 5-2) are obtained. This is followed by the theory and some examples of the analysis of spectra of some other nuclear systems which do not satisfy these conditions.

6-4. Simple First-order Spectra

a. **One Set of Equivalent Nuclei.** As stated in Chap. 5, a single set of equivalent nuclei (that is, nuclei with the same chemical shift) gives rise to only a single signal, even if there are spin coupling constants between the nuclei. This is easily confirmed in the simplest cases. For two equivalent nuclei, for example, the stationary-state functions are the basic symmetry functions given in Table 6-1. The selection rules on F_z and symmetry immediately show that only two transitions are possible

$$\beta\beta \to \frac{\alpha\beta + \beta\alpha}{\sqrt{2}}$$

$$\frac{\alpha\beta + \beta\alpha}{\sqrt{2}} \to \alpha\alpha \tag{6-35}$$

The energies are just the diagonal matrix elements of the total Hamiltonian for these three functions and are

State	Energy
$\alpha\alpha$	$(\gamma H/2\pi) + \tfrac{1}{4}J$
$(\alpha\beta + \beta\alpha)/\sqrt{2}$	$\tfrac{1}{4}J$
$\beta\beta$	$-(\gamma H/2\pi) + \tfrac{1}{4}J$

It follows that the two transitions both have an energy $\gamma H/2\pi$ independent of the spin coupling constant J.

A general proof of this result for a set of n equivalent nuclei is as follows: Since all the nuclei have the same chemical shift, the Hamiltonian can be written

$$\mathcal{K} = \mathcal{K}^{(0)} + \mathcal{K}^{(1)}$$

$$= \frac{\gamma H}{2\pi} F_z + \sum_{i<j} J_{ij} \mathbf{I}_i \cdot \mathbf{I}_j \qquad (6\text{-}36)$$

But it has already been established that the stationary-state functions are also eigenfunctions of F_z, so they must be eigenfunctions of the two parts of the Hamiltonian separately. The total energy $\mathcal{E}$, which is the eigenvalue of $\mathcal{K}$, can therefore be written

$$\mathcal{E} = \mathcal{E}^{(0)} + \mathcal{E}^{(1)} \qquad (6\text{-}37)$$

where $\mathcal{E}^{(0)}$ and $\mathcal{E}^{(1)}$ are the eigenvalues of $\mathcal{K}^{(0)}$ and $\mathcal{K}^{(1)}$, respectively.

The transition probability between the two states is proportional to the square of the matrix element of the x component of the magnetic moment M_x, which in turn is proportional to the x component of the total spin

$$F_x = \sum_i I_x(i) \qquad (6\text{-}38)$$

since the nuclei all have the same magnetogyric ratio. But F_x commutes with the spin coupling Hamiltonian $\mathcal{K}^{(1)}$. (The proof of this is identical with the corresponding proof for F_z given in Sec. 6-1.) It follows that the matrix element of M_x between two stationary states is

$$(a|M_x|b) = 0 \qquad (6\text{-}39)$$

unless the states a and b have the same value of the spin coupling energy $\mathcal{E}^{(1)}$. In other words, the difference between the energies of two states between which a transition is allowed will be independent of the spin coupling constants and, since $\Delta F_z = \pm 1$, will be simply $\gamma H/2\pi$.

It is interesting to observe that this proof does not appeal to symmetry in any manner. Thus a set of nuclei with accidentally identical chemical shifts will give rise to only a single signal, whatever the spin coupling constants between them.

b. Two Sets of Equivalent Nuclei. The simple multiplet rules for two sets of equivalent nuclei (Sec. 5-2), first obtained by Gutowsky, McCall, and Slichter,[166] can be derived *provided that all the spin coupling constants between a nucleus of one set and a nucleus of the other are equal.* This condition is by no means always satisfied. For example, in the molecule 1,1'-difluoroethylene:

there are two equivalent sets of nuclei (C^{12} having no magnetic moment) but there are two distinct HF coupling constants, cis and trans.

Suppose we consider a set of n_A equivalent nuclei of type A, all having the same spin coupling constant J_{AX} with each member of another equivalent set of n_X nuclei of type X. It will be assumed that A and X are different species or have a chemical shift large compared with J_{AX}. (If this were not so, we should refer to the sets as A and B according to the nomenclature explained in Sec. 5-2.) Then the total Hamiltonian can be written

$$\mathcal{H} = \frac{\gamma_A H_A}{2\pi} F_z(A) + \frac{\gamma_X H_X}{2\pi} F_z(X) + \sum_{i<j}^{A} J_{ij}\mathbf{I}_i \cdot \mathbf{I}_j$$
$$+ \sum_{i<j}^{X} J_{ij}\mathbf{I}_i \cdot \mathbf{I}_j + J_{AX} \sum_{i}^{A} \sum_{j}^{X} \mathbf{I}_i \cdot \mathbf{I}_j$$
$$= \mathcal{H}^{(0)}(A) + \mathcal{H}^{(0)}(X) + \mathcal{H}^{(1)}(A) + \mathcal{H}^{(1)}(X) + \mathcal{H}^{(1)}(AX) \qquad (6\text{-}40)$$

The first two terms represent the interaction of the A and X nuclei with the magnetic fields H_A and H_X. The third and fourth terms represent the effects of spin coupling within the two groups. The final term is the coupling between the groups and can be written in the alternative form

$$\mathcal{H}^{(1)}(AX) = J_{AX}\mathbf{F}(A) \cdot \mathbf{F}(X) = J_{AX}[F_x(A)F_x(X) + F_y(A)F_y(X) + F_z(A)F_z(X)] \qquad (6\text{-}41)$$

where $\mathbf{F}(A)$ and $\mathbf{F}(X)$ are the total spin vectors for the two equivalent sets

$$\mathbf{F}(A) = \sum_{i}^{A} \mathbf{I}(i) \qquad \mathbf{F}(X) = \sum_{i}^{X} \mathbf{I}(i) \qquad (6\text{-}42)$$

Now it has already been shown that each component of $\mathbf{F}(A)$ commutes with $\mathcal{H}^{(1)}(A)$, so the latter must commute with $\mathcal{H}^{(1)}(AX)$. $\mathcal{H}^{(1)}(A)$ also commutes with all the other parts of the complete Hamiltonian (6-40), so it follows that stationary states are eigenstates of it. But $\mathcal{H}^{(1)}(A)$ also commutes with the x component of the total nuclear magnetic moment, which is now

$$M_x = \gamma_A F_x(A) + \gamma_X F_x(X) \qquad (6\text{-}43)$$

So we deduce that, as for the single set of equivalent nuclei, transitions are allowed only between states that have the same value of $\mathcal{H}^{(1)}(A)$. The same applies to $\mathcal{H}^{(1)}(X)$. This leads to the important rule that *the spectrum due to two equivalent sets of nuclei, with all coupling constants between nuclei in different sets equal, will be independent of the coupling constants within the sets.* We may therefore obtain the transition energies more simply by omitting $\mathfrak{IC}^{(1)}(A)$ and $\mathfrak{IC}^{(1)}(X)$ from the Hamiltonian altogether. It should be noted that the argument leading to this rule does not depend on the chemical shift being large.

If the chemical shift is large, then the stationary-state functions become eigenfunctions of $F_z(A)$ and $F_z(X)$ separately and, as explained in Sec. 6-1, transitions in which the value of either $F_z(A)$ or $F_z(X)$ changes by ± 1 are the only ones that occur. Under these conditions it is easily shown that the diagonal matrix element of $\mathbf{F}(A) \cdot \mathbf{F}(X)$ in any stationary state is equal to the product of the values of the operators $F_z(A)$ and $F_z(X)$. These values, which give the total z spin component of A and X nuclei, will be written m_A and m_X, respectively. Writing ν_A and ν_X for $\gamma_A H_A / 2\pi$ and $\gamma_X H_X / 2\pi$, the energy of the state corresponding to m_A and m_X is

$$\mathcal{E}(m_A, m_X) = \nu_A m_A + \nu_X m_X + J_{AX} m_A m_X \qquad (6\text{-}44)$$

The energy of an A transition in which m_A changes by 1 is therefore

$$\Delta \mathcal{E}_A = \nu_A + J_{AX} m_X \qquad (6\text{-}45)$$

But m_X can take any of the values $-\frac{1}{2} n_X$, $-\frac{1}{2} n_X + 1$, $\ldots$, $\frac{1}{2} n_X$, so the spectrum will consist of $n_X + 1$ lines with a spacing of J_{AX}. The intensity of any one line will be proportional to the number of ways of arranging the n_X spins to give the required total spin component m_X. This will be equal to the binomial coefficient

$$\frac{(n_X)!}{(\frac{1}{2} n_X + m_X)!(\frac{1}{2} n_X - m_X)!}$$

A similar complementary spectrum will be obtained for the X nuclei.

The first-order spectra for more than two sets of equivalent nuclei are given by a direct extension. If the sets are labeled by R, Eq. (6-45) is replaced by

$$\Delta \mathcal{E}_A = \nu_A + \sum_R J_{AR} m_R \qquad (6\text{-}46)$$

where m_R is the value of the spin component $F_z(R)$.

Most of the theory also applies if the sets are made up of nuclei with spin greater than $\frac{1}{2}$. For large chemical shifts, or different nuclear species, Eq. (6-45) still applies (for two sets), so that there will be $2 n_X I_X + 1$ A transitions with spacing J_{AX}. The intensities will no longer have a binomial distribution, however. If $I_X = 1$, for example, then a single X nucleus gives a $1:1:1$ triplet for the spectrum of a neighboring set. If $n_X = 2$, so that there are two nuclei of spin 1, m_X can take values 2, 1, 0, -1, -2. The value of 2 can arise in only one way: with both spins having $I_z = 1$. The value of 1, on the other hand, can arise in two ways:

one of the two nuclei having $I_z = 1$, and the other $I_z = 0$. Similarly the value 0 can arise in three distinct ways: $1, -1; 0, 0;$ and $-1, 1$. Thus the quintet spectrum of a neighboring set will have an intensity distribution $1:2:3:2:1$. The form of the multiplet structure can always be predicted from simple considerations of this sort.

6-5. Spectra of Nuclear Groups AB_n

The spectra of groups of nuclei consisting of an equivalent set B_n and one other magnetic nucleus A can be analyzed in a comparatively simple and systematic manner. If the n nuclei of set B_n are equivalent for reasons of symmetry (or effective symmetry due to averaging by some internal motion), the coupling constants between A and each nucleus of the B set will be identical. This means that the whole spectrum will be independent of the coupling constants (Sec. 6-4) within the B set and we may proceed to calculate transitions putting them all equal to zero. Consequently the form of an AB_n spectrum will depend only on the chemical shift and the AB spin coupling constant. Clearly, if both these parameters were increased by the same factor, the only effect would be to change the scale of the whole spectrum without changing the relative intensities and spacings of the lines, so we need only investigate the way in which the spectrum varies as we change the ratio of the spin coupling constant to the chemical shift. It is this dependence on only a single parameter that makes AB_n spectra relatively easy to recognize and analyze. The positions of the energy levels for these groups were first investigated by Hahn and Maxwell[179] in connection with spin-echo experiments. We shall deal with the spectra for a slow-passage experiment for $n = 1, 2, 3$, including some examples of practical analysis.

a. **Two Nuclei AB.** The simplest system in which the effects of chemical shift and spin coupling are intermingled consists of two nonequivalent nuclei (spin 1/2) of the same species isolated from the effects of any other nuclei. If the chemical shift is large enough, the simple first-order rules apply and the spectrum consists of a pair of doublets, the doublet splitting being equal to the spin coupling constant. If the chemical shift is zero, we have a pair of equivalent nuclei, and only a single line will be observed. We shall now investigate the form of the spectrum in the intermediate range.

If the screening constants of the two nuclei are σ_A and σ_B, the local fields at the nuclei can be written

$$H_A = H_0(1 - \sigma_A)$$
$$H_B = H_0(1 - \sigma_B) \tag{6-47}$$

The relative chemical shift can be measured by the difference $\sigma_B - \sigma_A$, which may, of course, take either sign. The spin coupling constant will be written J. Since there are no effective elements of symmetry, the basic functions are most conveniently taken to be the simple product functions $\alpha\alpha$, $\alpha\beta$, $\beta\alpha$, and $\beta\beta$, which are numbered 1 to 4 (Table 6-3).

TABLE 6-3. BASIC FUNCTIONS AND DIAGONAL MATRIX ELEMENTS
FOR TWO NUCLEI AB

n	ψ_n	F_z	$\mathcal{3C}_{nn}$
1	$\alpha\alpha$	1	$\nu_0(1 - \tfrac{1}{2}\sigma_A - \tfrac{1}{2}\sigma_B) + \tfrac{1}{4}J$
2	$\alpha\beta$	0	$\nu_0(-\tfrac{1}{2}\sigma_A + \tfrac{1}{2}\sigma_B) - \tfrac{1}{4}J$
3	$\beta\alpha$	0	$\nu_0(\tfrac{1}{2}\sigma_A - \tfrac{1}{2}\sigma_B) - \tfrac{1}{4}J$
4	$\beta\beta$	-1	$\nu_0(-1 + \tfrac{1}{2}\sigma_A + \tfrac{1}{2}\sigma_B) + \tfrac{1}{4}J$

The corresponding diagonal matrix elements of the Hamiltonian are easily evaluated by the rules already given. In this table ν_0 has been written† for the frequency, in cycles per second, of a transition for a single unscreened nucleus of this species:

$$\nu_0 = \frac{\gamma H_0}{2\pi} \tag{6-48}$$

The only nonvanishing off-diagonal element is

$$\mathcal{3C}_{23} = \tfrac{1}{2}J \tag{6-49}$$

By the F_z mixing rule, the functions $\alpha\alpha$ and $\beta\beta$ will themselves be stationary-state functions. However, mixing will occur between $\alpha\beta$ and $\beta\alpha$. To evaluate the resulting energies it is convenient to define a positive quantity C and an angle θ (between 0 and π) by

$$\begin{aligned} C\cos 2\theta &= \tfrac{1}{2}\nu_0(\sigma_B - \sigma_A) \\ C\sin 2\theta &= \tfrac{1}{2}J \end{aligned} \tag{6-50}$$

so that, if $\delta = \sigma_B - \sigma_A$,

$$C = +\tfrac{1}{2}[(\nu_0\delta)^2 + J^2]^{1/2} \tag{6-51}$$

and we can write the energies E_n and the wave functions Φ_n explicitly in terms of C and θ. These are given in Table 6-4.

Since F_z can change only by ± 1, there are only four allowed transitions. The relative intensities are proportional to the squares of the appropriate matrix elements of the x component of the spin $I_x(A) + I_x(B)$. Thus

† It is to be noted that $\nu_0\delta$ is the chemical shift, in cycles per second, where $\delta = \sigma_B - \sigma_A$.

TABLE 6-4. WAVE FUNCTIONS AND ENERGY LEVELS FOR TWO NUCLEI AB

n	Φ_n	E_n
1	$\alpha\alpha$	$\nu_0(1 - \tfrac{1}{2}\sigma_A - \tfrac{1}{2}\sigma_B) + \tfrac{1}{4}J$
2	$\cos\theta(\alpha\beta) + \sin\theta(\beta\alpha)$	$-\tfrac{1}{4}J + C$
3	$-\sin\theta(\alpha\beta) + \cos\theta(\beta\alpha)$	$-\tfrac{1}{4}J - C$
4	$\beta\beta$	$\nu_0(-1 + \tfrac{1}{2}\sigma_A + \tfrac{1}{2}\sigma_B) + \tfrac{1}{4}J$

for the transition $2 \rightarrow 1$, for example, we have

$$[\cos\theta(\alpha\beta) + \sin\theta(\beta\alpha)|I_z(A) + I_z(B)|\alpha\alpha]^2 = \tfrac{1}{4}(\cos\theta + \sin\theta)^2$$
$$= \tfrac{1}{4}(1 + \sin 2\theta) \quad (6\text{-}52)$$

The transition energies [relative to the mean, $\nu_0(1 - \tfrac{1}{2}\sigma_A - \tfrac{1}{2}\sigma_B)$] and relative intensities are given in Table 6-5.

TABLE 6-5. TRANSITION ENERGIES AND INTENSITIES FOR TWO NUCLEI AB

Transition	Energy	Relative intensity
$3 \rightarrow 1$	$\tfrac{1}{2}J + C$	$1 - \sin 2\theta$
$4 \rightarrow 2$	$-\tfrac{1}{2}J + C$	$1 + \sin 2\theta$
$2 \rightarrow 1$	$\tfrac{1}{2}J - C$	$1 + \sin 2\theta$
$4 \rightarrow 3$	$-\tfrac{1}{2}J - C$	$1 - \sin 2\theta$

The general appearance of this spectrum depends only on the absolute ratio $|J/\nu_0\delta|$ and is independent of the signs of J and $\sigma_B - \sigma_A$. The assignment of lines in terms of the numbering used, however, will depend on the signs of both these quantities. If we suppose $\sigma_B > \sigma_A$ and $J > 0$ for illustrative purposes, then 2θ will lie between 0 and $\pi/2$ and the spectrum will be as illustrated in Fig. 6-1. As we start from small J, the spectrum changes from two simple doublets into a symmetrical group of four lines, the inner pair of lines being stronger than the outer. Eventually the two central lines degenerate into a single line and the outer ones become forbidden, so that only a single signal is observed (corresponding in the limit to the grouping A_2). In the intermediate stage we may still describe the left-hand pair qualitatively as predominantly A lines, although the actual transition is a mixed one in which there is some change of spin of the B nucleus.

If either or both of $\sigma_B - \sigma_A$ and J change sign, a relabeling of the lines in Fig. 6-1 is necessary. If $\sigma_B < \sigma_A$, the B signals will appear at lower field. If $J < 0$, $\sin 2\theta$ will be negative and $3 \rightarrow 1$ and $4 \rightarrow 3$ will become the inner transitions. It is clear that, from an AB spectrum, it is not possible to determine which nucleus is more screened, nor is it possible to obtain the sign of the coupling constant.

The numerical analysis of such a spectrum is straight forward. The separation between either the right-hand pair or the left-hand pair is

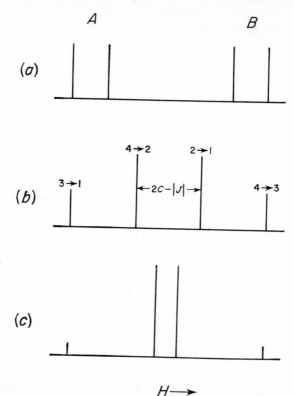

FIG. 6-1. Typical spectra for two nuclei AB. (a) $J \ll \nu_0\delta$. (b) $J \approx \nu_0\delta$. (c) $J \gg \nu_0\delta$. It is assumed that $\sigma_B > \sigma_A$ ($\delta > 0$) and $J > 0$.

equal to $|J|$. The separation between the inner lines is $2C - |J|$, giving C and hence, by Eq. (6-51), the chemical shift $|\delta|$.

2-Bromo-5-chlorothiophene. An example of a compound with an AB proton spectrum uncomplicated by other nuclei is 2-bromo-5-chlorothiophene:

In this molecule carbon and sulfur nuclei have no moments and the effects of chlorine and bromine do not show up in the proton spectrum because of rapid quadrupole relaxation. This compound was first investigated by spin-echo methods by Hahn and Maxwell,[179] and its slow-passage spec-

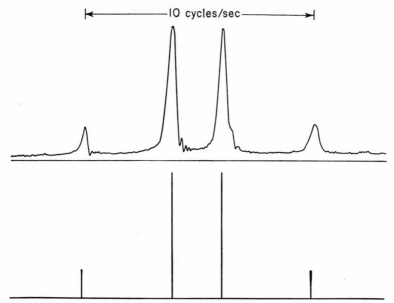

|←————————10 cycles/sec————————→|

FIG. 6-2. Proton spectrum of 2-bromo-5-chlorothiophene at 30.5 Mc/sec. The theoretical spectrum is given below. (Anderson.[10])

trum was recorded by Anderson.[10]   The latter is shown in Fig. 6-2.   By analysis of this spectrum, Anderson obtained

$$|\nu_0 \delta| = 4.7 \pm 0.2 \text{ cycles/sec}$$
$$|J| = 3.9 \pm 0.2 \text{ cycles/sec} \tag{6-53}$$

Using these parameters, the ratio of the intensities of the outer and inner lines is calculated to be 0.22 ± 0.01, which is to be compared with the experimental value of 0.195 ± 0.020. This good agreement with the experimental data is, of course, strong support for the empirical Hamiltonian that is used.

    b. Three Nuclei AB$_2$.   For a system of three nuclei, two of which are equivalent, there are two different spin coupling constants J and J'.

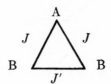

This arrangement has, as an element of symmetry, a reflection in the plane bisecting the BB line, so it is convenient to use a set of basic symmetry functions. For the two B nuclei, these functions are $\alpha\alpha$, $(\alpha\beta + \beta\alpha)/\sqrt{2}$, $(\alpha\beta - \beta\alpha)/\sqrt{2}$, and $\beta\beta$. Combining these with α or β for nucleus A, we get the basic set listed in Table 6-6, together with the corresponding

TABLE 6-6. BASIC SYMMETRY FUNCTIONS AND DIAGONAL MATRIX ELEMENTS
FOR THREE NUCLEI AB₂

Function	Basic symmetry function	Diagonal matrix element $\mathcal{K}_{nn}$
$s_{3/2}$	$\alpha\alpha\alpha$	$\nu_0(3/2 - 1/2\sigma_A - \sigma_B) + 1/2 J + 1/4 J'$
$1s_{1/2}$	$\alpha(\alpha\beta + \beta\alpha)/\sqrt{2}$	$\nu_0(1/2 - 1/2\sigma_A) + 1/4 J'$
$2s_{1/2}$	$\beta\alpha\alpha$	$\nu_0(1/2 + 1/2\sigma_A - \sigma_B) - 1/2 J + 1/4 J'$
$1s_{-1/2}$	$\alpha\beta\beta$	$\nu_0(-1/2 - 1/2\sigma_A + \sigma_B) - 1/2 J + 1/4 J'$
$2s_{-1/2}$	$\beta(\alpha\beta + \beta\alpha)/\sqrt{2}$	$\nu_0(-1/2 + 1/2\sigma_A) + 1/4 J'$
$s_{-3/2}$	$\beta\beta\beta$	$\nu_0(-3/2 + 1/2\sigma_A + \sigma_B) + 1/2 J + 1/4 J'$
$a_{1/2}$	$\alpha(\alpha\beta - \beta\alpha)/\sqrt{2}$	$\nu_0(1/2 - 1/2\sigma_A) - 3/4 J'$
$a_{-1/2}$	$\beta(\alpha\beta - \beta\alpha)/\sqrt{2}$	$\nu_0(-1/2 + 1/2\sigma_A) - 3/4 J'$

diagonal matrix element of $\mathcal{K}$. The symbols s and a are used to denote symmetric and antisymmetric functions. The value of the total spin F_z is appended as a suffix. The only off-diagonal matrix elements are

$$(1s_{1/2}|\mathcal{K}|2s_{1/2}) = (1s_{-1/2}|\mathcal{K}|2s_{-1/2}) = \frac{J}{\sqrt{2}} \qquad (6.54)$$

The functions $s_{3/2}$, $a_{1/2}$, $a_{-1/2}$, and $s_{-3/2}$ do not mix and are therefore themselves stationary-state wave functions. To find the symmetric stationary-state functions with $F_z = \pm 1/2$, we have to solve 2×2 secular equations. We define positive quantities C_+, C_- and angles θ_+, θ_- by

$$C_+ \cos 2\theta_+ = 1/2\nu_0(\sigma_B - \sigma_A) + 1/4 J$$

$$C_+ \sin 2\theta_+ = \frac{J}{\sqrt{2}}$$

$$C_- \cos 2\theta_- = 1/2\nu_0(\sigma_B - \sigma_A) - 1/4 J$$

$$C_- \sin 2\theta_- = \frac{J}{\sqrt{2}} \qquad (6-55)$$

so that, since
$$\delta = \sigma_B - \sigma_A \qquad (6-56)$$

one obtains
$$C_+ = 1/2[(\nu_0\delta)^2 + (\nu_0\delta)J + 9/4 J^2]^{1/2}$$
$$C_- = 1/2[(\nu_0\delta)^2 - (\nu_0\delta)J + 9/4 J^2]^{1/2} \qquad (6-57)$$

The corresponding wave functions and energies are given in Table 6-7.

The states are labeled according to their behavior in the limit when the chemical shift is large, in which case the basic functions become stationary-state functions. Thus we define the state $1s'_{1/2}$ as that state for which the wave function goes continuously into the basic function $1s_{1/2}$ as the chemical shift δ becomes large.

TABLE 6-7. WAVE FUNCTIONS AND ENERGY LEVELS FOR THREE NUCLEI AB₂

State	Wave function	Energy
$1s'_{1/2}$	$\cos\theta_+\alpha(\alpha\beta+\beta\alpha)/\sqrt{2}+\sin\theta_+\beta\alpha\alpha$	$\tfrac{1}{2}\nu_0(1-\sigma_B)+\tfrac{1}{4}(J'-J)+C_+$
$2s'_{1/2}$	$-\sin\theta_+\alpha(\alpha\beta+\beta\alpha)/\sqrt{2}+\cos\theta_+\beta\alpha\alpha$	$\tfrac{1}{2}\nu_0(1-\sigma_B)+\tfrac{1}{4}(J'-J)-C_+$
$1s'_{-1/2}$	$\cos\theta_-\alpha\beta\beta+\sin\theta_-\beta(\alpha\beta+\beta\alpha)/\sqrt{2}$	$\tfrac{1}{2}\nu_0(-1+\sigma_B)+\tfrac{1}{4}(J'-J)+C_-$
$2s'_{-1/2}$	$-\sin\theta_-\alpha\beta\beta+\cos\theta_-\beta(\alpha\beta+\beta\alpha)/\sqrt{2}$	$\tfrac{1}{2}\nu_0(-1+\sigma_B)+\tfrac{1}{4}(J'-J)-C_-$

Since transitions are allowed only between states of the same symmetry and for which $\Delta F_z = \pm 1$, it is clear that there are nine transitions in all, eight symmetrical and one antisymmetrical. The transition energies and relative intensities are given in Table 6-8. Each transition may be

TABLE 6-8. TRANSITION ENERGIES AND RELATIVE INTENSITIES FOR THREE NUCLEI AB₂

Transition	Origin†	Energy	Relative intensity
1. $2s'_{1/2}\to s_{3/2}$	A	$\nu_0[1-\tfrac{1}{2}(\sigma_A+\sigma_B)]+\tfrac{3}{4}J+C_+$	$(\sqrt{2}\sin\theta_+-\cos\theta_+)^2$
2. $2s'_{-1/2}\to 1s'_{1/2}$	A	$\nu_0(1-\sigma_B)+C_++C_-$	$[\sqrt{2}\sin(\theta_+-\theta_-)+\cos\theta_+\cos\theta_-]^2$
3. $a_{-1/2}\to a_{1/2}$	A	$\nu_0(1-\sigma_A)$	1
4. $s_{-3/2}\to 1s'_{-1/2}$	A	$\nu_0[1-\tfrac{1}{2}(\sigma_A+\sigma_B)]-\tfrac{3}{4}J+C_-$	$(\sqrt{2}\sin\theta_-+\cos\theta_-)^2$
5. $1s'_{-1/2}\to 1s'_{1/2}$	B	$\nu_0(1-\sigma_B)+C_+-C_-$	$[\sqrt{2}\cos(\theta_+-\theta_-)+\cos\theta_+\sin\theta_-]^2$
6. $1s'_{1/2}\to s_{3/2}$	B	$\nu_0[1-\tfrac{1}{2}(\sigma_A+\sigma_B)]+\tfrac{3}{4}J-C_+$	$(\sqrt{2}\cos\theta_++\sin\theta_+)^2$
7. $2s'_{-1/2}\to 2s'_{1/2}$	B	$\nu_0(1-\sigma_B)-C_++C_-$	$[\sqrt{2}\cos(\theta_+-\theta_-)-\sin\theta_+\cos\theta_-]^2$
8. $s_{-3/2}\to 2s'_{-1/2}$	B	$\nu_0[1-\tfrac{1}{2}(\sigma_A+\sigma_B)]-\tfrac{3}{4}J-C_-$	$(\sqrt{2}\cos\theta_--\sin\theta_-)^2$
9. $1s_{-1/2}\to 2s'_{1/2}$	Comb.	$\nu_0(1-\sigma_B)-C_+-C_-$	$[\sqrt{2}\sin(\theta_+-\theta_-)+\sin\theta_+\sin\theta_-]^2$

† Based on $\sigma_B > \sigma_A$.

labeled an A or B transition according to its behavior in the limit of large chemical shift. The labeling given in the table is appropriate for the case $\sigma_B > \sigma_A$, that is, the B nuclei are more shielded than the A. In this case θ_+ and $\theta_-\to 0$ as $\delta\to\infty$. Thus, for example, the transition $2s'_{1/2}\to s_{3/2}$ becomes $\beta\alpha\alpha\to\alpha\alpha\alpha$ and is therefore called an A transition, since in this limit only the A spin is changed. The transition $1s'_{-1/2}\to 2s'_{1/2}$, on the other hand, becomes $\alpha\beta\beta\to\beta\alpha\alpha$ and cannot be described as A or B. In the limit it will correspond to the simultaneous change of spin of all three nuclei and may be referred to as a *combination line*. It is actually forbidden in the limit but will have a small, nonzero intensity in the general case. The same transition also becomes forbidden in the other limit of zero chemical shift. If $\sigma_B < \sigma_A$, that is, if the single nucleus is more highly screened, θ_+ and $\theta_- \rightarrow \pi/2$ as $\delta \rightarrow -\infty$, so that some relabeling is necessary in Table 6-8.

All the transition energies and intensities are independent of the BB coupling constant, a particular case of the general result proved in

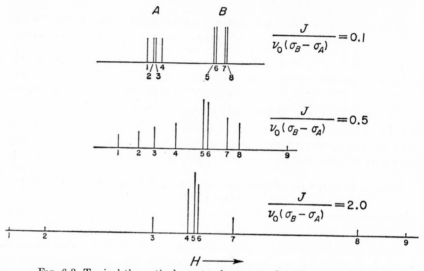

FIG. 6-3. Typical theoretical spectra for two nuclei AB_2 with $\sigma_B > \sigma_A$.

the last section. Apart from a scaling factor, the structure of the spectrum is a function only of the nondimensional ratio $J/\nu_0\delta$. The pattern of lines for a series of values of this ratio is illustrated in Fig. 6-3 for $\sigma_B > \sigma_A$ ($\delta > 0$) and $J > 0$. If $\sigma_B > \sigma_A$ and $J < 0$, the appearance of the spectrum is identical, although the assignment in terms of the numbering in Table 6-8 needs revision. If $\sigma_B < \sigma_A$, the patterns must be reversed, the B signal appearing at lower field. From an AB_2 spectrum, therefore, it is possible to determine the sign of $\sigma_B - \sigma_A$, but only the magnitude of the spin coupling constant J.

The following features, which are of use in the practical analysis of a spectrum, may be noted from Table 6-8:

1. Line 3 immediately gives the band origin for the A nucleus, unmodified by spin coupling.

2. The corresponding position for the B nuclei is the mean of the transitions 5 and 7.

Numerical values of the transition energies in Table 6-8 are given for a range of values of the ratio $J/\nu_0(\sigma_B - \sigma_A)$ in Table 6-9. All energies are measured relative to the A line (line 3) and the scale is so adjusted that the chemical shift is one unit.

TABLE 6-9. REDUCED TRANSITION ENERGIES FOR THREE NUCLEI AB$_2$[†]

$\dfrac{J}{\nu_0(\sigma_B - \sigma_A)}$	1(A)	2(A)	3(A)	4(A)	5(B)	6(B)	7(B)	8(B)	9 (comb.)
0	0	0	0	0	−1	−1	−1	−1	−2
0.1	0.105	0.010	0	−0.095	−0.950	−0.955	−1.050	−1.055	−2.010
0.2	0.218	0.040	0	−0.178	−0.904	−0.918	−1.096	−1.122	−2.040
0.3	0.338	0.088	0	−0.250	−0.862	−0.888	−1.138	−1.200	−2.088
0.4	0.463	0.153	0	−0.310	−0.826	−0.863	−1.174	−1.290	−2.153
0.5	0.593	0.233	0	−0.360	−0.797	−0.843	−1.203	−1.390	−2.233
0.6	0.726	0.326	0	−0.400	−0.774	−0.826	−1.226	−1.500	−2.326
0.7	0.862	0.429	0	−0.433	−0.755	−0.812	−1.245	−1.617	−2.429
0.8	1.000	0.540	0	−0.460	−0.740	−0.800	−1.260	−1.740	−2.540
0.9	1.140	0.658	0	−0.482	−0.729	−0.790	−1.271	−1.868	−2.658
1.0	1.281	0.781	0	−0.500	−0.719	−0.781	−1.281	−2.000	−2.781
1.2	1.566	1.038	0	−0.528	−0.706	−0.766	−1.294	−2.272	−3.038
1.4	1.855	1.306	0	−0.549	−0.696	−0.755	−1.304	−2.551	−3.306
1.6	2.146	1.581	0	−0.564	−0.690	−0.746	−1.310	−2.836	−3.581
1.8	2.438	1.862	0	−0.576	−0.685	−0.738	−1.315	−3.124	−3.862
2.0	2.732	2.146	0	−0.586	−0.682	−0.732	−1.318	−3.414	−4.146

[†] Energies are measured in multiples of the chemical shift relative to line 3.

In the practical analysis of a spectrum, there may be difficulties in resolving lines which are closely spaced, particularly 5 and 6. Values of J and the chemical shift δ are best obtained by adjusting the ratio of $J/\nu_0\delta$, using Table 6-9 until the best fit of the pattern is obtained.

An example of an AB$_2$ spectrum has already been given in Sec. 5-2, where the F^{19} spectrum of ClF$_3$ for a series of different applied fields was illustrated (Fig. 5-6). This illustrates how the A and B signals can be separated by increasing the applied field H_0 and consequently reducing the ratio $J/\nu_0\delta$. In practice, however, frequently there are spectra for which this ratio cannot be made small enough, even at the highest attainable fields, for a simple first-order analysis to be valid.

2,6-*Lutidine.* The ring-proton spectrum of 2,6-lutidine at a frequency of 40 Mc/sec was measured and analyzed as an example of AB$_2$ by Bernstein, Pople, and Schneider.[37]   In this molecule, the ring protons should show an isolated spectrum if the coupling constants with the methyl protons are small because of the extra separation.   The observed spectrum, reproduced in Fig. 6-4, is clearly of the AB_2 type.   A good over-all

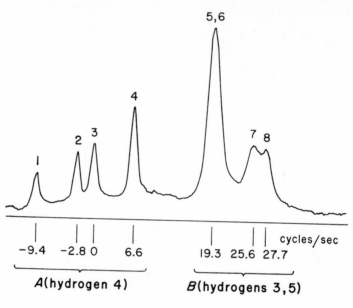

FIG. 6-4. Ring-proton spectrum of 2,6-lutidine at 40 Mc/sec.   The transitions are numbered as in Table 6-8.   (Bernstein, Pople, and Schneider.[37])

fit of pattern is obtained with the ratio $J/\nu_0\delta$ equal to 0.375.   Adjustment of the scale then gives

$$\nu_0(\sigma_B - \sigma_A) = 21.9 \text{ cycles/sec}$$
$$J = \pm 8.2 \text{ cycles/sec} \qquad (6\text{-}58)$$

The calculated energies and intensities using these parameters are compared with observed values in Table 6-10.   Lines 5 and 6 are unresolved; this is consistent with the small calculated separation.   The combination line 9 is not observed because of its low intensity.

c. Four Nuclei AB_3.   The spectrum of a system of four nuclei, three of which are equivalent, can be dealt with in a similar manner.   Because of the three equivalent B nuclei, we may classify states as A_1 or E according to C_{3v} symmetry.   To avoid an additional suffix we shall label them A or E as for C_3 symmetry.   The basic symmetry functions for B_3 have already been tabulated (Table 6-2), so we need only combine each of these with α or β for the A nucleus to get a complete set.   But since the E states

TABLE 6-10. COMPARISON OF CALCULATED AND OBSERVED
SPECTRUM OF 2,6-LUTIDINE

Line	Energy (cycles/sec relative to line 3)		Relative intensity	
	Calculated	Observed	Calculated	Observed
1	-9.4	-9.4	0.47	0.45
2	-3.0	-2.8	0.68	0.75
3	0	0	1.00	0.9
4	6.5	6.6	1.86	1.6
5	18.3 ⎫	19.3	2.85 ⎫	5.0
6	19.0 ⎭		2.52 ⎭	
7	25.5 ⎫	25.6	1.46 ⎫	3.3
8	27.7 ⎭	27.7	1.16 ⎭	
9	46.7		0.0025	

are all doubly degenerate, it is unnecessary to repeat calculations for both components, so we need only consider one component of each and double all the final intensities for E transitions. We shall therefore deal with only the E basic functions $(\alpha\alpha\beta - \alpha\beta\alpha)/\sqrt{2}$ and $(\beta\beta\alpha - \beta\alpha\beta)/\sqrt{2}$ for the B nuclei, omitting the other set given in Table 6-2.

The set of basic functions obtained in this way is given in Table 6-11,

TABLE 6-11. BASIC FUNCTIONS AND MATRIX ELEMENTS OF HAMILTONIAN
FOR FOUR NUCLEI AB$_3$

State	Basic function	Diagonal matrix elements	Off-diagonal matrix elements
A_2	$\alpha\alpha\alpha\alpha$	$\nu_0(2 - \tfrac{1}{2}\sigma_A - \tfrac{3}{2}\sigma_B) + \tfrac{3}{4}J$	
$1A_1$	$\alpha(\alpha\alpha\beta + \alpha\beta\alpha + \beta\alpha\alpha)/\sqrt{3}$	$\nu_0(1 - \tfrac{1}{2}\sigma_A - \tfrac{1}{2}\sigma_B) + \tfrac{1}{4}J$ ⎫	$\sqrt{3}\,J/2$
$2A_1$	$\beta\alpha\alpha\alpha$	$\nu_0(1 + \tfrac{1}{2}\sigma_A - \tfrac{3}{2}\sigma_B) - \tfrac{3}{4}J$ ⎭	
$1A_0$	$\alpha(\beta\beta\alpha + \beta\alpha\beta + \alpha\beta\beta)/\sqrt{3}$	$\nu_0(-\tfrac{1}{2}\sigma_A + \tfrac{1}{2}\sigma_B) - \tfrac{1}{4}J$ ⎫	J
$2A_0$	$\beta(\alpha\alpha\beta + \alpha\beta\alpha + \beta\alpha\alpha)/\sqrt{3}$	$\nu_0(\tfrac{1}{2}\sigma_A - \tfrac{1}{2}\sigma_B) - \tfrac{1}{4}J$ ⎭	
$1A_{-1}$	$\alpha\beta\beta\beta$	$\nu_0(-1 - \tfrac{1}{2}\sigma_A + \tfrac{3}{2}\sigma_B) - \tfrac{3}{4}J$ ⎫	$\sqrt{3}\,J/2$
$2A_{-1}$	$\beta(\beta\beta\alpha + \beta\alpha\beta + \alpha\beta\beta)/\sqrt{3}$	$\nu_0(-1 + \tfrac{1}{2}\sigma_A + \tfrac{1}{2}\sigma_B) + \tfrac{1}{4}J$ ⎭	
A_{-2}	$\beta\beta\beta\beta$	$\nu_0(-2 + \tfrac{1}{2}\sigma_A + \tfrac{3}{2}\sigma_B) + \tfrac{3}{4}J$	
E_1	$\alpha\alpha(\alpha\beta - \beta\alpha)/\sqrt{2}$	$\nu_0(1 - \tfrac{1}{2}\sigma_A - \tfrac{1}{2}\sigma_B) + \tfrac{1}{4}J$	
$1E_0$	$\alpha\beta(\beta\alpha - \alpha\beta)/\sqrt{2}$	$\nu_0(-\tfrac{1}{2}\sigma_A + \tfrac{1}{2}\sigma_B) - \tfrac{1}{4}J$ ⎫	$-\tfrac{1}{2}J$
$2E_0$	$\beta\alpha(\alpha\beta - \beta\alpha)/\sqrt{2}$	$\nu_0(+\tfrac{1}{2}\sigma_A + \tfrac{1}{2}\sigma_B) - \tfrac{1}{4}J$ ⎭	
E_{-1}	$\beta\beta(\beta\alpha - \alpha\beta)/\sqrt{2}$	$\nu_0(-1 + \tfrac{1}{2}\sigma_A + \tfrac{1}{2}\sigma_B) + \tfrac{1}{4}J$	

together with the corresponding diagonal matrix elements of the Hamiltonian. (The coupling constant between B nuclei has been omitted, since it is known not to affect the observable spectrum.) The energies are found by diagonalizing the submatrices in Table 6-11, and transition energies then follow by using the $\Delta F_z = \pm 1$ and symmetry selection rules. If we again define

$$\delta = \sigma_B - \sigma_A$$

and four new quantities

$$D_1 = \tfrac{1}{2}[(\nu_0\delta + J)^2 + 3J^2]^{\frac{1}{2}}$$
$$D_0 = \tfrac{1}{2}[(\nu_0\delta)^2 + 4J^2]^{\frac{1}{2}}$$
$$D_{-1} = \tfrac{1}{2}[(\nu_0\delta - J)^2 + 3J^2]^{\frac{1}{2}}$$
$$D_0' = \tfrac{1}{2}[(\nu_0\delta)^2 + J^2]^{\frac{1}{2}}$$

(6-59)

it becomes possible to write all the transition energies in explicit form. These are given in Table 6-12 (only one component of each E transition

TABLE 6-12. TRANSITION ENERGIES FOR FOUR NUCLEI AB$_3$
[Relative to $\nu_0(1 - \tfrac{1}{2}\sigma_A - \tfrac{1}{2}\sigma_B)$]

Transition	Origin†	Energy
1. $2A_1' \to A_2$	A	$J + D_1$
2. $2A_0' \to 1A_1'$	A	$-\tfrac{1}{2}\nu_0\delta + D_1 + D_0$
3. $2E_0' \to E_1$	A	$\tfrac{1}{2}J + D_0'$
4. $2A_{-1}' \to 1A_0'$	A	$-\tfrac{1}{2}\nu_0\delta + D_0 + D_{-1}$
5. $E_{-1} \to 1E_0'$	A	$-\tfrac{1}{2}J + D_0'$
6. $A_{-2} \to 1A_{-1}'$	A	$-J + D_{-1}$
7. $1A_{-1}' \to 1A_0'$	B	$-\tfrac{1}{2}\nu_0\delta + D_0 - D_{-1}$
8. $1E_0' \to E_1$	B	$\tfrac{1}{2}J - D_0'$
9. $1A_0' \to 1A_1'$	B	$-\tfrac{1}{2}\nu_0\delta + D_1 - D_0$
10. $1A_1' \to A_2$	B	$J - D_1$
11. $2A_0' \to 2A_1'$	B	$-\tfrac{1}{2}\nu_0\delta - D_1 + D_0$
12. $2A_{-1}' \to 2A_0'$	B	$-\tfrac{1}{2}\nu_0\delta - D_0 + D_{-1}$
13. $E_{-1} \to 2E_0'$	B	$-\tfrac{1}{2}J - D_0'$
14. $A_{-2} \to 2A_{-1}'$	B	$-J - D_{-1}$
15. $1A_{-1}' \to 2A_0'$	Comb.	$-\tfrac{1}{2}\nu_0\delta - D_0 - D_{-1}$
16. $1A_0' \to 2A_1'$	Comb.	$-\tfrac{1}{2}\nu_0\delta - D_1 - D_0$

† Based on $\sigma_B > \sigma_A$.

being quoted) together with the origin of the line. For an AB$_3$ spectrum it is seen that there are two combination lines. An observed spectrum of this type is the proton resonance spectrum of methyl mercaptan.[4]

6-6. Spectra of Unsymmetrical Three-spin Systems

We shall now consider the form of the spectrum from a set of three nonequivalent nuclei ABC, each of spin 1/2. No elements of symmetry are present in such a system.   If the nuclei are not all of the same species, however, or if some of the chemical shifts are large, there are simplifying features and the analysis of a spectrum can be carried out in a systematic manner.

a. First-order Spectra for Three Nuclei of Spin 1/2.   The three-spin spectrum takes the simplest form if *all* the nuclei are of different species or if the chemical shifts involved are all large compared with the spin coupling constants.   Under these circumstances, the basic product functions will be good approximations of the stationary-state wave functions, and the simple first-order treatment can be applied.   The spectrum will then consist of a simple quartet of four equally intense lines for each nucleus.   The A signal will be split into a doublet by the coupling with the B nucleus, and each component will be split into

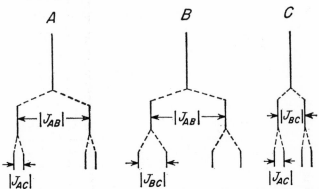

Fig. 6-5. First-order spectra of three nonequivalent nuclei.   The separation between each quartet is large compared with the coupling constants.

another doublet by the AC coupling.   Similar considerations apply to the other two nuclei.   This is illustrated in Fig. 6-5.

The separation between the outer members of the A quartet is $|J_{AB}| + |J_{AC}|$, and that between the inner members is $|(|J_{AB}| - |J_{AC}|)|$.   It is not possible to determine which of $|J_{AB}|$ and $|J_{AC}|$ is the greater from the A spectrum alone, but this information can be obtained from the B and C spectra, where the separations between outer pairs are $|J_{AB}| + |J_{BC}|$ and $|J_{BC}| + |J_{AC}|$, respectively.   The value of $|J_{AB}| - |J_{AC}|$ including its sign follows as the difference.   From a first-order spectrum, therefore, it is possible to determine the magnitudes of three coupling constants $|J_{AB}|$, $|J_{BC}|$, and $|J_{AC}|$, but not their signs.   We shall see below that some information about relative signs may be obtained when chemical shifts are of the same order as the spin coupling constants.

b. General Spectrum for Three Nuclei ABC.   To be able to treat all cases of three nuclei with spin 1/2, we need to set up the full matrix of the Hamiltonian.   Since we wish to deal with situations in which two species of nuclei occur, we shall adopt a modified notation using ν_A, ν_B, and ν_C for the frequencies, in cycles per second, at which the three nuclei would absorb in a field H_0 if there were no spin coupling present. Thus

$$\nu_i = \frac{\gamma_i H_0}{2\pi}(1 - \sigma_i) \qquad i = A, B, C \tag{6-60}$$

The complete set of basic product functions and the diagonal matrix elements are given in Table 6-13. The nonvanishing off-diagonal matrix

TABLE 6-13. BASIC FUNCTIONS AND DIAGONAL MATRIX ELEMENTS
FOR THREE NUCLEI ABC

Basic function†	F_z	Diagonal matrix element $\mathfrak{IC}_{nn}$
1. $\alpha\alpha\alpha$	3/2	$\frac{1}{2}(\nu_A + \nu_B + \nu_C) + \frac{1}{4}(J_{AB} + J_{BC} + J_{CA})$
2. $\alpha\alpha\beta$	1/2	$\frac{1}{2}(\nu_A + \nu_B - \nu_C) + \frac{1}{4}(J_{AB} - J_{BC} - J_{CA})$
3. $\alpha\beta\alpha$	1/2	$\frac{1}{2}(\nu_A - \nu_B + \nu_C) + \frac{1}{4}(-J_{AB} - J_{BC} + J_{CA})$
4. $\beta\alpha\alpha$	1/2	$\frac{1}{2}(-\nu_A + \nu_B + \nu_C) + \frac{1}{4}(-J_{AB} + J_{BC} - J_{CA})$
5. $\alpha\beta\beta$	-1/2	$\frac{1}{2}(\nu_A - \nu_B - \nu_C) + \frac{1}{4}(-J_{AB} + J_{BC} - J_{CA})$
6. $\beta\alpha\beta$	-1/2	$\frac{1}{2}(-\nu_A + \nu_B - \nu_C) + \frac{1}{4}(-J_{AB} - J_{BC} + J_{CA})$
7. $\beta\beta\alpha$	-1/2	$\frac{1}{2}(-\nu_A - \nu_B + \nu_C) + \frac{1}{4}(J_{AB} - J_{BC} - J_{CA})$
8. $\beta\beta\beta$	-3/2	$\frac{1}{2}(-\nu_A - \nu_B - \nu_C) + \frac{1}{4}(J_{AB} + J_{BC} + J_{CA})$

† As in previous tables, the order in which the individual spin functions are written is the same as the alphabetical order of labeling of the nuclei, e.g., $\alpha\beta\alpha = \alpha(A)\beta(B)\alpha(C)$.

elements are

$$\mathfrak{IC}_{23} = \mathfrak{IC}_{67} = \frac{1}{2}J_{BC}$$
$$\mathfrak{IC}_{34} = \mathfrak{IC}_{56} = \frac{1}{2}J_{AB}$$
$$\mathfrak{IC}_{24} = \mathfrak{IC}_{57} = \frac{1}{2}J_{AC} \tag{6-61}$$

Using the selection rule $\Delta F_z = \pm 1$, it is seen that there are 15 transitions possible (as against 12 in the first-order spectrum). Systematic analysis of such a spectrum is not usually possible, however, for it is necessary to solve cubic secular equations to obtain the energy levels from a given set of parameters.

c. Spectrum for Three Nuclei ABX. More progress is possible if one of the three nuclei is of different species or if its signals are well separated from those of the other two. This is referred to as an ABX system, and its spectrum has been discussed in several papers.[464,37,161]

The complete matrix of the Hamiltonian for ABX is given in Table 6-13 and Eq. (6-61), X replacing C. The additional simplification is that basic product functions with different X spin cannot be mixed, so that functions 2 and 7 become approximate stationary-state functions and only 2×2 secular equations remain to be solved. The final energy levels and wave functions can then be written in explicit analytical form. If we define positive quantities D_+, D_- and angles ϕ_+ and ϕ_- by

$$
\begin{aligned}
D_+ \cos 2\phi_+ &= \tfrac{1}{2}(\nu_A - \nu_B) + \tfrac{1}{4}(J_{AX} - J_{BX}) \\
D_+ \sin 2\phi_+ &= \tfrac{1}{2}J_{AB} \\
D_- \cos 2\phi_- &= \tfrac{1}{2}(\nu_A - \nu_B) - \tfrac{1}{4}(J_{AX} - J_{BX}) \\
D_- \sin 2\phi_- &= \tfrac{1}{2}J_{AB}
\end{aligned}
\tag{6-62}
$$

so that

$$
D_\pm = \tfrac{1}{2}\{[\nu_A - \nu_B \pm \tfrac{1}{2}(J_{AX} - J_{BX})]^2 + J_{AB}{}^2\}^{\frac{1}{2}}
\tag{6-63}
$$

the mixed wave functions can be written in the form given in Table 6-14.

TABLE 6-14. MIXED WAVE FUNCTIONS AND ENERGY LEVELS
FOR THREE NUCLEI ABX

State	Wave function	Energy
3'	$\cos \phi_+(\alpha\beta\alpha) + \sin \phi_+(\beta\alpha\alpha)$	$\tfrac{1}{2}\nu_X - \tfrac{1}{4}J_{AB} + D_+$
4'	$- \sin \phi_+(\alpha\beta\alpha) + \cos \phi_+(\beta\alpha\alpha)$	$\tfrac{1}{2}\nu_X - \tfrac{1}{4}J_{AB} - D_+$
5'	$\cos \phi_-(\alpha\beta\beta) + \sin \phi_-(\beta\alpha\beta)$	$-\tfrac{1}{2}\nu_X - \tfrac{1}{4}J_{AB} + D_-$
6'	$- \sin \phi_-(\alpha\beta\beta) + \cos \phi_-(\beta\alpha\beta)$	$-\tfrac{1}{2}\nu_X - \tfrac{1}{4}J_{AB} - D_-$

We are concerned with the case where A and B are of the same species, so $\nu_A - \nu_B$ is just the chemical shift between A and B. We shall assume, without loss of generality, that σ_B is greater than σ_A, so that $\nu_A > \nu_B$. The states are labeled 3', 4', 5', and 6' so that their wave functions would reduce to the basic product functions 3, 4, 5, and 6 if $\nu_A - \nu_B$ became large.

We can now write down explicit expressions for the energies and relative intensities of the 15 transitions; they are summarized in Table 6-15. We have written

$$
\nu_{AB} = \tfrac{1}{2}(\nu_A + \nu_B)
\tag{6-64}
$$

for the mean frequency of A and B signals. The various transitions may be classified according to the first-order transitions that they go into as the chemical shift $\nu_A - \nu_B$ is steadily increased. The last three transitions become forbidden in this limit and are therefore combination lines in this sense. Transition 13 is forbidden whatever the value of $\nu_A - \nu_B$, so that an ABX spectrum cannot consist of more than 14 lines. If the chemical shift $\nu_A - \nu_B$ becomes very small, lines 14 and 15 may become strong and are effectively X lines.

To analyze an ABX spectrum, certain significant features about the transition energies in Table 6-15 may be noted. In the first place, the AB part (transitions 1 to 8) consists of two separate quartets (1, 3,

5, 7 and **2, 4, 6, 8**), each of which is identical in appearance with a two-spin AB spectrum (Sec. 6-5). The separation between outer pairs in both these quartets is equal to J_{AB}, and the separation of the centers is equal to $\frac{1}{2}|J_{AX} + J_{BX}|$. This is shown in Fig. 6-6. The ordering of the transitions will not always be as illustrated but will depend on the various parameters involved.

The first task in analyzing the AB part of an ABX spectrum is to pick out the two quartets. The interval $|J_{AB}|$ occurs four times, and there

TABLE 6-15. Transition Energies and Relative Intensities
for Three Nuclei ABX

Transition	Origin†	Energy	Relative intensity
1. $8 \to 6'$	B	$\nu_{AB} + \frac{1}{4}(-2J_{AB} - J_{AX} - J_{BX}) - D_-$	$1 - \sin 2\phi_-$
2. $7 \to 4'$	B	$\nu_{AB} + \frac{1}{4}(-2J_{AB} + J_{AX} + J_{BX}) - D_+$	$1 - \sin 2\phi_+$
3. $5' \to 2$	B	$\nu_{AB} + \frac{1}{4}(2J_{AB} - J_{AX} - J_{BX}) - D_-$	$1 + \sin 2\phi_-$
4. $3' \to 1$	B	$\nu_{AB} + \frac{1}{4}(2J_{AB} + J_{AX} + J_{BX}) - D_+$	$1 + \sin 2\phi_+$
5. $8 \to 5'$	A	$\nu_{AB} + \frac{1}{4}(-2J_{AB} - J_{AX} - J_{BX}) + D_-$	$1 + \sin 2\phi_-$
6. $7 \to 3'$	A	$\nu_{AB} + \frac{1}{4}(-2J_{AB} + J_{AX} + J_{BX}) + D_+$	$1 + \sin 2\phi_+$
7. $6' \to 2$	A	$\nu_{AB} + \frac{1}{4}(2J_{AB} - J_{AX} - J_{BX}) + D_-$	$1 - \sin 2\phi_-$
8. $4' \to 1$	A	$\nu_{AB} + \frac{1}{4}(2J_{AB} + J_{AX} + J_{BX}) + D_+$	$1 - \sin 2\phi_+$
9. $8 \to 7$	X	$\nu_X - \frac{1}{2}(J_{AX} + J_{BX})$	1
10. $5' \to 3'$	X	$\nu_X + D_+ - D_-$	$\cos^2(\phi_+ - \phi_-)$
11. $6' \to 4'$	X	$\nu_X - D_+ + D_-$	$\cos^2(\phi_+ - \phi_-)$
12. $2 \to 1$	X	$\nu_X + \frac{1}{2}(J_{AX} + J_{BX})$	1
13. $7 \to 2$	Comb.	$2\nu_{AB} - \nu_X$	0
14. $5' \to 4'$	Comb. (X)	$\nu_X - D_+ - D_-$	$\sin^2(\phi_+ - \phi_-)$
15. $6' \to 3'$	Comb. (X)	$\nu_X + D_+ + D_-$	$\sin^2(\phi_+ - \phi_-)$

† See text.

may be more than one way of doing it. If so, it may be possible to pick out the correct assignment by the intensities or by means of cross checks with the X spectrum described below. If the two quartets are picked out, it is possible to obtain values for $|J_{AB}|$, $|J_{AX} + J_{BX}|$, D_+, and D_-, although the latter are known only as a pair which cannot be separately identified.

Turning to the X spectrum, this is seen to consist of six lines (if we include 14 and 15), symmetrical in three pairs about the central position ν_X. The strongest pair (transitions 9 and 12) will be separated by $|J_{AX} + J_{BX}|$. This is just twice the separation of the centers of the quartets in the AB spectrum, so that a cross check is possible here. The separations between the other pairs are $2(D_+ + D_-)$ and $2|D_+ - D_-|$, which can also be checked against the AB spectrum. This is illustrated schematically in Fig. 6-7.

The total amount of information that can be deduced from the spectrum is limited. In the first place the whole calculated spectrum is unaltered if J_{AB} is replaced by $-J_{AB}$. Consequently we can determine only $|J_{AB}|$. Also we cannot determine the absolute signs of J_{AX} and J_{BX}; for if both were reversed in sign, nothing observable would be changed.

We can, however, get information about the *relative* sign of J_{AX} and J_{BX}. Thus if we arbitrarily suppose that $D_+ > D_-$ (this being one of the things we cannot determine) and then use the observed value of J_{AB} (arbitrarily taking it to be positive), we can use Eq. (6-62) to get $D_+ \cos 2\phi_+$ and $D_- \cos 2\phi_-$. But this can be done in either of two ways, taking them to be of the same sign or opposite signs. These two assignments lead to the same transition energies but different distributions of intensities. Also the spectrum will change in a different manner when the external field is altered. If one can distinguish between these two assignments, then it is possible to find whether J_{AX} and J_{BX} have like or unlike signs.

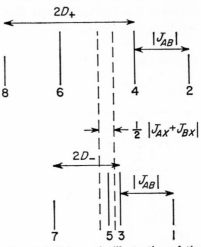

FIG. 6-6. Schematic illustration of the AB part of an ABX spectrum as the superposition of two quartets. 1, 2, 3, 4 are B lines; 5, 6, 7, 8 are A lines. The numbering of lines applies if $J_{AX} > J_{BX} > 0$; $\nu_A > \nu_B$.

2-Fluoro-4,6-dichlorophenol. As an example of the analysis of an ABX spectrum and the determination of relative signs of coupling constants,

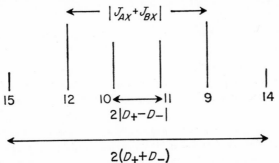

FIG. 6-7. Schematic illustration of the X part of an ABX spectrum. The numbering of lines applies if $J_{AX} > J_{BX} > 0$; $\nu_A > \nu_B$.

we shall describe the proton and fluorine spectra of 2-fluoro-4,6-dichlorophenol, which, with spectra of other compounds of the same type, were measured and analyzed by Gutowsky, Holm, Saika, and Williams.[161] The spectra were measured in a field of 4,165 gauss; they are illustrated in Fig. 6-8.

In the F^{19} spectrum (X spectrum) all six lines are observed. The strongest pair (b and e) must be transitions 9 and 12 (Table 6-15); their splitting of 7.9 cycles/sec is $|J_{AX} + J_{BX}|$. The other two splittings of 12.6 and 0.9 cycles/sec are respectively $2(D_+ + D_-)$ and $2|D_+ - D_-|$.

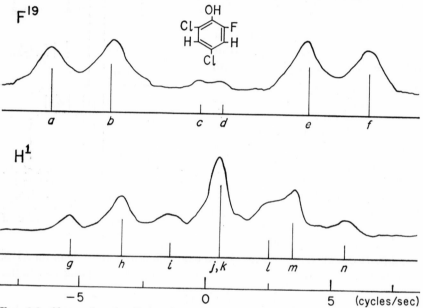

Fig. 6-8. Observed and calculated proton and fluorine spectra at 4,165 gauss for 2-fluoro-4,6-dichlorophenol. (Gutowsky, Holm, Saika, and Williams.[161])

The pairing of proton lines for the quartets can be done on the basis of intensities and splittings. The four equal splittings are gh, ij, kl, and mn, giving $|J_{AB}| = 2.3 \pm 0.1$ cycles/sec. The pairs can be grouped into quartets either as $ghmn$ and $ijkl$ or as $ghkl$ and $ijmn$. The first assignment gives a separation between the quartet centers of 0.4 cycle/sec and the second of 3.9 cycles/sec. Since this must be equal to one-half of the separation of the strong lines in the F^{19} spectrum (X spectrum), the second must be correct. The values of $D_+ + D_-$ and $|D_+ - D_-|$ also check with those obtained from the fluorine spectrum. Arbitrarily taking $D_+ > D_-$, we obtain $D_+ = 3.35$ cycles/sec, $D_- = 2.95$ cycles/sec.

For further progress we need to examine the intensities. The fact that the outer lines of the fluorine spectrum are *strong* (unlike Fig. 6-7) indicates (Table 6-15) that $\sin^2(\phi_+ - \phi_-) \approx 1$, or $\phi_+ - \phi_- \approx \pm\pi/2$.

This in turn [Eq. (6-62)] means that $\cos 2\phi_+$ and $\cos 2\phi_-$ have opposite sign, so that $\frac{1}{2}(\nu_A - \nu_B) - \frac{1}{4}(J_{AX} - J_{BX})$ and $\frac{1}{2}(\nu_A - \nu_B) + \frac{1}{4}(J_{AX} - J_{BX})$ have opposite signs. This implies that $|J_{AX} - J_{BX}|$ must be larger than $2(\nu_A - \nu_B)$. The actual values are easily found by using Eq. (6-62). $|J_{AX} - J_{BX}|$ turns out to be larger than the sum $|J_{AX} + J_{BX}|$, so that the two must have opposite sign. The magnitudes of J_{AX} and J_{BX} are 9.6 and 2.1 cycles/sec, and the proton chemical shift is 2.1 cycles/sec. Comparison with other compounds suggests that the coupling constant of 9.6 cycles/sec is to be assigned to the proton and fluorine nuclei in ortho positions.

In other spectra of the ABX type, it may not always be possible to observe the weaker lines in the X spectrum. Under these circumstances, it may still be possible to distinguish between the two assignments on the basis of intensities in the AB part. Other examples where this is done are given by Gutowsky, Holm, Saika, and Williams.[161]

2,3-*Lutidine.* An example of an ABX system in which all three nuclei are of the same species is the ring-proton spectrum of 2,3-lutidine:

This was measured and analyzed by Bernstein, Pople, and Schneider.[37] The observed spectrum, shown in Fig. 6-9, consists of one set of signals X well separated from the remainder AB. All eight signals are resolved in the AB part, but the X region shows only four lines as against six in the previous example.

This spectrum is an example in which the A and B regions do not overlap, and it is possible to treat it as a typical AB spectrum which is modified by coupling with the X nucleus. If the proton giving signals at highest field is labeled B, the B quartet (Fig. 6-9) shows a greater splitting due to the X coupling than does the A quartet, so that $|J_{BX}| > |J_{AX}|$. If both J_{AX} and J_{BX} have the same sign, the assignment is then as in Fig. 6-10. Alternatively, the same assignment could have been made by picking out the two separate AB-type quartets 1, 3, 5, 7 and 2, 4, 6, 8 (Fig. 6-6). The coupling constant J_{AB} follows from the separations 1, 3; 2, 4; 5, 7; and 6, 8; and it is 7.35 cycles/sec. The remaining analysis is straightforward, using Table 6-15, and gives $J_{BX} = 5.0$ cycles/sec and

$J_{AX} = 1.3$ cycles/sec. The chemical shifts of the A and B protons to the high-field side of X are 43.4 and 55.1 cycles/sec, respectively. Another assignment is possible with the labeling in Fig. 6-10 reading 7, 8, 5, 6, 4, 3, 2, 1 from left to right, leading to opposite sign for J_{AX} and J_{BX}. In this spectrum, however, it is not possible to distinguish between the two

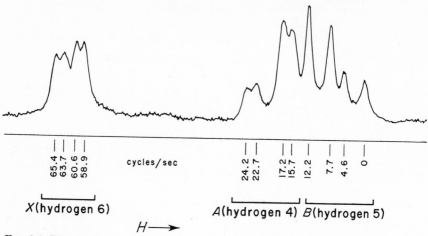

Fig. 6-9. Ring-proton spectrum of 2,3-lutidine at 40 Mc/sec. (Bernstein, Pople, and Schneider.[37])

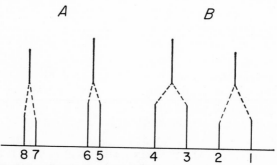

Fig. 6-10. Relation of AB region of ABX spectrum to the pure AB spectrum.

assignments from intensity considerations because the observed line intensities are not sufficiently precise.

6-7. Two Pairs of Two Equivalent Nuclei

In this section we shall discuss the spectrum of a system of four nuclei of spin 1/2, consisting of two pairs. If the two pairs are of different species, or have a large chemical shift, this would be referred to as A_2X_2.

The theory for A_2X_2 was first given by McConnell, McLean, and Reilly,[273] and the extension to the general case A_2B_2 where the chemical shift is not large was discussed by Pople, Schneider, and Bernstein.[342]

We begin by setting up the complete matrix for A_2B_2. Let ν_A and ν_B be the frequencies the lines would have if there were no spin coupling constants, so that

$$\nu_A = \frac{\gamma_A H_0}{2\pi}(1 - \sigma_A) \qquad \nu_B = \frac{\gamma_B H_0}{2\pi}(1 - \sigma_B) \qquad (6\text{-}65)$$

We shall suppose $\nu_A > \nu_B$, so that, if the nuclei are of the same species, σ_B will be greater than σ_A and, if the experiment is performed by varying the external field to obtain resonance at a given frequency, the B signals will appear at higher field.

In general there will be four different spin coupling constants, as shown in Fig. 6-11. If there is a plane of symmetry, the coupling constants J_{13} and J_{24} will be equal to J', and the pair J_{23} and J_{14} will equal J. But in general $J \neq J'$. We shall find it convenient to define new quantities

$$K = J_A + J_B \qquad L = J - J'$$
$$M = J_A - J_B \qquad N = J + J' \qquad (6\text{-}66)$$

The basic functions will be chosen as symmetry functions which are either symmetrical (s) or anti-symmetrical (a) with respect to reflection in the plane of symmetry. We already have symmetrical basic functions for A_2 and B_2 separately. A complete set for A_2B_2 can then be obtained by taking all possible products; it is given in Table 6-16. The value of F_z is again indicated by a suffix. It should be noted that the function $3s_0$, which is a product of antisymmetric functions, is symmetric. This is not the only possible choice of basic symmetry functions, of course. The functions $3s_0$ and $4s_0$, for example, could be replaced by

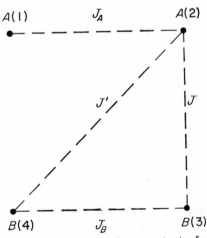

FIG. 6-11. Spin-coupling constants for four nuclei A_2B_2.

$(\alpha\beta\alpha\beta + \beta\alpha\beta\alpha)/\sqrt{2}$ and $(\alpha\beta\beta\alpha + \beta\alpha\alpha\beta)/\sqrt{2}$. However, the final energies and wave functions will not depend on this choice.

The matrix elements of the Hamiltonian can be evaluated as before; they also are given in Table 6-16. The energies and wave functions for the stationary states can then be obtained by diagonalizing the submatrices of $\mathcal{H}$ for various symmetries and values of F_z. In general, the energy levels for the s_0 set require the solution of a quartic secular equation, and explicit analytical expressions are not possible.

TABLE 6-16. BASIC FUNCTIONS AND COMPLETE MATRIX OF HAMILTONIAN $\mathcal{H}$
FOR FOUR NUCLEI A_2B_2

Function†	A	B	Diagonal matrix elements‡	Off-diagonal matrix elements
s_2	$\alpha\alpha$	$\alpha\alpha$	$\nu_A + \nu_B + \tfrac{1}{2}N$	
$1s_1$	$2^{-\frac{1}{2}}(\alpha\beta + \beta\alpha)$	$\alpha\alpha$	ν_B	$(1s_1\|\mathcal{H}\|2s_1) = \tfrac{1}{2}N$
$2s_1$	$\alpha\alpha$	$2^{-\frac{1}{2}}(\alpha\beta + \beta\alpha)$	ν_A	
$1s_0$	$\beta\beta$	$\alpha\alpha$	$-\nu_A + \nu_B - \tfrac{1}{2}N$	$(1s_0\|\mathcal{H}\|2s_0) = 0 \quad (2s_0\|\mathcal{H}\|3s_0) = \tfrac{1}{2}L$
$2s_0$	$\alpha\alpha$	$\beta\beta$	$\nu_A - \nu_B - \tfrac{1}{2}N$	$(1s_0\|\mathcal{H}\|3s_0) = \tfrac{1}{2}L (2s_0\|\mathcal{H}\|4s_0) = \tfrac{1}{2}N$
$3s_0$	$2^{-\frac{1}{2}}(\alpha\beta - \beta\alpha)$	$2^{-\frac{1}{2}}(\alpha\beta - \beta\alpha)$	$-K$	$(1s_0\|\mathcal{H}\|4s_0) = \tfrac{1}{2}N(3s_0\|\mathcal{H}\|4s_0) = -\tfrac{1}{2}L$
$4s_0$	$2^{-\frac{1}{2}}(\alpha\beta + \beta\alpha)$	$2^{-\frac{1}{2}}(\alpha\beta + \beta\alpha)$	0	
$1s_{-1}$	$2^{-\frac{1}{2}}(\alpha\beta + \beta\alpha)$	$\beta\beta$	$-\nu_B$	
$2s_{-1}$	$\beta\beta$	$2^{-\frac{1}{2}}(\alpha\beta + \beta\alpha)$	$-\nu_A$	$(1s_{-1}\|\mathcal{H}\|2s_{-1}) = \tfrac{1}{2}N$
s_{-2}	$\beta\beta$	$\beta\beta$	$-\nu_A - \nu_B + \tfrac{1}{2}N$	
$1a_1$	$2^{-\frac{1}{2}}(\alpha\beta - \beta\alpha)$	$\alpha\alpha$	$\nu_B - \tfrac{1}{2}K - \tfrac{1}{2}M$	$(1a_1\|\mathcal{H}\|2a_1) = -\tfrac{1}{2}L$
$2a_1$	$\alpha\alpha$	$2^{-\frac{1}{2}}(\alpha\beta - \beta\alpha)$	$\nu_A - \tfrac{1}{2}K + \tfrac{1}{2}M$	
$1a_0$	$2^{-\frac{1}{2}}(\alpha\beta + \beta\alpha)$	$2^{-\frac{1}{2}}(\alpha\beta - \beta\alpha)$	$-\tfrac{1}{2}K + \tfrac{1}{2}M$	$(1a_0\|\mathcal{H}\|2a_0) = -\tfrac{1}{2}L$
$2a_0$	$2^{-\frac{1}{2}}(\alpha\beta - \beta\alpha)$	$2^{-\frac{1}{2}}(\alpha\beta + \beta\alpha)$	$-\tfrac{1}{2}K - \tfrac{1}{2}M$	
$1a_{-1}$	$2^{-\frac{1}{2}}(\alpha\beta - \beta\alpha)$	$\beta\beta$	$-\nu_B - \tfrac{1}{2}K - \tfrac{1}{2}M$	$(1a_{-1}\|\mathcal{H}\|2a_{-1}) = -\tfrac{1}{2}L$
$2a_{-1}$	$\beta\beta$	$2^{-\frac{1}{2}}(\alpha\beta - \beta\alpha)$	$-\nu_A - \tfrac{1}{2}K + \tfrac{1}{2}M$	

† A serial notation is used. Thus $\alpha\alpha\beta\beta$ means $\alpha(1)\alpha(2)\beta(3)\beta(4)$, the numbering being as in Fig. 6-11.
‡ For convenience, $\tfrac{1}{4}K$ is subtracted from all diagonal matrix elements. This makes no difference in calculating transition energies.

a. **Spectra of Four Nuclei A_2X_2.** The analysis is considerably simplified if the AB chemical shift is large, or if the nuclei are of different species. Many of the secular determinants then break up into smaller ones. Inspection of Table 6-16 shows that the only basic functions which may still mix are the pairs $3s_0$, $4s_0$ and $1a_0$, $2a_0$. If we define angles θ_s and θ_a by

$$\cos 2\theta_s : \sin 2\theta_s : 1 = K : L : (K^2 + L^2)^{\frac{1}{2}} \qquad (6\text{-}67)$$
$$\cos 2\theta_a : \sin 2\theta_a : 1 = M : L : (M^2 + L^2)^{\frac{1}{2}} \qquad (6\text{-}68)$$

the stationary-state functions and energies corresponding to the basic functions are as given in Table 6-17. The remaining energies are just the diagonal matrix elements of $\mathcal{H}$ given in Table 6-16 (with ν_B replaced by ν_X).

The possible transitions can be found by using the symmetry selection rule and either $\Delta F_z(A)$ or $\Delta F_z(X) = \pm 1$. Thus, a transition such as $2s_0 \rightarrow 1s_1$ is forbidden even though $\Delta F_z = 1$, since $\Delta F_z(X) = 2$ (combina-

TABLE 6-17. STATIONARY-STATE WAVE FUNCTIONS AND ENERGIES
FOR FOUR NUCLEI A_2X_2

State	Wave function	Energy
$3s_0'$	$(3s_0) \cos \theta_s + (4s_0) \sin \theta_s$	$-\frac{1}{2}K - \frac{1}{2}(K^2 + L^2)^{\frac{1}{2}}$
$4s_0'$	$-(3s_0) \sin \theta_s + (4s_0) \cos \theta_s$	$-\frac{1}{2}K + \frac{1}{2}(K^2 + L^2)^{\frac{1}{2}}$
$1a_0'$	$(1a_0) \cos \theta_a - (2a_0) \sin \theta_a$	$-\frac{1}{2}K + \frac{1}{2}(M^2 + L^2)^{\frac{1}{2}}$
$2a_0'$	$(1a_0) \sin \theta_a + (2a_0) \cos \theta_a$	$-\frac{1}{2}K - \frac{1}{2}(M^2 + L^2)^{\frac{1}{2}}$

tion transition). This results in a total of 24 transitions, of which 12 are
A transitions $[\Delta F_z(A) = \pm 1]$ and the remaining 12 are X transitions
$[\Delta F_z(X) = \pm 1]$. The energies and relative intensities of the A transitions are given in Table 6-18. An exactly similar set of transitions

TABLE 6-18. ENERGIES AND RELATIVE INTENSITIES OF A TRANSITIONS
FOR FOUR NUCLEI A_2X_2

Transition	Energy relative to ν_A	Relative intensity
1. $1s_1 \rightarrow s_2$	$\frac{1}{2}N$	1
2. $1s_0 \rightarrow 1s_1$	$\frac{1}{2}N$	1
3. $s_{-2} \rightarrow 1s_{-1}$	$-\frac{1}{2}N$	1
4. $1s_{-1} \rightarrow 2s_0$	$-\frac{1}{2}N$	1
5. $3s_0' \rightarrow 2s_1$	$\frac{1}{2}K + \frac{1}{2}(K^2 + L^2)^{\frac{1}{2}}$	$\sin^2 \theta_s$
6. $2s_{-1} \rightarrow 4s_0'$	$-\frac{1}{2}K + \frac{1}{2}(K^2 + L^2)^{\frac{1}{2}}$	$\cos^2 \theta_s$
7. $4s_0' \rightarrow 2s_1$	$\frac{1}{2}K - \frac{1}{2}(K^2 + L^2)^{\frac{1}{2}}$	$\cos^2 \theta_s$
8. $2s_{-1} \rightarrow 3s_0'$	$-\frac{1}{2}K - \frac{1}{2}(K^2 + L^2)^{\frac{1}{2}}$	$\sin^2 \theta_s$
9. $2a_0' \rightarrow 2a_1$	$\frac{1}{2}M + \frac{1}{2}(M^2 + L^2)^{\frac{1}{2}}$	$\sin^2 \theta_a$
10. $2a_{-1} \rightarrow 1a_0'$	$-\frac{1}{2}M + \frac{1}{2}(M^2 + L^2)^{\frac{1}{2}}$	$\cos^2 \theta_a$
11. $1a_0' \rightarrow 2a_1$	$\frac{1}{2}M - \frac{1}{2}(M^2 + L^2)^{\frac{1}{2}}$	$\cos^2 \theta_a$
12. $2a_{-1} \rightarrow 2a_0'$	$-\frac{1}{2}M - \frac{1}{2}(M^2 + L^2)^{\frac{1}{2}}$	$\sin^2 \theta_a$

(centered about ν_X) is obtained for the 12 X transitions.

Inspection of Table 6-18 shows the A spectrum will consist of:

1. A strong doublet (lines 1, 2, 3, 4) centered on the frequency ν_A, the separation being $N = J + J'$.

2. Two symmetrical quartets (5, 6, 7, 8 and 9, 10, 11, 12) also centered on ν_A. The assignments of the outer and inner lines of each quartet depend on the signs of K and M, but the inner lines are always more intense.

If these features of the spectrum can be separated, it becomes possible to determine the *magnitudes* of L and N separately and the magnitudes of K and M. However, it is not possible to distinguish between K and M.

Accordingly the signs of the spin coupling constants are not determined from the analysis, and J_A cannot be distinguished from J_B, nor J from J'.

1,1-*Difluoroethylene.* A good example of an A_2X_2 system is 1,1-difluoroethylene:

The proton and fluorine spectra were measured (at a fixed frequency of 40 Mc/sec) and analyzed by McConnell, McLean, and Reilly.[273]   The two spectra are identical, in agreement with the theory.   The F^{19} spectrum is illustrated in Fig. 6-12.

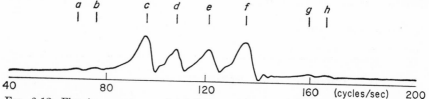

Fig. 6-12. Fluorine spectrum of 1,1-difluoroethylene at 40 Mc/sec. (McConnell, McLean, and Reilly.[273])

The general features predicted show up fairly clearly in this spectrum. The strongest signals c and f correspond to the strong doublet; and the four outermost weak signals (a, b, g, and h) are the outer members of the two quartets.   The inner members of the two quartets are evidently superposed at d and e.   The complete analysis yields the following absolute values for the spin coupling constants:

$$J_{HH} \approx 4 \text{ cycles/sec} \qquad J_{HF,cis} \approx 1 \text{ cycle/sec}$$
$$J_{FF} = 37 \text{ cycles/sec} \qquad J_{HF,trans} = 34 \text{ cycles/sec} \qquad (6\text{-}69)$$

where $J_{HH} = J_A$, $J_{FF} = J_X$, $J_{HF,cis} = J$, and $J_{HF,trans} = J'$.   Owing to the limitations discussed above, it is not possible to deduce from this spectrum alone whether the coupling constant of 37 cycles/sec is J_{FF} or J_{HH}, nor is it possible to distinguish between the cis and trans coupling constants. The assignments made were based on comparisons with coupling constants in other molecules.[273]

b. Analysis of A_2B_2 Spectra. If the chemical shift between the two pairs is not large compared with the spin coupling constants, it becomes necessary to solve the 4 × 4 secular equation for the s_0 functions.   However, all the other secular determinants do not exceed the second order, so it is still possible to give explicit analytical forms for the energies and wave functions of the remaining states.   It is convenient to define further angles by

$$\cos 2\phi : \sin 2\phi : 1 = \nu_0\delta : N : [(\nu_0\delta)^2 + N^2]^{1/2}$$
$$\cos 2\psi_{\pm} : \sin 2\psi_{\pm} : 1 = (\nu_0\delta \pm M) : L : [(\nu_0\delta \pm M)^2 + L^2]^{1/2} \quad (6\text{-}70)$$

where we have written

$$\nu_0\delta = \nu_0(\sigma_B - \sigma_A) = \nu_A - \nu_B \quad (6\text{-}71)$$

The energies and wave functions of all states except those for s_0 states are then as in Table 6-19.

TABLE 6-19. EXPLICIT EXPRESSION FOR ENERGIES AND WAVE FUNCTIONS FOR FOUR NUCLEI A_2B_2

State	Energy	Wave function
s_2	$\nu_A + \nu_B + \tfrac{1}{2}N$	s_2
$1s_1'$	$\tfrac{1}{2}(\nu_A + \nu_B) - \tfrac{1}{2}[(\nu_0\delta)^2 + N^2]^{1/2}$	$(1s_1)\cos\phi - (2s_1)\sin\phi$
$2s_1'$	$\tfrac{1}{2}(\nu_A + \nu_B) + \tfrac{1}{2}[(\nu_0\delta)^2 + N^2]^{1/2}$	$(1s_1)\sin\phi + (2s_1)\cos\phi$
$1s_{-1}'$	$-\tfrac{1}{2}(\nu_A + \nu_B) + \tfrac{1}{2}[(\nu_0\delta)^2 + N^2]^{1/2}$	$(1s_{-1})\cos\phi + (2s_{-1})\sin\phi$
$2s_{-1}'$	$-\tfrac{1}{2}(\nu_A + \nu_B) - \tfrac{1}{2}[(\nu_0\delta)^2 + N^2]^{1/2}$	$-(1s_{-1})\sin\phi + (2s_{-1})\cos\phi$
s_{-2}	$-(\nu_A + \nu_B) + \tfrac{1}{2}N$	s_{-2}
$1a_1'$	$\tfrac{1}{2}(\nu_A + \nu_B) - \tfrac{1}{2}K - \tfrac{1}{2}[(\nu_0\delta + M)^2 + L^2]^{1/2}$	$(1a_1)\cos\psi_+ + (2a_1)\sin\psi_+$
$2a_1'$	$\tfrac{1}{2}(\nu_A + \nu_B) - \tfrac{1}{2}K + \tfrac{1}{2}[(\nu_0\delta + M)^2 + L^2]^{1/2}$	$-(1a_1)\sin\psi_+ + (2a_1)\cos\psi_+$
$1a_0'$	$-\tfrac{1}{2}K + \tfrac{1}{2}(M^2 + L^2)^{1/2}$	$(1a_0)\cos\theta_a - (2a_0)\sin\theta_a$
$2a_0'$	$-\tfrac{1}{2}K - \tfrac{1}{2}(M^2 + L^2)^{1/2}$	$(1a_0)\sin\theta_a + (2a_0)\cos\theta_a$
$1a_{-1}'$	$-\tfrac{1}{2}(\nu_A + \nu_B) - \tfrac{1}{2}K + \tfrac{1}{2}[(\nu_0\delta - M)^2 + L^2]^{1/2}$	$(1a_{-1})\cos\psi_- - (2a_{-1})\sin\psi_-$
$2a_{-1}'$	$-\tfrac{1}{2}(\nu_A + \nu_B) - \tfrac{1}{2}K - \tfrac{1}{2}[(\nu_0\delta - M)^2 + L^2]^{1/2}$	$(1a_{-1})\sin\psi_- + (2a_{-1})\cos\psi_-$

The possible transitions are labeled according to the type they become as the chemical shift continuously increases. Thus, the transition $1s_1' \to s_2$, for example, is an A transition. Certain other transitions such as $1s_{-1}' \to 1s_0'$ involve changing the spins of three nuclei in the limit (where they are forbidden). There are four such transitions, and they give rise to combination lines of weak intensity. They will not be considered explicitly. The remaining 24 transitions go over into the two separate sets of 12 already considered if the chemical shift is sufficiently large. Detailed inspection of the Hamiltonian matrix shows that the set of A lines is always a mirror image of the set of B lines with respect to the central position, $\tfrac{1}{2}(\nu_A + \nu_B)$. We need therefore only examine the theoretical expressions for the energies and intensities of the 12 A transitions, which become the set given in Table 6-18 in the limiting case of large δ. We shall number them in the same way.

Of the 12 transitions, 6 will involve states of type s_0, but the remainder have transition energies and intensities as given in Table 6-20.

TABLE 6-20. ENERGIES AND INTENSITIES OF A TRANSITIONS FOR FOUR NUCLEI A_2B_2

Transition	Energy relative to $\frac{1}{2}(\nu_A + \nu_B)$	Intensity
1. $1s_1' \rightarrow s_2$ 2. $1s_0' \rightarrow 1s_1'$	$\frac{1}{2}N + \frac{1}{2}[(\nu_0\delta)^2 + N^2]^{\frac{1}{2}}$	$1 - \sin 2\phi$
3. $s_{-2} \rightarrow 1s_{-1}'$ 4. $1s_{-1}' \rightarrow 2s_0'$	$-\frac{1}{2}N + \frac{1}{2}[(\nu_0\delta)^2 + N^2]^{\frac{1}{2}}$	$1 + \sin 2\phi$
5. $3s_0' \rightarrow 2s_1'$		
6. $2s_{-1}' \rightarrow 4s_0'$		
7. $4s_0' \rightarrow 2s_1'$		
8. $2s_{-1}' \rightarrow 3s_0'$		
9. $2a_0' \rightarrow 2a_1'$	$\frac{1}{2}[(\nu_0\delta + M)^2 + L^2]^{\frac{1}{2}} + \frac{1}{2}(M^2 + L^2)^{\frac{1}{2}}$	$\sin^2(\theta_a - \psi_+)$
10. $2a_{-1}' \rightarrow 1a_0'$	$\frac{1}{2}[(\nu_0\delta - M)^2 + L^2]^{\frac{1}{2}} + \frac{1}{2}(M^2 + L^2)^{\frac{1}{2}}$	$\cos^2(\theta_a + \psi_-)$
11. $1a_0' \rightarrow 2a_1'$	$\frac{1}{2}[(\nu_0\delta + M)^2 + L^2]^{\frac{1}{2}} - \frac{1}{2}(M^2 + L^2)^{\frac{1}{2}}$	$\cos^2(\theta_a - \psi_+)$
12. $2a_{-1}' \rightarrow 2a_0'$	$\frac{1}{2}[(\nu_0\delta - M)^2 + L^2]^{\frac{1}{2}} - \frac{1}{2}(M^2 + L^2)^{\frac{1}{2}}$	$\sin^2(\theta_a + \psi_-)$

c. A_2B_2 Spectra with Equal AB Coupling Constants. If the two AB coupling constants J and J' (Fig. 6-11) are equal, then, as shown in Sec. 6-4, the spectrum will become independent of J_A and J_B and its shape will depend only on the ratio $J/\nu_0\delta$. This can also be confirmed by examining the complete energy matrix (Table 6-16). Since $L = 0$, the basic function $3s_0$ does not mix with any others, so it becomes a stationary-state function. At the same time, the transitions 5 and 8 involving $3s_0$ become forbidden. Also there is no mixing in the antisymmetrical part of the matrix. This means that transitions 9 and 12 become forbidden.

TABLE 6-21. ENERGIES OF A TRANSITIONS FOR A_2B_2 WITH TWO EQUAL AB COUPLING CONSTANTS IN UNITS OF $\nu_0\delta$†

$J/\nu_0\delta$	Transition (see Table 6-20)						
	4	3	10, 11	6	7	2	1
0.1	0.401	0.410	0.500	0.508	0.512	0.599	0.610
0.2	0.309	0.339	0.500	0.524	0.554	0.694	0.739
0.3	0.233	0.283	0.500	0.535	0.631	0.785	0.883
0.4	0.176	0.240	0.500	0.536	0.744	0.872	1.040
0.5	0.134	0.207	0.500	0.528	0.886	0.955	1.207
0.75	0.077	0.151	0.500	0.482	1.320	1.158	1.651
1.00	0.052	0.118	0.500	0.429	1.807	1.363	2.118

† Relative to the center of band.

The number of allowed A transitions is now reduced to eight, two of them (10 and 11 in Table 6-20) being always degenerate. The complete spectrum is still symmetrical about the mid-point. Numerical values for the A-transition energies are given for a range of values of $J/\nu_0\delta$ in Table 6-21. The energies are measured relative to the center of the spectrum in units of $\nu_0\delta$. The form of a typical half spectrum is given in Fig. 6-13, together with a correlation between the lines and the triplet of the A_2X_2 limit. It is useful to note that the position of the degenerate pair gives directly the frequency ν_A, and consequently the chemical shift.

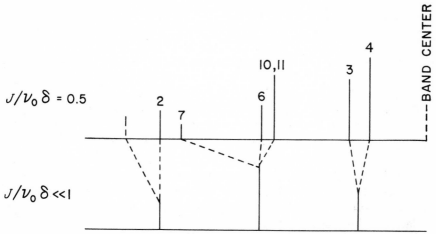

FIG. 6-13. Typical half spectrum for A_2B_2 with equal AB coupling constants, including correlation with components of triplet in the limit of large chemical shift.

β-Propiolactone. An example of an A_2B_2 spectrum of this type is the proton spectrum of β-propiolactone:

$$H_2C\!-\!\!-CH_2$$
$$O\!-\!\!-C\!=\!O$$

which was measured at a frequency of 30.5 Mc/sec and analyzed by Anderson.[10] The spectrum is shown in Fig. 6-14. The equality of the two AB coupling constants in a ring compound of this type is accidental.

d. Complex A_2B_2 Spectra. The general spectrum for A_2B_2 depends on the relative chemical-shift and spin coupling constants in a rather complicated way, and it is no longer possible to give such a direct deductive method of analysis as was possible for the simpler groups. However, there are certain general classes of A_2B_2 spectra which are likely to be found in a variety of molecules and which have a form sufficiently characteristic to allow at least a partial assignment to be made. Once a satisfactory assignment is made, it is possible to get values for the parameters from the explicit expressions for the transition energies in Table 6-20, together with a certain amount of trial-and-error fitting. Some help in the assignment may also be obtained from a study of the way in which a theoretical spectrum changes from an A_2X_2 type as the chemical shift is continuously reduced.

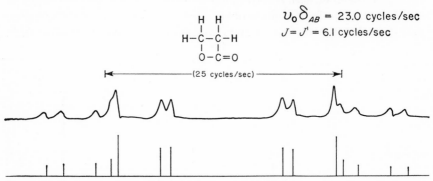

FIG. 6-14. Proton spectrum of β-propiolactone at 30.5 Mc/sec. The theoretical spectrum is shown below. (Anderson.[10])

One important class of A_2B_2 spectra occurs in molecules where the four nuclei are so arranged that one of the pairs (B_2, say) is more strongly coupled than the other. Such groups often occur if the two B nuclei are relatively close together and each A nucleus is close to one B nucleus, as is true of the protons in a symmetrical ortho disubstituted benzene:

$$A \!\!\!\bigotimes\limits_{\substack{B \; B \\ R \; R}}\!\!\! A$$

The largest spin coupling constants in such a system will probably be J and J_B (notation as in Fig. 6-11). Information about signs of coupling constants is difficult to obtain from A_2B_2 spectra, and the analyses published have been made on the assumption that the signs are all positive. Therefore we examine the form of the spectrum under the conditions

$$J \gg J' > 0$$
$$J_B \gg J_A \geqslant 0 \qquad\qquad (6\text{-}72)$$

It is still arbitrarily assumed that $\sigma_B > \sigma_A$ for convenience in numbering the transitions, although it will not be possible to determine whether that is so, owing to the symmetrical form of the spectrum.

In the A_2X_2 limit, the spectrum is of the form already described; it is illustrated schematically in Fig. 6-15a. (The numbering takes this form because $M = J_A - J_B$ is negative.) It consists of two strong lines, each of which is a degenerate pair, 1, 2 and 3, 4, together with two quartets, 5, 6, 7, 8 and 10, 9, 12, 11. If $J_A = 0$, so that $K = -M$, the pairs 5, 10; 9, 6; 7, 12; and 11, 8 coalesce. The B spectrum, which is to the right of the figure, is identical.

As the AB chemical shift decreases, this spectrum becomes modified in a characteristic manner (Fig. 6-15b). The part which is closest to the B spectrum becomes more intense at the expense of the outer components. In fact, the signals 5 and 10 may become so weak that they are practically unobservable. The two degenerate pairs 1, 2 and 3, 4 split slightly and there is a tendency for the separation of both the inner pairs (9, 6 and

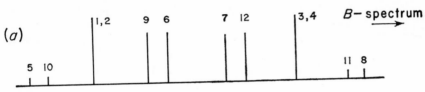

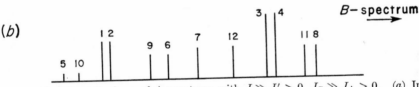

FIG. 6-15. Schematic form of A spectrum with $J \gg J' > 0$, $J_B \gg J_A > 0$. (a) In A_2X_2 limit. (b) General case.

7, 12) to increase. If J' is not too small, the separation of the pair 7, 12 is usually increased most. The outermost right-hand pair may cross the corresponding B lines if the chemical shift is sufficiently small.

In the practical analysis of a spectrum of this type, the pairs 1, 2 and 3, 4 are usually easily recognized and lines 1 and 3 can be used (Table 6-20) to obtain the chemical shift $\nu_0\delta$ and $N \ (= J + J')$. The positions of the inner lines can then be used to obtain values for the other combinations of spin coupling constants.

Naphthalene. The proton resonance spectrum of naphthalene has been analyzed as an example of an A_2B_2 system by Pople, Schneider, and Bernstein.[342] Strictly, the protons of naphthalene are A_4B_4, but they can be dealt with approximately as a superposition of two A_2B_2 sets if the spin coupling between protons in different rings is neglected.

The complete proton resonance spectrum of naphthalene in dioxane solution at 40 Mc/sec is shown in Fig. 6-16, together with the mean positions of the signals relative to the center. Following the notation developed earlier in this section, the two α protons are labeled A and the two β protons B. We assume $\sigma_B > \sigma_A$. This is not implicit in the spectrum but was confirmed by a measurement of β-deuteronaphthalene. An

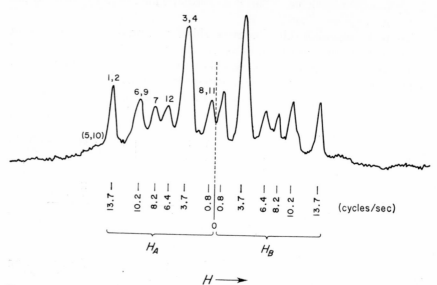

FIG. 6-16. Complete proton resonance spectrum and assignment of A lines of naphthalene at 40 Mc/sec. (Pople, Schneider, and Bernstein.[342])

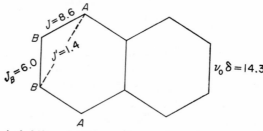

FIG. 6-17. Chemical-shift and spin coupling constants for naphthalene, in cycles per second.

assignment of signals is made on the basis of Fig. 6-15. The signals at 3.75 and 13.7 cycles/sec are assigned to the pairs 3, 4 and 1, 2. There should be four lines between these pairs, but only three are observed. However, the line at 10.2 cycles/sec does show some sign of being a doublet, so the assignment illustrated in Fig. 6-16 is indicated. On the basis of this assignment, it is possible to obtain numerical values for the parameters and carry out internal checks. From the positions of lines

1, 3, 9, 11, and 12 (Table 6-20)

$$N = E_1 - E_3 = 9.95 \text{ cycles/sec}$$
$$(M^2 + L^2)^{1/2} = E_9 - E_{11} = 9.4 \text{ cycles/sec}$$
$$[(\nu_0\delta)^2 + N^2]^{1/2} = E_1 + E_3 = 17.45 \text{ cycles/sec}$$
$$[(\nu_0\delta + M)^2 + L^2]^{1/2} = E_9 + E_{11} = 11.0 \text{ cycles/sec} \qquad (6\text{-}73)$$

To get a complete set of constants, we also need K. It cannot be found in a direct manner, so it is assumed that $K = -M$. This corresponds to $J_A = 0$, which is reasonable because the A protons are far apart. The complete set of basic parameters is then as shown in Fig. 6-17. The complete calculated spectrum is compared with the experimental one in Table 6-22.

TABLE 6-22. COMPARISON OF CALCULATED AND OBSERVED PROTON
SPECTRA OF NAPHTHALENE

Line	Energy relative to center of band, cycles/sec		Relative intensity	
	Calculated	Observed	Calculated	Observed†
11	0.8⎫	0.8	0.52⎫	1.1
8	1.6⎭		0.45⎭	
4	3.2⎫	3.7	1.87⎫	2.8
3	3.7⎭		1.57⎭	
12	6.1	6.4	0.93	0.9
7	7.5	8.2	0.62	0.6
6	9.9⎫	10.2	0.53⎫	1.3
9	10.2⎭		0.49⎭	
2	13.2⎫	13.7	0.46⎫	1.1
1	13.7⎭		0.43⎭	
10	15.5		0.07	
5	15.8		0.07	

† Normalized to same total intensity as calculated values.

1,2-*Chlorobromoethane.* Chlorobromoethane (CH_2ClCH_2Br) is characteristic of a rather different class of molecules giving A_2B_2 spectra. Its proton spectrum at 40 Mc/sec is shown in Fig. 6-18.

It is well known that molecules of this type may exist in either of two isomeric forms. One possibility is that the two halogen atoms may be trans relative to the CC bond, and the alternative is that they are gauche, or skew. If the molecule were in one of the two gauche forms for a sufficiently long period, it would give a spectrum of four nonequivalent nuclei (type ABCD). In fact, the observed spectrum is completely symmetrical, from which we may deduce that the molecule either is in the trans form or is rotating from one configuration to another sufficiently rapidly for it to be necessary to replace the coupling constants by their averaged values.† It should be noted, however, that even if the molecule is rotating about the central bond, the average spin coupling constants between one of the A protons and the two B protons are not necessarily equal (i.e., $J \neq J'$). The fact that the observed spectrum contains at least 20 lines confirms this, since for the case where $J = J'$ there would be only 14 separate lines, as discussed earlier in this section.

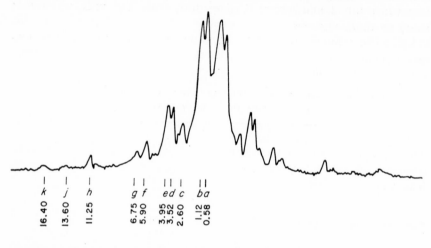

$H \longrightarrow$

FIG. 6-18. Complete proton resonance spectrum of 1,2-chlorobromoethane (liquid) at 40 Mc/sec. Energies are given in cycles per second measured from the band center. (Pople, Schneider, and Bernstein.[342])

In the analysis of this spectrum, it is assumed as a preliminary hypothesis that the coupling constants between protons attached to the same carbon atom will be greater than those between protons attached to different carbon atoms. This implies that the constant K ($= J_A + J_B$) is large. Inspection of the complete matrix (Table 6-16) then shows that the basic function $3s_0$ will not mix with $1s_0$, $2s_0$, and $4s_0$. As a consequence of this, transitions 5 and 8 are forbidden, so the number of A transitions is reduced from 12 to 10 as observed. A further consequence is that all the *symmetrical* energy levels become independent of L ($= J - J'$), so that the positions of the symmetrical transitions 1, 2, 3, 4, 6, and 7 will be the same as the spectrum with $J = J'$ (Table 6-21). The outermost signal at k is therefore assigned to transition 1, and signal b to transition 3. From the explicit expressions for the energies of these transitions (Table 6-20) we get the values of N ($= J + J'$) and the chemical shift $\nu_0\delta$.

† A more detailed discussion of the effects of rotational isomerism on the spectra of substituted ethanes is given in Sec. 13-4.

Although K $(= J_A + J_B)$ is large, the difference M $(= J_A - J_B)$ may be small and the antisymmetric transitions 9, 10, 11, and 12 may all be distinct. The energy expressions given in Table 6-20 show that they should consist of two equally spaced pairs. These are most satisfactorily assigned to signals g, f, d, and c, leading to numerical values for M and L $(= J - J')$. It is then possible to calculate the positions of the remaining lines, and it is found that signals a, e, h, and j correspond to transitions 4, 6, 2, and 7 within experimental error, providing an internal check on the assignment.

Values for the chemical-shift and spin coupling constants for this molecule are

$$\nu_0 \delta = \pm 8.9 \text{ cycles/sec}$$
$$N = J + J' = 15.2 \text{ cycles/sec}$$
$$L = J - J' = \pm 3.1 \text{ cycles/sec}$$
$$M = J_A - J_B = \pm 1.0 \text{ cycle/sec} \tag{6-74}$$

The value of K $(= J_A + J_B)$ cannot be determined, but it appears to be large enough to prevent any significant mixing of the basic function $3s_0$ with other functions.

6-8. Perturbation Methods

In general, spectra in which the signals from nonequivalent nuclei are closely spaced or overlapping must be analyzed by using the full solution of the secular equation. In many cases, however, the spacings of such signals are large enough for the spectrum to bear a close resemblance to a first-order multiplet pattern corresponding to large chemical shifts. Under these circumstances, a perturbation method may be more appropriate than a complete treatment.

Anderson[10] developed a perturbation theory for the spectra of several sets of equivalent nuclei A, B, C, . . . satisfying the condition that there is only one coupling constant between nuclei in any given pair of sets. This is just the condition under which first-order theory applies if the signals are sufficiently separated. As demonstrated in Sec. 6-4, such spectra are completely independent of the coupling constants *within* an equivalent set. These may therefore be ignored.

To begin with, let us consider two sets A and B containing n_A and n_B nuclei, respectively. If the common coupling constant is J_{AB}, then, following Sec. 6-4, the Hamiltonian may be written

$$\mathcal{H} = \mathcal{H}^{(0)} + \mathcal{H}^{(1)}$$
$$\mathcal{H}^{(0)} = \nu_A F_z(A) + \nu_B F_z(B)$$
$$\mathcal{H}^{(1)} = J_{AB} \mathbf{F}(A) \cdot \mathbf{F}(B) \tag{6-75}$$

where $\mathbf{F}(A)$ and $\mathbf{F}(B)$ are the total spins of the two sets [Eq. (6-42)]. The procedure is then to treat the spin coupling Hamiltonian $\mathcal{3C}^{(1)}$ as a perturbation of the energy levels and wave functions of $\mathcal{3C}^{(0)}$. First-order perturbation theory gives the simple multiplet rules derived in Sec. 6-4. Here we shall be concerned with splittings and displacements due to higher orders.

The construction of basic symmetry functions for a set of n_A equivalent nuclei was discussed in Sec. 6-2. Since the operator $[\mathbf{F}(A)]^2$ commutes with $F_z(A)$, the wave functions can be chosen to be eigenfunctions of both operators. Consequently we shall label the basic functions by quantum numbers F_A and m_A, where $F_A(F_A + 1)$ is the eigenvalue of $[\mathbf{F}(A)]^2$ and m_A the eigenvalue of $F_z(A)$. F_A can take positive values $\frac{1}{2}n_A$, $\frac{1}{2}n_A - 1$, . . . , and m_A any of the values F_A, $F_A - 1$, ... The basic symmetry functions for the set of n_B nuclei can be labeled by quantum numbers F_B, m_B in a similar manner. This classification is similar to that made on the basis of symmetry groups in Sec. 6-2. Thus, for two equivalent nuclei, the three symmetrical functions (Table 6-1) correspond to $F = 1$ and $m = 0, \pm 1$, while the antisymmetrical function $(\alpha\beta - \beta\alpha)/\sqrt{2}$ has $F = 0$, $m = 0$. It is important to note, however, that the states of sets of more than two equivalent nuclei are not *completely* specified by the quantum numbers F and m. For a set of three nuclei, for example, F can take values $3/2$ or $1/2$. There are four states with $F = 3/2$ corresponding to the four possible values of m, but there are *two* states with $F = 1/2$, $m = 1/2$ and *two* with $F = 1/2$, $m = -1/2$. Referring to the functions given explicitly in Table 6-2, these are the degenerate pairs $(E)_{1/2}$ and $(E)_{-1/2}$. This must be taken into account when intensities are calculated.

Each state can now be labeled by the four quantum numbers F_A, m_A, F_B, and m_B corresponding to the values in the limit when the chemical shift is large. Application of first-order perturbation theory then gives

$$\mathcal{E}(F_A, m_A, F_B, m_B) = \nu_A m_A + \nu_B m_B + J_{AB} m_A m_B \qquad \text{to 1st order} \qquad (6\text{-}76)$$

In second-order perturbation theory, account must be taken of the mixing of pairs of states between which there is an off-diagonal matrix element.† This leads to a second-order energy[52,10]

$$\mathcal{E}^{(2)}(F_A, m_A, F_B, m_B) = \frac{1}{2}\frac{J_{AB}^2}{\nu_A - \nu_B}\{m_A[F_B(F_B + 1) - m_B^2]$$
$$- m_B[F_A(F_A + 1) - m_A^2]\} \qquad (6\text{-}77)$$

This must be added to Eq. (6-76) to give the corrected energy.

---

† The only nonvanishing off-diagonal matrix elements can be evaluated by using shift operators (Condon and Shortley[97]) and are

$$\langle F_A, m_A \pm 1, F_B, m_B \mp 1 | \mathbf{F}(A) \cdot \mathbf{F}(B) | F_A, m_A, F_B, m_B \rangle$$
$$= [(F_A - m_A)(F_A + m_A + 1)(F_B + m_B)(F_B - m_B + 1)]^{1/2}$$

The transition energy between states $(F_A, m_A - 1, F_B, m_B)$ and (F_A, m_A, F_B, m_B) (an A transition) is obtained by subtracting the corresponding total energies and is given by

$$\nu = \nu_A + J_{AB}m_B + \frac{1}{2}\frac{J_{AB}{}^2}{\nu_A - \nu_B}[F_B(F_B + 1) - m_B(m_B + 1) \\ + 2m_Am_B] \quad (6\text{-}78)$$

The first two terms on the right-hand side of this equation give the simple multiplets. The third correcting term gives rise to some splitting.

This result is easily extended to any number of equivalent sets satisfying the same conditions. If the sets are denoted by R $(= A, B, \ldots)$, the modified form of Eq. (6-78) for the frequency of an A transition is†

$$\nu = \nu_A + \sum_{R(\neq A)} J_{AR}m_R + \frac{1}{2}\sum_{R(\neq A)}\frac{J_{AR}{}^2}{\nu_A - \nu_R}[F_R(F_R + 1) \\ - m_R(m_R + 1) + 2m_Am_R] \quad (6\text{-}79)$$

The relative intensity of the corresponding transition is, to the same order,

$$(F_A - m_A + 1)(F_A + m_A)\left(1 - 2\sum_{R(\neq A)}\frac{J_{AR}m_R}{\nu_A - \nu_R}\right) \quad (6\text{-}80)$$

The perturbation theory can be extended to higher orders. The general third-order result was given by Anderson.[10] In the present notation and units, his result is that the second- and third-order energy corrections to a state with quantum numbers $F_A, m_A, F_B, m_B, \ldots$ are

$$\mathcal{E}^{(2)}(F_A, m_A, F_B, m_B, \ldots) \\ = \frac{1}{4}\sum_R \sum_{S(\neq R)}\frac{J_{RS}{}^2}{\nu_R - \nu_S}[m_R(F_S{}^2 + F_S - m_S{}^2) \\ - m_S(F_R{}^2 + F_R - m_R{}^2)] \quad (6\text{-}81)$$

$$\mathcal{E}^{(3)}(F_A, m_A, F_B, m_B, \ldots) \\ = -\sum_R \sum_{S(\neq R)}\frac{J_{RS}{}^3 G(R)}{2(\nu_R - \nu_S)^2}[\tfrac{1}{2}G(S) + m_S(1 - m_S + m_R)] \\ -\sum_R \sum_{S(\neq R)} \sum_{T(\neq R,S)}\frac{J_{RS}{}^2 J_{RT}m_T}{2(\nu_R - \nu_S)^2}[G(S)m_R - G(R)m_S] \\ -\sum_R \sum_{S(\neq R)} \sum_{T(\neq R,S)}\frac{J_{RS}J_{ST}J_{TR}G(T)m_Rm_S}{2(\nu_S - \nu_T)(\nu_T - \nu_R)} \quad (6\text{-}82)$$

where

$$G(R) = (F_R - m_R)(F_R + m_R + 1) \quad (6\text{-}83)$$

† This formula differs in notation from that given by Anderson,[10] primarily because Anderson measures all energies in radians per second instead of cycles per second. Also he uses the symbol J_{AR} for the spin coupling constant in radians per second.

The third-order correction to a transition energy is the difference between the energies $\mathcal{E}^{(3)}$ of the states involved.

a. Five Nuclei A_2B_3. The general formulas of the previous section can be illustrated by a calculation of the spectrum of two sets of equivalent nuclei A_2B_3, with all AB coupling constants equal. This is of some interest, because a spectrum of this type is frequently found for ethyl compounds CH_3CH_2X, where X has nuclei which do not couple with the protons. (The effective symmetry is increased by rapid rotation about the CC bond.)

The quantum number F_A can take the value 0 or 1, while F_B can be 1/2 or 3/2. According to the second-order expression (6-78), the fre-

TABLE 6-23. TRANSITION ENERGIES AND INTENSITIES FOR A_2B_3
CALCULATED TO SECOND ORDER

m_A	(F_B, m_B)	First-order energy	Second-order energy†	Intensity
\multicolumn{5}{c}{A Transitions, $m_A - 1$ to m_A}
1	(3/2,3/2)	$\frac{3}{2}J$	$\frac{3}{2}J^2/\nu_0\delta$	$2(1 - 3J/\nu_0\delta)$
0	(3/2,3/2)	$\frac{3}{2}J$	0	$2(1 - 3J/\nu_0\delta)$
1	(3/2,1/2)	$\frac{1}{2}J$	$2J^2/\nu_0\delta$	$2(1 - J/\nu_0\delta)$
0	(3/2,1/2)	$\frac{1}{2}J$	$\frac{3}{2}J^2/\nu_0\delta$	$2(1 - J/\nu_0\delta)$
1	(1/2,1/2)	$\frac{1}{2}J$	$\frac{1}{2}J^2/\nu_0\delta$	$4(1 - J/\nu_0\delta)\ddagger$
0	(1/2,1/2)	$\frac{1}{2}J$	0	$4(1 - J/\nu_0\delta)\ddagger$
0	(3/2,−1/2)	$-\frac{1}{2}J$	$2J^2/\nu_0\delta$	$2(1 + J/\nu_0\delta)$
1	(3/2,−1/2)	$-\frac{1}{2}J$	$\frac{3}{2}J^2/\nu_0\delta$	$2(1 + J/\nu_0\delta)$
0	(1/2,−1/2)	$-\frac{1}{2}J$	$\frac{1}{2}J^2/\nu_0\delta$	$4(1 + J/\nu_0\delta)\ddagger$
1	(1/2,−1/2)	$-\frac{1}{2}J$	0	$4(1 + J/\nu_0\delta)\ddagger$
0	(3/2,−3/2)	$-\frac{3}{2}J$	$\frac{3}{2}J^2/\nu_0\delta$	$2(1 + 3J/\nu_0\delta)$
1	(3/2,−3/2)	$-\frac{3}{2}J$	0	$2(1 + 3J/\nu_0\delta)$

m_B	(F_A, m_A)	First-order energy	Second-order energy	Intensity
\multicolumn{5}{c}{B Transitions, $m_B - 1$ to m_B}
−1/2	(1,1)	J	$\frac{1}{2}J^2/\nu_0\delta$	$3(1 + 2J/\nu_0\delta)$
1/2	(1,1)	J	$-\frac{1}{2}J^2/\nu_0\delta$	$6(1 + 2J/\nu_0\delta)\ddagger$
3/2	(1,1)	J	$-\frac{3}{2}J^2/\nu_0\delta$	$3(1 + 2J/\nu_0\delta)$
3/2, 1/2, −1/2	(1,0)	0	$-\frac{1}{2}J^2/\nu_0\delta$	$12\ddagger$
3/2, 1/2, −1/2	(0,0)	0	0	$12\ddagger$
3/2	(1,−1)	$-J$	$\frac{1}{2}J^2/\nu_0\delta$	$3(1 - 2J/\nu_0\delta)$
1/2	(1,−1)	$-J$	$-\frac{1}{2}J^2/\nu_0\delta$	$6(1 - 2J/\nu_0\delta)\ddagger$
−1/2	(1,−1)	$-J$	$-\frac{3}{2}J^2/\nu_0\delta$	$3(1 - 2J/\nu_0\delta)$

† $\nu_0\delta$ is written for the chemical shift $\nu_A - \nu_B$.

‡ These intensities arise from the superposition of more than one transition with the quantum numbers specified.

quency of an A transition between states $m_A - 1$ and m_A depends on the quantum numbers m_A, F_B, and m_B.   A similar result holds for B transitions.   The first- and second-order contributions for all transitions are listed in Table 6-23, together with the intensity according to Eq. (6-80) (noting that some transitions entered in the table are really superpositions of degenerate transitions).

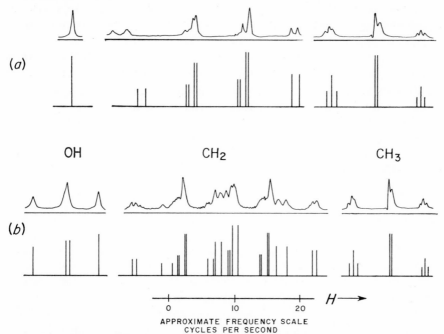

FIG. 6-19. High-resolution spectrum of the hydroxyl, methylene, and methyl protons of ethyl alcohol in sequence from left to right (a) for acidified alcohol and (b) for pure alcohol.   Theoretical spectra calculated by second-order perturbation theory are given below.   (Arnold.[20])

Ethyl Alcohol.   The most ambitious analysis carried out by perturbation methods is that of the high-resolution spectrum of ethyl alcohol by Arnold.[20]   As mentioned in Sec. 5-4, a trace of acid is sufficient to cause rapid exchange of the hydroxyl protons of different molecules, so that the spectrum of the remaining protons will be of the A_2B_3 type just described. The upper part of Fig. 6-19 shows the observed spectrum at 30 Mc/sec together with that calculated from the second-order expressions given in Table 6-23.   Arnold also carried out a calculation to the third order, which gave a further improvement in the agreement with the experimental spectrum.

The lower part of Fig. 6-19 shows the spectrum of purified ethyl alcohol, in which hydroxyl-proton exchange does not take place rapidly enough to remove the effects of spin coupling. The spectrum of the methylene protons then becomes considerably more complicated, but the details are satisfactorily reproduced by the second-order calculation of Arnold.

6-9. Miscellaneous Aids in Spectral Analysis

When spectra become highly complex and a complete or perturbation-type analysis is difficult, there are a number of ways in which a limited amount of information about chemical shifts and spin coupling constants can be obtained. In other cases, the spectra may be too simple to give information required, as with coupling constants between nuclei of an equivalent set (having the same chemical shift). In this section we shall describe three techniques which have proved of value in these respects. They are the measurement of spectral moments, the use of simultaneous irradiation by two frequencies, and measurements on isotopically substituted molecules.

   a. The Use of Moments. Even for very complicated spectra, it may be possible to derive information from the *spectral moments*. The theory was developed by Anderson and McConnell[14] and is in many ways similar to the work of Van Vleck[446] on the moments of spectra due to dipole interaction in solids. Before proceeding to this theory, however, it should be emphasized that, in experimental measurements of spectral moments, particular care must be taken to avoid saturation. Also, drifts in the radio frequency or the magnetic field or any nonlinearity of the sweep will cause distortion and lead to errors.

The moment theory is simplest when applied to the spectrum of a group of nuclei of one species, for which the relative chemical shifts are of the same order as the coupling constants involved. Anderson and McConnell refer to such a system as a single *basic group* of nuclei and the spectrum as a single *basic multiplet*. (If more than one species of nucleus is involved, or if there are large chemical shifts, it will be possible to divide the complete spectrum into several basic multiplets and to measure moments for each.)

If the various lines of the spectrum are measured on a frequency scale relative to an arbitrary origin, ν_{nm} being the transition frequency from state m to state n and L_{mn} its intensity, the rth moment is defined as

$$\langle \nu^r \rangle = \frac{\sum_{mn} (\nu_{mn})^r L_{mn}}{\sum_{mn} L_{mn}} \tag{6-84}$$

This definition is clearly independent of the choice of units for line intensities. In practice the intensities can be estimated from the areas under the absorption curves.

The first moment $\langle \nu \rangle$ gives the mean frequency, or center, of the multiplet. The positions of other lines can then be measured relative to the mean by quantities

$$\Delta \nu = \nu - \langle \nu \rangle \qquad (6\text{-}85)$$

Moments relative to the mean $\langle (\Delta \nu)^r \rangle$ are then connected with the moments $\langle \nu^r \rangle$ by the well-known formulas

$$\langle \Delta \nu \rangle = 0$$
$$\langle (\Delta \nu)^2 \rangle = \langle \nu^2 \rangle - \langle \nu \rangle^2$$
$$\langle (\Delta \nu)^3 \rangle = \langle \nu^3 \rangle - 3\langle \nu^2 \rangle \langle \nu \rangle + 2\langle \nu \rangle^3$$
$$\langle (\Delta \nu)^4 \rangle = \langle \nu^4 \rangle - 4\langle \nu^3 \rangle \langle \nu \rangle + 6\langle \nu^2 \rangle^2 - 3\langle \nu \rangle^4 \qquad (6\text{-}86)$$

Anderson and McConnell[14] derived expressions for these moments relative to the mean in terms of the chemical shifts and spin coupling constants. It is also convenient to measure chemical shifts relative to the mean frequency $\langle \nu \rangle$. Thus if ν_i is the frequency for nucleus i in the absence of the spin coupling Hamiltonian, we define

$$\Delta \nu_i = \nu_i - \langle \nu \rangle \qquad (6\text{-}87)$$

If there are N nuclei in the group, each with spin I, Anderson and McConnell showed that the lower moments are given by†

$$\langle \Delta \nu \rangle = N^{-1} \sum_i \Delta \nu_i = 0 \qquad (6\text{-}88)$$

$$\langle (\Delta \nu)^2 \rangle = N^{-1} \sum_i (\Delta \nu_i)^2 \qquad (6\text{-}89)$$

$$\langle (\Delta \nu)^3 \rangle = N^{-1} \sum_i (\Delta \nu_i)^3 \qquad (6\text{-}90)$$

$$\langle (\Delta \nu)^4 \rangle = N^{-1} \left[\sum_i (\Delta \nu_i)^4 + \tfrac{2}{3} I(I+1) \sum_{i<j} (\Delta \nu_i - \Delta \nu_j)^2 J_{ij}^2 \right] \qquad (6\text{-}91)$$

Equation (6-88) indicates that the mean frequency of the observed spectrum is also the mean of the signals unperturbed by spin coupling. Equations (6-89) and (6-90) show that both the second and third moments relative to the mean are also independent of the coupling constants. It is not until the fourth moment (6-91) that J_{ij} appears.

† Anderson and McConnell actually developed their theory in terms of angular frequencies and used the symbol J to denote spin coupling constant in radians per second rather than cycles per second. The notation used here is altered to be consistent with the earlier part of the chapter.

One Basic Multiplet with Two Nonequivalent Groups of Nuclei. The application of the moment method is simplest for systems with only two distinct nonequivalent groups of nuclei. If there are N_1 and N_2 nuclei in these groups and $\Delta\nu_1$ and $\Delta\nu_2$ are the corresponding frequency displacements from the mean, then

$$N_1 \Delta\nu_1 + N_2 \Delta\nu_2 = 0 \qquad (6\text{-}92)$$

The second moment equation (6-89) can be written in the form

$$(\Delta\nu_1 - \Delta\nu_2)^2 = N_1^{-1}N_2^{-1}(N_1 + N_2)^2 \langle (\Delta\nu)^2 \rangle \qquad (6\text{-}93)$$

Thus, the magnitude of the chemical shift $\Delta\nu_1 - \Delta\nu_2$ can be calculated immediately from a measurement of the second moment.

The fourth moment equation (6-91) can be written

$$\frac{\sum\limits_{i}^{N_1}\sum\limits_{j}^{N_2} J_{ij}^2}{(\Delta\nu_1 - \Delta\nu_2)^2} = \frac{3N_1^2N_2^2}{2I(I+1)(N_1+N_2)^3} \left\{ \frac{\langle (\Delta\nu)^4 \rangle}{\langle (\Delta\nu)^2 \rangle^2} - \frac{N_1^3 + N_2^3}{N_1N_2(N_1+N_2)} \right\} \qquad (6\text{-}94)$$

The fourth moment, therefore, gives the *mean-square coupling constant* between the nuclei in *different* chemical groups. It is still independent of the coupling constants between nuclei in the same chemical group.

Anderson and McConnell applied this method to the 30-Mc/sec proton spectrum of *o*-dichlorobenzene.

This is an A_2B_2 system, so that Eqs. (6-93) and (6-94) may be applied with $N_1 = N_2 = 2$. In this way it was found that

$$|\Delta\nu_1 - \Delta\nu_2| = 7.8 \pm 0.5 \text{ cycles/sec}$$
$$(J_{12}^2 + J_{13}^2)^{1/2} = 8.1 \pm 0.5 \text{ cycles/sec} \qquad (6\text{-}95)$$

A complete analysis of the proton resonance spectrum of this molecule at 40 Mc/sec was carried out independently by Pople, Schneider, and Bernstein.[342] They found the chemical shift to be 0.25 ppm and $J_{12} = 8.3$ cycles/sec, $J_{13} = 1.7$ cycles/sec, $J_{23} = 8.3$ cycles/sec, $J_{14} \approx 0$. The results obtained by the moment method are thus in satisfactory agreement with these values.

One Basic Multiplet with Three Nonequivalent Groups of Nuclei. If there are three distinct chemical groups of N_1, N_2, N_3 nuclei all contributing to one basic multiplet, complete analysis is difficult because of

the large number of spin coupling constants. The moment method can
be used, however, to obtain information about chemical shifts from the

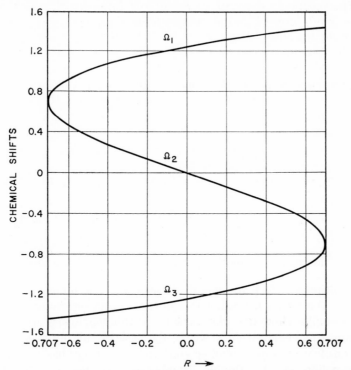

FIG. 6-20. Chemical shifts of a spin system containing three chemical groups with
$N_1 = N_2 = N_3$. (Anderson and McConnell.[14])

second and third moments, which are independent of the coupling constants. The three equations for $\Delta\nu_1$, $\Delta\nu_2$, and $\Delta\nu_3$ are

$$N_1 \Delta\nu_1 + N_2 \Delta\nu_2 + N_3 \Delta\nu_3 = 0$$
$$N_1(\Delta\nu_1)^2 + N_2(\Delta\nu_2)^2 + N_3(\Delta\nu_3)^2 = N\langle(\Delta\nu)^2\rangle$$
$$N_1(\Delta\nu_1)^3 + N_2(\Delta\nu_2)^3 + N_3(\Delta\nu_3)^3 = N\langle(\Delta\nu)^3\rangle \qquad (6\text{-}96)$$

These equations are best solved graphically for a given set of N_1, N_2, N_3.
It is convenient to define a reduced third moment

$$R = \langle(\Delta\nu)^3\rangle\langle(\Delta\nu)^2\rangle^{-\frac{3}{2}} \qquad (6\text{-}97)$$

and a reduced chemical shift

$$\Omega_i = \Delta\nu_i\langle(\Delta\nu)^2\rangle^{-\frac{1}{2}} \qquad (6\text{-}98)$$

Ω_i is then a function of R only. The function is illustrated in Fig. 6-20
for the case $N_1 = N_2 = N_3$. It would apply, in particular, to three non-

equivalent nuclei ABC.   For each value of R there are three values of Ω, giving the three chemical shifts.   Similar curves for other values of N_1, N_2, and N_3 are also given by Anderson and McConnell.[14]   The solution of Eq. (6-96), however, is not always unique.

Moments for Several Basic Multiplets.   If there is more than one basic multiplet (arising from two nuclear species or well-separated signals), an extended version of this theory can be applied to the moments of each multiplet separately.   If the nuclei giving rise to the basic multiplet under consideration are also coupled to other groups, the formulas for the first three moments become

$$\langle \Delta \nu \rangle = N^{-1} \sum_i \Delta \nu_i = 0 \tag{6-99}$$

$$\langle (\Delta \nu)^2 \rangle = N^{-1} \left[\sum_i (\Delta \nu_i)^2 + \tfrac{1}{3} \sum_i \sum_m{}^* I_m(I_m + 1)J_{im}{}^2 \right] \tag{6-100}$$

$$\langle (\Delta \nu)^3 \rangle = N^{-1} \left[\sum_i (\Delta \nu_i)^3 + \sum_i \sum_m{}^* I_m(I_m + 1) \, \Delta \nu_i \, J_{im}{}^2 \right] \tag{6-101}$$

where $\sum_m{}^*$ indicates summation over all nuclei which give rise to other basic multiplets. I_m is the spin of nucleus m.   The summation over i is still over the nuclei belonging to the basic group under consideration. These formulas show that the second and third moments are no longer determined by chemical shifts within the basic group, but also have contributions from the spin coupling constants with other basic groups.

b. Simplification by Double Irradiation.   An important technique which is of some assistance in simplifying a complex spectrum is the double-irradiation method due originally to Bloch.[50]   The aim is to remove the effect of some spin coupling by the application of a second rf field in addition to the one used for observation.   The method is applicable if the chemical shift is large compared with spin coupling constants; it consists in disturbing one group of nuclei with a strong rf field close to their corresponding resonance frequency.   This leads to saturation and frequent transitions between the states of these nuclei, so that they become effectively decoupled from the remaining nuclei.   A full theory of the effect, due to Bloom and Shoolery,[63] will be described in Sec. 10-3.

A number of examples of the application of double irradiation in spectral analysis were given by Anderson.[10]   The proton spectrum of 2,3-dibromopropene at 30.5 Mc/sec is shown in Fig. 6-21.   This clearly shows three groups of nonequivalent protons, the doublet to the right (group C) corresponding to the CH_2Br protons, which become equivalent by virtue of internal rotation.   The other two signals (groups B and A) correspond to the two protons attached to the double bond.   These do not appear as a simple AB quartet, however, because of the complicating effect of coupling with the —CH_2Br group. This complication, however, was removed by Anderson by using the double-irradiation technique. Figure 6-21b shows groups B and A before a large rf field was applied to

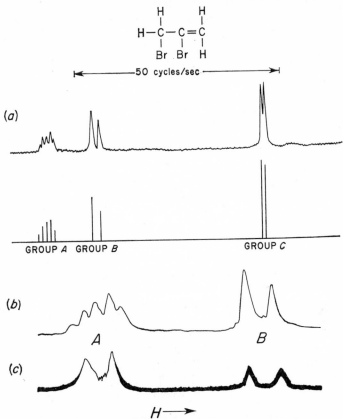

FIG. 6-21. Proton spectrum of 2,3-dibromopropene at 30.5 Mc/sec, including the effect of double irradiation. (Anderson.[10])

group C. Figure 6-21c shows the corresponding region while the additional field was present. This now shows the characteristic spectrum of two protons without any effect of coupling with other nuclei.

Other examples of the application of the double-irradiation method to simplify the interpretation of spectra, particularly those of the borohydrides, will be given in Chap. 12.

c. Isotopic Substitution in Complex Molecules. Some help in the analysis of a complex spectrum may often be obtained by comparison with the spectrum of an isotopically substituted molecule. The most important instance, of course, is the substitution of hydrogen by deuterium.   Isotopic substitution has only a very minor effect on the electronic structure of a molecule, so the chemical shifts of remaining nuclei will be practically unaltered.   If the isotope substituted has zero spin, all complications due to spin coupling with it will be removed.   Deuterons are not in this category, but they often fill the role of a nonmagnetic substituent, presumably because spin coupling is eliminated by quadrupole relaxation (Sec. 10-3).   Deuteration is of use both in identifying proton signals (by

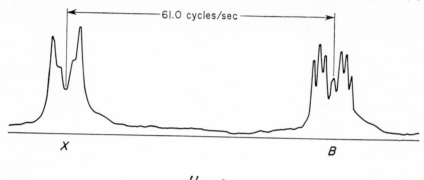

Fig. 6-22. Proton spectrum of 4d-pyridine at 40 Mc/sec.   (Schneider, Bernstein, and Pople.[401])

observing which disappear) and in simplifying the spectra of those that remain.

A number of deuterated pyridines have been used to assist in the analysis of the complex proton spectrum of pyridine.[401]   This is an exam-

$$\begin{array}{c} 4 \\ 5 \diagup \diagdown 3 \\ 6 \diagdown_{N} \diagup 2 \end{array}$$

ple of an AB_2X_2 system; for the signals from the 2 and 6 protons are well separated from the remainder (see Fig. 11-17).   The absorption region due to the 3,4,5 protons is very complicated, but a direct determination of the 3,4 coupling constant and chemical shift can be made from the spectrum of 2,6-pyridine-d_2, which is an AB_2 example (no effects of coupling with deuterons being observable).   Another example is 4d-pyridine, the proton spectrum of which is shown in Fig. 6-22.   This is of type A_2X_2, and a partial analysis can be carried out by using the methods of Sec. 6-7.   It is interesting to note that the signals from the 3,5 positions do show additional structure presumably due to coupling with the deuteron in position 4.

d. Isotopic Substitution in Symmetrical Molecules.   As we have noted earlier in this chapter, coupling constants between nuclei in an equivalent set cannot be determined from the nuclear resonance spectrum. It may still be possible to find these constants, however, by replacing one or more members of the equivalent set by an isotope, and using the theoretical rule (Chap. 8) that the coupling constants are proportional to the products of the magnetogyric ratios and a factor depending only on the electronic structure. The electronic structure is practically unaffected by the isotopic substitution, so the unknown coupling constants are easily found.

The first application of this device was the determination of the proton coupling constant in H_2 from that observed[85] in HD. It has also been used by Gutowsky, Meyer, and McClure[170] to obtain proton coupling constants in CH_4 (12.4 ± 0.6 cycles/sec), CH_3CCl_3 (12.4 ± 0.6 cycles/sec), and C_2H_2 (9.1 ± 2.0 cycles/sec).

Another interesting method for determining coupling constants in symmetrical molecules has been described recently by Cohen, Sheppard, and Turner.[95] This makes use of an isotope of a species which is normally magnetically inactive. The method is best illustrated by the effect of C^{13} nuclei on the proton spectra of organic compounds. The principal isotope of carbon C^{12} has zero spin, and it does not affect the spectra of other nuclei. However C^{13} has spin 1/2 and, if present, will lead to further splittings, particularly for protons directly bonded to it. The spin coupling constant betweeen C^{13} and H directly bonded is usually of the order of 150 cycles/sec, considerably larger than proton-proton constants. In a sample of molecules with a single equivalent set of protons bonded to a single carbon atom, such as chloroform, therefore, the complete proton spectrum consists of a strong central line due to $C^{12}H_3Cl$ and a weak doublet (of about 150 cycles/sec spacing) centered in the same position due to the protons in $C^{13}H_3Cl$ in natural abundance (~1 per cent). The intensity of these weak signals can be enhanced by using samples enriched in C^{13}.

If the molecule contains more than one carbon atom, the components of the doublet sometimes possess fine structure due to proton-proton coupling. A good example investigated by Cohen, Sheppard, and Turner[95] is 1,4-dioxane ($OCH_2CH_2OCH_2CH_2$), the proton spectrum of which is shown in Fig. 6-23. In the molecule containing only C^{12}, all protons are equivalent by virtue of the rapid interchange of the two chair forms of the six-membered ring. However, there is about a 4 per cent concentration of molecules with one C^{13} nucleus which possess the grouping

$$H_2C^{13}\!\!-\!\!C^{12}H_2$$
$$\diagup \qquad\quad \diagdown$$
$$O \qquad\qquad\quad O$$

These give rise to the side signals shown in Fig. 6-23. These two sets of signals arise from protons bonded directly to C^{13}, one for C^{13} nuclei with α spin and the other for those with β spin. The corresponding signals from the other hydrogens (which would also show some fine structure) are presumably buried under the central peak. The effect of bonding a proton to a C^{13} nucleus with a definite spin is identical with giving it a chemical shift of $\pm J^*$ cycles/sec, where J^* is the corresponding $C^{13}H$ coupling constant, provided this coupling constant is large compared with

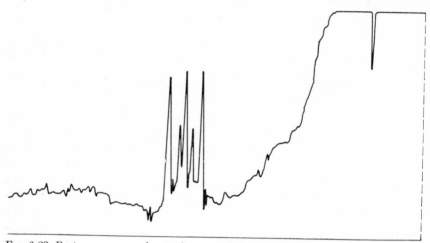

FIG. 6-23. Proton resonance due to the natural abundance of $C^{13}H_2$ groups in dioxane. The low-field portion of the spectrum is shown; the center of the much stronger resonance due to $C^{12}H_2$ groups is indicated by the dashed line on the right-hand side of the diagram. (Cohen, Sheppard, and Turner.[95])

other couplings in the molecule. Hence if we ignore coupling between protons on opposite sides of the molecule (i.e., separated by oxygen atoms), each of the multiplets observed is half of an A_2X_2 spectrum, and an analysis using the methods of Sec. 6-7 can be carried out. In this way, Cohen, Sheppard, and Turner were able to find the two coupling constants between protons attached to neighboring carbon atoms. Assuming positive values, they found $J = 2.7$ cycles/sec and $J' = 6.1$ cycles/sec. These must be interpreted as averages of the coupling constants between pairs of protons in both the chair forms. If it is assumed that the axial/equatorial and equatorial/equatorial constants are equal (both being between protons gauche with respect to the single bond) and differ from the axial/axial constant (this being trans), this leads to $J_{trans} = 9.4$ cycles/sec and $J_{gauche} = 2.7$ cycles/sec. These will be compared with other coupling constants in saturated six-membered rings in Chap. 14.

CHAPTER 7

THEORY OF CHEMICAL SHIFTS

7-1. Atomic Screening

The simplest system for which it is possible to calculate the magnetic shielding of a nucleus due to the induced electronic currents is a free atom with no orbital or spin angular momentum (i.e., in a ^1S state). It has already been shown in Sec. 2-2 that the effect of a uniform external magnetic field $\mathbf{H}$ is to cause a rotation of the whole electronic system about the direction of $\mathbf{H}$ with an angular frequency $eH/2mc$. At the nucleus, there will be a secondary magnetic field set up by these currents, which will be opposed to $\mathbf{H}$. The magnitude of this secondary field can be found by integrating over all elemental currents such as the one illustrated in Fig. 2-1. Using the notation in that figure, the element of current shown is of magnitude $-e^2H/4\pi mc$. It will give rise to a magnetic field at the nucleus of

$$-\frac{e^2 H \sin^2 \theta}{2mc^2 r} \tag{7-1}$$

Multiplying by an appropriate probability factor and integrating, the local field acting at the nucleus is therefore

$$\mathbf{H} - \frac{e^2\mathbf{H}}{3mc^2} \sum_i \overline{\left(\frac{1}{r_i}\right)} \tag{7-2}$$

This must be equal to $\mathbf{H}(1 - \sigma)$, where σ is the screening constant, so we obtain

$$\sigma = \frac{e^2}{3mc^2} \sum_i \overline{\left(\frac{1}{r_i}\right)} = \frac{e^2}{3mc^2} \int \frac{\rho(r)}{r}\, d\tau$$

$$= \frac{4\pi e^2}{3mc^2} \int_0^\infty r\rho(r)\, dr \tag{7-3}$$

where $\rho(r)$ is the electron density at a distance r from the nucleus. This important result was first obtained by Lamb[228] and is generally known as

Lamb's formula. Like the classical calculation of the diamagnetic susceptibility of an atom, it can be justified by a more rigorous quantum-mechanical argument to be presented shortly.

Equation (7-3) shows that the screening constant is proportional to the electrostatic potential energy of interaction between the nucleus and

TABLE 7-1. INTERNAL DIAMAGNETIC CORRECTION FOR NEUTRAL ATOMS[119]

Z	100σ	Z	100σ	Z	100σ
1	0.0018	32	0.273	63	0.693
2	0.0060	33	0.285	64	0.709
3	0.0101	34	0.296	65	0.724
4	0.0149	35	0.308	66	0.740
5	0.0199	36	0.321	67	0.756
6	0.0261	37	0.333	68	0.772
7	0.0325	38	0.345	69	0.788
8	0.0395	39	0.358	70	0.804
9	0.0464	40	0.371	71	0.820
10	0.0547	41	0.384	72	0.837
11	0.0629	42	0.397	73	0.853
12	0.0710	43	0.411	74	0.869
13	0.0795	44	0.425	75	0.885
14	0.0881	45	0.438	76	0.901
15	0.0970	46	0.452	77	0.917
16	0.106	47	0.465	78	0.933
17	0.115	48	0.478	79	0.949
18	0.124	49	0.491	80	0.965
19	0.133	50	0.504	81	0.982
20	0.142	51	0.517	82	0.998
21	0.151	52	0.531	83	1.01
22	0.161	53	0.545	84	1.03
23	0.171	54	0.559	85	1.05
24	0.181	55	0.573	86	1.06
25	0.191	56	0.587	87	1.08
26	0.202	57	0.602	88	1.10
27	0.214	58	0.616	89	1.11
28	0.226	59	0.631	90	1.13
29	0.238	60	0.647	91	1.15
30	0.249	61	0.662	92	1.16
31	0.261	62	0.678		

electrons. The most complete calculations using this formula are those of Dickinson,[119] who used Hartree-type self-consistent functions where available and interpolated elsewhere. His results for neutral atoms are reproduced in Table 7-1. They are estimated to be reliable to within 5 per cent except for the heaviest elements, where relativistic effects may be appreciable. It should be emphasized, however, that the figures are really applicable only to atoms in S states and may be completely wrong in molecular environments.

7-2. General Theory of Nuclear Screening in Molecules

If the nucleus is in a molecule so that the electrons are not free to move in circles around the direction of the applied magnetic field, the theoretical expression for the screening constant will be more complicated. The general expression for an isolated molecule which we shall now derive was first obtained by Ramsey.[364]

If we consider a molecule with a fixed nuclear configuration and apply a uniform magnetic field H in any direction, the secondary field $\mathbf{H'}$ due to the induced currents is not necessarily parallel to $\mathbf{H}$ at any nucleus. In other words, the relation between $\mathbf{H'}$ and $\mathbf{H}$ should be written

$$\mathbf{H'} = -\boldsymbol{\sigma}\mathbf{H} \tag{7-4}$$

where $\boldsymbol{\sigma}$ is a second-rank tensor characteristic of the position of the nucleus in the molecule. In general, only if the applied field is along one of the principal axes of this tensor will the secondary field be in the same direction. In practice, however, the position of the nuclear resonance signal in liquids is determined by the mean component of $\mathbf{H'}$ along the direction of $\mathbf{H}$ averaged over many rotations; for molecular rotation is rapid compared with any signal width due to anisotropy of the screening tensor. If we carry out this averaging, the tensor $\boldsymbol{\sigma}$ can be replaced by a scalar σ which is the mean of the three principal components:

$$\sigma = \tfrac{1}{3}(\sigma_{11} + \sigma_{22} + \sigma_{33}) \tag{7-5}$$

Although it is not directly measured in a liquid spectrum, it will be seen later in this chapter that significant anisotropy of $\boldsymbol{\sigma}$ is expected on theoretical grounds for a number of molecules. It could, in principle, be detected in solids under conditions in which dipole-dipole broadening did not dominate it; for the rotational averaging would not then be appropriate. An example might be the C^{13} resonance in CS_2. The only experimental determinations of anisotropy in $\boldsymbol{\sigma}$, however, are some very approximate ones of Gutowsky and Woessner[173] based on the observations of the spin-lattice relaxation time (Sec. 9-2).

To find the screening constant at a particular nucleus in a molecule with the external field in a certain direction (taken to be the z axis), we consider the perturbation of the energy of the system due to the joint action of the external field $\mathbf{H}$ and a parallel magnetic dipole $\boldsymbol{\mu}$ at the nuclear position under investigation. The total vector potential can then be written

$$\begin{aligned}\mathbf{A} &= \tfrac{1}{2}(\mathbf{H} \times \mathbf{r}) + r^{-3}(\boldsymbol{\mu} \times \mathbf{r}) \\ &= (\tfrac{1}{2}H + \mu r^{-3})(-y,x,0)\end{aligned} \tag{7-6}$$

where the origin is taken at the nucleus. If the energy of the system is now expanded in powers of H and μ, the cross term in μH is equal to the energy of interaction of the dipole $\mathbf{\mu}$ with the currents induced by the field $\mathbf{H}$. It can then be equated to $\sigma_{zz}\mu H$, σ_{zz} being the screening constant appropriate to this direction.

The Hamiltonian representing the perturbation is

$$\mathcal{K}_1 + \mathcal{K}_2 = \frac{e}{mc} \sum_j \mathbf{A}_j \cdot \mathbf{p}_j + \frac{e^2}{2mc^2} \sum_j \mathbf{A}_j{}^2 \tag{7-7}$$

where $\mathbf{p}_j$ is the momentum of electron j and $\mathbf{A}_j$ is the value of the vector potential (7-6) at the position of electron j. The change of energy that is of second order in μ and H is obtained by applying first-order perturbation theory to $\mathcal{K}_2$ and second-order theory to $\mathcal{K}_1$, giving

$$\delta\mathcal{E} = (0|\mathcal{K}_2|0) - \sum_{n(\neq 0)} \frac{(0|\mathcal{K}_1|n)(n|\mathcal{K}_1|0)}{E_n - E_0} \tag{7-8}$$

when the sum over n is over all excited states and $E_n - E_0$ is the excitation energy. Now

$$\mathbf{A}_j{}^2 = (\tfrac{1}{2}H + \mu r_j^{-3})^2 (x_j{}^2 + y_j{}^2) \tag{7-9}$$

and

$$\mathbf{A}_j \cdot \mathbf{p}_j = (\tfrac{1}{2}H + \mu r_j^{-3})(x_j p_{jy} - y_j p_{jx})$$

$$= -i\hbar(\tfrac{1}{2}H + \mu r_j^{-3})\left(x_j \frac{\partial}{\partial y_j} - y_j \frac{\partial}{\partial x_j}\right)$$

$$= -i\hbar(\tfrac{1}{2}H + \mu r_j^{-3})\frac{\partial}{\partial \phi_j} \tag{7-10}$$

where ϕ_j is the azimuthal angle for rotation about the z axis. If Eqs. (7-9) and (7-10) are substituted in the energy expression (7-8), the cross term in μH is easily picked out and we obtain

$$\sigma_{zz} = \frac{e^2}{2mc^2} \int \frac{x^2 + y^2}{r^3} \rho \, d\tau + \frac{e^2\hbar^2}{2m^2c^2} \sum_{n\neq 0} (E_n - E_0)^{-1}\left[\left(0\left|\Sigma_j \frac{\partial}{\partial \phi_j}\right|n\right) \times\right.$$

$$\left.\left(n\left|\Sigma_k r_k^{-3}\frac{\partial}{\partial \phi_k}\right|0\right) + \left(0\left|\Sigma_k r_k^{-3}\frac{\partial}{\partial \phi_k}\right|n\right)\left(n\left|\Sigma_j \frac{\partial}{\partial \phi_j}\right|0\right)\right] \tag{7-11}$$

This is Ramsey's formula; it is analogous to the general Van Vleck formula for molecular diamagnetism.[445] The mean screening constant follows by averaging over all directions.

The first term in the Ramsey formula is similar to the Lamb formula for atoms and becomes identical with it when averaged over all directions. It should be noted that the integral is taken over the entire molecule, not just the atom to which the nucleus belongs. So physically it corresponds to what the shielding would be if the whole electronic structure of the molecule rotated about the nucleus with the Larmor angular velocity, irrespective of the position of the other nuclei. The second term, which vanishes if the system is axially symmetric about the z axis, effectively corrects for the hindrance to this free rotation by the nuclear field. It corresponds closely to the paramagnetic term in the Van Vleck equation for the magnetic susceptibility.

To evaluate the second term precisely, it would be necessary to have detailed knowledge of the energies and wave functions of all the excited electronic states, including those in the continuum. A rather simpler, but less exact, form can be obtained if all the electronic excitation energies $E_n - E_0$ are replaced by an average value ΔE. The sum over excited states can then be carried out by using the quantum-mechanical sum rule leading to an expression for σ_{zz} involving only the ground-state wave functions

$$\sigma_{zz} = \frac{e^2}{2mc^2} \int \frac{x^2 + y^2}{r^3} \rho \, d\tau + \frac{e^2 \hbar^2}{m^2 c^2 \, \Delta E} \left(0 \left| \Sigma_{jk} r_k^{-3} \frac{\partial^2}{\partial \phi_j \, \partial \phi_k} \right| 0 \right) \quad (7\text{-}12)$$

Even in this form, however, the Ramsey formula is not suitable for the calculation of the screening constants in any but the smallest molecules. The principal difficulty lies in the fact that, for a large molecule, both terms become large and mainly cancel each other, as in the corresponding theory of the magnetic susceptibility. In order to deal with a large system, or to be able to make comparative studies of a series of related compounds, it is necessary to develop a theory which breaks up the total screening into local contributions in some manner.

7-3. Screening Constant of Molecular Hydrogen

The value of the screening constant for the protons in the hydrogen molecule has been the subject of a number of investigations. Apart from being the simplest molecular system to which any theory can be applied, the screening constant is of some practical importance because it provides a reference point for all other protons. Once the value of σ for molecular hydrogen is known, it is possible to obtain absolute screening constants for protons in any other molecule by measuring the chemical shift relative to hydrogen gas.

Early calculations of the value of σ were based purely on the Lamb formula and were inaccurate because of the neglect of the second term in the general formula (7-11). Ramsey[364] showed how the task of evaluating that complicated term could be avoided by appealing to other experimental data. In fact, he showed that, for linear molecules, the second term in Eq. (7-11) is proportional to the nuclear spin-rotational interaction constant, which can be measured experimentally (by molecular-beam techniques).   Combining the experimental value for the second part with a value of the Lamb term calculated from available wave functions, Ramsey obtained a value for the mean screening constant σ.   His values were slightly modified by Newell,[301] who obtained $\sigma = 32.1 \times 10^{-6}$ by using the Lamb term only and, after correcting for the second term, $\sigma = 26.6 \times 10^{-6}$.

More recently some calculations of the paramagnetic contribution to σ have been made by using a variational method rather than the perturbation procedure leading to the Ramsey formula.   The paramagnetic term really allows for the change in the wave function brought about by the external field, or the mixing between ground and excited states.   Das and Bersohn[109] suggested that this change could be found by writing the wave function in the presence of a magnetic field in the form

$$\psi = \psi_0(1 + \mathbf{g} \cdot \mathbf{H}) \qquad (7\text{-}13)$$

where ψ_0 is the unperturbed function and $\mathbf{g}$ is a vector function which can be varied to minimize the energy.   In the case of a hydrogen molecule, the wave function would be unmodified if the magnetic field is along the axis, but for fields perpendicular to the axis it is necessary to put in an explicit form for $\mathbf{g}$ containing parameters which can be varied. Using the center of the molecule as origin and the leading term in a power-series expansion for $\mathbf{g}$, Das and Bersohn[109] obtained† values of -5.3×10^{-6}, -4.9×10^{-6}, and -5.2×10^{-6} for the paramagnetic contribution to σ with the unperturbed wave functions due to Coulson, Wang, and Weinbaum, respectively.   This compares well with the indirect experimental value of Newell, -5.5×10^{-6}.

McGarvey[277] and Stephen[431] have carried out variational calculations of this type on other diatomic molecules and on the proton screening in CH bonds.   It seems likely that variational methods will prove more useful in accurate calculations of shielding constants than will direct application of the Ramsey formula.

7-4. Local Contributions to Nuclear Screening

We have already seen that the general formula of Ramsey [Eq. (7-11)] consists of two terms, the diamagnetic and paramagnetic terms, which largely cancel for a molecule of any size.   In fact, the terms would tend to $\pm \infty$ as the molecule became indefinitely large.   An important step forward was taken by Saika and Slichter,[393] who suggested that the

---

† Stephen[431] has pointed out that the formula for σ_{yy} given by Das and Bersohn is incorrect.   However, their numerical results appear to be correct.

screening could be approximately divided into separate atomic contributions.   They divided the total screening into three parts:

1. The diamagnetic correction for the atom in question
2. The paramagnetic correction for the atom in question
3. The contribution from other atoms

The physical significance of this separation can be appreciated if we consider the details of the current density induced by the external field. Suppose it is possible to divide up the total electron distribution into separate parts for individual atoms.   Then if the effect of the external

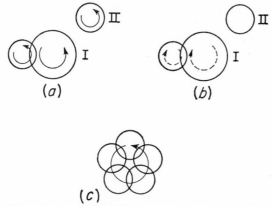

(a)   (b)

(c)

FIG. 7-1. Molecular currents.   (a) Local diamagnetic currents in a diatomic molecule I and atom II.   (b) Local paramagnetic currents in molecule I only.   (c) Interatomic ring currents in a cyclic molecule.

field were merely to rotate the electrons of each atom *about its own nucleus* with the Larmor frequency (Fig. 7-1a), the resultant screening of a nucleus due to the electrons of its own atom (effect 1) would be given by the Lamb formula, the integration being restricted to the local atomic electron density.   However, for an atom in a molecule the environment is not spherically symmetric, and there will be hindrance to these atomic circulations.   The resultant reduced circulation may be represented by a superposition of an atomic *paramagnetic* current on the diamagnetic part. This would vanish for an isolated atom (Fig. 7-1b).   The screening effect of an atomic paramagnetic current on the nucleus of the same atom is effect 2 of Saika and Slichter.   Effect 3 is the combined effect of diamagnetic and paramagnetic atomic currents on other atoms.   The mathematical basis of this breakdown into atomic currents has been discussed by Pople[337] and McConnell.[269]

The subdivision proposed by Saika and Slichter[393] does not take account of the possible magnetic effects of *interatomic* currents in which electrons flow from one atom to another.   We shall see later that interatomic currents can make a significant contribution to proton chemical shifts,[336] particularly in systems in which it is possible for electrons to flow round a ring of bonded atoms (Fig. 7-1c). We therefore complete the breakdown of the screening constant by adding:

4. The contribution from interatomic currents

a. **Fluorine Chemical Shifts.** Saika and Slichter[393] developed a quantitative theory of the atomic contributions to the chemical shifts observed in fluorine magnetic resonance experiments. The experimental observations of Gutowsky and Hoffman,[159] some of which are shown in Fig. 5-2a, showed a fairly good correlation with the electronegativity of the atom to which the fluorine is bonded, a covalently bonded F^{19} nucleus being less shielded than an ionic one. The chemical shift of the partly ionic molecule HF relative to the nonionic molecule F_2 is 625 ppm.

The simplest explanation of this shift would be in terms of the increase of electron density on the fluorine atom in the ionic compounds and the consequent increase in the diamagnetic Lamb term. This is quantitatively inadequate, however; for in going from F_2 to F^-, only a $2p$ electron is added. If the radial part of the p function is taken to be proportional to $re^{-Zr/2}$, the corresponding value of $\overline{r^{-1}}$ is $\frac{1}{4}Z$ (in atomic units). Taking the Slater value $Z = 5.2$, the contribution to the local diamagnetic shielding of this extra electron is only 2.3×10^{-5}. The actual change may be smaller still, since the other electrons move in expanded orbitals in the negative ion, leading to a reduction in $\overline{r^{-1}}$.

Saika and Slichter therefore suggested that the principal cause of chemical shifts in these compounds was variation of the paramagnetic term for the atom. This would be zero in the spherically symmetric F^- ion, and it would lead to a negative contribution to σ for a covalently bonded atom. To make a quantitative investigation, the molecule F_2 was dealt with in more detail. Since it is diatomic and in a $^1\Sigma_g^+$ state, the electron distribution is axially symmetric and there will be no paramagnetic contribution if the applied field is along the molecular axis. If the applied field is perpendicular to the axis, the ground state will be mixed with certain excited states, leading to a paramagnetic term. The excited state must be such that it can be mixed with the $^1\Sigma_g^+$ state by the rotational operator $\Sigma_k \, \partial/\partial\phi_k$. The appropriate symmetry is $^1\Pi_g$. In molecular-orbital terms a state of this symmetry can be obtained by the excitation of an electron from a bonding π orbital to the antibonding σ orbital which is unoccupied in the ground state. By using simple valence-bond wave functions for the ground and excited states, Saika and Slichter were able to calculate the matrix element of the rotational operator for one atom, neglecting any contribution from the other. This gives a paramagnetic contribution

$$\Delta\sigma^\perp = -\frac{e^2\hbar^2}{m^2c^2}\left\langle\frac{1}{r^3}\right\rangle_{\mathrm{av}}\frac{1}{\Delta E} \tag{7-14}$$

where $\langle 1/r^3\rangle_{\mathrm{av}}$ is the average of $1/r^3$ for $2p$ electrons and ΔE is the excitation energy from the $^1\Sigma_g^+$ to the $^1\Pi_g$ state. Since the corresponding quantity $\Delta\sigma^\|$ is zero, the paramagnetic contribution to the mean screening constant is

$$\Delta\sigma = \tfrac{2}{3}\Delta\sigma^\perp \tag{7-15}$$

Using 4.3 ev for ΔE (the same as to the $^1\Pi_u$ state) and $8.89a_0^{-3}$ for $\langle 1/r^3\rangle_{\mathrm{av}}$, where a_0 is the Bohr radius, Saika and Slichter obtained $\Delta\sigma = -20 \times 10^{-4}$. Actually the $^1\Pi_g$ state is probably at a higher energy than the $^1\Pi_u$, so this may well be an overestimate.

The calculated paramagnetic contribution should correspond to the difference between a purely covalent and purely ionic bond, and its sign is in agreement with the experimental fact that fluorine nuclei in F_2 are less shielded than in other fluorine compounds. For a bond with an intermediate amount of ionic character, it is reasonable to suppose that the paramagnetic contribution would be partly reduced, leading to an approximately linear dependence on the electronegativity of the neighboring atom or group. The magnitude $\Delta\sigma = -20 \times 10^{-4}$ is rather larger than the observed difference between F_2 and HF (-6.25×10^{-4}), but part of the discrepancy can be attributed to the partially covalent character of the HF bond. The fluorine resonance for F^- ions in aqueous solution actually appears on the low-field side of HF, which is not in agreement with the theory. However, the effect of hydration is not known.

The general conclusion derived from this study is that, for a number of fluorine compounds, variations in the local paramagnetic term are the dominant cause of chemical shifts, being more important than changes in the Lamb term. Further, again for fluorine compounds, this paramagnetic contribution is a shift toward low field (low screening), which is largest for covalent bonds.

It should be possible to extend this theory to other nuclei in the first row of the periodic table, such as carbon, nitrogen, and oxygen. Although no extensive quantitative work has been published, one general prediction can be made on the basis of formulas of the type used for fluorine. The paramagnetic contribution to the shift should be approximately inversely proportional to a mean electronic excitation energy ΔE, so that unsaturated organic compounds with low-lying excited states should be less screened (resonating at lower field) than saturated molecules. A correlation of this sort is apparent from the tabulations of C^{13}, N^{14}, and O^{17} shifts given in Chap. 12. For example, acetone has a low-lying electronic state arising from an $n \to \pi$ transition centered mainly on the carbonyl oxygen atom. Its O^{17} resonance (Fig. 12-11) is indeed found at lower field than for most other oxygen compounds.

b. Chemical Shifts in Cobalt Complexes. Another set of chemical-shift data which has been successfully interpreted along similar lines is the range of cobalt resonant frequencies for a number of octahedral cobaltic complexes. Surprisingly large chemical shifts in these compounds were observed by Proctor and Yu,[354] who attributed them to the temperature-independent paramagnetism. The fact that some complexes are weakly paramagnetic, in spite of having all electrons paired in the ground state, was attributed by Van Vleck[445] to the effect of mixing of the ground and low-lying excited states by the magnetic field.

A quantitative theory of the paramagnetism and the nuclear resonance shifts has been developed along these lines by Griffith and Orgel,[148] using crystal-field theory. In an octahedral field, the five atomic d orbitals split into a group of three which is of symmetry t_{2g} and a group of two of symmetry e_g, the t_{2g} orbitals being the more stable. The electronic configuration of the cobaltic ion is $(t_{2g})^6$ in the ground state with an over-all symmetry A_{1g}. There are various excited states with configuration $(t_{2g})^{6-n} (e_g)^n$, including a triply degenerate set of symmetry T_{1g}, which can be mixed with the ground state by a magnetic field. From the forms of the d orbitals, the matrix element of the operator $\Sigma_k \, \partial/\partial\phi_k$ can be evaluated for the T_{1g} function corresponding to the same direction. One finds

$$\left[\psi(A_{1g}) \left| \Sigma_k \frac{\partial}{\partial\phi_k} \right| \psi(T_{1g}) \right] = 2 \sqrt{2} \qquad (7\text{-}16)$$

In an octahedral system, there will be no anisotropy in σ, so we may evaluate the paramagnetic contribution to the screening constant for an arbitrary direction. Replacing r_k^{-3} by a mean value $\langle r^{-3} \rangle_{av}$ in the Ramsey formula (7-11) and neglecting contributions from the ligands, Griffith and Orgel[148] obtain a paramagnetic contribution from the T_{1g} state of

$$\Delta\sigma = - \frac{8e^2\hbar^2}{m^2c^2 \, \Delta E} \left\langle \frac{1}{r^3} \right\rangle_{av} \qquad (7\text{-}17)$$

where ΔE is the excitation energy which is known for many complexes from optical data. Comparison with the corresponding formula for fluorine [Eq. (7-14)] shows that cobalt paramagnetic shifts are substantially larger. The predictions of Eq. (7-17) are in very good agreement with the experimental data on cobalt resonances (see Sec. 12-10).

7-5. Proton Chemical Shifts

From the large number of measurements of proton chemical shifts, it is clear that the theoretical interpretation has to be more complex than for nuclei where the shielding is dominated by one effect. In the first place, the total range of chemical shifts is much smaller than for other nuclei, being of the order of 10^{-5} instead of 10^{-3} to 10^{-2} as for many other nuclei. This is clearly because the total number of electrons in the vicinity of a proton is so much smaller than for any other nucleus. Further, the local paramagnetic effect, which appears to give the dominant contribution to chemical shifts in the fluorine and cobalt compounds, will be far less important, because there are no low-lying p orbitals associated with a hydrogen atom and consequently matrix elements of the operators $\partial/\partial\phi$ will be small.

Secondly, the results of many measurements show that the proton chemical shifts often do not correlate with the ionic character of the bond as measured by properties such as acidity. This lack of correlation may be expected, however, since the total electron density on the hydrogen atom is relatively small and the proton will be more exposed to currents flowing in other parts of the molecule, which may not necessarily bear any direct relationship to electronegativity.

The contribution of local diamagnetic currents on the hydrogen atom itself can be estimated from the Lamb formula

$$\sigma_{\text{local diamagnetic}} = \frac{e^2}{3mc^2} \int \frac{\rho}{r} \, d\tau \tag{7-18}$$

where ρ is the electron density of the electrons associated with the hydrogen atom. This density is not a precisely defined quantity, of course, but it may be represented approximately by

$$\rho = \lambda\psi_{1s}^2 \tag{7-19}$$

where λ measures the effective number of electrons in the hydrogen $1s$ atomic orbital ψ_{1s} ($= \pi^{-\frac{1}{2}}e^{-r}$ in atomic units). The integral is easily evaluated, and we obtain

$$\sigma_{\text{local diamagnetic}} = \frac{\lambda e^2}{3mc^2 a_0} = 17.8\lambda \times 10^{-6} \tag{7-20}$$

The atomic orbital appropriate for a free hydrogen atom is probably more diffuse than that for hydrogen atoms in molecules. Experience derived from variational calculations on molecular hydrogen suggests that $\psi_{1s} \propto e^{-1.2r}$ (r in atomic units again) would be a better choice. This would raise the numerical result in Eq. (7-20) to $21.4\lambda \times 10^{-6}$. Unlike fluorine shifts, therefore, variations in the electron density around the proton give changes in the screening constant which are of the order of the experimentally observed range. Some correlation of the proton screening with the electronegativity of the group to which hydrogen is bonded is, therefore, not unexpected. It is difficult to estimate any local paramagnetic contributions arising from the nonspherical environment of the hydrogen atom. However, on account of the absence of low-lying $2p$ orbitals, it is likely to be much smaller than for other atoms. In any case, it is difficult to see any reason why such a contribution should not correlate strongly with the ionic character of the bond like the local diamagnetic term.

Inspection of data for proton chemical shifts, either in the vapor phase for simple hydrides (Table 5-1) or in the more extensive liquid-phase measurements discussed in Chap. 11, shows that, although there is some correlation with the electron density on the hydrogen atom for certain groups of compounds, there are many discrepancies. Examples which show a good correlation of this type are the methyl protons of the methyl halides and the α protons of the ethyl halides, which are progressively less shielded in the series iodide, bromide, chloride.[423] Again the hydroxyl proton of phenol is less shielded than that of an alcohol. Among the more striking anomalies, however, are the facts that the protons in water (in the gas phase) are more shielded than in ethane and that the acetylene signal appears between ethane and ethylene, although on grounds of ionic character and acidity, the acetylene proton would be expected to be the least shielded of the three hydrocarbon protons. Also, the α protons in the isopropyl halides become *more* shielded as the halogen electronegativity is increased.[72] To understand some of these apparent anomalies, it is necessary to consider the magnetic effects of currents flowing in other parts of the molecule.

a. The Neighbor-anisotropy Effect. If the electronic currents in a molecule are divided up into atomic contributions in the manner outlined at the beginning of Sec. 7-4, the proton magnetic moment is likely to experience a considerable magnetic field due to local circulations in the atom X to which it is bonded. The simplest way to estimate the magnitude of such an effect, adopted by Pople[338] and McConnell,[269] is to replace the currents on the other atom by point magnetic dipoles at the atom's center. This corresponds to dividing up the total magnetic susceptibility of a molecule into atomic contributions χ_{atomic} and, to find the secondary field at the proton due to other atoms, placing appropriate magnetic dipoles $\chi_{atomic}H_0$ at the positions of all other nuclei. This is only an approximation, of course, particularly for an immediate neighbor, but it should serve to give an order of magnitude for the other-atom contribution to the screening constant.

The secondary field due to the currents on the neighboring atom X will depend strongly on the relative directions of the XH line and the applied field H_0. Therefore the contribution to the screening tensor will be anisotropic. If the field is parallel to the XH line, the induced moment on the X atom will be $\chi_{atomic}^{\parallel} H_0$, where $\chi_{atomic}^{\parallel}$ is the contribution to the atomic susceptibility for this direction. (We shall suppose to begin with that this is one of the principal axes.) The secondary field at the proton due to this

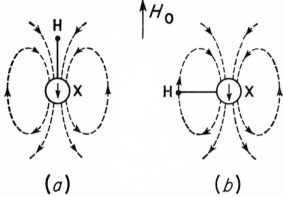

(a) (b)

FIG. 7-2. Secondary magnetic field due to diamagnetism of neighboring atom. (a) Primary field parallel to XH. (b) Primary field perpendicular to XH. Dashed lines represent magnetic lines of force.

moment (Fig. 7-2a) will be opposed to the primary field, so there will be a positive contribution to the shielding constant

$$\Delta\sigma^{\parallel} = -2R^{-3}\chi_{atomic}^{\parallel} \qquad (7\text{-}21)$$

where R is the XH distance and χ is negative. If the primary field is perpendicular to the XH line, however, the corresponding secondary field reinforces H_0 at the proton position and leads to a negative contribution to the shielding constant (Fig. 7-2b)

$$\Delta\sigma^{\perp} = R^{-3}\chi_{atomic}^{\perp} \qquad (7\text{-}22)$$

In general, there will be two perpendicular susceptibilities $\chi_{atomic}^{\perp}$ and $\chi_{atomic}^{\perp *}$. Because we observe only the mean value of σ averaged over all directions of H_0 relative to the XH line, the resultant contribution is

$$\Delta\sigma = -\tfrac{1}{3}R^{-3}(2\chi_{atomic}^{\parallel} - \chi_{atomic}^{\perp} - \chi_{atomic}^{\perp *}) \qquad (7\text{-}23)$$

In this approximation, therefore, there is a resultant effect only if the local atomic susceptibility on the neighboring atom is anisotropic. *If the neighboring atom has a greater diamagnetic susceptibility along the XH bond than perpendicular to it, the proton will experience increased shielding.*

A qualitatively similar conclusion also follows if the source of the anisotropy is located in the XH bond rather than on the X atom.

Equation (7-23) is easily extended to the case where the XH line is not one of the principal axes of the atomic susceptibility of atom X. Suppose the three principal susceptibilities of X are $\chi_{\text{atomic}}^{(i)}$ ($i = 1, 2, 3$) in directions which make angles γ_i with the XH line. Then, if the primary field H_0 is in the i direction, the induced moment will be $\chi_{\text{atomic}}^{(i)} H_0$ and the component of the secondary field at the proton in the direction of H_0 will be

$$R^{-3}\chi_{\text{atomic}}^{(i)}H_0(3\cos^2\gamma_i - 1) \qquad (7\text{-}24)$$

The mean contribution to the proton screening constant is obtained by averaging over the three directions i and is therefore

$$\Delta\sigma = \tfrac{1}{3}R^{-3} \sum_{i=1,2,3} \chi_{\text{atomic}}^{(i)}(1 - 3\cos^2\gamma_i) \qquad (7\text{-}25)$$

If two of the susceptibilities $\chi_{\text{atomic}}^{(i)}$ are equal, so that the X atom has an effective axis of symmetry, Eq. (7-25) simplifies to

$$\Delta\sigma = \tfrac{1}{3}R^{-3}\Delta\chi_{\text{atomic}}(1 - 3\cos^2\gamma) \qquad (7\text{-}26)$$

where $\Delta\chi_{\text{atomic}}$ is the anisotropy†

$$\Delta\chi_{\text{atomic}} = \chi_{\text{atomic}}\ (\| \text{ to axis}) - \chi_{\text{atomic}}\ (\perp \text{ to axis}) \qquad (7\text{-}27)$$

and γ is the angle between the axis of symmetry in X and the XH line.

The anisotropy of the local susceptibility on an atom can be separated into an anisotropy of the purely diamagnetic part (corresponding to the simple rotation with the Larmor frequency) and the paramagnetic part arising from the mixing of the ground state with excited electronic states by the magnetic field. In most atoms, the distribution of electrons is not likely to be very nonspherical, so it is expected that most of the anisotropy will arise from the paramagnetic part.

The effect of magnetic anisotropy on the neighboring atom is likely to be largest in linear molecules in $^1\Sigma$ states. Examples are the hydrogen halides, hydrogen cyanide, and acetylene. Since the electron distribution is axially symmetric about the molecular axis, there will be no paramagnetic contributions to the susceptibility if the applied field is parallel to the axis, whereas this is not so if the field is in a perpendicular direction. We expect, therefore, that the proton signals in linear molecules will be found further to high field (that is, with higher screening constants) than would be expected on grounds of electronegativity. Inspection of the simple hydride data in Table 5-1 shows that this does account for some of the anomalies.

† It should be noted that $\Delta\sigma$ is a *contribution to the average value* of the screening tensor, whereas $\Delta\chi$ is the anisotropy of the susceptibility tensor.

In particular the neighbor-anisotropy effect can account for the anomalous position of the acetylene-proton resonance in the series ethane, ethylene, and acetylene, characterizing sp^3, sp^2, and sp hybridization. In the gas-phase measurements (Table 5-1), it is found that the acetylene signal appears at 0.6×10^{-6} to the low-field side of ethane, whereas that for ethylene is 4.4×10^{-6} to the low-field side. In terms of the local circulations in the hydrogen atoms, it would be expected that the acetylene proton would appear at lowest field. However, acetylene is a linear molecule, so that its proton signal will be shifted to high field by the magnetic anisotropy of the neighboring carbon atom. The corresponding effect in the other two compounds is likely to be smaller. In the ethane molecule the shielding should be similar to that in methane, where the local circulation on the carbon atom has to be isotropic by symmetry. This theory predicts that the anisotropy of the proton-screening-constant tensor itself should be greater in acetylene.

Unfortunately, no data are available on the principal magnetic susceptibilities of acetylene. An approximate theoretical estimate for the neighbor-anisotropy shift was made by Pople.[338] The anisotropy arises because, when the applied field is perpendicular to the molecular axis, there will be a mixing of the ground state with some $\sigma \rightarrow \pi$ excited states.† Approximate molecular-orbital wave functions can be set up for these states by using linear combinations of atomic orbitals and the magnitudes of the paramagnetic currents estimated. This calculation gives for the change in shielding at the proton

$$\Delta\sigma = \frac{e^2\hbar^2}{2m^2c^2\,\Delta E\,R^3} \tag{7-28}$$

where ΔE is the mean excitation energy of the $\sigma \rightarrow \pi$ states† involved and R is the CH distance. Substituting $R = 1.06$ A and $\Delta E = 9$ ev, this gives $\Delta\sigma = 10 \times 10^{-6}$. Although this estimate is very rough because of the approximations implicit in Eq. (7-28), it is clearly large enough to displace the acetylene signal from a position to the low-field (low-screening) side of ethylene to its observed position near ethane.

A further point of interest is presented by the rather large differences in chemical shifts of the hydrogen halides. For HCl, HBr, and HI in the vapor phase, the proton resonance signals (Table 5-1) are 0.45×10^{-6}, 4.35×10^{-6}, and 13.25×10^{-6} to the *high*-field side of methane gas. All being linear molecules, the neighbor-anisotropy effect displaces the signals to high field. The magnitude of the paramagnetic contributions which give rise to the anisotropy probably increases along the series because of the increasing availability of other orbitals (d-, f-type atomic orbitals, etc.)

† The spectroscopic notation used here is not to be confused with the screening constant.

into which electrons can be excited, so that the biggest effect is expected for hydrogen iodide. It should be noted, however, that electronegativity differences give a similar ordering among the set. It is the position of the whole set relative to methane which suggests that the neighbor effect is operative.

Turning to other molecules, it is noteworthy that the proton resonance signals from NH and OH groups in ammonia, water, and alcohols are all surprisingly close to the methyl signals in paraffins, if effects due to hydrogen bonding are eliminated by carrying out the measurements in the vapor phase or as a dilute solution in a nonpolar solvent (Tables 5-1 and 15-3). Here it is possible that the effect of anisotropy in the paramagnetic circulations may compensate the change due to the removal of electrons from the hydrogen orbital as we move along the series C, N, O, F. This has been investigated quantitatively[338] for the series of isoelectronic molecules CH_4, NH_3, H_2O, and HF. In each of these molecules significant paramagnetic circulations will occur only about the central atom. Using molecular-orbital theory for the lowest excited states, it is possible to obtain the following expression for the induced paramagnetic moment μ_z^{para} in one of the principal directions.

$$\mu_z^{para} = \frac{e^2h^2H_0}{16\pi^2m^2c^2\,\Delta E}\,[P_{xx}(2 - P_{yy}) + P_{yy}(2 - P_{xx})] \qquad (7\text{-}29)$$

where ΔE is again a mean excitation energy and P_{xx} and P_{yy} are the "gross populations" of Mulliken[298] associated with the $2px$ and $2py$ atomic orbitals. Values of these are available from self-consistent wave functions, and it is therefore possible to estimate the magnetic anisotropy of the central atom (assuming the diamagnetic contribution to be isotropic). For methane, of course, there can be no anisotropy on the carbon. For ammonia, water, and hydrogen fluoride, this method gives shifts of 0.25×10^{-6}, 2.75×10^{-6}, 3.0×10^{-6}, respectively (all to high field), due to the neighbor effect. This increasing effect as we proceed along the series is in the direction opposite to the electronegativity effect which removes electrons from the hydrogen orbital and reduces the shielding. It seems reasonable to propose, therefore, that the relatively small variation of the total shift along the series is largely due to the cancellation of these two effects.

b. The Ring-current Effect. *Aromatic Compounds.* Up to this point we have considered only the magnetic effects of current circulations which are localized on or near individual atoms. In aromatic molecules, however, there are additional interatomic currents which flow around closed conjugated loops. The effect of these ring currents on the magnetic susceptibility and its anisotropy have already been discussed in detail in

Sec. 2-5.   In this section we shall consider the effect on the screening constant of protons in the vicinity.

The simplest system to consider is the benzene molecule, in which there are six mobile π electrons.   As we have seen in the theory of the magnetic susceptibility, these electrons behave much like charged particles free to move on a circular wire.   If a magnetic field H_0 is applied

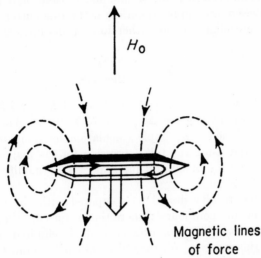

Fig. 7-3. Current and magnetic lines of force induced in benzene by a primary field H_0.

perpendicularly to the wire, the electrons circulate with angular frequency $eH_0/2mc$, leading to a current of

$$j = \frac{3e^2H_0}{2\pi mc} \qquad (7\text{-}30)$$

The direction of this current will be such as to lead to a diamagnetic moment opposed to the primary field, and there will be magnetic lines of force as shown in Fig. 7-3.   It is evident that the secondary magnetic field at the positions of the aromatic protons at the side of the ring will reinforce the primary field H_0 and will therefore give a negative contribution to the screening constant.   Other things being equal, therefore, it is expected that aromatic protons will resonate at lower field than others.

A simple estimate of the magnitude of this effect can be made[336] if the current j is replaced by a magnetic dipole $j\pi a^2/c$ at the center of the ring and perpendicular to it (a being the radius of the ring).   If R is the distance of the proton from the center of the ring, the corresponding approximation for the secondary magnetic field at this point is

$$\frac{j\pi a^2}{cR^3} = \frac{3e^2 H_0 a^2}{2mc^2 R^3} \tag{7-31}$$

Dividing by $-H_0$, the contribution to the screening constant *for this direction* is obtained. If the applied field is in the plane of the molecule, there will be no induced ring current and no contribution to proton screening. The corresponding approximation of the ring-current contribution to the mean screening constant, therefore, is obtained by dividing by three and is

$$\Delta\sigma = -\frac{e^2 a^2}{2mc^2 R^3} \tag{7-32}$$

Substituting the values $a = 1.4 \times 10^{-8}$ cm and $R = 2.5 \times 10^{-8}$ cm for benzene, this equation gives $\Delta\sigma = -1.75 \times 10^{-6}$. Waugh and Fessenden[456] have refined this simple calculation by removing the dipole approximation and using the full expression for the magnetic field of a circular wire in terms of elliptic integrals. This modified calculation gives $\Delta\sigma = -2.2 \times 10^{-6}$.

The calculated results should be compared with the chemical shift between benzene and compounds where the protons are similarly bonded except that the possibility of ring currents is eliminated. Ethylenic protons are in this category, for the CH bond has the same hybridization. From an examination of many organic compounds in the liquid state, Meyer, Saika, and Gutowsky[286] found that the aromatic-proton signals in benzene were displaced by about 1.4×10^{-6} to the low-field side of ethylenic protons. It is more appropriate to compare systems in the same environment, however, so Waugh and Fessenden[456] measured chemical shifts of compounds of this type in dilute solution in carbon tetrachloride. They found, for example, that the chemical shift between benzene and the ethylenic protons of cyclohexadiene-1,3 is 1.48×10^{-6}, the benzene protons having a lower screening constant.

Further evidence supporting the ring-current hypothesis comes from the proton resonance spectra of 1,4-polymethylenebenzenes, which were measured by Waugh and Fessenden.[456] Some of the methylene protons

in such a compound will be held in a position directly above the ring. They should, therefore, experience a magnetic field from the aromatic ring current which is opposite in direction to that associated with the aromatic protons. These methylene protons will consequently be shifted to high field relative to the normal methylene position. Waugh and Fessenden[456] made a quantitative estimate of the shift expected and found reasonably good agreement with the data for 1,4-decamethylenebenzene.

The considerable success of this simple theory in predicting shifts in aromatic compounds gives strong support to the basic hypothesis of the effect of ring currents on proton chemical shifts. In later chapters, many other examples of similar effects will be described, both in polycyclic systems and in connection with aromatic solvents.

Nonaromatic Compounds. Although the existence of induced ring currents in aromatic compounds is a well-established phenomenon, comparatively little is known about currents around saturated or partly saturated rings. Molecules such as cyclohexane do possess a continuous distribution of electronic charge around which such currents can flow, and a free-electron model would predict currents of a magnitude similar to that for benzene. However, the free-electron picture is less applicable to saturated molecules and would undoubtedly overestimate the effect.

There is no direct magnetic evidence on the magnitude of saturated ring currents. As we shall see in Chap. 14, there is a consistent tendency for the signals of the equatorial protons in six-membered rings to appear at lower field than those from axial protons. This could be due in part to a ring current; for the equatorial protons are in a position analogous to the ring protons in benzene.

CHAPTER 8

THEORY OF NUCLEAR SPIN-SPIN INTERACTIONS

In this chapter we shall be concerned with the theoretical calculation and interpretation of the nuclear spin-spin interactions discovered by Gutowsky and McCall[162] and by Hahn and Maxwell.[177] Early theoretical interpretations did not give quantitative values as large as those observed. A full and successful theory based on the complete Hamiltonian for electron-nuclear interactions was first outlined by Ramsey and Purcell[368] and developed in more detail in a later paper by Ramsey.[366] This general theory will be described first, followed by some account of its application to individual molecules.

8-1. General Theory

The Hamiltonian for the motion of the electrons in the field of nuclei which possess magnetic moments may be divided into the three principal parts

$$\mathcal{3C} = \mathcal{3C}_1 + \mathcal{3C}_2 + \mathcal{3C}_3 \tag{8-1}$$

The first part is

$$\mathcal{3C}_1 = \sum_k \frac{1}{2m} \left(\frac{\hbar}{i} \nabla_k + \frac{e}{c} \sum_N \hbar \gamma_N \mathbf{I}_N \times \frac{\mathbf{r}_{kN}}{r_{kN}^3} \right)^2 + V + \mathcal{3C}_{LL} + \mathcal{3C}_{LS} + \mathcal{3C}_{SS} \tag{8-2}$$

where m is the electron mass, γ_N is the magnetogyric ratio of nucleus N (so that $\hbar \gamma_N \mathbf{I}_N$ is its magnetic moment), and $\mathbf{r}_{kN}$ is $\mathbf{r}_k - \mathbf{r}_N$. The first term in the parentheses allows for the kinetic energy of the electrons and their interaction as moving charged particles in the magnetic field of the nuclei. The remaining terms, V, $\mathcal{3C}_{LL}$, $\mathcal{3C}_{LS}$, $\mathcal{3C}_{SS}$, are respectively the electrostatic potential energy and the electron orbital-orbital, spin-orbital, and spin-spin interactions, none of which involve the nuclear spin vectors $\mathbf{I}_N$.

The second term is

$$\mathcal{3C}_2 = 2\beta\hbar \sum_k \sum_N \gamma_N [3(\mathbf{S}_k \cdot \mathbf{r}_{kN})(\mathbf{I}_N \cdot \mathbf{r}_{kN}) r_{kN}^{-5} - (\mathbf{S}_k \cdot \mathbf{I}_N) r_{kN}^{-3}] \tag{8-3}$$

and represents the *dipole-dipole* interactions between the nuclear magnetic moments and the electronic magnetic moments. S_k is the electron spin vector and β is the Bohr magneton $e\hbar/2mc$.

The third part

$$\mathcal{3C}_3 = \frac{16\pi\beta\hbar}{3} \sum_k \sum_N \gamma_N\, \delta(\mathbf{r}_{kN})\, \mathbf{S}_k \cdot \mathbf{I}_N \qquad (8\text{-}4)$$

is less easy to interpret in classical terms. $\delta(\mathbf{r}_{kN})$ is a Dirac δ function which picks out the value at $\mathbf{r}_{kN} = 0$ in any integration over the coordinates of electron k.   A term of this sort was introduced by Fermi[135] to explain hyperfine structure in atomic spectra, and it is also used in the discussion of hyperfine structure in electron resonance experiments.[2] Since the δ function depends on the properties of electrons at the nucleus, it is sometimes referred to as the *contact term*.   Its magnitude for a one-electron system can be deduced from relativistic quantum mechanics.[97]

To find the nuclear-coupling energies by interaction via the electronic system, it is necessary to treat those parts of the Hamiltonian which depend on $\mathbf{I}_N$ as a perturbation on the remainder and carry the perturbation calculation to second order.   (For molecules in singlet ground states with no resultant orbital angular momentum, all first-order terms vanish.) The perturbation Hamiltonian can be divided into the part involving the interaction of the electron orbital motion with the nuclear magnetic moments (appropriate terms in $\mathcal{3C}_1$) and the part involving the corresponding interaction of the electron spins ($\mathcal{3C}_2$ and $\mathcal{3C}_3$).   These can be dealt with separately as cross terms vanish.

a. Nuclear Spin Coupling via Electron Spins.   The most important term giving a nuclear spin coupling is the contact Hamiltonian $\mathcal{3C}_3$. This operator will have nonvanishing matrix elements between the singlet ground electronic state and excited triplet states.   The corresponding second-order perturbation energy is

$$-\sum_{n(\neq 0)} \frac{(0|\mathcal{3C}_3|n)(n|\mathcal{3C}_3|0)}{E_n - E_0} \qquad (8\text{-}5)$$

where the sum is over excited states of the unperturbed system and $E_n - E_0$ is the corresponding excitation energy.   If the full form (8-4) is substituted for $\mathcal{3C}_3$, a double summation is obtained.   To find the spin coupling between a particular pair of nuclei N and N', it is necessary to pick out those terms involving $\mathbf{I}_N$ and $\mathbf{I}_{N'}$, which gives the perturbation energy for this pair as

$$\mathcal{E}_{NN'}^{(3)} = -2\left(\frac{16\pi\beta\hbar}{3}\right)^2 \gamma_N\gamma_{N'} \sum_{n(\neq 0)} \sum_k \sum_j (E_n - E_0)^{-1} \times$$

$$[0|\delta(\mathbf{r}_{kN})\, \mathbf{S}_k \cdot \mathbf{I}_N|n][n|\delta(\mathbf{r}_{jN'})\, \mathbf{S}_j \cdot \mathbf{I}_{N'}|0] \qquad (8\text{-}6)$$

The matrix elements in Eq. (8-6) imply integration over electronic coordinates, so that the nuclear spin vectors I_N and $I_{N'}$ can be taken outside the summations. The total expression is not proportional to the scalar product $I_N \cdot I_{N'}$, however. Rather it takes the form

$$U_{\alpha\beta}I_{N\alpha}I_{N'\beta} \qquad (8\text{-}7)$$

where $U_{\alpha\beta}$ is a second-order tensor with principal axes fixed in the molecule. But in liquids and gases, where rapid molecular tumbling occurs, we have to average over all orientations to get the effective interaction, so that $U_{\alpha\beta}$ has to be replaced by its rotational average

$$\langle U_{\alpha\beta} \rangle_{\text{av}} = \tfrac{1}{3} U_{\gamma\gamma} \delta_{\alpha\beta} \qquad (8\text{-}8)$$

where $U_{\gamma\gamma}$ is the trace of $U_{\alpha\beta}$. The interaction energy (8-7) then becomes proportional to the scalar product and can be written

$$h J^{(3)}_{NN'} I_N \cdot I_{N'} \qquad (8\text{-}9)$$

where $J^{(3)}_{NN'}$ is the contribution of $\mathfrak{K}_3$ to the spin coupling constant (measured in cycles per second). Thus

$$J^{(3)}_{NN'} = -\frac{2}{3h}\left(\frac{16\pi\beta\hbar}{3}\right)^2 \gamma_N\gamma_{N'} \sum_{n(\neq 0)} \sum_k \sum_j (E_n - E_0)^{-1} \times$$
$$[0|\delta(r_{kN})\,S_k|n] \cdot [n|\delta(r_{jN'})\,S_j|0] \qquad (8\text{-}10)$$

If we make the approximation of replacing all the triplet excitation energies by a mean value ΔE, the remaining sum over excited states can be evaluated by the quantum-mechanical sum rule[121b]

$$\sum_n |n\rangle\langle n| = 1$$

This leads to the result

$$J^{(3)}_{NN'} = -\frac{2}{3h}\left(\frac{16\pi\beta\hbar}{3}\right)^2 \gamma_N\gamma_{N'} \frac{1}{\Delta E} \times$$
$$\left[0 \left| \sum_k \sum_j \delta(r_{kN})\,\delta(r_{jN'})\,S_k \cdot S_j \right| 0 \right] \qquad (8\text{-}11)$$

The evaluation of the matrix element in Eq. (8-11) requires only a knowledge of the wave function for the electronic ground state. This will be elaborated in later sections of the chapter.

The perturbation energy due to the direct magnetic dipole interaction between electronic and nuclear spins (Hamiltonian $\mathfrak{K}_2$) can be handled in a very similar manner. There is a contribution $J^{(2)}_{NN'}$ to the spin coupling constant given by

$$J_{NN'}^{(2)} = - \frac{2}{3\hbar} (2\beta\hbar)^2 \gamma_N \gamma_{N'} \sum_{n(\neq 0)} \sum_k \sum_j (E_n - E_0)^{-1} \times$$
$$\{0|[3(\mathbf{S}_k \cdot \mathbf{r}_{kN})\mathbf{r}_{kN} r_{kN}^{-5} - \mathbf{S}_k r_{kN}^{-3}]|n\} \cdot$$
$$\{n|[3(\mathbf{S}_j \cdot \mathbf{r}_{jN'})\mathbf{r}_{jN'} r_{jN'}^{-5} - \mathbf{S}_j r_{jN'}^{-3}]|0\} \quad (8\text{-}12)$$

Again if $E_n - E_0$ is replaced by ΔE, this simplifies to

$$J_{NN'}^{(2)} = - \frac{2}{3\hbar} (2\beta\hbar)^2 \gamma_N \gamma_{N'} \frac{1}{\Delta E} \times$$
$$\{0|[3(\mathbf{S}_k \cdot \mathbf{r}_{kN})\mathbf{r}_{kN} r_{kN}^{-5} - \mathbf{S}_k r_{kN}^{-3}] \cdot$$
$$[3(\mathbf{S}_j \cdot \mathbf{r}_{jN'})\mathbf{r}_{jN'} r_{jN'}^{-5} - \mathbf{S}_j r_{jN'}^{-3}]|0\} \quad (8\text{-}13)$$

It is also possible to obtain cross terms by the common interaction of $\mathcal{K}_2$ and $\mathcal{K}_3$. Ramsey,[366] however, showed that they would average to zero under conditions of frequent collisions, so we shall not consider them further.

b. Nuclear Spin Coupling via Electron Orbital Motion. The remaining contributions to the total spin coupling constant $J_{NN'}$ arise from the interaction of the orbital electronic currents with the nuclear magnetic moments. This can be thought of in simple classical terms, for each nuclear magnetic moment will induce certain currents in the molecule which, in turn, will set up a secondary magnetic field experienced by other nuclei. In general this contribution will not average to zero over rotations.

When expanded, there are two terms in the Hamiltonian $\mathcal{K}_1$ which involve the nuclear spins. They are

$$\mathcal{K}_1^{(a)} = \frac{e^2\hbar^2}{2mc^2} \sum_N \sum_{N'} \sum_k \gamma_N \gamma_{N'} \left(\mathbf{I}_N \times \frac{\mathbf{r}_{kN}}{r_{kN}^3} \right) \cdot \left(\mathbf{I}_{N'} \times \frac{\mathbf{r}_{kN'}}{r_{kN'}^3} \right)$$
$$= \frac{e^2\hbar^2}{2mc^2} \sum_N \sum_{N'} \sum_k \gamma_N \gamma_{N'} r_{kN}^{-3} r_{kN'}^{-3} \times$$
$$[(\mathbf{I}_N \cdot \mathbf{I}_{N'})(\mathbf{r}_{kN} \cdot \mathbf{r}_{kN'}) - (\mathbf{I}_N \cdot \mathbf{r}_{kN'})(\mathbf{I}_{N'} \cdot \mathbf{r}_{kN})] \quad (8\text{-}14)$$

and

$$\mathcal{K}_1^{(b)} = \frac{e\hbar^2}{mci} \sum_N \sum_k \gamma_N r_{kN}^{-3}(\mathbf{I}_N \times \mathbf{r}_{kN}) \cdot \nabla_k$$
$$= \frac{e\hbar^2}{mci} \sum_N \sum_k \gamma_N r_{kN}^{-3} \mathbf{I}_N \cdot (\mathbf{r}_{kN} \times \nabla_k) \quad (8\text{-}15)$$

$\mathcal{K}_1^{(a)}$ is already of second order in the nuclear spins, and we may pick out the term in $I_N I_{N'}$ in the first-order matrix element $(0|\mathcal{3C}_1^{(a)}|0)$. $\mathcal{3C}_1^{(b)}$ can be handled by the same methods as used for $\mathcal{3C}_2$ and $\mathcal{3C}_3$. The contributions to $J_{NN'}$ are

$$J_{NN'}^{(1a)} = \frac{4}{3h} \frac{e^2\hbar^2}{2mc^2} \gamma_N\gamma_{N'} \left(0 \left| \sum_k \mathbf{r}_{kN} \cdot \mathbf{r}_{kN'} r_{kN}^{-3} r_{kN'}^{-3} \right| 0\right) \tag{8-16}$$

$$J_{NN'}^{(1b)} = -\frac{8}{3h} \beta^2\hbar^2\gamma_N\gamma_{N'} \frac{1}{\Delta E} \times$$

$$\left[0 \left| \sum_k \sum_j r_{kN}^{-3} r_{jN'}^{-3} (\mathbf{r}_{kN} \times \nabla_k) \cdot (\mathbf{r}_{jN'} \times \nabla_j) \right| 0\right] \tag{8-17}$$

using the approximate excitation energy ΔE.

One important point that can be noted from this analysis is that all the contributions to $J_{NN'}$ are proportional to the product of the magnetogyric ratios $\gamma_N\gamma_{N'}$. This gives a simple relation between the spin coupling constants involving various isotopes of the same nuclear species.

8-2. Spin–Spin Coupling in the Hydrogen Molecule

As with the theory of the chemical shift, the simplest application is to the coupling between the two protons in the hydrogen molecule. Ramsey[366] carried out such a calculation of the main terms described in the previous section. In practice, of course, the spin coupling constant of the hydrogen molecule H_2 cannot be observed directly because the two protons are in equivalent positions. However, the spectrum of the isotopic species HD will show splitting in both the proton and deuterium spectra, and the coupling constant in the HD molecule is just γ_D/γ_H times that in H_2.

For a two-electron system, the approximate form (8-11) for the contact term can be written

$$J_{NN'}^{(3)} = -\frac{4}{3h} \left(\frac{16\pi\beta\hbar}{3}\right)^2 \gamma_N\gamma_{N'} \frac{1}{\Delta E} [0|\delta(\mathbf{r}_{1N}) \, \delta(\mathbf{r}_{2N'}) \, \mathbf{S}_1 \cdot \mathbf{S}_2|0] \tag{8-18}$$

[Note that matrix elements of expressions such as $\delta(\mathbf{r}_{1N}) \, \delta(\mathbf{r}_{1N'})$ vanish.] Now to a good approximation, the ground-state electronic wave function for the hydrogen molecule is separable into a product of a function of position coordinates and a function of spin coordinates. Further

$$\mathbf{S}_1 \cdot \mathbf{S}_2 = \tfrac{1}{2}(\mathbf{S}^2 - \mathbf{S}_1^2 - \mathbf{S}_2^2) \tag{8-19}$$

where $\mathbf{S}$ is the total electron spin. But since the state is a singlet, the expectation value of $\mathbf{S}^2$ is zero, while that of $\mathbf{S}_1^2$ and $\mathbf{S}_2^2$ is 3/4 [that is,

$S_1(S_1 + 1)$, where $S_1 = 1/2$]. Thus $\mathbf{S_1 \cdot S_2}$ can be replaced by $(-3/4)$ and then

$$J_{NN'}^{(3)} = \frac{1}{h\,\Delta E}\left(\frac{16\pi\beta\hbar}{3}\right)^2 \gamma_N\gamma_{N'}[0|\delta(\mathbf{r}_{1N})\,\delta(\mathbf{r}_{2N'})|0] \qquad (8\text{-}20)$$

The matrix element is now simply the value of the wave function when electron 1 is at nucleus N and electron 2 is at nucleus N'. For the accurate James-Coolidge function[207]

$$[0|\delta(\mathbf{r}_{1N})\,\delta(\mathbf{r}_{2N'})|0] = 0.0600 a_0^{-6} \qquad (8\text{-}21)$$

where a_0 is the Bohr radius. Using numerical values for the other quantities in Eq. (8-20), this gives

$$J_{HD}^{(3)} = \frac{55.8}{\Delta E} \qquad \text{cycles/sec} \qquad (8\text{-}22)$$

where ΔE is expressed in Rydberg units.

There is no clear unique way of obtaining a mean excitation energy ΔE. However, the reasonable value of 1.4 Rydbergs gives a coupling constant of about 40 cycles/sec. The best experimental value is 43.5 ± 1 cycles/sec from pulse-type measurements of Carr and Purcell.[85] This suggests that the contact-term part of the coupling gives the main contribution for this molecule.

Ramsey also made estimates of the other contributions, using the expression derived previously. By evaluating the integrals approximately, he concluded that the other interaction $J_{HD}^{(2)}$ via the electron spins was about 3 cycles/sec and that the orbital contributions were probably less than 0.5 cycle/sec.

8-3. Proton Spin Coupling in Other Molecules

The Fermi-type coupling is also likely to give the principal contribution to the coupling constant between protons in other molecules where there is no direct bond. This is primarily because the electrons on a hydrogen atom are well represented by a $1s$-type atomic orbital, whereas the other spin-coupling terms considered in Sec. 8-1 depend on the presence of angular-dependent atomic orbitals of types $p, d, f, \ldots$ It should be possible, therefore, to interpret the observations on proton-proton couplings in terms of the matrix element [Eq. (8-11)]

$$\left[0\left|\sum_k \sum_j \delta(\mathbf{r}_{kN})\,\delta(\mathbf{r}_{jN'})\,\mathbf{S}_k \cdot \mathbf{S}_j\right|0\right] \qquad (8\text{-}23)$$

together with a value of the mean triplet excitation energy ΔE. To develop Eq. (8-23) at all, it is necessary to specify the ground-state total electronic wave function. Theories using both molecular-orbital and valence-bond wave functions have been given for this purpose.

a. Molecular-orbital Theory. The calculation of spin coupling constants by molecular-orbital theory was first developed in full by McConnell.[267] For a molecule with a closed-shell ground state, the wave function in this theory consists of a single determinant built up from molecular orbitals ψ_1, ψ_2, . . . , each being doubly occupied. The matrix element can be evaluated by using this function, and Eq. (8-11) then gives

$$J_{NN'} = (\tfrac{8}{3}\beta\gamma)^2 h(\Delta E)^{-1} \sum_{st} \psi_s^*(N)\psi_t^*(N')\psi_t(N)\psi_s(N') \qquad (8\text{-}24)$$

where γ is the proton magnetogyric ratio and $\psi_s(N)$ is the value of the molecular orbital ψ_s at the nucleus N. This expression has an interesting physical interpretation. If we write $P^{\alpha\alpha}(1,2)$ for the probability per unit volume of there being simultaneously electrons of α spin at positions 1 and 2 and $P^{\alpha\beta}(1,2)$ for the corresponding probability of an electron of α spin at position 1 and an electron of β spin at position 2, then the expression (8-24) for $J_{NN'}$ is proportional to

$$P^{\alpha\beta}(N,N') - P^{\alpha\alpha}(N,N') \qquad (8\text{-}25)$$

Thus the spin coupling constant is approximately proportional to the excess of β electrons over α electrons at the position of nucleus N', given that there is an α electron at nucleus N.

It is well known that there is some degree of flexibility in the choice of the orbitals ψ_1, ψ_2, . . . , without causing any change in the total wave function or the predicted value of any observable property. In particular, the delocalized orbitals ψ can be replaced by a set of semilocalized or equivalent orbitals χ which correspond to individual bonds, lone pairs, and inner shells.[244] If a set of such orbitals which were completely localized and nonoverlapping could be found, then Eq. (8-24) (with ψ_s, ψ_t replaced by χ_s, χ_t) would predict no coupling constant between protons in different bonds. The existence of such coupling constants, therefore, is an indication of intrinsic delocalization of the bonding orbitals.

The next approximation commonly made in molecular-orbital theory is to write the molecular orbitals ψ_s as linear combinations of atomic orbitals (LCAO) ϕ_μ:

$$\psi_s = \sum_\mu C_{s\mu}\phi_\mu \qquad (8\text{-}26)$$

By substituting this and a similar expression for ψ_t in Eq. (8-24) and further assuming that the values of all atomic orbitals (except local $1s$ orbitals) were negligible at the proton positions, McConnell obtained the simple formula[267]

$$J_{NN'} = \tfrac{16}{9}\beta^2\gamma^2h(\Delta E)^{-1}[\phi(0)]^4\eta_{NN'}{}^2 \qquad (8\text{-}27)$$

where

$$\eta_{NN'} = 2\sum_s C_{sN}C_{sN'} \qquad (8\text{-}28)$$

Here $\phi(0)$ is the value of a hydrogen $1s$ atomic orbital at its center and C_{sN} is the LCAO coefficient of the orbital centered on proton N. The quantity $\eta_{NN'}$ is the usual definition of the bond order between atoms N and N' in LCAO molecular-orbital theory.[108] (It has usually been used in theories concerned with the $2p\pi$ orbitals in aromatic compounds, but the concept can be extended to give a partial bond order between any pair of atomic orbitals.)

If ΔE is taken to be 10 ev and the effective charge in the $1s$ orbital is assumed to be 1.00, Eq. (8-27) becomes

$$J_{NN'} \approx 200\eta_{NN'}{}^2 \qquad \text{cycles/sec} \qquad (8\text{-}29)$$

For the hydrogen molecule, where $\eta_{NN'} = 1$, this gives $J_{NN'} \approx 200$ cycles/sec, to be compared with the experimental value 280 cycles/sec. For other molecules, the formula can be applied if it is possible to make an estimate of the proton-proton bond order. The theory predicts that the coupling constant between protons is always positive (as long as configuration interaction is neglected). There is experimental evidence, however, that suggests that proton-proton coupling constants may have either sign.[6] This indicates that a molecular-orbital theory without configuration interaction does not always give an accurate picture of the relative electron distribution.

b. Valence-bond Theory. The use of valence-bond wave functions in calculating proton spin coupling constants has been reported by Karplus, Anderson, Farrar, and Gutowsky.[215] Using only the Fermi interaction, they find that $J_{NN'}$ takes the form

$$J_{NN'} = \frac{3.025 \times 10^{-46}}{\Delta E}[\phi(0)]^4 \sum_{lm} C_l C_m\, 2^{-n+i(l,m)}[1 + 2f(l,m,p_{NN'})] \qquad (8\text{-}30)$$

Here the complete wave function is written

$$\Psi = \sum_l C_l\psi_l \qquad (8\text{-}31)$$

where ψ_l denotes the functions for the canonical valence-bond structures; n, $i(l,m)$, $f(l,m,p_{NN'})$ are quantities occurring in the evaluation of matrix elements between valence-bond functions ψ_l and ψ_m.[324] A calculation for methane gives $J = 10.4$ cycles/sec, compared with the experimental value of 12.4 cycles/sec. The calculations have been extended by Karplus and Gutowsky[215a] for nontetrahedral HCH angles. It was shown that the valence-bond theory predicts that J decreases from 27 to 2.8 cycles/sec as the angle changes from 100 to 120°. For angles greater than 125°, the calculated value is negative.

These calculations have also been made for hydrogen atoms bonded to neighboring carbon atoms.[214a] For ethylene, values of 6.1 and 11.9 cycles/sec are obtained for the cis and trans coupling constants, respectively. For ethane in a staggered configuration, the values are 1.7 and 9.2 cycles/sec for the gauche and trans positions. These results are in good agreement with some of the experimental data described below and indicate that the valence-bond theory is likely to prove a powerful theoretical tool in this field.

c. Discussion of Experimental Data. A considerable number of proton-proton coupling constants have been determined and, although no extensive detailed interpretation has been attempted, certain empirical regularities are apparent. It is not possible to determine the absolute signs of coupling constants, although, in some molecules, relative signs can be found. For example, different signs are claimed[6] in butene-1. Many analyses of proton spectra, however, have been carried out by assuming all positive signs.

Some characteristic values of proton-proton coupling constants in a variety of compounds are given in Table 8-1. They show a number of significant features. One of the most striking is the relatively small values of the proton coupling constants between protons attached to the same carbon atom: they are of the same order as those between protons attached to neighboring carbon atoms. The very small value for gem protons in ethylenic compounds is particularly remarkable. A rough qualitative interpretation of this can be made in terms of the molecular-orbital expression (8-24). If the orbitals used are partially localized equivalent bond orbitals, χ_1 and χ_2 for two CH bonds, and if all other orbitals are ignored, this gives

$$J_{12} = (\tfrac{8}{3}\beta\gamma)^2 h(\Delta E)^{-1}[\chi_1{}^2(1)\chi_1{}^2(2) + \chi_2{}^2(1)\chi_2{}^2(2) + 2\chi_1(1)\chi_2(1)\chi_1(2)\chi_2(2)]$$

$$= (\tfrac{8}{3}\beta\gamma)^2 h(\Delta E)^{-1} 4A^2B^2 \tag{8-32}$$

where $A = \chi_1(1) = \chi_2(2)$ is the value of a bond orbital at the position of its own proton and $B = \chi_2(1) = \chi_1(2)$ is the value at the other proton, so that B is considerably smaller than A. Hence if one bond orbital has a node passing close to the position of the other proton, the coupling constant is likely to be small. This is to be expected for both tetrahedral and trigonal carbon atoms; for the corresponding hybrid atomic orbitals on the carbon atom have just this property (assuming equal radial parts

TABLE 8-1. CHARACTERISTIC PROTON-PROTON COUPLING CONSTANTS

Compound	Configuration	Type	J, cycles/sec	Ref.
	H_2		280	85
	CH_4 and CH_3X		12.4	215 (by deuteration)
	C_2H_2		9.1	215 (by deuteration)
Ethylenic compounds	C=C (H, H gem)	Gem	1–2	Sec. 11-2
	C=C (cis)	Cis	8–11	Sec. 11-2
	C=C (trans)	Trans	17–18	Sec. 11-2
Ethyl groups	CH_3CH_2X		6–8	20, 69
Saturated six-membered rings	CHX—CHY	Axial/axial	5–8	Chap. 14
		Axial/equatorial and equatorial/equatorial	2–3.5	Chap. 14
Benzene- and pyridine-type rings		Ortho	5–8.5	161, 37, 342, 401
		Meta	1–3	161, 37, 342, 401
		Para	~1	161, 401
Five-membered rings		$\alpha\beta$	1.3	Sec. 11-6
			3.5	403
Seven-membered rings			10–12	37, 403
			13	403

for 2*s* and 2*p* functions) (Fig. 8-1).   Quantitatively these small coupling constants are reproduced by the valence-bond calculations of Karplus and Gutowsky,[215a] which also give the smaller value for trigonal carbon atoms.

Another feature of interest concerns the coupling constants between protons at different ends of a double bond.   Here the trans value is consistently larger than the cis.   A similar and possibly related fact is that axial/axial coupling constants between protons on neighboring carbon atoms in saturated six-membered rings are larger than the others.   Here axial/axial positions are trans relative to the CC single bond, while all others are gauche (Fig. 8-2).   In both cases, therefore, the observed coupling constant is largest between the protons which are separated by the greatest distance.

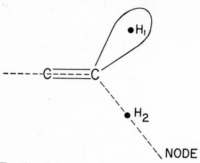

FIG. 8-1. Schematic diagram of a trigonal CH bonding orbital with a node passing through a neighboring proton.

The third point of general interest concerns the values of the coupling constants between protons attached to carbon atoms in aromatic rings. One possibility, which has been examined in detail by McConnell,[270] is that they are partly determined by interactions via the mobile π electron system.   In simple molecular-orbital theory, there is no direct contribution, since the π orbitals all have nodes through the protons if the

trans (axial/axial)

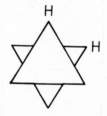

gauche (axial/equatorial
and equatorial/
equatorial)

FIG. 8-2. Relative positions of protons with respect to a carbon-carbon single bond.

molecule is planar.   However, an indirect effect is possible if configuration interaction is included.   (McConnell has shown that a similar effect can explain observed proton hyperfine structure in aromatic free radicals in which the odd electron is in a π orbital.[268])   Quantitatively, however, the magnitude of the contribution of π electrons to the coupling constant turns out to be relatively small. For the ortho coupling constant in benzene, for example, McConnell estimates[270] a contribution of 0.80 cycle/sec. It seems likely, therefore, that the coupling constant between protons ortho to each other is dominated by interaction through the σ system.

The experimental data on aromatic coupling constants do not show any marked correlation with the corresponding π-bond order. Rather it seems that the most important factor is the size of ring to which the protons are attached. The coupling constants between protons attached to neighboring atoms apparently increase from 1 to 4 cycles/sec for five-membered rings to 5 to 9 cycles/sec and 10 to 13 cycles/sec for six- and seven-membered rings, respectively. This trend may be caused by the fact that, as the internal bond angle in the ring is increased, neighboring CH bonds are forced closer together. This introduces delocalization by overlap (as with interacting helium atoms), leading to increased coupling.

8-4. Coupling Constants Involving Nuclei Other than Hydrogen

The theory of the coupling between nuclei of atoms other than hydrogen is more complicated, owing to the larger contribution of the electron-dipole term [Eq. (8-13)] and the electron-orbital term [Eq. (8-16)]. The fullest treatment is that of McConnell,[267] who applied molecular-orbital theory to the further development of the general expressions due to Ramsey, breaking them down into local contributions as with the contact part discussed in the previous section.

An approximate estimate of the magnitude of the orbital contributions can be made by noting that there is a connection with the theory of the screening constant in an external field.[341a] In particular, the electron-orbital currents induced by one nucleus will interact with an external field by the same amount as the nucleus interacts with the currents induced by the external field. Thus if the screening constant is σ, the total orbital magnetic moment induced by the nuclear moment $\mathbf{u}$ is $-\sigma\mathbf{u}$. If it is assumed that the currents giving rise to this moment are mostly localized in the vicinity of the nuclear moment $\mathbf{u}$, their effect can be equated to that of a point dipole, so that $\mathbf{u}$ is replaced by $(1 - \sigma)\mathbf{u}$ at the same point. Clearly, if σ is independent of direction, this will only scale down the effective magnitude of $\mathbf{u}$, and the interaction with another moment will average out on rotation. If the screening is *anisotropic*, however, there will be a resultant effect. Detailed development of this theory then gives [341a]†

$$J_{NN'}^{(1)} = -\tfrac{1}{3}h^{-1}\gamma_N\gamma_{N'}\hbar^2 R^{-3} \times$$
$$[\Delta\sigma\,(1 - 3\cos^2\theta) + \Delta\sigma'\,(1 - 3\cos^2\theta')] \quad (8\text{-}33)$$

† The expressions given in reference 341a are too large by a factor of two.

TABLE 8-2. CHARACTERISTIC COUPLING CONSTANTS INVOLVING NUCLEI OTHER THAN PROTONS

Group	Molecules	Coupling constant, cycles/sec	Ref.
	H Directly Bonded to Other Atoms		
HB	B_2H_6	125	304
HB	$(CH_3)_2PHBH_3$	93	419
HB (bridge)	B_2H_6	43	304
HC	$(C^*H_3)_4C$	120	Table 12-2
	C_6H_6	159	Table 12-2
	$CHBr_3$	208	Table 12-2
HN^{14}	$N^{14}H_3$	46	309
HN^{15}	$N^{15}H_3$	64	309
HF	HF	615	430
HSi	$C_6H_5SiH_3$	211	195
HP	$(CH_3)_2PHBH_3$	350	419
	PH_3	183	166
	H with Other Atoms Two Bonds Removed		
HCF	CH_3CH_2F	60	169
	Fluorinated methanes	44–81	285
HCP	$(CH_3)_2PHBH_3$	12	419
HBP	$(CH_3)_2PHBH_3$	12	419
	H with Other Atoms More than Two Bonds Removed		
HCCF	CH_3CH_2F	20	169
	$CF_2X\!-\!CHYZ$	6–15	125
	$CF_2X\!-\!CH_2Y$	4–29	422
$HC{=}CF$ (cis)	$HR_1C{=}CFR_2$	1–8	275
$HC{=}CF$ (trans)	$HR_1C{=}CFR_2$	12–40	275
(ortho H–F fluorobenzene structure)	Fluorobenzenes	6–10	161
(meta H–F fluorobenzene structure)	Fluorobenzenes	6–8	161
(para H–F fluorobenzene structure)	Fluorobenzenes	~2	161
	F Directly Bonded to Other Atoms		
FC	CF_3COOH	275	166
FN	FNO_2	113	307
FSi	$(CH_3)_3SiF$	268	195
FP	PF_3	1,400	166
FSb	$NaSb^{121}F_6$	1,940	354

TABLE 8-2. CHARACTERISTIC COUPLING CONSTANTS INVOLVING NUCLEI
OTHER THAN PROTONS (*Continued*)

Group	Molecules	Coupling constant, cycles/sec	Ref.
	F with F Two Bonds Removed		
FCF	CF_2X—$CHYZ$	158	125
	Subst. cyclobutanes	190–224	331
	Subst. cyclopropane	157	331
FBrF	BF_5	76	166
FIF	IF_5	84	166
F—Cl (with F, F)	ClF_3	~400	291
FSF	SF_4	78	105a
=C (with F, F)	R_1R_2C=CF_2	28–87	275
	F with F More than Two Bonds Removed		
FCCF	CF_2Br—CBr_2F	18	299
FCCCF	$(CF_3)_2CHCF_2OCH_3$	11	297
FC=CF (cis)	R_1FC=CFR_2	33–58	275
FC=CF (trans)	R_1FC=CFR_2	115–124	275
(ortho difluorobenzene)	Fluorobenzenes	20	161
(meta difluorobenzene)	Fluorobenzenes	2–4	161
(para difluorobenzene)	Fluorobenzenes	12–15	161

where $\Delta\sigma$, $\Delta\sigma'$ are the screening anisotropies ($\sigma^{\parallel} - \sigma^{\perp}$, assuming axial symmetry) and θ, θ' are the angles between the axial directions and the internuclear line NN'. Application of this formula to coupling constants involving fluorine nuclei (where $\Delta\sigma \approx 10^{-3}$) suggests that the orbital contribution is usually positive but is still a small fraction of the total observed value.

In his molecular-orbital theory of spin coupling, McConnell[267] obtained an expression for the contribution of the nucleus–electron dipole inter-action.   If the molecular orbitals are ψ_α, the expression [developed from Eq. (8-13)] is

$$J_{NN'}^{(2)} = -h^{-1}(2\beta\hbar)^2\gamma_N\gamma_{N'} \frac{1}{\Delta E} \times$$

$$\left\{ \sum_\alpha [\psi_\alpha(s)|(3\cos^2\theta_{ss} - 1)r_{sN}^{-3}r_{sN'}^{-3}|\psi_\alpha(s)] \right.$$

$$\left. - \sum_{\alpha,\beta} [\psi_\alpha(s)\psi_\beta(t)|(3\cos^2\theta_{st} - 1)r_{sN}^{-3}r_{tN'}^{-3}|\psi_\alpha(t)\psi_\beta(s)] \right\} \quad (8\text{-}34)$$

where θ_{st} is the angle between the vectors $\mathbf{r}_{sN}$ and $\mathbf{r}_{tN'}$.   The two parts of Eq. (8-34) are one- and two-electron contributions.   Physically, the one-electron parts arise because nucleus N induces a local electron perturba-tion, producing a magnetic field which then acts across space on the second nucleus.   The two-electron parts, on the other hand, arise because one nucleus induces a perturbation on its own atom, which in turn affects the distribution of a second electron on the other atom, and so on the second nucleus.   In this case the perturbation proceeds via the electronic structure.   McConnell[267] made estimates of the one-electron contribu-tions through the π electrons in tetrafluoroethylene and found appreciable contributions.   Calculation of the two-electron part is difficult owing to the lack of knowledge of detailed molecular orbitals for such molecules. Much the same applies to the calculation of the contact part, which depends, among other things, on the amount of s character in the bonding orbitals.

A considerable amount of data on spin coupling constants involving atoms other than protons has been collected, and some typical values are presented in Table 8-2.   Once again signs are usually indeterminate, but it is of interest to note that opposite signs for two HF coupling con-stants have been discovered in at least one substituted benzene molecule.[161]

CHAPTER 9

SPIN-LATTICE RELAXATION

9-1. Introduction

The role of the rate of energy transfer between the nuclear spin and other degrees of freedom in determining the line widths of nuclear resonance spectra in liquids has already been discussed in Chap. 3. In this chapter the various mechanisms that lead to this spin-lattice relaxation will be dealt with in more detail.

Nuclei with spin $I = 1/2$ are the simplest to consider, for they have only a magnetic moment associated with the spin and consequently can only interact with magnetic fields. Thermal equilibration of the spins with the other degrees of freedom can then take place only through any local magnetic fields which are present. There are several ways in which molecular motion can give rise to fluctuating local magnetic fields, the most important being:

1. Fields due to the magnetic moments of other nuclei
2. Fields due to the spins of unpaired electrons
3. Fields due to variable electronic screening of the static field H_0 (intra- or intermolecular)

Investigations of these factors are considered in turn in the next section.

For nuclei with spin $I > 1/2$, however, nuclear electric quadrupole moments can interact with variable electric fields coupled to the other degrees of freedom. This leads to *electrical* relaxation as an additional mechanism. It is described separately in Sec. 9-3.

9-2. Magnetic Relaxation in Liquids

Before going into the detailed origins of local magnetic fields which act on a nucleus, we shall consider the general problem of finding the probability of a single nucleus undergoing transitions in the presence of a magnetic field which is fluctuating in some random manner. Transitions between the energy levels of a given nucleus brought about by spin-lattice interaction can be thought of in terms very similar to those of the radiation-induced transitions which are the basis of NMR spectroscopy. Thus if the static field H_0 is in the z direction, transitions can be induced by magnetic fields in the x and y directions oscillating with the appropriate frequency

$$\nu_0 = \frac{\gamma H_0}{2\pi} \qquad (9\text{-}1)$$

If we analyze the noise of the fluctuating field in a distribution among frequencies, then the component with frequency ν_0 can also be effective in producing a transition. The extent of spin-lattice interaction, therefore, will depend on two factors:

1. The magnitude of local fields
2. The rate of fluctuation of local fields

In this section we shall limit the theoretical discussion to nuclei with spin $I = 1/2$, so that only one transition probability is involved. If the fluctuating field is $\mathbf{H}'(t)$, the components H'_x and H'_y will be able to cause transitions. The interaction Hamiltonian is

$$\mathcal{H}' = -\gamma\hbar\mathbf{I}\cdot\mathbf{H}'(t) \qquad (9\text{-}2)$$

and its matrix element between the state $I_z = -1/2$ and the state $I_z = 1/2$ is

$$\begin{aligned}(-\tfrac{1}{2}|\mathcal{H}'|\tfrac{1}{2}) &= -\gamma\hbar[(-\tfrac{1}{2}|I_x|\tfrac{1}{2})H'_x + (-\tfrac{1}{2}|I_y|\tfrac{1}{2})H'_y] \\ &= -\tfrac{1}{2}\gamma\hbar[H'_x(t) + iH'_y(t)]\end{aligned} \qquad (9\text{-}3)$$

This matrix element will be a fluctuating function of time with a mean-square value

$$\overline{|(-\tfrac{1}{2}|\mathcal{H}'|\tfrac{1}{2})|^2} = \tfrac{1}{4}\gamma^2\hbar^2(\overline{H'^2_x + H'^2_y}) = \tfrac{1}{2}\gamma^2\hbar\overline{H'^2_x} \qquad (9\text{-}4)$$

The theory of the transition probability due to a fluctuating Hamiltonian of this type is given in Appendix B.

Further development of the theory requires some information about the nature of the fluctuations. Under certain conditions it is possible to make use of results of the theory of Brownian motion, a procedure adopted by Bloembergen, Purcell, and Pound,[59] on whose work most of the theory is based. The fluctuations in the field $\mathbf{H}'(t)$ arise from the rotational and translational motion of individual molecules, perturbed from time to time by collisions. The basic condition for the theory of Brownian motion to be valid under these circumstances is that many collisions take place during the time a molecule takes to turn around or move through a distance characteristic of one molecular spacing. This is likely to be a reasonable approximation in many liquids (and is, in fact, used in the theory of dielectric relaxation[113]). On the other hand it is not generally applicable in gases, where a molecule may rotate many times between collisions.

The Brownian-motion assumptions lead to a particular form of noise spectrum for the frequency distribution.   This is

$$K(\nu) \propto \frac{2\tau_c}{1 + 4\pi^2\nu^2\tau_c^2} \tag{9-5}$$

where τ_c is a time characteristic of the random motion which we shall call the *correlation time*.   It is a measure of the time taken for the field $H'(t)$ to "lose memory" of a previous value.

Substituting in the complete formula [Eq. (B-9)] derived in Appendix B, we obtain for the transition probability between the states

$$W_{-1/2 \to 1/2} = \frac{\gamma^2 \overline{H_x'^2}\tau_c}{1 + 4\pi^2\nu_0^2\tau_c^2} \tag{9-6}$$

where ν_0 is the Larmor frequency ($= \gamma H_0/2\pi$).   If the correlation time τ_c is short compared with the inverse Larmor frequency ν_0^{-1}, so that many fluctuations occur during one rotation of the magnetic moment, the denominator in Eq. (9-6) can be replaced by unity.   The spin-lattice relaxation time is then given by [compare Eq. (3-12)]

$$\frac{1}{T_1} = 2W_{-1/2 \to 1/2} = 2\gamma^2\overline{H_x'^2}\tau_c \tag{9-7}$$

It should be noted that, for fluctuating fields that are not introduced by the application of the external field $\mathbf{H}_0$, the spin-lattice relaxation time according to Eq. (9-7) is independent of the frequency ν_0. If the fluctuating field $\mathbf{H}'$ is isotropic, we have

$$\frac{1}{T_1} = \tfrac{2}{3}\gamma^2\overline{H'^2}\tau_c \tag{9-8}$$

These formulas can now be applied to various types of local magnetic field $\mathbf{H}'$.

a. Relaxation Due to Nuclear Magnetic Dipole Interaction.   We begin by considering the magnetic fields due to other nuclei.   They may be divided into those in the same molecule (intramolecular) and those in different molecules (intermolecular).   We shall deal with intramolecular relaxation first.

If the molecule is approximately rigid, we may treat the internuclear distance as a constant b and average only over orientations.   Now the mean-square field at a distance b from a dipole moment μ' is† $2\mu'^2/b^6$.

† The radial and transverse components of the field are $(2\mu' \cos\theta)/b^3$ and $(\mu' \sin\theta)/b^3$. The mean-square field is therefore
$$\frac{\overline{(4\cos^2\theta + \sin^2\theta)}\mu'^2}{b^6} = \frac{2\mu'^2}{b^6}$$

Quantum mechanically, μ'^2 must be replaced by

$$\hbar^2\gamma'^2 I(I+1)$$

where γ' is the magnetogyric ratio for the other nucleus. Since we are dealing with $I = 1/2$, the mean-square field is $\frac{3}{2}\hbar^2\gamma'^2/b^6$. Substituting in the basic formula (9-8), we obtain

$$\frac{1}{T_1} = \frac{\hbar^2\gamma^2\gamma'^2}{b^6}\,\tau_c \qquad (9\text{-}9)$$

This applies only to nonidentical nuclei ($\gamma \neq \gamma'$). If the nuclei are of the same species, the simple treatment given above no longer leads to the correct result. A more complete treatment based on the wave functions for the two nuclei together gives

$$\frac{1}{T_1} = \frac{\frac{3}{2}\hbar^2\gamma^4}{b^6}\,\tau_c \qquad (9\text{-}10)$$

This result was obtained by Kubo and Tomita[227] and also by Solomon,[429] correcting a slightly different result obtained originally by Bloembergen, Purcell, and Pound.[59] Solomon[429] also gave a more complete derivation of the different-nuclei formula (9-9).

It now remains only to find a correlation time τ_c for the rotational motion of the molecule in the liquid. Bloembergen, Purcell, and Pound[59] did this by an extension of the Debye[113] theory of dielectric dispersion. This is based on a model of a sphere turning in a viscous fluid and gives

$$\tau_c = \frac{4\pi\eta a^3}{3kT} \qquad (9\text{-}11)$$

where η is the viscosity and a the radius of the sphere. Combining this with Eq. (9-10), we obtain a complete formula for the contribution of the intramolecular effect to $1/T_1$.

$$\left(\frac{1}{T_1}\right)_{\text{intra}} = \frac{2\pi\eta a^3\hbar^2\gamma^4}{b^6 kT} \qquad (9\text{-}12)$$

Bloembergen, Purcell, and Pound applied their theory to water at 20°C, using $\eta = 0.01$ poise, $a = b = 1.5 \times 10^{-8}$ cm. This gives†
$\tau_c = 0.35 \times 10^{-11}$ sec and $(1/T_1)_{\text{intra}} = 0.26$ sec^{-1}.

Intermolecular contributions to T_1, that is, contributions arising from the magnetic fields of nuclei in other molecules, were related to the diffusion process by these authors. To be specific, we suppose that there are two nuclei per molecule so that the result can be applied to water. We

† Numerical values differ slightly from those in ref. 59 because of the afore-mentioned changes in the formulas.

consider nuclei whose distances from the central molecule lie between r and $r + dr$. From such a nucleus there is a contribution $(\frac{3}{2}\hbar^2\gamma^4/b^6)\tau_c$ after averaging over all directions. τ_c is estimated as the time a molecule takes to diffuse across a relative distance r. This is $r^2/12D$, where D is the diffusion coefficient (noting that both molecules move). The total contribution is then obtained by multiplying by the number of nuclei per unit volume $2N_0$ (N_0 being the number of molecules per unit volume) and integrating over all space outside the sphere $r = 2a$, corresponding to two spheres in contact. This gives

$$\begin{aligned}\left(\frac{1}{T_1}\right)_{inter} &= 2N_0 \int_{2a}^{\infty} \frac{\frac{3}{2}\hbar^2\gamma^4}{r^6} \frac{r^2}{12D} 4\pi r^2\, dr \\ &= \frac{\pi N_0 \hbar^2 \gamma^4}{2Da}\end{aligned}$$ (9-13)

The diffusion coefficient D may be related to the viscosity η by the Stokes-Einstein relation $D = kT/6\pi\eta a$, giving the final result

$$\left(\frac{1}{T_1}\right)_{inter} = \frac{3\pi^2\gamma^4\hbar^2\eta N_0}{kT}$$ (9-14)

Substitution of the same numerical values as before gives $0.15~\mathrm{sec}^{-1}$ for this translational contribution. Adding the two terms, we get $1/T_1 = 0.4~\mathrm{sec}^{-1}$, or $T_1 = 2.5$ sec, in good agreement with the experimental values of 2 to 3 sec.[59] The rather precise correspondence between the two figures must be regarded as partly fortuitous because of the crude nature of the model, but the order-of-magnitude agreement is a satisfactory confirmation of the mechanism.

These results for the intra- and intermolecular contributions to $1/T_1$ are easily extended to systems with many nuclei. The generalized expressions are, in a form similar to that given by Gutowsky and Woessner,[173]

$$\left(\frac{1}{T_{1i}}\right)_{intra} = \frac{2\pi\hbar^2\gamma_i^2\eta a^3}{3kT}\left(3\gamma_i^2 \sum_j r_{ij}^{-6} + 2\sum_f^* \gamma_f^2 r_{if}^{-6}\right)$$ (9-15)

$$\left(\frac{1}{T_{1i}}\right)_{inter} = \frac{\pi^2\hbar^2\gamma_i^2\eta N_0 a}{kT}\left(3\gamma_i^2 \sum_j \frac{1}{r_{ij}^0} + 2\sum_f^* \gamma_f^2 \frac{1}{r_{if}^0}\right)$$ (9-16)

In these formulas for the relaxation time of a nucleus i, summations $\sum_j$ are over nuclei of the same species and $\sum_f^*$ over all others. In Eq. (9-15) the summations are over nuclei in the same molecule as the one under consideration; in Eq. (9-16) they are over nuclei of a neighboring molecule, $1/r_{ij}^0$ being the mean value of $1/r_{ij}$ for two molecules in contact. In the crudest approximation, all the quantities $(1/r_{ij}^0)$ can be replaced by $2a$. The distance a can be estimated from the molar volume.

b. Experiments on Spin-lattice Relaxation by Nuclear-dipole Interaction. Both the intra- and intermolecular contributions to the inverse spin-lattice relaxation time $1/T_1$ are predicted to be proportional to the ratio of the viscosity to the temperature η/T by the theory of Bloembergen, Purcell, and Pound.[59] The authors carried out a number of experiments to verify this prediction.

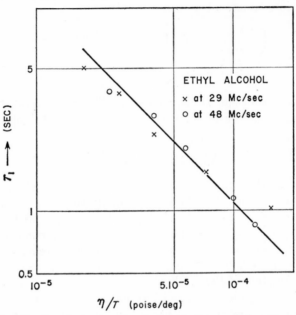

FIG. 9-1. Relaxation time for protons in ethyl alcohol, measured at 29 and 48 Mc/sec. (Bloembergen, Purcell, and Pound.[59])

Measurements of the spin-lattice relaxation time for liquid ethyl alcohol at a series of temperatures are shown in Fig. 9-1 in the form of a logarithmic plot. The plot shows that $1/T_1$ is indeed proportional to η/T, as indicated by the line with slope -1 drawn on the graph. Measurements at two different frequencies confirm that $1/T_1$ is independent of the Larmor frequency ν_0 in this range, also in agreement with the theory.

A wider range in η/T is accessible by measurements with glycerine as a function of temperature. As the temperature is lowered, the viscosity increases and the relaxation time decreases according to Eqs. (9-12) and (9-14). With glycerine a stage at which the correlation time τ_c becomes long enough to be comparable with the Larmor precession period can be reached. The appropriate Fourier component of the fluctuations then goes through a maximum and thereafter decreases. Consequently the spin-lattice relaxation time passes through a minimum and increases again when the viscosity increases further. According to Eq. (9-5), the position of this minimum depends on the frequency ν_0. The predictions were all confirmed by the measurements.[59]

It may be noted that the condition $\tau_c \ll \nu_0^{-1}$ is also the condition for the transverse and longitudinal relaxation times to be equal. When τ_c increases beyond the critical value $(2\pi\nu_0)^{-1}$, the fluctuations become slower than the Larmor precession, and spin-lattice relaxation again

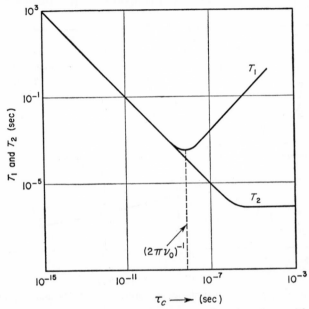

FIG. 9-2. Schematic respresentation of variation of relaxation times with correlation time τ_c. (Bloembergen, Purcell, and Pound.[59])

becomes less effective. T_1 therefore increases again. T_2, on the other hand, continues to decrease and eventually approaches a limiting value which is a measure of the dipole broadening of nuclear resonance lines for molecules held rigidly in a solid. This is illustrated schematically in Fig. 9-2. The conditions in most liquids and gases, however, are well to the left in the figure, although certain low-frequency exchange processes may modify this situation (Chap. 10). For a full theoretical treatment of the relaxation times throughout the whole range, the reader may consult the paper of Kubo and Tomita.[227]

The predicted inverse proportionality between relaxation time T_1 and viscosity η was investigated for a number of liquids under pressure by Benedek and Purcell.[36] In all the liquids examined T_1 was found to decrease with increasing pressure. The behavior of n-hexane, illustrated in Fig. 9-3, is typical. The viscosity rises more rapidly, however, so that the product $T_1\eta$ actually increases with pressure. For n-hexane, for example, the viscosity increases by a factor of about 30 when the pressure is increased to 8,000 kg/cm², while T_1 decreases by a factor of only 6. Other liquids show similar relative behavior.

Benedek and Purcell attribute the failure of the theory in these experiments to different behavior of the inter- and intramolecular contributions to the spin-lattice relaxation time. The theory actually relates the intermolecular part to the self-diffusion constant D [Eq. (9-13)] and then to

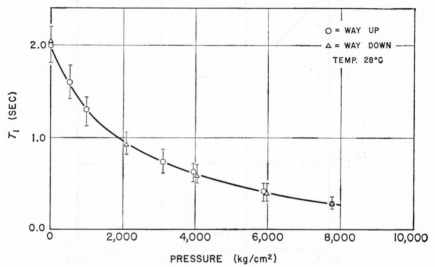

FIG. 9-3. Spin-lattice relaxation time vs. pressure for n-hexane. (Benedek and Purcell.[36])

the viscosity by using the Stokes-Einstein relation. Investigations of the diffusion constant itself, however, showed that the product $D\eta$ was approximately independent of pressure, in agreement with the Stokes-Einstein formula. The disagreement is therefore attributed to the failure of Eq. (9-12) for the intramolecular part. This requires that the *reorientation* correlation time τ_c should be proportional to the viscosity. While this assumption may be reasonable for temperature variation at constant pressure, it is plausible that the reduction of the free volume of the liquid by compression should affect the freedom to migrate more drastically than the freedom to rotate. As a result, the intramolecular contribution to the spin-lattice relaxation will not fall off as rapidly as the intermolecular contribution. Since the intramolecular contribution is generally the larger, T_1 will not fall as rapidly as predicted by the Bloembergen, Purcell, and Pound theory.

A number of measurements of spin-lattice relaxation times for protons are listed in Table 9-1.   One interesting feature is that some substances show distinct relaxation times for chemically nonequivalent protons in the same molecule.   This possibility was suggested by Wertz, Jain, and Batdorf[461] and by Nederbragt and Reilly.[300]   The latter made a series of comparative measurements of T_1 for the aliphatic and aromatic protons in some methylated benzenes.   The low value for T_1 of benzene in the presence of air is due to the presence of dissolved oxygen, which has a large effect on relaxation.   This will be discussed further in the next section.   The large value for a dilute solution of benzene in CS_2 (which

TABLE 9-1. PROTON SPIN-LATTICE RELAXATION TIMES

Substance	T_1, sec	Temp, °C	Ref.
Water	3.6 ± 0.2		91
Ethyl alcohol	2.2	20	59
Acetic acid	2.4	20	59
Sulfuric acid	0.7	20	59
Glycerine	0.023	20	59
n-Pentane	4.3	27	36
n-Hexane	2.0	28	36
Methyl iodide	3.8	29	36
Benzene	19.3	25	300
Benzene (in presence of air)	2.7		142
Benzene in CS_2 (11% vol)	60	25	300
Toluene (aromatic)	16	25	300
Toluene (—CH_3)	9	25	300

has very few magnetic nuclei) suggests that the intermolecular relaxation makes a considerable contribution to the total spin-lattice relaxation of pure benzene.

c. Relaxation by Paramagnetic Substances.   Another important mechanism of spin-lattice relaxation is the action of the magnetic fields due to unpaired electrons in paramagnetic substances.   Bloch, Hansen, and Packard[54] were the first to observe that the addition of paramagnetic ions to water substantially reduced the proton relaxation time.   The effect was further examined by Bloembergen, Purcell, and Pound,[59] who developed a theory similar to that for nuclear-dipole relaxation.   The relaxation is attributed to the diffusional Brownian motion of water molecules in the vicinity of the ion, so the only difference in the theoretical expression is that an effective mean-square magnetic moment of the electrons on an ion μ_{eff}^2 replaces the nuclear square moment $\frac{3}{4}\gamma^2\hbar^2$.   Thus the contribution to $1/T_1$ is,† by comparison with Eq. (9-14),

$$\frac{1}{T_1} = \frac{4\pi^2\gamma^2\eta N_p\mu_{eff}^2}{kT} \tag{9-17}$$

† The numerical factor is again different from the value quoted in ref. 59.

where N_p is the number of paramagnetic molecules or ions per cubic centimeter. For all but the smallest concentrations, this mechanism is more important than nuclear-dipole relaxation, because the magnetic moment of an unpaired electron is of the order of 10^3 times as large as the moment of a nucleus.

According to Eq. (9-17), the relaxation time of protons in ionic solutions should be inversely proportional to the ionic concentration and to

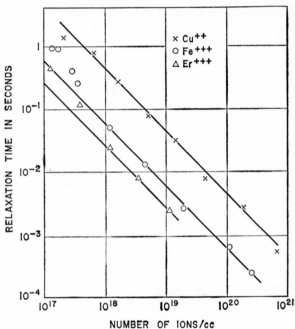

FIG. 9-4. Relaxation time T_1 for solutions of paramagnetic ions, measured at 29 Mc/sec. (Bloembergen, Purcell, and Pound.[59])

the square of the magnetic moment μ_{eff}^2. The first prediction was confirmed (except for some variations at low concentrations) by measuring T_1 as a function of concentration for several ions. This is illustrated in Fig. 9-4.

The predicted proportionality to μ_{eff}^2 can be tested by comparison with magnetic-susceptibility measurements, which provide a direct measure of the effective moment. Instead of using a value of the constant of proportionality derived from the viscosity, Bloembergen, Purcell, and Pound arbitrarily assumed a constant such that the value of μ_{eff} for Cu^{++} was 2.0 Bohr magnetons, in approximate agreement with susceptibility data. Use of the same constant of proportionality for other ions then leads to a "nuclear relaxation value" of μ_{eff} for other ions, which can be compared with the susceptibility value. It should be emphasized that use of Eq. (9-17) is not a good alternative method of finding μ_{eff}; the purpose is merely to test the predicted proportionality. The measurements presented in this manner are summarized in Table 9-2, which includes data

TABLE 9-2. COMPARISON OF MAGNETIC MOMENTS OF IONS INFERRED FROM PROTON SPIN-LATTICE RELAXATION TIMES AND FROM MAGNETIC SUSCEPTIBILITIES

Ion	Ground state	μ_{eff} (from T_1), Bohr magnetons	μ_{eff} (susceptibility), Bohr magnetons	Ref.
Cr^{3+}	$3d^3$ $^5D_0$	4.1 4.8 5.6	3.8	59 98 289
Mn^{++}	$3d^5$ ^6S	6.1 5.7	5.9	98 289
Fe^{3+}	$3d^5$ ^6S	5.5 5.6 6.4	5.9	59 98 289
Fe^{++}	$3d^6$ $^5D_4$	1.5	5.3	98
Co^{++}	$3d^7$ $^4F_{9/2}$	1.1 0.89 1.0	4.4–5.3	59 98 289
Ni^{++}	$3d^8$ $^3F_4$	1.8 1.4 2.1	3.2	59 98 289
Cu^{++}	$3d^9$ $^2D_{5/2}$	2.0†	2.0	
Ce^{3+}	$4f$ $^2F_{5/2}$	0.35	2.1	98
Pr^{3+}	$4f^2$ $^3H_4$	0.38	3.4	98
Nd^{3+}	$4f^3$ $^4I_{9/2}$	0.35	3.5	98
Sm^{3+}	$4f^5$ $^6H_{5/2}$	0.30	1.6	98
Eu^{3+}	$4f^6$ $^7H_0$	0.20	3.9	98
Eu^{++}	$4f^7$ ^8S	3.0	7.9	98
Gd^{3+}	$4f^7$ ^8S	10.8	7.9	98
Tb^{3+}	$4f^8$ $^7F_6$	1.95	9.8	98
Dy^{3+}	$4f^9$ $^6H_{15/2}$	1.47	10.9	98
Er^{3+}	$4f^{11}$ $^4I_{15/2}$	1.75	9.5	98
Yb^{3+}	$4f^{13}$ $^2F_{7/2}$	0.50	4.5	98

† Assumed as standard.

obtained more recently by other workers. The corresponding electronic ground states of the free ions are also listed.

It is clear from Table 9-2 that there are substantial deviations from the predicted relationship with the susceptibility. Ions such as Co^{++} and most of the rare earths are considerably less effective in reducing T_1.

The variations in the table can be understood in a qualitative manner if we note that the derivation of Eq. (9-15) assumed that each electron moment *maintained its orientation during the course of the diffusion* which leads to relaxation. This is valid only if the spin-lattice relaxation time of the electron spin is long compared with the correlation time for diffusion. If this is not so, that is, if the electron spin changes its direction frequently, the magnetic field at the neighboring proton will fluctuate more rapidly. Consequently the decay time τ_c in Eq. (9-8) must be replaced by the electron spin-lattice time τ_s, and the proton spin-lattice relaxation time will be longer.

The ions in Table 9-2 that are comparatively ineffective in proton-spin relaxation are just those which might be expected to have short electron spin-lattice relaxation times, the electron spin being strongly coupled to motions of the molecular framework. In the first transition series, Fe^{++} and Co^{++} have orbital degeneracy in the octahedral field of six water molecules, so that spin-orbit coupling and distortion of the hydration shell will lead to rapid electron-spin relaxation. The ferric and manganous ions, on the other hand, have half-filled shells and are in ^6S states. The field of neighboring water molecules cannot lead to any splitting and the spin-orbit coupling is relatively small. This means that the electron-spin orientation is only loosely coupled to the environment, so that the ions are relatively efficient in proton relaxation. Similar arguments apply to Cr^{3+} ions for the electron-spin Hamiltonian is nearly isotropic.[2]

In the rare earth series, the ions Eu^{++} and Gd^{3+} with a half-filled shell (f^7) are again the most effective, since the free ions are in S states. The most ineffective of all (relative to its susceptibility) is Eu^{3+}. The magnetic susceptibility of this ion is known to be anomalous,[445] the free ion possessing no resultant moment in its lowest state.

The proton spin-lattice relaxation times in aqueous solutions of a number of other chromium (III) complexes have been examined by Morgan, Nolle, Hull, and Murphy.[289] $CrF_6{}^{3-}$, $Cr(NH_3)_6{}^{3+}$, $Cr(C_2O_4)_3{}^{3-}$, and $Cr(CN)_6{}^{3-}$ are all less effective than $Cr(H_2O)^{3+}$. The values of the product $N_{ion}T_1$ vary from 7.4×10^{-4} sec mole/liter for $CrF_6{}^{3-}$ to 20.5×10^{-4} for $Cr(CN)_6{}^{3-}$, compared with 1.35×10^{-4} for $Cr(H_2O)^{3+}$. This lowering of effectiveness is probably due to the closer approach of the protons to the unpaired electrons in the hydrated ion. [There may be exchange between protons in the hydrated shell and other water molecules in solutions of $Cr(H_2O)^{3+}$.]

Relatively little work has been done on the effect of nonionic paramagnetic substances. Perhaps the most interesting is the oxygen molecule, which is often present in small quantities. Chiarotti and Giulotto[91] measured the effect of dissolved oxygen on the proton relaxation time of water and found that $\mu_{eff} = 1.2$ Bohr magnetons, compared with the susceptibility value of 2.8.   This suggests that electronic relaxation may be a significant effect.

Some evidence that the relaxation theory based on the Brownian motion of H_2O molecules is not altogether satisfactory has been given by Rivkind.[384]   He investigated the proton relaxation times in solutions of paramagnetic ions in H_2O-D_2O mixtures.   The proton relaxation time was found to increase by as much as a factor of 10 if the D_2O concentration was increased to 90 per cent, which is more than can be accounted for by viscosity changes.   Rivkind suggested that the principal motion of protons near the paramagnetic ion was by proton exchange across hydrogen bonds rather than by molecular motion.   This would be more sharply reduced by the presence of deuterons.   In any case, the first shell of water molecules is probably tightly bound and could not take part in the Brownian motion envisaged in the derivation of Eq. (9-17).

Another mechanism contributing to proton relaxation times has been proposed by Bloembergen.[55]   It is based on the fact that, if the unpaired electron has, or the unpaired electrons have, a wave function that actually extends to the proton positions, there is a term in the Hamiltonian of the type $A\mathbf{I} \cdot \mathbf{S}$, where A is a constant and $\mathbf{S}$ is the electron spin.   This energy is the origin of nuclear hyperfine structure in electron magnetic resonance spectra; it gives a fluctuating magnetic field at the proton with a correlation time equal to the electron spin-lattice relaxation time τ_s (this usually being shorter than the time the proton remains close to the ion).   If τ_s is sufficiently long, there will be low-frequency oscillations of this field which will contribute[55] to the transverse relaxation time T_2 but not to T_1.   Under these circumstances, the ratio T_1/T_2 may be greater than unity.   Such an effect had already been observed by Zimmerman[473] and by Laukien and Schlüter[234] for solutions of Mn^{++} and Gd^{3+}.   Both of these ions are half-filled shells in S states (Table 9-2), so that τ_s is expected to be long.   With Mn^{++}, $\tau_s = 3 \times 10^{-9}$ sec (long enough to permit the observation of electron-spin resonance), whereas the usual value is 10^{-11} or 10^{-12} sec.   Bloembergen showed that the theoretical order of magnitude of the effect was sufficient to explain the observed value of $T_1/T_2 = 7.1$ for Mn^{++}.   In very small external fields, the mechanism also contributes to T_1, so that eventually $T_1 = T_2$ again.   This has been observed by Bloom.[60]

The Overhauser Effect.   An effect closely connected with spin-lattice relaxation of nuclei by unpaired electrons is the Overhauser nuclear polarization.[310]   Overhauser predicted that, if nuclear spin-lattice relaxation was governed principally by an interaction $A\mathbf{I} \cdot \mathbf{S}$, then saturation of the electron resonance should lead to an increase in the nuclear polarization.   The prediction was originally made for metals, but it can, in principle, also operate in other paramagnetic substances.

The effect is most easily understood in terms of Fig. 9-5, which shows the energy levels of the system of one unpaired electron and one nucleus of spin 1/2 in a magnetic field. (It should be noted that the magneto-gyric ratio of the electron is negative. This means that states with $S_z = 1/2$ are above those with $S_z = -1/2$.) The effect of a small coupling Hamiltonian $A\mathbf{I} \cdot \mathbf{S}$ is two-fold. In the first place, AI_zS_z changes the energy levels slightly; secondly, the part $A(I_xS_x + I_yS_y)$ can give rise to a transition in which the spins interchange, that is, the transition $1 \rightleftharpoons 4$ shown by a dashed line in the figure. We suppose, in fact, that this is the principal method of nuclear spin-lattice relaxation.

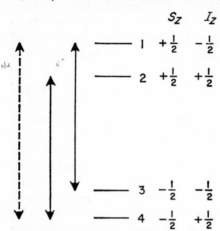

FIG. 9-5. Energy levels of an electron and a nucleus in a magnetic field. The solid lines indicate electron transitions, and the dashed line the transition leading to nuclear relaxation.

The effect of saturating the electron resonance is to equalize the populations of states connected by the solid lines. Thus if the populations are p_1, p_2, p_3, p_4, we have

$$p_1 = p_3 \qquad p_2 = p_4 \qquad (9\text{-}18)$$

The spin-exchange transitions $1 \rightleftharpoons 4$, however, are unaffected by the saturation and ensure the correct thermal ratio between p_1 and p_4:

$$\frac{p_1}{p_4} = \exp\left(-\frac{\Delta E}{kT}\right) \qquad (9\text{-}19)$$

where ΔE is the energy difference between the highest and lowest states. Combining with Eq. (9-18), we get for the ratio of nuclear spin polarizations

$$\frac{p_1 + p_3}{p_2 + p_4} = \exp\left(-\frac{\Delta E}{kT}\right) \qquad (9\text{-}20)$$

Since the energy ΔE is much larger than the separation between the nuclear Zeeman levels (being determined, rather, by the electron magnetic moment), the nuclear polarization is greatly increased. This effect has been observed in metals by Carver and Slichter[88] and in an organic free radical by Belgers, van der Kint, and van Wieringen.[34]

d. **Relaxation Due to Anisotropic Electronic Shielding.** Another possible mechanism for spin-lattice magnetic relaxation was suggested by Gutowsky and Woessner[173] and by McConnell and Holm.[272] If the chemical shielding is not isotropic, the secondary magnetic field due to electronic currents will not generally be parallel to the applied field, and there will therefore be a component in a perpendicular direction. As the molecule rotates, this component will oscillate and may cause transitions between the nuclear spin states. Unlike the mechanisms previously discussed, this requires the presence of an external field H_0 and will lead to a spin-lattice relaxation time dependent on the magnitude of H_0 even when the correlation time τ_c is small.

As already discussed in Chap. 7, the electronic shielding should really be represented by a tensor $\mathbf{\sigma}$, so that the field acting on the nucleus when the applied field is $\mathbf{H}_0$ will be

$$\mathbf{H} = \mathbf{H}_0 - \mathbf{\sigma} \cdot \mathbf{H}_0 \qquad (9\text{-}21)$$

If $\mathbf{H}_0$ is in the z direction, the x component of $\mathbf{H}$ will be

$$H_x = -\sigma_{xz}H_0 \qquad (9\text{-}22)$$

To apply the general theory developed earlier in this section [Eq. (9-6)], we need the mean-square value of $\sigma_{xz}H_0$. The correlation time τ_c will be the same as for intramolecular relaxation. The mean-square value of σ_{xz}, averaged over orientations, can be expressed in terms of the principal values of $\mathbf{\sigma}$, which we shall write σ_{11}, σ_{22}, and σ_{33}. Then, by standard tensor theory

$$\overline{H_0{}^2\sigma_{xz}{}^2} = \tfrac{1}{15}H_0{}^2(\sigma_{11}{}^2 + \sigma_{22}{}^2 + \sigma_{33}{}^2 - \sigma_{22}\sigma_{33} - \sigma_{33}\sigma_{11} - \sigma_{11}\sigma_{22}) \qquad (9\text{-}23)$$

The expression for T_1 then follows by substitution in Eq. (9-6). If the correlation time τ_c is small and if we assume that the tensor $\mathbf{\sigma}$ is axially symmetric, then we obtain the McConnell-Holm formula[272]

$$\frac{1}{T_1} = \tfrac{2}{15}\gamma^2 H_0{}^2 \, (\Delta\sigma)^2 \, \tau_c \qquad (9\text{-}24)$$

where $\Delta\sigma$ is the difference between the values of σ parallel and perpendicular to the axis of symmetry. This mechanism, therefore, gives a contribution to $1/T_1$ which is proportional to $H_0{}^2$.

McConnell and Holm[272] quoted some data on C^{13} relaxation in support of the above mechanism. They found that the observed value for T_1 for $C^{13}S_2$ was shorter than for $C^{13}Cl_4$ in unenriched samples. In $C^{13}S_2$, the dipole-interaction mechanism cannot be important because of the low density of magnetic nuclei, so much of the observed relaxation may be due to anisotropic shielding. In $C^{13}Cl_4$, however, the tensor $\mathbf{\sigma}$ must be isotropic because of the tetrahedral symmetry, so this mechanism cannot be effective.

Quantitative investigations of the dependence of T_1 on the strength of the external field H_0 were carried out by Gutowsky and Woessner.[173] They examined proton and fluorine spin-lattice relaxation times in

CH_2FCl, CHF_2Cl, $CHFCl_2$, and 1,3,5-trifluorobenzene at frequencies of 20 and 26.5 Mc/sec. These compounds have structures such that the values of $1/T_1$ according to the formulas for direct magnetic dipole interaction are nearly identical. In fact, the fluorine T_1 values are found to be much shorter than the proton values and to decrease with increasing field H_0, as would be expected if the anisotropic shielding mechanism were effective. Gutowsky and Woessner used their data to estimate the screening-constant anisotropy $\Delta\sigma$ from Eq. (9-24) and the theoretical expressions for the dipole-dipole contributions in the case of 1,3,5-trifluorobenzene. They found $\Delta\sigma = 7.5 \times 10^{-4}$, in reasonable agreement with the prediction of the theory of electronic screening (Chap. 7). The data on the Freons lead to a similar value for the anisotropy, although here the value of the ratio T_{1H}/T_{1F} extrapolated to zero field did not agree with the ratio predicted by the dipole mechanism.

9-3. Electric Quadrupole Relaxation in Liquids

The possibility of spin relaxation by the interaction of nuclear-quadrupole moments with fluctuating electric-field gradients arises only for nuclei with spin $I \geqslant 1$. Before proceeding to a theory of this effect, it is necessary to generalize the relation between T_1 and the transition probabilities, which was given in Sec. 3-2 for nuclei with $I = 1/2$. This will be done only for $I = 1$, where there are three possible states.

The three states corresponding to $I_z = 1$, 0, and -1 can be labeled $+$, 0, $-$, respectively. If the magnitude of the external field is H_0, the corresponding energies will be $-\gamma\hbar H_0$, 0, and $\gamma\hbar H_0$. The six transition probabilities may then be denoted by symbols such as $W_{0\to+}$. If the populations of the states are n_+, n_0, and n_-, the resultant magnetic moment will be proportional to $n_+ - n_-$, where

$$\frac{dn_+}{dt} = -n_+(W_{+\to 0} + W_{+\to -}) + n_0 W_{0\to +} + n_- W_{-\to +}$$

$$\frac{dn_-}{dt} = n_+ W_{+\to -} + n_0 W_{0\to -} - n_-(W_{-\to 0} + W_{-\to +}) \qquad (9\text{-}25)$$

If it is assumed that n_0 is always the average of n_+ and n_-, the probabilities W can be related by detailed balancing [as in Eq. (3-8)]. Subtraction of the two parts of Eq. (9-25) then gives (in a small field H_0)

$$\frac{d}{dt}(n_+ - n_-) = -\frac{1}{T_1}[(n_+ - n_-) - (n_+ - n_-)_{eq}] \qquad (9\text{-}26)$$

where the spin-lattice relaxation time T_1 is given by

$$\frac{1}{T_1} = W_1 + 2W_2 \qquad (9\text{-}27)$$

In this equation W_1 is the mean of the one-quantum transition probabilities $W_{0\to+}$, $W_{0\to-}$, $W_{+\to 0}$, $W_{-\to 0}$ (which are nearly equal in a small field) and W_2 is the mean of the two-quantum probabilities $W_{+\to-}$, $W_{-\to+}$. This is the required extension of Eq. (3-12).

To calculate the one- and two-quantum transition probabilities W_1 and W_2, we have to set up the Hamiltonian for the interaction of the nuclear quadrupole with the electric-field gradient. We shall follow the notation used by Pound[343] in his work on pure quadrupole spectroscopy. Both the quadrupole moment $\mathbf{Q}$ and the field gradient $\nabla\mathbf{E}$ are second-order tensors, and the interaction F may be written in the form

$$F = \mathbf{Q} \cdot \nabla\mathbf{E} = \sum_{p=-2}^{2} (-1)^p Q_p (\nabla E)_{-p} \qquad (9\text{-}28)$$

The complex components of the field gradient $(\nabla E)_p$ are

$$(\nabla E)_0 = -\tfrac{1}{2} \frac{\partial E_z}{\partial z}$$
$$(\nabla E)_{\pm 1} = \pm 6^{-\frac{1}{2}} \left(\frac{\partial E_x}{\partial z} \pm i \frac{\partial E_y}{\partial z} \right)$$
$$(\nabla E)_{\pm 2} = -6^{-\frac{1}{2}} \left(\frac{\partial E_x}{\partial x} - \frac{\partial E_y}{\partial y} \pm 2i \frac{\partial E_x}{\partial y} \right) \qquad (9\text{-}29)$$

If (1) the electric-field gradient is axially symmetric, (2) the axis of symmetry makes an angle θ with the z direction, and (3) the projection on Oxy makes an angle ϕ with Ox, then the components take the form

$$(\nabla E)_0 = \tfrac{1}{4} eq (3 \cos^2 \theta - 1)$$
$$(\nabla E)_{\pm 1} = \pm \tfrac{1}{4} 6^{\frac{1}{2}} eq \sin \theta\, e^{\pm i\phi}$$
$$(\nabla E)_{\pm 2} = \tfrac{1}{8} 6^{\frac{1}{2}} eq \sin^2 \theta\, e^{\pm 2i\phi} \qquad (9\text{-}30)$$

where the field gradient eq is given by an average of the field of the neighboring electrons and nuclei:

$$eq = -e \sum_{j} \langle (3 \cos^2 \theta_j - 1) r_j^{-3} \rangle_{\text{av}} \qquad (9\text{-}31)$$

θ_j being the angle between the direction of electron j and the symmetry axis.

If the external magnetic field is in the z direction, we require the matrix elements of the operator F between states corresponding to different values of I_z. These can be obtained from the matrix elements of the quadrupole moment.[57] For a nucleus with spin $I = 1$, the only elements required are

$$(0|F|\pm 1) = -\tfrac{1}{2} 3^{\frac{1}{2}} eQ(\nabla E)_{\pm 1}$$
$$(\pm 1|F|\mp 1) = \tfrac{1}{2} 6^{\frac{1}{2}} eQ(\nabla E)_{\pm 2} \qquad (9\text{-}32)$$

where eQ is the nuclear-quadrupole moment.

The theory of transitions in random fields (Appendix B) can now be used to get the transition probabilities W_1 and W_2. The mean-square moduli of $(\nabla E)_q$ can be found from Eq. (9-30) and are all equal to $\frac{1}{20}e^2q^2$. It follows that the required quantities are

$$W_1 = \frac{3}{80} e^4 q^2 Q^2 \hbar^2 \frac{2\tau_c}{1 + 4\pi^2 \nu_0^2 \tau_c^2}$$

$$W_2 = \frac{3}{40} e^4 q^2 Q^2 \hbar^2 \frac{2\tau_c}{1 + 16\pi^2 \nu_0^2 \tau_c^2} \tag{9-33}$$

where τ_c is the correlation time, determined by the molecular rotation as with the intramolecular dipolar mechanism. Making the usual assumption $\nu_0 \tau_c \ll 1$, we finally obtain

$$\frac{1}{T_1} = \frac{3}{8} e^4 \hbar^2 q^2 Q^2 \tau_c \tag{9-34}$$

Bloembergen, Purcell, and Pound[59] measured the spin-lattice relaxation time of deuterium (which has spin $I = 1$) in a sample of 50 per cent heavy water. They found it to be 0.5 sec, compared with 3.0 sec for the protons. Since the magnetic moment of the deuteron is less than that of the proton, the magnetic dipolar mechanism would lead to a *longer* relaxation time for deuterium. It appears then that the relaxation of deuterium is determined mainly by the quadrupole effect. Using a value of τ_c estimated from the proton relaxation and the value $Q = 2.73 \times 10^{-27}$ cm², Bloembergen[57] calculated that the value of the field gradient eq was the same as that produced by one elementary charge at a distance of 1 A.

The dependence of T_1 on the field gradient eq is shown up rather strikingly by observations on the spectrum of a nucleus with a quadrupole when it is placed in an environment in which there can be no field gradient. In the ammonium ion,[308] for example, the N^{14} nucleus can experience only a small field gradient, and the spectrum is sharper (Fig. 5-8) than is normal for this nucleus.

9-4. Spin-lattice Relaxation in Gases

Nuclear magnetic resonance absorption in hydrogen gas was first observed by Purcell, Pound, and Bloembergen,[356] and the interpretation of the observed spin-lattice relaxation times was discussed in their later paper.[59] At room temperature and a pressure of 10 atm, T_1 was found to be approximately 0.015 sec and to increase with increasing pressure. Subsequent measurements have shown that T_1 is proportional to the pressure both at room temperature[316] and at 20.4°K.[64] Similar behavior has been reported for ethane.[451]

The mechanism of spin-lattice relaxation for protons is again the effect of local magnetic fields which fluctuate more rapidly than the basic Larmor frequency ν_0. In the hydrogen molecule there are two distinct magnetic fields, one arising from the molecular rotation and the other from the magnetic moment of the other nucleus. These interactions depend on the rotational quantum number J and its component m_J. The correlation time τ_c for such fields, then, will be of the order of the time in which J or m_J changes, which will be of the order of the time between collisions. For hydrogen at 10 atm this is approximately 10^{-11} sec, so that $2\pi\nu_0\tau_c \ll 1$, and we therefore have a situation in which $T_1 = T_2$, and $T_1 \propto 1/\tau_c$. Since the time between collisions is inversely proportional to the pressure P, we obtain the observed proportionality $T_1 \propto P$.

A quantitative theory of spin-lattice relaxation in hydrogen gas was developed by Schwinger and reported by Bloembergen.[57] Using this theory, Bloembergen, Purcell, and Pound found $T_1 = 0.03$ sec, in approximate agreement with the experimental data. A fuller study of spin-lattice relaxation in hydrogen gas at lower temperatures has been carried out by Bloom,[64] who also investigated the dependence of T_1 on ortho-para concentration and concentration of added helium.

CHAPTER 10

TIME-DEPENDENT FACTORS INFLUENCING
SIGNAL SHAPE

10-1. Introduction

As has already been pointed out in Chap. 5, the shape and width of nuclear magnetic resonances are sensitive to time-dependent processes which occur at rates of the order of the extent of the spectrum measured in frequency units (e.g., cycles per second). For processes slow compared with this critical rate, spectra appear as superpositions of distinct parts corresponding to the individual species or environments present. For rapid processes, on the other hand, the spectra are determined by the time-average environment of the nuclei under investigation.

There are a number of ways in which nuclear spins can be disturbed from steady-state motion in a uniform magnetic field. Some of these occur naturally, as with intermolecular exchange and internal rotation, whereas others can be introduced by suitable experimental techniques, as with double irradiation. All of these phenomena, however, are closely related in that each involves some time averaging or partial time averaging of the nuclear environment. For processes taking place at something near the critical rate, NMR spectroscopy can be a valuable tool in quantitative rate investigations. In this chapter we shall consider in detail the effect of processes of this sort.

10-2. Collapse of Signals by Exchange between Different Chemical Positions

a. **Two Sites.** Perhaps the simplest example of a rate process which modifies the nuclear resonance spectrum is a system in which the individual nuclei are moving from position to position in a random statistical manner. To begin with, we shall neglect any spin coupling and suppose that the positions or sites are of two types with different chemical shifts. Some of the protons in a mixture of water and alcohol, for example, will be exchanging between water molecules and the hydroxyl position in the alcohol. If the exchange rate is slow, the spectrum will consist of two separate signals; if it is rapid, there will be only one signal in an appropriately averaged position.

The quantitative description of this system is best developed by suitable modifications of the Bloch phenomenological equations introduced in Chap. 3. This approach was first used by Gutowsky, McCall, and Slichter[166] and has since been presented in a simplified form by McConnell.[270a] The solutions (3-48) to (3-50) give the variation of the macroscopic moment (M_x, M_y, M_z) per unit volume. It is more convenient to discuss the components in the coordinate frame which is rotating with the applied rf field (Fig. 3-2). Thus if u and v are the transverse components of M along and perpendicular to the rotating field H_1, Eqs. (3-55) to (3-57) apply. The out-of-phase component v is then proportional to the absorption intensity. If the oscillating field H_1 is not too large, the polarization M_z is not appreciably altered from its equilibrium value M_0, and the equations for u and v become

$$\frac{du}{dt} + \frac{u}{T_2} + (\omega_0 - \omega)v = 0 \qquad (10\text{-}1)$$

$$\frac{dv}{dt} + \frac{v}{T_2} - (\omega_0 - \omega)u = -\gamma H_1 M_0 \qquad (10\text{-}2)$$

Equations (10-1) and (10-2) are the real and imaginary parts of a complex equation. If we define a complex moment

$$G = u + iv \qquad (10\text{-}3)$$

the equation for G is

$$\frac{dG}{dt} + \left[\frac{1}{T_2} - i(\omega_0 - \omega)\right]G = -i\gamma H_1 M_0 \qquad (10\text{-}4)$$

The Bloch equations in their simplest form apply to the macroscopic moment $\mathbf{M}$ when all nuclei are acted on by the same field H_0. Now if there are two positions with different screening constants, this is no longer correct, and instead there will be two possible fields and correspondingly two Larmor frequencies, which we shall write ω_A and ω_B. The chemical shift in cycles per second is then $(\omega_A - \omega_B)/2\pi$. If no exchange of nuclei occurs between A and B positions, there will be two independent macroscopic moments, with complex G components obeying equations

$$\frac{dG_A}{dt} + \alpha_A G_A = -i\gamma H_1 M_{0A} \qquad (10\text{-}5)$$

$$\frac{dG_B}{dt} + \alpha_B G_B = -i\gamma H_1 M_{0B} \qquad (10\text{-}6)$$

where α_A and α_B are complex quantities defined by

$$\alpha_A = T_{2A}^{-1} - i(\omega_A - \omega) \tag{10-7}$$
$$\alpha_B = T_{2B}^{-1} - i(\omega_B - \omega) \tag{10-8}$$

T_{2A} and T_{2B} being the transverse relaxation times of nuclei in the two positions in the absence of exchange.

These equations now have to be modified to take account of the possibility of exchange between A and B positions. We shall follow a procedure similar to that proposed by McConnell.[270a] It will be supposed that all nuclei remain in one position until they make a sudden rapid jump to another, the nuclear precession during the jump being neglected. Under these circumstances it is clear that a nuclear exchange between positions *of the same type* will have no effect. We shall therefore ignore such exchanges and consider only interchanges between positions of types A and B. It will be assumed that, while a nucleus is in an A position, there is a constant probability τ_A^{-1} per unit time of its making a jump to a B position. τ_A is then the mean lifetime for a stay on A sites. Another corresponding time τ_B can be defined for the lifetime of B positions. The fractional populations of A and B sites p_A and p_B $(= 1 - p_A)$ are related to τ_A and τ_B by

$$p_A = \frac{\tau_A}{\tau_A + \tau_B} \qquad p_B = \frac{\tau_B}{\tau_A + \tau_B} \tag{10-9}$$

by considerations of detailed balancing.

The modified Bloch equations proposed by McConnell[270a] are

$$\frac{dG_A}{dt} + \alpha_A G_A = -i\gamma H_1 M_{0A} + \tau_B^{-1}G_B - \tau_A^{-1}G_A \tag{10-10}$$

$$\frac{dG_B}{dt} + \alpha_B G_B = -i\gamma H_1 M_{0B} + \tau_A^{-1}G_A - \tau_B^{-1}G_B \tag{10-11}$$

Equations (10-10) and (10-11) differ from Eqs. (10-5) and (10-6) by the addition of terms to allow for the exchange. Thus $\tau_B^{-1}G_B$ in Eq. (10-10) represents the rate of increase of G_A due to transfer of magnetization from B to A sites. Similarly, $\tau_A^{-1}G_A$ is the corresponding rate of loss. McConnell gave the equations in a more general form which did not assume a small rf field H_1, but we shall require only Eqs. (10-10) and (10-11).

The solution of Eqs. (10-10) and (10-11) appropriate for slow passage is obtained by putting

$$\frac{dG_A}{dt} = \frac{dG_B}{dt} = 0 \tag{10-12}$$

The equations can then be solved for G_A and G_B. Noting that

$$M_{0A} = p_A M_0 \qquad M_{0B} = p_B M_0 \tag{10-13}$$

the total complex moment is given by

$$
\begin{aligned}
G &= G_A + G_B \\
&= -i\gamma H_1 M_0 \frac{\tau_A + \tau_B + \tau_A \tau_B(\alpha_A p_A + \alpha_B p_B)}{(1 + \alpha_A \tau_A)(1 + \alpha_B \tau_B) - 1}
\end{aligned} \tag{10-14}
$$

This was first obtained by Gutowsky, McCall, and Slichter,[166] using a more complicated argument. The intensity of absorption at frequency ω is then proportional to the imaginary part of G. Before considering this in full, we shall examine its behavior in the two limiting cases when the lifetimes τ_A and τ_B are long and short.

Slow Exchange. If the lifetimes τ_A and τ_B are sufficiently large compared with the inverse of the separation $(\omega_A - \omega_B)^{-1}$, the spectrum will consist of distinct signals in the vicinity of the frequencies ω_A and ω_B. For example, if the radio frequency ω is close to ω_A, and thus far away from ω_B, G_B is effectively zero and the solution becomes

$$G \approx G_A \approx -i\gamma H_1 M_0 \frac{p_A \tau_A}{1 + \alpha_A \tau_A} \tag{10-15}$$

The imaginary part is

$$v = -\gamma H_1 M_0 \frac{p_A T'_{2A}}{1 + (T'_{2A})^2(\omega_A - \omega)^2} \tag{10-16}$$

a broadened signal centered at ω_A with width given by the parameter

$$T'^{-1}_{2A} = T_{2A}^{-1} + \tau_A^{-1} \tag{10-17}$$

There will be a corresponding signal centered on ω_B. This shows that the exchange leads to an *additional* broadening of the individual signals. If T_{2A}^{-1} is known, measurements of the width of these broadened signals provide a means of estimating τ_A. This procedure is valid, provided the broadening is not large enough to cause appreciable overlap of the signals.

Rapid Exchange. In the limit of rapid exchange, τ_A and τ_B are small and Eq. (10-14) reduces to [using Eq. (10-10)]

$$G = -i\gamma H_1 M_0 \frac{\tau_A + \tau_B}{\alpha_A \tau_A + \alpha_B \tau_B} = -\frac{i\gamma H_1 M_0}{p_A \alpha_A + p_B \alpha_B} \tag{10-18}$$

The imaginary part is

$$v = -\gamma H_1 M_0 \frac{T'_2}{1 + T'^2_2(p_A \omega_A + p_B \omega_B - \omega)^2} \tag{10-19}$$

representing a resonance line centered on a mean frequency

$$\omega_{\text{mean}} = p_A \omega_A + p_B \omega_B \tag{10-20}$$

with a line width given by

$$\frac{1}{T_2'} = \frac{p_A}{T_{2A}} + \frac{p_B}{T_{2B}}$$ (10-21)

If the exchange is not quite rapid enough to give complete collapse, the central signal centered on ω_{mean} will appear to have a larger width than that given by Eq. (10-21). A corrected form of Eq. (10-21) can be obtained by putting $\omega = \omega_{mean}$ in Eq. (10-14) and expanding in powers of τ. This gives an effective transverse relaxation time

$$\frac{1}{T_2'} = \frac{p_A}{T_{2A}} + \frac{p_B}{T_{2B}} + p_A{}^2 p_B{}^2 (\omega_A - \omega_B)^2 (\tau_A + \tau_B)$$ (10-22)

Experimentally, this effect may lead to a transverse relaxation time T_2 which is appreciably shorter than the longitudinal time T_1. Equation (10-22) has been used by Meiboom, Luz, and Gill[282] to interpret the difference between T_1 and T_2 for water in terms of the breaking and re-forming of hydrogen bonds (Chap. 15).

Intermediate Rate of Exchange. The transition from a spectrum of two lines to one line occurs when the lifetimes τ_A and τ_B are of the order of $(\omega_A - \omega_B)^{-1}$. The full expression for the intensity of absorption in this intermediate range is obtained from the imaginary part of the general expression for the complex moment G [Eq. (10-14)]. Gutowsky and Holm[160] give the expression in the following form when the two transverse relaxation times T_{2A} and T_{2B} are equal.

$$v = -\frac{\gamma H_1 M_0 (1 + \tau/T_2) P + QR}{P^2 + R^2}$$ (10-23)

where

$$\tau = \frac{\tau_A \tau_B}{\tau_A + \tau_B}$$ (10-24)

and

$$P = \tau \left\{ \left(\frac{1}{T_2}\right)^2 - [\tfrac{1}{2}(\omega_A + \omega_B) - \omega]^2 + \tfrac{1}{4}(\omega_A - \omega_B)^2 \right\} + \frac{1}{T_2}$$

$$Q = \tau[\tfrac{1}{2}(\omega_A + \omega_B) - \omega - \tfrac{1}{2}(p_A - p_B)(\omega_A - \omega_B)]$$

$$R = [\tfrac{1}{2}(\omega_A + \omega_B) - \omega] \left(1 + \frac{2\tau}{T_2}\right) + \tfrac{1}{2}(p_A - p_B)(\omega_A - \omega_B)$$ (10-25)

Rather than develop this complicated expression any further we shall examine the intermediate behavior under the following simplifying conditions:

1. Equal populations and lifetimes so that

$$p_A = p_B = \tfrac{1}{2} \qquad \tau_A = \tau_B = 2\tau$$ (10-26)

2. Large transverse relaxation times so that we may take

$$T_{2A}{}^{-1} = T_{2B}{}^{-1} = 0$$ (10-27)

This means that we are dealing with signals whose width in the absence of exchange is small compared with their separation. Under these conditions, the intensity of absorption is proportional to

$$v = -\tfrac{1}{4}\gamma H_1 M_0 \frac{\tau(\omega_A - \omega_B)^2}{[\tfrac{1}{2}(\omega_A + \omega_B) - \omega]^2 + \tau^2(\omega_A - \omega)^2(\omega_B - \omega)^2} \tag{10-28}$$

For the purpose of applying it to actual cases, this formula can be

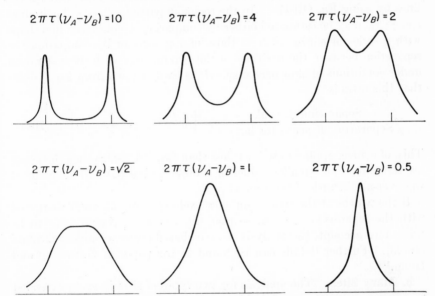

FIG. 10-1. Change of shape function $g(\nu)$ for increasing exchange rate between two positions with equal populations. (Note that τ is half of the lifetime of either site. The intensities are not on comparable scales.)

expressed in terms of frequencies ν $(= \omega/2\pi)$, measurements being in cycles per second. This gives the shape function $g(\nu)$:

$$g(\nu) = K \frac{\tau(\nu_A - \nu_B)^2}{[\tfrac{1}{2}(\nu_A + \nu_B) - \nu]^2 + 4\pi^2\tau^2(\nu_A - \nu)^2(\nu_B - \nu)^2} \tag{10-29}$$

where K is a normalizing constant. It turns out that the actual shape of this function depends only on the product $\tau|\nu_A - \nu_B|$. It is easily seen that for large τ it gives two lines at ν_A and ν_B, while for small τ it gives one line halfway between. The form of the function for some intermediate values of $\tau(\nu_A - \nu_B)$ is shown in Fig. 10-1. These diagrams show that, as τ decreases from infinity, the two individual signals broaden and their maxima draw closer together. This continues until τ reaches the intermediate value

$$\frac{\sqrt{2}}{2\pi(\nu_A - \nu_B)} \tag{10-30}$$

when the peaks coalesce into one broad signal with a maximum at the mean position. As τ decreases below this value, the central peak sharpens until eventually there is a single sharp line.

From the observed shape of the curve, it is possible to estimate the time τ, provided, of course, that the conditions about the relaxation times T_2 are satisfied. If τ is relatively large, so that the principal effect is a broadening of the individual signals, it can be found from the width of the lines by using Eq. (10-17). In the region of partial collapse, the product $\tau|\nu_A - \nu_B|$ may be estimated either by comparing the observed line shape with a series of curves such as those of Fig. 10-1 or by comparing the separation between the positions of the two maxima with the separation under conditions of slow exchange. It is easily shown from Eq. (10-29) that this ratio is

$$\frac{\text{Separation of peaks}}{\text{Separation of peaks for large } \tau} = \left[1 - \frac{1}{2\pi^2\tau^2(\nu_A - \nu_B)^2} \right]^{\frac{1}{2}} \quad (10\text{-}31)$$

This, of course, applies only if τ is less than Eq. (10-30), so that the peaks are separate. For smaller values of τ, observations have to be made on the over-all breadth of the central peak.

If the widths of the signals for slow exchange are not small compared with the separation $\nu_A - \nu_B$, so that the relaxation time T_2 has to be taken into account, the analysis must be based on the complete formula (10-23). Further details can be found in the paper of Gutowsky and Holm.[160]

b. Many Sites. The analysis for two types of sites is easily extended to n types. The results for this more general problem have been discussed in detail by Anderson,[9] Kubo,[226] and Sack,[391] together with a fuller treatment of the basic assumptions. In this section, however, we shall indicate only the lines along which the analysis of Sec. 10-2a can be extended.

If there are n types of site with natural Larmor frequencies ω_j and transverse relaxation times T_{2j} ($j = 1, 2, \ldots, n$), we define

$$\alpha_j = T_{2j}^{-1} - i(\omega_j - \omega) \quad (10\text{-}32)$$

Further it is supposed that, if a nucleus is on a j site, there is a constant probability $1/\tau_{jk}$ per unit time of its making a jump to a k site. If the fractional population of the j sites is p_j, then, for a steady state,

$$p_j \sum_k \frac{1}{\tau_{jk}} = \sum_k p_k \frac{1}{\tau_{kj}} \quad (10\text{-}33)$$

Since jumps between two sites of the same types are ineffective, $1/\tau_{jk}$ is taken to be nonzero only if $j \neq k$.

The differential equations determining the rates of change of the complex moments G_j corresponding to j sites are easily written down as generalizations of Eqs. (10-10) and (10-11).   Thus

$$\frac{dG_j}{dt} + \alpha_j G_j = -i\gamma H_1 M_{0j} + \sum_k (\tau_{kj}^{-1}G_k - \tau_{jk}^{-1}G_j) \qquad (10\text{-}34)$$

The steady solution follows by putting $dG_j/dt = 0$, solving the resulting linear equations, and taking the imaginary part of

$$G = \sum_j G_j \qquad (10\text{-}35)$$

Slow Exchange.   Again if the exchange processes are slow, the signals will be only broadened and the solution of Eq. (10-34) with $dG_j/dt = 0$ becomes

$$G_j = -i\gamma H_1 M_0 \frac{p_j\tau_j}{1 + \alpha_j\tau_j} \qquad (10\text{-}36)$$

leading to a width given by

$$T_{2j}'^{-1} = T_{2j}^{-1} + \tau_j^{-1} \qquad (10\text{-}37)$$

where $\tau_j^{-1}\left(= \sum_k \tau_{jk}^{-1}\right)$ is the probability per unit time of a nucleus on a j site moving to one of another kind.   Thus if the other contributions to broadening (represented by T_{2j}^{-1}) are negligible or otherwise known, the width of the j signal can give information about the lifetime of the nucleus on a j site, independently of the details of all the other sites.

10-3. Collapse of Spin Multiplets

In the previous section we have been concerned with the collapse of signals arising from nuclei in different chemical positions, that is, the collapse of a chemical shift.   It is also frequently found that the components of a spin multiplet may be partly or completely collapsed by similar mechanisms.   If the spin coupling Hamiltonian $J\mathbf{I}_1 \cdot \mathbf{I}_2$ is replaced by the simpler form $JI_{1z}I_{2z}$ (it has been shown in Chap. 6 that this makes no difference to the spectrum if the multiplets are well separated), a theory of multiplet collapse can be developed along lines very similar to those of Sec. 10-2.   This procedure was adopted by Gutowsky, McCall, and Slichter.[166]   The energy $JI_{1z}I_{2z}$ is equivalent to the interaction of nucleus 2 with a magnetic field proportional to JI_{1z} in the z direction. The proximity of a neighboring nucleus with a specified spin, therefore, acts in a similar manner to a contribution to electronic screening.   If nucleus 1 is a proton, for example, a jump of nucleus 2 from the proximity of an α proton ($I_{1z} = 1/2$) to a β proton ($I_{1z} = -1/2$) is analogous to the process considered previously. This change can occur either by nucleus 2 moving from one molecule to another (exchange collapse) or by nucleus 1 undergoing frequent transitions between its states. We shall consider these separately.

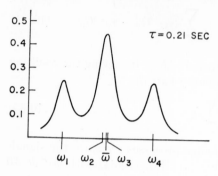

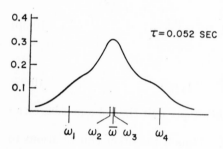

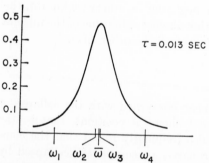

Fig. 10-2. Calculated shapes of hydroxyl-proton resonances in ethyl alcohol for three values of the exchange time τ. (Arnold.[20])

a. **Exchange Processes.** The collapse of spin multiplets can be caused by the exchange of nuclei between identical molecules. This effect was demonstrated very clearly by Arnold[20] for the hydroxyl protons of ethyl alcohol, which show a triplet spectrum (due to coupling with the methylene protons) in the absence of exchange but collapse to a singlet if the exchange rate is increased by addition of acid (Fig. 5-7). There are four possible spin states for the methylene group, and it may be assumed that, on leaving one molecule, a hydroxyl proton is equally likely to attach itself to a molecule with any of the four orientations. Thus, using the notation of Sec. 10-2b, all $1/\tau_{jk}$ for $j \neq k$ are equal and all p_j are $1/4$. Actually, two of the frequencies ω_j are nearly equal (and would be exactly equal were it not for second-order corrections). Using the steady-state solution of equations corresponding to (10-34), Arnold calculated the line shapes shown in Fig. 10-2 for various values of τ, the mean lifetime between exchange events. By comparing these shapes with observed spectra for a series of concentrations of HCl and NaOH, he was able to estimate values of τ varying from 1 to about 0.01 sec.

The neglect of the x and y parts of the scalar product $\mathbf{I}_1 \cdot \mathbf{I}_2$ is, in fact, only a good approximation for slow exchange rates. As the exchange rate becomes more rapid, so that the signal approximates to a broadened single line, the other parts become more important. Solomon and Bloembergen[430] have considered the theory for hydrogen fluoride where only single signals are observed rather than two doublets. The signals are broadened and relaxation-time measurements show that $T_2 < T_1$. In this limit of rapid exchange, these authors derive a formula for the contribution of exchange to $1/T_2$ which is twice as large as that given by the Gutowsky, McCall, and Slichter treatment.[166]

A full theory of exchange broadening and collapse has been developed by Kaplan.[212] It is based on a study of the complete density matrix and is valid even if the spin coupling constants and chemical shifts are of the same order of magnitude, so that the spectrum is not of the simple first-order type. It has been applied in detail to the case of a molecule with two nonequivalent protons AB, one of which may exchange with a molecule with one proton. Kaplan's general method, which we shall not describe in detail, reduces to that of Gutowsky, McCall, and Slichter[166] in the slow-exchange limit and to the formula of Solomon and Bloembergen[430] for two nuclei with rapid exchange.

b. Quadrupole Relaxation. Spin multiplets may also be collapsed by rapid disturbance or relaxation of the second nucleus causing the splitting. This effect is particularly marked if the second nucleus possesses an electric quadrupole moment, so that part of its spin-lattice relaxation arises from fluctuating electric-field gradients (Sec. 9-3). In many cases where the quadrupole relaxation is rapid, multiplets will be completely collapsed and the nuclei are apparently decoupled. This is the case with the proton spectra of molecules containing chlorine, for example. In other situations, notably for protons bonded to N^{14}, an intermediate situation occurs: sometimes a single broad line is found and elsewhere a partly resolvable triplet structure (see Roberts,[386] for example). The effect was shown very clearly by Ogg and Ray,[309] who compared the proton spectra of anhydrous $N^{14}H_3$ and $N^{15}H_3$. The latter gives a sharp doublet (N^{15} has spin 1/2), whereas $N^{14}H_3$ gives a group of three much broader signals.

An approximate quantitative theory of this collapse mechanism can be developed[340] if it is assumed that the nucleus possessing the quadrupole moment makes sudden transitions between its possible states. This has the same effect on the nucleus whose spectrum is under investigation as a change of environment by intermolecular exchange.

To be explicit, let us consider a proton bonded to an N^{14} nucleus, so that the undisturbed spectrum would consist of a 1:1:1 triplet. The three lines of this triplet correspond to proton transitions occurring in molecules where the N^{14} nuclei have spin components $I_z = -1, 0, 1$.

If the relaxation is not too rapid, therefore, the individual components of the triplet will only be broadened and each will have a shape function

$$g_j(\nu) = \frac{2\tau_j}{1 + 4\pi^2\tau_j^2(\nu_j - \nu)^2} \qquad j = 0, \pm 1 \qquad (10\text{-}38)$$

where τ_j is the lifetime of the state of the N^{14} nucleus with $I_z = j$. The probabilities of transitions between the states of the N^{14} nucleus due to fluctuating electric-field gradients have already been found in Sec. 9-3. There it was shown that, under typical conditions, the probabilities of transitions in which $\Delta j = \pm 1$ or ± 2 were respectively $\frac{3}{40}e^4q^2Q^2\hbar^2\tau_c$ and $\frac{3}{20}e^4q^2Q^2\hbar^2\tau_c$, where q measures the field gradient, Q measures the nuclear-quadrupole moment, and τ_c is a correlation time for molecular rotation.

The fact that the double transition $\Delta j = \pm 2$ is twice as probable as $\Delta j = \pm 1$ means that the lifetimes of the states $j = \pm 1$ are shorter than the lifetime of $j = 0$ by a factor $\frac{2}{3}$; for a nucleus can leave $j = 1$ by $\Delta j = -1$ or -2 but can leave $j = 0$ only by $\Delta j = \pm 1$. Consequently the broadening of the outer components of the proton triplet spectrum should be three-halves as great as that of the central component. This shows up very well in the spectrum of anhydrous $N^{14}H_3$ measured by Ogg and Ray,[309] which is shown in Fig. 5-8a. By comparison with Eq. (9-34) for the spin-lattice relaxation time of N^{14} itself, it is clear that the broadening of the outer and central components of the proton triplet should be respectively three- and two-fifths that of the N^{14} multiplet [each component of which will have the form (10-38) with τ_j replaced by T_1]. The quartet N^{14} spectrum of ammonia has also been measured by Ogg and Ray[308] and does indeed show greater broadening than any of the proton components.

The theory is readily extended to the broadening of multiplet components for protons bonded to nuclei with spin greater than unity.[340] For spin 3/2, it turns out that all components of the proton 1:1:1:1 quartet should be equally broadened. There is no good example on which to test this prediction, but it appears to be consistent with the partly resolved spectrum of the terminal protons in diborane[419] (B^{11} has spin 3/2).

The theory has also been extended[340] to more rapid rates of quadrupole relaxation by using the Gutowsky, McCall, and Slichter approximation (neglect of the effects of the x and y components of the scalar product). As with the exchange effect between two sites, the outer peaks draw together as they broaden, until eventually the whole structure collapses into one broad central component. However, the neglect of the remainder of the scalar product again leads to inaccuracy in the theory for rapid relaxation.

c. Double Irradiation. Another method by which spin multiplets can be collapsed is by the application of a strong rf magnetic field, the frequency being adjusted to cause saturation of the spins of a second nucleus. This causes frequent transitions between the states of the second nucleus and, just as with the quadrupole collapse, this nucleus becomes effectively decoupled from the remainder of the nuclear system. The use of this method as an aid in spectral analysis has already been mentioned in Sec. 6-9.

The double-irradiation technique was developed and first applied by Bloch,[50] Royden,[390] and Bloom and Shoolery.[63] Bloom and Shoolery presented a theory and carried out a number of experiments to confirm it in detail. They considered a system of two nuclei with magnetogyric ratios γ_1 and γ_2, so that the Hamiltonian in the absence of rf fields is†

$$\mathcal{H} = -\hbar[\gamma_1(\mathbf{I}_1 \cdot \mathbf{H}_0) + \gamma_2(\mathbf{I}_2 \cdot \mathbf{H}_0) + 2\pi J(\mathbf{I}_1 \cdot \mathbf{I}_2)] \qquad (10\text{-}39)$$

It is then supposed that a strong rf field H_2 is applied, rotating in the xy plane with angular frequency ω_2 in the vicinity of $\gamma_2 H_0$. Simultaneously the transitions in the vicinity of $\gamma_1 H_0$ are investigated by the usual weak rf field H_1 with angular frequency ω_1.

By transforming to a rotating coordinate system, Bloom and Shoolery[63] were able to show that, if $\omega_2 = \gamma_2 H_0$ (that is, the strong rf field is at the resonance frequency of nucleus 2), resonance of nucleus 1 would occur if H_0 were replaced by $H_0 + \Delta H$ (ΔH being a sweep field), where

$$\Delta H = 0 \qquad (10\text{-}40)$$

or

$$(\Delta H)^2 = \frac{\pi^2 J^2(\gamma_1{}^2 - \gamma_2{}^2) + \gamma_1{}^2\gamma_2{}^2 H_2{}^2}{\gamma_1{}^2(\gamma_1{}^2 - \gamma_2{}^2)} \qquad (10\text{-}41)$$

The intensities of the central and outer components are respectively proportional to

$$\frac{\gamma_2{}^2 H_2{}^2}{\pi^2 J^2 + \gamma_2{}^2 H_2{}^2} \quad \text{and} \quad \frac{\pi^2 J^2}{\pi^2 J^2 + \gamma_2{}^2 H_2{}^2} \qquad (10\text{-}42)$$

These results mean that, as the intensity of the strong field H_2 is gradually increased from zero, a central component $\Delta H = 0$ will appear and the two components of the original doublet will spread out and become weaker if $\gamma_1 > \gamma_2$. If $\gamma_1 < \gamma_2$, they will collapse, giving only a single signal for $2\gamma_2 H_2 \gtrsim \pi J$.

The theory was tested on the phosphorus and fluorine nuclei of an aqueous solution of Na_2PO_3F. The strong field H_2 was applied to the phosphorus nuclei at 12.91 Mc/sec, and the fluorine spectrum was

---

† J is measured in cycles per second. In their original paper, Bloom and Shoolery used the symbol J for the coupling constant in radians per second.

investigated at 30.00 Mc/sec.   The form of the fluorine spectrum for a series of values of H_2 is shown in Fig. 10-3, which clearly shows the properties predicted by Eqs. (10-40) to (10-42).   Bloom and Shoolery

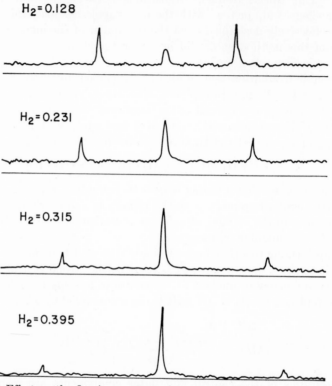

$H_2 = 0.128$

$H_2 = 0.231$

$H_2 = 0.315$

$H_2 = 0.395$

FIG. 10-3. Effect on the fluorine spectrum (aqueous Na_2PO_3F) of varying the phosphorus amplitude H_2, with $\omega_2 = \gamma_2 H_0$.   (Bloom and Shoolery.[63])

also investigated the effect of varying the frequency ω_2 through the value $\gamma_2 H_0$.   Under these circumstances, the two components of the spin-interaction doublet eventually collapse to the central line when $\omega_2 = \gamma_2 H_0$. At the same time the two other signals appear on the wings.

PART 2

APPLICATIONS

CHAPTER 11

PROTON MAGNETIC RESONANCE SPECTRA
AND MOLECULAR STRUCTURE

11-1. Introduction

The general features of NMR spectra, the experimental techniques, and the analysis of the multiplet structure due to spin-spin coupling have been described in previous chapters. The theories of some proton chemical shifts and spin interaction have also been discussed. Organic compounds provide examples of these spectra, exhibiting all of the features of structural and theoretical interest. Hydrogen is one of the most prevalent elements and is present in a very wide variety of chemical compounds. For this reason, and the fact that protons give a stronger resonance signal than most nuclei, the field of proton magnetic resonance spectroscopy is a particularly fruitful one. Further, proton resonance spectra are not complicated by quadrupole relaxation effects present in the spectra of nuclei with spin greater than 1/2. In the present chapter, we shall deal with the magnetic resonance spectra obtained for hydrogen atoms which are present in many different classes of organic compounds and their correlation with molecular structure. The spectra of other common magnetic nuclei will be described in Chap. 12.

We recall that three important types of information may be obtained from an NMR spectrum. In the first place, the position of the signal in the applied field, that is, its chemical shift referred to some reference compound, is an indication of the kind of environment in which the particular proton under observation finds itself within the molecule. One would expect, therefore, that protons in similar environments in different molecules would have a characteristic chemical shift, so that a knowledge of such shifts would be useful in identifying particular protons in chemical compounds just as the group characteristic vibrational frequency in infrared and Raman spectroscopy is an aid in identifying certain groups in a molecule. Secondly, each proton in the molecule contributes one unit of intensity to the resonance signal, so that the relative number of equivalent protons can be obtained from intensity considerations. Finally, the analysis of the fine structure of the signals very often

233

gives unambiguous information on the kind of first neighbors near a particular proton or group of protons.   Use of all three kinds of information provides a powerful tool for identifying and verifying molecular structures.

In certain cases, supplementary information may be gained by observing the NMR spectra of other magnetic nuclei in the molecule for which the proton spectrum has been obtained.   Also, in some cases where a spectrum is complicated by spin-spin coupling with more than one species of magnetic nucleus, it is often possible to simplify the spectrum due to the protons by exciting the perturbing nuclei by means of the double-irradiation technique (Sec. 10-3).   Further, simplification of a spectrum is often achieved by making use of isotopically substituted compounds.

In many cases unambiguous information with regard to structure can be obtained simply from an inspection of the NMR spectrum.   Compared to other techniques such as Raman and infrared spectroscopy, the proton magnetic resonance spectrum has the advantage of relative simplicity, since only protons are detected and other common nuclei—C^{12} and O^{16}, for example—do not complicate the spectrum because they do not possess magnetic moments.   In the following sections, proton resonance spectra of typical molecules belonging to various classes of compounds are illustrated and discussed in terms of chemical shifts, intensities, and the fine structure due to spin coupling.   Where chemical-shift data have been corrected for bulk susceptibility according to Eq. (4-6), this is indicated in the individual tables.   *In the experimental spectra shown in the figures, the chemical shifts given are those measured from the particular reference compound chosen, without susceptibility correction.*

11-2. Saturated Hydrocarbons

The proton magnetic resonance spectra of saturated hydrocarbons resemble one another to the extent that they are confined to a rather narrow spectral region and usually consist of unresolved bands.   This is due to the fact that the spin-spin coupling constants and chemical shifts are of the same order of magnitude and not very large.   The spectra for methane, ethane, and neopentane consist of only one single line, owing to the equivalence of all protons in the molecules.   The proton chemical shifts measured for these molecules are given in Table 11-1. In Fig. 11-1, spectra showing several signals due to the nonequivalent protons of the hydrocarbons containing up to five carbon atoms are reproduced.   The spectra of propane, n-butane, n-pentane, and isopentane are not sufficiently well resolved to obtain accurate chemical shifts, so only approximate values have been given in Table 11-1.   Isobutane possesses two types of protons: the nine protons belonging to methyl groups and the tertiary hydrogen. A complete analysis of the spectrum must be made therefore on the basis of the grouping AB_9. However, in the limit AX_9, the simple rules for predicting the number and intensity of the lines

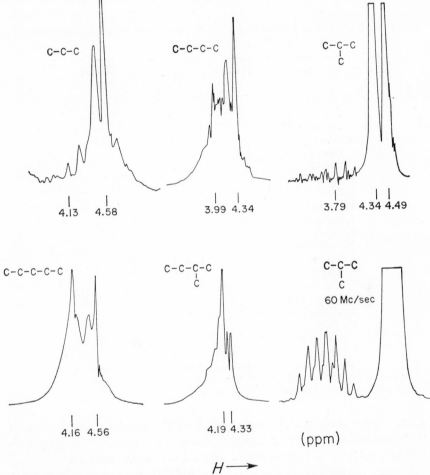

FIG. 11-1. The proton resonance spectra of some paraffins at 40 Mc/sec. The reference compound is water in a capillary tube. The 60-Mc/sec spectrum of isobutane is also shown. (*Courtesy of Varian Associates.*)

due to spin-spin coupling apply, and the spectrum should consist of a series of 10 equally spaced lines, with total intensity of one, and a symmetrical doublet of the same spacing, with total intensity of nine. It is apparent from the 60-Mc/sec spectrum in Fig. 11-1 that the observed spectrum is approximately as predicted. From the doublet spacing of the strong signal at high field the spin-spin coupling constant J_{CH,CH_3} is found to be about 5 cycles/sec. Estimates of the chemical shifts are given in Table 11-1.

The spectra of all the isomeric hexanes are shown in Fig. 11-2, and the chemical shifts of the various types of protons are given in Table

TABLE 11-1. PROTON CHEMICAL SHIFTS IN SOME SATURATED HYDROCARBONS†
(In ppm referred to water)

Hydrocarbon‡	CH$_3$	CH$_2$	CH
Methane:			
Gas	4.8		
Liquid ($-95°$)	4.8		
Ethane:			
Gas	4.1		
Liquid	4.1		
Propane	4.1	3.7	
n-Butane	4.0		
Isobutane	4.1		3.5
n-Pentane	4.1	3.7	
Isopentane	4.0		
Neopentane	4.0		
n-Hexane	4.1	3.7	
2-Methylpentane	4.1	3.7	
3-Methylpentane	4.1		
2,3-Dimethylbutane	4.0		3.5
2,2-Dimethylbutane	4.0		
Cyclopropane		4.5	
Cyclopentane		3.3	
Cyclohexane		3.4	

† Corrected for bulk diamagnetic susceptibility.
‡ Liquids at room temperature unless otherwise indicated.

11-1.   From the doublet spacing of the CH$_3$ signals in the spectra of 2,3-dimethylbutane and 2-methylpentane, the spin-spin coupling constants are $J_{CH,CH_3} \approx 5.5$ cycles/sec and 5.2 cycles/sec, respectively.

The chemical shifts of the CH$_3$,CH$_2$, and CH protons may be directly compared in these compounds because the bulk diamagnetic-susceptibility corrections (due to the cylindrical sample shape used) have been made according to Eq. (4-6) of Sec. 4-9. Within the experimental error of estimating chemical shifts in incompletely resolved spectra, it is apparent that the chemical shifts for the CH$_3$, CH$_2$, and CH groups in the acyclic molecules are nearly constant and have values of 4.1, 3.7, and 3.5 ppm, respectively, referred to water.

Table 11-1 also includes the chemical shifts for some cyclic saturated hydrocarbons. The chemical shift of the protons of the CH_2 group in the cyclic five- and six-membered rings is somewhat lower than for CH_2

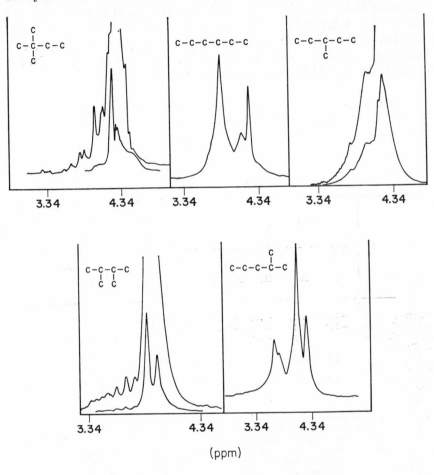

(ppm)

H ⟶

FIG. 11-2. The proton magnetic resonance spectra of the isomeric hexanes at 40 Mc/sec. The reference compound is H_2O in a capillary tube. Traces at two different amplifications are shown in some spectra.

groups in the acyclic compounds, whereas that for cyclopropane is considerably higher, even higher than the chemical shift for the aliphatic CH_3 group. There are extremely few proton signals in the spectra of organic molecules which occur in this high-field region, and the appearance of a signal here is a strong indication of the presence of a cyclopropane ring.

11-3. Unsaturated Hydrocarbons

a. Olefinic Compounds. The spectra of olefinic hydrocarbons possess two main features: a high-field signal due to the alkyl groups in the side chains and a low-field signal due to the ethylenic hydrogens. The position of the ethylenic hydrogens at low field (corresponding to less shielding) may be associated with the increased s character of the sp^2 carbon atom to which these protons are bound.

TABLE 11-2. CHEMICAL SHIFTS[†] AND SPIN-SPIN COUPLING CONSTANTS
OF STYRENE AND SOME METHYL-SUBSTITUTED STYRENES[‡]

$$H_2 \quad H_3$$
$$\diagdown \qquad \diagup$$
$$C{=}C$$
$$\diagup \qquad \diagdown$$
$$\phi \qquad H_4$$

| Compound | Chemical shifts, ppm | | | | | Coupling constants, cycles/sec | | | | | |
| | | | | | | H,H | | | H,CH$_3$ | | |
	H_2	H_3	H_4	Ring protons	CH$_3$	$J_{2,3}$	$J_{2,4}$	$J_{3,4}$	$J_{2,3}$	$J_{2,4}$	$J_{3,4}$
Styrene§	-1.4	0.1_5	-0.4	-1.9		10.6	17.2	1.2			
p-Methylstyrene	-1.4	0.1	-0.5	-1.8		10.2	17.3	1.3			
α-Methylstyrene		0.2	-0.1	-2.0	3.3			~1.4	~1.4	~0.7	
cis-Propenyl-benzene	-1.2	-0.5		-2.0	3.5	11.4				1.4	6.7
trans-Propenyl-benzene¶	~-1.0		~-0.9	-2.0	3.5						~6.0
ββ-Dimethyl-styrene	-1.1			-2.0	3.5						

† In ppm from water and corrected for bulk diamagnetic susceptibilities.

‡ The authors are indebted to G. F. Wright for these compounds.

§ Similar values for chemical shifts and coupling constants in styrene have been obtained by Fessenden and Waugh,[135a] who also established that all coupling constants were of the same sign.

¶ This compound contained some impurity which made it impossible to analyze the spectrum completely. The chemical shifts and coupling constants are approximate.

Styrene and Methyl Styrenes. The assignment of the ethylenic-proton signals can be made for styrene with the aid of some methyl derivatives. The spectrum of *cis*-propenylbenzene, for example (Fig. 11-3a), can be analyzed completely. The unperturbed AB-type quartet due to H_3 and H_2 is shown in the figure, and the components of the doublet associated with the H_3 proton are split into quartets by the methyl group (Fig. 11-3a). Thus the chemical shifts for H_2 and H_3 are immediately assigned and the value for the cis coupling constant between ethylenic

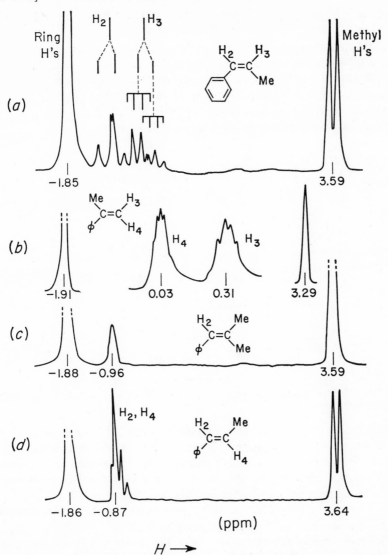

FIG. 11-3. Proton magnetic resonance spectra of some substituted styrenes: liquids at 40 Mc/sec; H_2O capillary as reference. (*a*) *cis*-Propenylbenzene. (*b*) α-Methyl-styrene (slower sweep for H_3, H_4 region). (*c*) ββ-Dimethylstyrene. (*d*) *trans*-Propenylbenzene.

protons is found to be 11.4 cycles/sec.   All chemical shifts and coupling constants for this molecule are shown in Table 11-2.

The spectrum of the ethylenic protons of α-methylstyrene (Fig. 11-3b) is essentially a narrow doublet (about 0.3 ppm separation) with some closely spaced fine structure.   The spectrum can be interpreted in terms of a small coupling constant between H_3 and H_4 which is about the same as the cis H,CH_3 coupling constant (Table 11-2).   A possible identification of the signals of the protons H_3 and H_4 is shown.

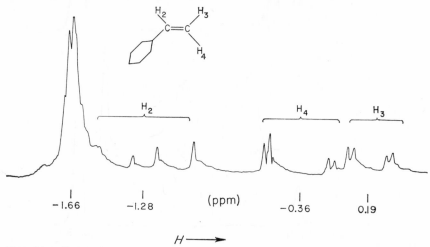

Fig. 11-4. Proton magnetic resonance spectrum of styrene at 40 Mc/sec; H_2O as external reference.

The spectrum of $\beta\beta$-dimethylstyrene confirms the assignment of the low-field signal in cis-propenylbenzene (Fig. 11-3c and Table 11-2). The spectrum of $trans$-propenylbenzene (Fig. 11-3d) can be interpreted on the basis of almost identical chemical shifts for H_2 and H_4, with the H_4 signal being split into a quartet by spin coupling with CH_3.   The outer pair of the unperturbed AB quartet expected for the H_2 and H_4 spectrum is presumably so weak that it was not observed.

The spectrum of styrene is shown in Fig. 11-4, and it can be readily assigned on the basis of an ABX type of grouping.   The X group is identified with the low-field signals of proton H_2 by analogy with $\beta\beta$-dimethylstyrene and cis-propenylbenzene.   The spacing in the X quartet indicates that the two coupling constants between H_2 and H_3, and H_2 and H_4, are about 17 and 10 cycles/sec, respectively.   Since one might expect the spin coupling constant between the cis protons, H_2 and H_3, to have about the same value as in cis-propenylbenzene, the quartet at highest field is immediately identified with the H_3 proton.   The coupling constant between trans protons, which is considerably larger than between cis protons,† corresponds to the spacing in the middle quartet. The small spacing in the doublets in the H_4 and H_3 quartets gives a small H_3,H_4 coupling constant consistent with that obtained for these protons in α-methylstyrene. This unambiguous assignment of chemical shifts in styrene is also consistent with the results expected from the ring-current model. The lowest-field signal corresponds to the shortest distance of the H_2 proton from the benzene ring, and the highest-field signal to the longest distance from the ring to H_3. However, a quantitative calculation similar to that described in Sec. 7-5 indicates that only part of the low-field shift can be explained in this manner. The coupling constants and chemical shifts are summarized in Table 11-2. The CH_3 signal for α-methylstyrene is at somewhat lower field than in the other compounds, again possibly due to the effect of the benzene ring current.

Olefins. The relative magnitudes of the spin coupling constants between H_2 and H_3, H_2 and H_4, and H_3 and H_4 given in Table 11-2 are of great assistance in the interpretation of the magnetic resonance spectra of the ethylenic protons in some alkyl-substituted ethylenes (Table 11-3). The spectra of the ethylenic protons in liquid ethylene, *cis*-butene-2, *trans*-butene-2, trimethylethylene, cyclohexene, and 2-methylpentene-2 are relatively simple. The spectrum of *trans*-hexene-2 is analogous to that of *trans*-propenylbenzene, where no evidence for the large trans coupling constant $J_{2,4}$ is obtained because the chemical shifts of H_2 and H_4 are almost identical. Thus the outer components of the unperturbed AB quartet expected for H_2 and H_4 are too weak to be observed. The other substituted ethylenes listed in Table 11-3 give rise to more complicated spectra. Two of the spectra (3,3-dimethylbutene-1 and butene-1) have been analyzed completely,[6] and two others (propylene and heptene-1) partially, to give spin coupling constants and chemical shifts. The low value for J_{H,CH_2} in cyclohexene is rather unexpected.

The spectrum of the vinyl group in 3,3-dimethylbutene-1 is shown in Fig. 11-5. The analysis of this typical ABC spectrum has been given by Alexander,[6] who also computed the theoretical spectrum for several sets of values for the chemical shifts and coupling constants. The best fit was obtained with coupling constants of 17.5, 10.8, and 1.4 cycles/sec and relative chemical shifts of 1.0 and 0.1 ppm. In this analysis no assignment of signals to protons was obtained. But by analogy with styrene, for which the values of the coupling constants are very similar, the lowest-field quartet may perhaps be assigned to the H_2 proton, and the H_4 quartet is immediately identified from the large trans coupling constant of 17.5 cycles/sec (Fig. 11-5).

† This is consistent with the relative magnitudes of the trans and cis coupling constants for 1,2-dichloroethylene, which have been obtained (for molecules containing C^{13} in natural abundance) by Cohen, Sheppard, and Turner.[95]

TABLE 11-3. SPIN COUPLING CONSTANTS AND CHEMICAL SHIFTS OF ETHYLENIC PROTONS
(In ppm referred to water as external reference)

Liquid hydrocarbon	Chemical shifts			Spin-coupling constants, cycles/sec				
	H_2	H_3	H_4	J_{H,CH_3}	J_{H,CH_2}	$J_{2,4}$	$J_{2,3}$	$J_{3,4}$
H_2,H_3 (top), H_1,H_4 (bottom), C=C, at −60°	0.14	0.14	0.14					
H,H / C=C / $(CH_3)_3C$,H		$\delta_{H_3} - \delta_{H_2} = 1.0$ ⎫ † $\delta_{H_3} - \delta_{H_4} = 0.1$ ⎬				17.5	10.8	1.4
H,H / C=C / CH_3,H	~−0.2	~0.4	~0.5	6.6(J_{12})			18	8.7
H,H / C=C / CH_3,CH_3	−0.06	−0.06		4.5(J_{12})				
H,CH_3 / C=C / CH_3,H	0.04		0.04	~4.5(J_{12})				
CH_3,CH_3 / C=C / CH_3,H			0.1	~6(J_{34})‡				
H,H / C=C / CH_3CH_2,H		$\delta_{H_3} - \delta_{H_2} = 0.94$ ⎫ † $\delta_{H_3} - \delta_{H_4} = 0.09$ ⎬			−6.3(J_{12})	17.4	10.4	1.9
H,H / C=C / $CH_3(CH_2)_3CH_2$,H	~−0.5	~−0.1	~0.1		6.1(J_{12})		18.3	8.6
H,H / C=C / H_2< >H_2 / H_2 H_2	−0.5	−0.5			~1.6(J_{12})			
H,CH_3 / C=C / $CH_3CH_2CH_2$,H	~−0.2		~−0.2	§	§			
CH_3,H / C=C / $(CH_3)_3CCH_2$,H		0.3 ⎵ 0.5						
CH_3,CH_2CH_3 / C=C / CH_3,H			0.14		~7			

† These are internal shifts relative to proton H_3 given by Alexander.[6] Measurements of chemical shift referred to a reference compound were not reported.
‡ From partially resolved HC= signal.
§ Not sufficiently well resolved for analysis of spin-coupling constants.

A complete analysis of the spectrum of butene-1 was made by Alexander[6] for several sets of coupling constants and chemical shifts.   In this spectrum each component of the H_2 quartet is further split into triplets by the CH_2 group.   Again by analogy with 3,3-dimethylbutene-1 and styrene, the signals may be identified (Table 11-3).   Some of the relative chemical shifts and spin coupling constants that gave the best agreement between the calculated and observed spectrum are given in Table 11-3.   Along with them, the additional values $J_{CH_2,H_3} = 1.3$ cycles/sec, $J_{CH_2,H_4} = 1.9$ cycles/sec, and $\delta_{CH_2} - \delta_{H_3} = 3.53$ ppm were derived from the complete analysis.

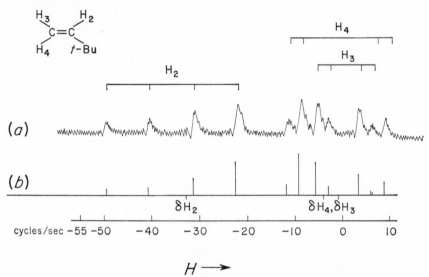

FIG. 11-5. The proton magnetic resonance spectrum at 3,3-dimethylbutene-1 at 31.6 Mc/sec. (Alexander.[6]) (a) Observed spectrum. (b) Calculated spectrum.

In Fig. 11-6 the spectra of propylene and heptene-1 are shown. The analysis of the H_2 spectrum is straightforward for both molecules, as indicated in the figure. Approximate values of spin coupling constants and chemical shifts are given in Table 11-3.

In order to compare the chemical shifts for the compounds listed in Table 11-3 (obtained in cylindrical sample tubes with an external reference), it is necessary to evaluate the corrected chemical shifts according to Eq. (4-6). In Table 11-4 the corrected shifts referred to water are given for the ethylenic protons, the protons of the CH_3—C=C and —CH_2—C=C groups as well as for the aliphatic CH_2 and CH_3 groups.

The CH_3 and CH_2 signals compare reasonably well with the values found for the alkanes (Table 11-1). The CH_2—C=C and CH_3—C=C groups are nearly constant at about 2.9 and 3.3 ppm, respectively, and displaced 1.1 and 0.7 ppm, to low field, respectively, from the signal of the methyl group in saturated hydrocarbons. The chemical shifts of the ethylenic protons given in Table 11-4 may be of some assistance in determining the degree of alkyl substitution at the double bond in olefins.

Some information about the effect of conjugation on the chemical shifts of the ethylenic hydrogens can be obtained from the proton resonance spectrum of isoprene, shown in Fig. 11-7 under moderate resolution. By analogy with propylene and heptene-1 the quartet at lowest

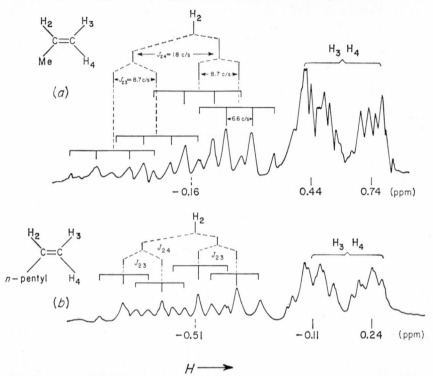

FIG. 11-6. (a) The magnetic resonance spectrum of the vinyl protons in propylene liquid at 40 Mc/sec. The reference is H_2O in a capillary tube. (b) Heptene-1, under the same experimental conditions.

field is due to the H_2 proton. (See Fig. 11-7 for labeling.) This signal originates from a widely spaced doublet ($J_{2,4} \approx 17.6$ cycles/sec) due to the trans coupling with H_4. Each of the components of this doublet is further split into doublets by the smaller cis coupling with proton H_3 ($J_{2,3} \approx 10.2$ cycles/sec) resulting in the observed quartet. One component of the H_4 doublet (spacing ≈ 17.6 cycles/sec) is at 0.13 ppm, and the other is under the band at 0.50 ppm. The coupling between H_3 and H_4 is very small (see propylene) and does not complicate the assignment. Similarly, one component of the H_3 doublet is at 0.33 ppm, and the other component is under the band at 0.50 ppm. The H_5 and H_6 proton signals are also under that band. By comparing (Table 11-5) the chemical

TABLE 11-4. CHEMICAL SHIFTS OF ALKYL-SUBSTITUTED ETHYLENES†
(In ppm referred to water)

$$\overset{2}{\diagdown}\underset{1}{\diagup}C{=}C\overset{3}{\diagup}\underset{4}{\diagdown}$$

Compound	H$_2$	H$_3$	H$_4$	CH$_2$—C=C	CH$_3$—C=C	CH$_2$	CH$_3$
Ethylene	−0.9	−0.9	−0.9				
Propylene	−0.8	−0.2	−0.1		3.3		
Heptene-1	−1.1	−0.4	−0.2	2.8		~3.5	4.0
2,4,4-Trimethyl-							
pentene-1		0.0	0.2	2.9	3.1		4.1
cis-Butene-2	−0.7	−0.7			3.3		
Cyclohexene	−0.7	−0.7		3.0		~3.3	
trans-Butene-2	−0.6		−0.6		3.3		
trans-Hexene-2	~−0.5		~−0.5				~4.0
Trimethylethylene			−0.3				
2-Methylpentene-2			−0.2	~2.9	3.3		~4.0

† Corrected for bulk diamagnetic susceptibility.

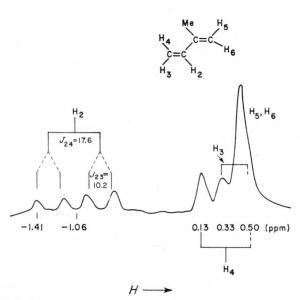

FIG. 11-7. The proton magnetic resonance spectrum of liquid isoprene at 40 Mc/sec; the methyl-group signal is not shown. Reference is H$_2$O in a capillary tube.

shifts (corrected for bulk diamagnetic susceptibility) of the ethylenic protons in isoprene with the mean shifts for the corresponding protons in heptene-1 and propylene, it is evident that the effect of conjugation is to displace the signal of proton H_2 about 0.6 ppm to low field. The other ethylenic protons exhibit little or no conjugation effect.

b. Acetylenic Compounds. One might have expected the proton resonance signal of acetylenic hydrogens (*sp* hybridization) to be observed

TABLE 11-5. CHEMICAL SHIFTS IN ISOPROPENE†
(Referred to water)

Proton	Isoprene chemical shift	Average chemical shift of heptene-1 and propylene‡
H_2	-1.6	-1.0
H_3	-0.2	-0.3
H_4	-0.1	-0.15
H_6, H_5	0	
CH_3	3.1	

† Corrected for bulk diamagnetic susceptibility by using Pascal's constants.
‡ From Table 11-4.

At even lower field than for ethylenic hydrogens. This expected larger shift to low field has been overcompensated, however, by a large paramagnetic contribution (Sec. 7-5), which moves the signal to high field into the region where the signals for protons in alkyl groups are observed. As a result the spectra of alkynes consist of overlapped signals crowded in a rather narrow spectral region.

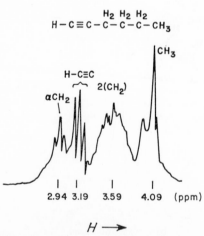

FIG. 11-8. Proton resonance spectrum of liquid hexyne-1 at 40 Mc/sec referred to H_2O capillary.

The spectrum of gaseous acetylene consists of a single line 3.46 ppm from the signal for water (corrected for susceptibility). The chemical shift for the liquid (corrected for susceptibility) is 2.17 ppm. This difference is due to the effect of association in liquid acetylene (Sec. 15-2).

The spectrum of liquid propyne consists of one line, from which one concludes that the H—C≡C and CH_3—C≡C signals must be superposed. The chemical shift is given in Table 11-6.

The magnetic resonance spectrum of liquid hexyne-1 is shown in Fig.

11-8.   From the position of the signal due to the acetylenic hydrogen in propyne, it seems probable that the signal at lowest field in the region 2.9 to 3.2 ppm is in part due to this type of hydrogen.   A definite identification of the H—C≡C signal with the triplet at 3.19 ppm was obtained by comparing the spectrum of the liquid with that obtained in a CCl₄ solution.   Dilution weakens the effect of association, shifting the H—C≡C signal to higher field but leaving all other signals practically unaltered. The assignment to the various protons is straightforward; it is shown in Fig. 11-8 as well as Table 11-6.   Table 11-6 includes characteristic

TABLE 11-6. CHEMICAL SHIFTS† AND COUPLING CONSTANT FOR SOME ALKYNES‡
(Referred to water)

Alkyne	H—C≡C	αCH₂	CH₂ (chain)	CH₃ (chain)	αCH₃	$J_{CH.CH_2}$
Acetylene gas	3.46					
Propyne	<3.0§				<3.0	
Hexyne-1	3.1	2.9	3.5	4.0		2.4

† In ppm.
‡ Corrected for bulk diamagnetic susceptibility by using Pascal's constants.
§ Bulk-susceptibility correction was made by using the density at −27°C.   The spectrum was obtained for the liquid at room temperature.

chemical shifts associated with alkyne groupings and the spin coupling constant (obtained from the triplet spacing) between the acetylenic hydrogen and hydrogens of the αCH₂ group.

It is of interest to compare the characteristic chemical shifts of methylene protons adjacent to single, double, and triple bonds, viz., 3.7, 2.9, and 2.9 ppm, respectively.   One might have expected that the trend to low field from the single to the double bond would have continued to give a signal at even lower field for the CH₂ group adjacent to a triple bond. However, the large neighbor-anisotropy effect in alkynes leads to a shift to high field of about 1 ppm (on the basis of a calculation analogous to that made for acetylene, Sec. 7-5a).

11-4. Aromatic Hydrocarbons

a. Alternant Hydrocarbons.   The magnetic resonance signals of the ring protons in benzene and other aromatic hydrocarbons are to be found at lower applied field than those for ethylenic protons (although the hybridization of the carbon atoms in both cases is sp^2 in character). This is because of the large diamagnetic circulation induced in the mobile π-electron systems of the carbon rings by the applied magnetic field (see Sec. 7-5).

The conjugated aromatic hydrocarbons containing six-membered rings (alternant hydrocarbons) have characteristic proton magnetic resonance

TABLE 11-7. ASSIGNMENT OF CHEMICAL SHIFTS IN CONJUGATED
AROMATIC HYDROCARBONS
(In ppm)

Compound	Chemical shift referred to cyclohexane	Relative intensity	Assignment	Calculated shift with adjusted mean
(benzene)	-5.75			(-5.75)
(naphthalene; positions 1, 2)	-6.0 -6.2	4 4	2 1	-5.92 -6.28
(anthracene; positions 9, 1, 2, 10)	-5.8 -6.1 -6.7	4 4 2	2 1 9	-5.75 -6.20 -6.65
(pyrene; positions 1, 2, 3)	-6.4	10	1,2,3	$-6.00, -6.42, -6.53$
(phenanthrene; positions 3,4,2,1,5,6,7,8,9,10)	-6.1 -7.1	8 2	1,2,3,10 4	$-6.30, -5.88, -5.92,$ -6.43 -6.78
(positions 5',6',4',3',8,9,7,6,5,10,4,3,2,1)	-6.3 -7.3 -7.7	10 or 9 1 or 2 1	5',4',3',3,4 5,6,7,8 6',10 9	$-6.22, -6.18, -6.60,$ $-6.73, -6.83$ $-6.65, -6.16, -6.17,$ -6.70 $-7.25, -7.15$ -7.62
(positions 5,4,6,3,2,1,6)	-6.1 -7.0	8 4	2,3,4,5 1,6	$-5.92, -5.88, -6.30,$ -6.48 $-6.85, -6.95$

TABLE 11-7. ASSIGNMENT OF CHEMICAL SHIFTS IN CONJUGATED
AROMATIC HYDROCARBONS (Continued)

Compound	Chemical shift referred to cyclohexane	Relative intensity	Assignment	Calculated shift with adjusted mean
(structure, positions 1,2,3,4,5,6)	−6.2	10	2,3,4,5,6	−6.30, −5.80, −6.22, −6.36, −6.40
	−7.9	2	1	−8.00
(structure, positions 1,2)	−6.0	6	2	−5.95
	−6.8	6	1	−6.83
(structure, positions 1,2,3)	−5.8	8	2,3	−5.62, −5.93
	−6.4	4	1	−6.56

spectra due to the nonequivalence of the protons. The chemical shifts of the signals in these compounds were measured† relative to suitable internal reference standards and are shown in Table 11-7 referred to cyclohexane.[39] The relative intensities of the signals are also given in the table. The spectra were under conditions of low resolution and consisted of rather broad bands. Since the chemical shifts were obtained with reference to internal standards, the solvent effect for these aromatic molecules could be appreciable (Sec. 16-2). For these reasons, comparison of the chemical shifts referred to cyclohexane in Table 11-7 for different molecules may be in error by about ±0.2 ppm. The internal chemical shifts, however, between signals of the same molecule are probably more accurate. In these poorly resolved spectra, the positions

† The spectra were obtained for the liquids about 10° above the melting point.

of intensity maxima may not give correct chemical shifts, so further errors may be introduced.

The numbering of the protons in the conjugated aromatic molecules and the assignment of the chemical shifts to the various protons in the molecule are also given in Table 11-7. The assignment of the lower-field signal to the 1 proton in naphthalene (see Chap. 6 for a complete analysis of the higher-resolution naphthalene spectrum) was confirmed by the spectrum of 1,4,5,8-naphthalene-d_4,[†] which possessed a single line only, at about -6.0 ppm, from cyclohexane. The assignment of the signals to protons of types 1 and 2 in anthracene follows by analogy with naphthalene. The signal of relative intensity 2 can arise only from the 9 and 10 protons on anthracene, and this was confirmed by its disappearance from the spectrum of 9,10-anthracene-d_2. The spectrum of pyrene consists of only one unresolved signal, although some structure appears under higher resolution.

The spectrum of phenanthrene under moderate resolution consists essentially of two bands with relative intensity $2:8$. Chemical arguments might suggest that the unique pair of protons are those at the 9,10 positions. However, the spectrum of 9-phenanthrene-d_1 gave two signals with intensity ratio of $2:7$, whereas $1:8$ would have been observed if this low-field signal had come from the 9,10 protons. Positive identification of the protons responsible for this low-field band came from the spectrum of 4-methylphenanthrene,[‡] which consisted of two bands separated by about the same chemical shift as in phenanthrene with intensity ratio of $1:8$. The protons at the 9,6' positions in 1,2-benzanthracene, the 1,6 positions in chrysene, the 1 position in benzo(c) phenanthrene, and the 1 position in both triphenylene and perylene are analogous to the 4 position in phenanthrene. On that basis the lowest-field signals are assigned to those protons, this being consistent with the relative intensities. This assignment in benzo(c) phenanthrene was confirmed by the absence of the low-field signal from the spectrum of 1,12-dimethyl-benzo(c) phenanthrene.[§] In the case of 1,2-benzanthracene the spectrum was not sufficiently resolved to enable distinguishing between the two sets of relative intensities given in Table 11-7, and the assignment was made on the basis of the calculations from the ring-current theory (see below).

A theoretical explanation and a semiquantitative description of the observed spectra can be given in terms of the ring-current model outlined in Sec. 7-5. According to Eq. (7-32), the chemical shift of the ring

[†] The authors are indebted to L. Leitch for these compounds.
[‡] *Ibid.*
[§] The authors are greatly indebted to M. S. Newman for providing this compound.

protons in benzene referred to ethylene is

$$\delta = -\frac{e^2 a^2}{2mc^2 R^3} \tag{11-1}$$

If in a polynuclear alternant hydrocarbon the current in each aromatic ring is assumed equal to that in benzene, the corresponding chemical shift of a particular proton is given by[39]

$$\delta = -\frac{e^2 a^2}{2mc^2} \Sigma_i R_i^{-3} \tag{11-2}$$

where R_i = distance to proton from center of ith hexagon
    a = radius of current ring
In the following calculations the CH distance and CC distance are taken to be the same and equal to a.   With a taken as 1.25 A, the

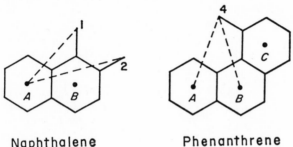

Naphthalene   Phenanthrene

FIG. 11-9

chemical shift of the protons in benzene due to the ring current is -1.41 ppm, relative to ethylene.   As an example, the method of calculation may be used to estimate the chemical shifts of the type 1 and 2 protons in naphthalene.   It is apparent from Fig. 11-9 that three distances are involved, namely R_{A1}, R_{A2}, and $R_{B1} = R_{B2}$.   Applying Eq. (11-2), the ring-current chemical shifts of protons 1 and 2 are

$$\delta_1 = -\frac{e^2 a^2}{2mc^2}\left(\frac{1}{R_{B1}^3} + \frac{1}{R_{A1}^3}\right)$$

and $$\delta_2 = -\frac{e^2 a^2}{2mc^2}\left(\frac{1}{R_{B2}^3} + \frac{1}{R_{A2}^3}\right)$$

This gives $\delta_2 = -1.64$ and $\delta_1 = -2.01$ ppm, or -0.23 and -0.60 ppm relative to benzene.   Since the chemical shift of benzene is -5.75 ppm relative to cyclohexane, the chemical shifts of the naphthalene protons are calculated to be $\delta_2 = -5.98$ and $\delta_1 = -6.35$ ppm relative to cyclohexane.   In a similar manner the chemical shifts for the protons in the other alternant hydrocarbons were calculated, assuming planar structures. These values could be referred to benzene and then compared with the observed values of Table 11-7. However, as mentioned previously, the relative shifts within a molecule are more accurately observed

TABLE 11-8. COMPARISON OF THEORETICAL CHEMICAL SHIFTS OF AROMATIC HYDROCARBONS WITH OBSERVATIONS AT INFINITE DILUTION

Compound	Proton	Calculated		Observed	
		Waugh and Fessenden[†]	From Eq. (11-2)	Infinite dilution CCl_4	Infinite dilution dioxane[‡]
Benzene		0	0	0	0
Naphthalene	2	−0.25	−0.23	−0.16[§]	−0.14
	1	−0.61	−0.60	−0.50[§]	−0.50
Anthracene	2	−0.31	−0.31	−0.40[†]	−0.2
	1	−0.80	−0.78	−0.90[†]	−0.8
	9	−1.25	−1.21	−1.37[†]	−1.2
Phenanthrene	2	−0.31	−0.32	Wide band with intensity max at −0.4[¶]	
	3	−0.38	−0.37		
	1	−0.76	−0.74		
	10	−0.88	−0.86		−0.4[¶]
	4	−1.19	−1.21	−1.31[†]	−1.4
Pyrene	1		−0.56		
	2		−0.98		−0.8
	3		−1.09		
Chrysene	3		−0.36		
	2		−0.42		−0.6
	4		−0.80		
	5		−0.98		
	1		−1.35		−1.4
	6		−1.45		

[†] Ref. 456.

[‡] Unpublished results obtained in the authors' laboratories.

[§] The chemical-shift separation between protons 1 and 2 furnished by a complete analysis of the spectrum has been used here (Sec. 6-7).

[¶] Identified by comparison of the spectrum of phenanthrene with that of 10-phenanthrene-d_1.

than are the absolute shifts. For this reason the calculated and observed shifts were so adjusted that their means (weighted for intensity) coincide; the calculated shifts and adjusted means are given in the last column of Table 11-7. In general, the gross features of the observed spectra are reproduced by the assumed model. In particular, the low-field signal in phenanthrene from the protons in the 4,5 positions is readily explained, as are all the lowest-field signals in the other compounds. It is clear from Fig. 11-9 that the value of $\Sigma_i R_i^{-3}$ is greater for the 4,5 protons in phenanthrene than for any other, since the distance from those protons to the centers of the other hexagons is shortest. Consequently the calculated value of the shift of the signal to low field is greatest. It may be observed from Table 11-7 that the simple ring-current model estimates too large a spread between the high-field signals arising from the remaining protons.

Waugh and Fessenden[456] modified the simple ring model by replacing the π-electron current by two loops equally spaced above and below the benzene ring and calculated the chemical shifts of the ring protons in naphthalene, anthracene, and phenanthrene relative to benzene. For comparison with the calculations they measured chemical shifts in spectra of these compounds at infinite dilution in CCl₄, thus avoiding effects due to interactions in aromatic solutions (Sec. 16-2). Their observed and calculated results are given in Table 11-8. In this table some infinite-dilution results in dioxane are given, as well as the results calculated from Eq. (11-2). The simple ring model and modified double-ring model give essentially the same calculated shifts.

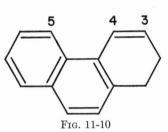

FIG. 11-10

Perhaps it is too much to expect that more refined calculations which do not take changes of charge densities at the carbon atoms and distortion from coplanarity into account will be appreciably better than the simple ring model. It is possible also that steric effects exist and account for some of the differences between the observed chemical shifts and those calculated on the basis of the ring model, since the protons in the 4,5 positions in phenanthrene and 1,12 positions in benzo(c) phenanthrene are quite close to one another. There is X-ray evidence[188] that the benzo(c) phenanthrene molecule is distorted out of the planar configuration because of these steric effects. An attempt to estimate the magnitude of the chemical shift due to steric effects was made by Reid.[378] For that purpose, the molecule shown in Fig. 11-10 was synthesized. In the absence of steric interference, the chemical-shift difference between protons 5 and 3, and between 4 and 3, should be given by a calculation based on the ring-current model. Although the 5-proton signal was not unambiguously identified,[378] the observed chemical shift ($\delta_{H_5} - \delta_{H_3}$) was found to be about 0.44 ppm larger than the theoretical value. This corresponds to the signal from H_5 being at lower field than expected on the basis of the calculation. The proton signals 4 and 3 were identified by deuteration, and the observed chemical shift was also found to be 0.44 ppm larger than calculated. Again the signal from proton 4 is at lower

field than expected.   Reid assumed that conjugation of the 4-3 bond with
the naphthalene ring did not affect the chemical shift of proton 4 and
attributed the differences to the steric effect.   However, as shown in
Sec. 11-3, the conjugation shift may be as much as 0.6 ppm (to low field).

   b. Azulene.   In Fig. 11-11a the proton spectrum of pure liquid azulene
(at 125°C) is shown, together with the spectra obtained from solutions
in dioxane.[403]   The numbering of the carbon atoms is shown in Fig. 11-12.

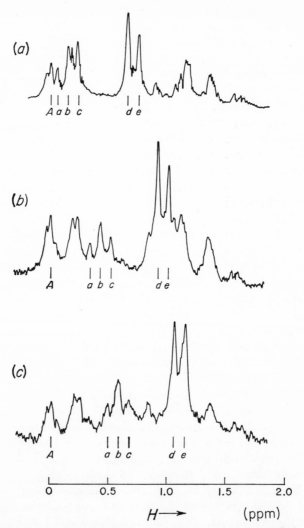

FIG. 11-11. The proton magnetic resonance spectra of azulene at 40 Mc/sec: (a) liquid
azulene at 125°C, (b) 20 mole per cent solution of azulene in dioxane, and (c) 3 mole
per cent solution of azulene in dioxane.   (Schneider, Bernstein, and Pople.[403])

The five-membered ring has three protons, two of which (H_1 and H_3) are equivalent.   The spectrum due to this group should be of the type AB_2 described in Sec. 6-5.   On comparing the three spectra at various dilutions (Fig. 11-11), it is apparent that the set of lines marked a, b, c, d, and e maintain nearly constant separations and relative intensities.   On

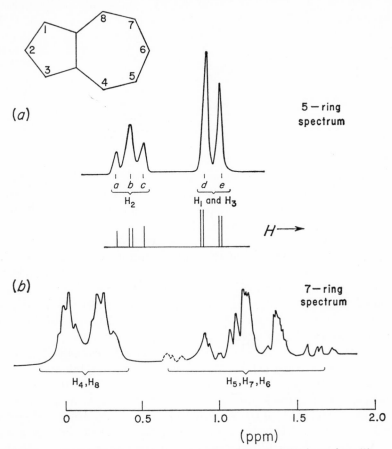

FIG. 11-12. The five- and seven-membered ring spectra in azulene.[403]

subtracting out these lines from Fig. 11-11c, the two spectra shown in Fig. 11-12 were constructed.   The spectrum in the upper field of the figure is an AB_2 type arising from the five-membered ring.   This assignment was confirmed by the spectra of 1-methyl- and 2-methylazulene.

The lower-field spectrum shown in Fig. 11-12 is that of the seven-membered ring obtained by subtraction and is therefore not too accurate. Its analysis was carried out with the simplifying assumption that spin-spin coupling between nonnearest neighbors was negligible.   Also, any

coupling between protons in different rings was neglected. The results
of the complete analysis are given in Table 11-9. The values of the

TABLE 11-9. CHEMICAL SHIFTS† AND SPIN-SPIN COUPLING
CONSTANTS‡ FOR AZULENE[403]

Dilution	Five-membered ring	Seven-membered ring
3 mole per cent solution	$\delta_1 - \delta_2 = 0.52$ $J_{1,2} = 3.5$	$\delta_6 - \delta_4 = 0.92$ $\delta_5 - \delta_4 = 1.32$ $J_{4,5} = J_{5,6} = 10.0$
20 mole per cent solution	$\delta_1 - \delta_2 = 0.54$ $J_{1,2} = 3.5$	
Liquid azulene (125°C)	$\delta_1 - \delta_2 = 0.60$ $J_{1,2} = 3.8$	

† In ppm.
‡ In cycles/sec.

chemical shifts in the 3 mole per cent solution of azulene in dioxane
(sufficiently dilute to minimize dilution effects) are shown schematically
in Fig. 11-13a. The assignment to the protons is given above the lines,
the heights of which denote relative intensities.

There are two effects which might be expected to contribute to the
values of the chemical shift of the various protons in azulene: (1) that
due to the aromatic ring currents and (2) that due to the variation of the
local charge density from carbon to carbon, leading to different shieldings
of the protons bound to the carbons. The second effect should be more
pronounced in nonalternants because, for alternant hydrocarbons, simple
molecular-orbital theory predicts uniform charge density. [355]

The chemical shifts due to rings currents† may be calculated by using
an equation of the type (11-2) and are shown in Fig. 11-13b drawn to the
same scale as the experimental results in (a). It is clear that the total
calculated spread is too small and that the H_1, H_3 signals are predicted to
lie on the low-field side of the H_2 signal, whereas the opposite is observed.

It is difficult to estimate quantitatively the effect of the charge distribution on the spectrum of azulene, but it is interesting to correlate
the order of the signals in the field with the π-electron charge density.
These charge densities have been calculated by Pariser[319] and are shown
in Fig. 11-13d. If the signal at a proton is assumed to be displaced to
low field by an amount proportional to the π-electron charge density on
the carbon atom to which it is bound, the spectrum shown in Fig. 11-13c
is obtained. No significance is to be attached to the scale in the figure,
the order of the signals in the field being of principal interest. It is

† The quantum-mechanical theory of ring currents indicates that the currents
flowing around the two rings of azulene are approximately equal.[339]

interesting to note that the H_4,H_8 signal is predicted at lowest field and the H_2,H_1,H_3 signals, as well as those for H_6,H_5,H_7, are given in the correct order.   It appears that, if these two effects are superposed, one obtains a set of chemical shifts resembling the observed ones except for the relative positions of H_2 and H_6.

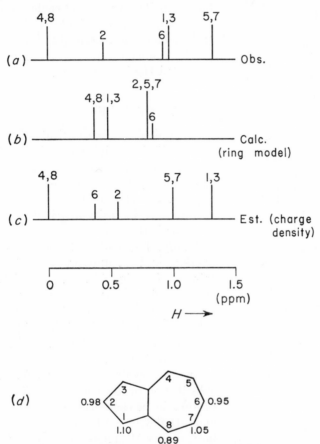

FIG. 11-13. The observed and calculated chemical shifts for azulene. (a) Observed in 3 mole per cent dioxane.   Heights are proportional to intensity; numbers refer to protons. (b) Calculated by ring model.   (c) Calculated order based on charge densities.   (d) Electron charge densities in azulene.

As might be expected, the spectrum of acepleiadylene, which has been partially analyzed,[403] shows features similar to that of azulene, and again the ring-current model is not satisfactory for explaining the positions of the signals.   In other five- and seven-membered aromatic rings, as in the cyclopentadienide anion, $C_5H_5^-$, and the tropylium cation, $C_7H_7^+$, similar disagreement was obtained.[244a]   Here the discrepancies may be attributed in part to the effect of the charge densities. The negative charge of the $C_5H_5^-$ ion results in higher proton screening relative to benzene, whereas the positive charge of $C_7H_7^+$ leads to a lower screening.

The interesting problem of the effect of dilution on the spectrum of azulene is discussed in more detail in Sec. 16-3. Evidence of proton exchange has been obtained[138] from the proton resonance spectra of azulene in concentrated H_2SO_4 and D_2SO_4.

11-5. Substituted Benzenes

The spectra of the substituted benzenes can be classified as shown in Table 11-10, depending on the nature of the substituents. Accordingly, the monosubstituted benzenes may be expected to have very complicated spectra with intensity distributed over many lines, or if the coupling constants and chemical shifts are small, all the allowed lines may overlap, and an unresolved spectrum is obtained. In Fig. 11-14 two typical AB_2C_2 spectra of monosubstituted benzenes are shown. Depending on the nature of the substituent, it is evident that the spectrum may appear at low or high field relative to benzene or toluene.

An extensive study of the effect of monosubstitution on the chemical shifts of the ring protons in benzene has been made by Corio and Dailey.[105] All chemical shifts were measured with reference to cyclohexane in solution at a concentration of 50 per cent by volume. As a result, no bulk-susceptibility corrections are required, but some dilution effects characteristic of aromatic compounds are no doubt present. Attempts were made to assign signals to meta and para protons in partially resolved spectra, so that some inaccuracy is to be expected in the chemical shifts obtained. The chemical shift of the para proton was identified with the strongest peak in the spectrum.[105] This identification was verified for nitrobenzene, by comparison with the spectrum of nitrobenzene which had

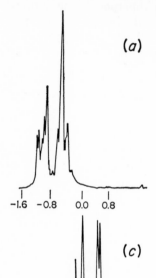

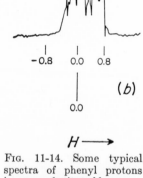

$H \longrightarrow$

FIG. 11-14. Some typical spectra of phenyl protons in monosubstituted benzenes (chemical shifts in ppm referred to dioxane and corrected for bulk susceptibility): (a) Nitrobenzene. (b) Position of unresolved toluene signal. (c) Aniline.

TABLE 11-10. TYPICAL PROTON GROUPINGS IN SUBSTITUTED BENZENES

Substitution	Symmetrical substitution	Asymmetrical substitution
Mono	AB_2C_2, AB_2X_2	
1,2	A_2B_2, A_2X_2	ABCD, ABXY, etc.
1,3	AB_2C, AB_2X	ABCX, etc.
1,4	A_4	A_2B_2, A_2X_2
1,2,3	AB_2, AX_2	ABC, ABX
1,2,4		ABC, ABX
1,3,5	A_3	ABC, ABX, AB_2
1,2,3,4	A_2	AB, AX
1,2,3,5	A_2	AB, AX
1,2,4,5	A_2	AB, AX
Penta	A	

TABLE 11-11. CHEMICAL SHIFTS OF ORTHO, META, AND PARA PROTONS
IN MONOSUBSTITUTED BENZENES
(In ppm from benzene)

Substituent	δ_{ortho}[†]	δ_{meta}[†]	δ_{para}[†]	δ_{para}[‡]
NO_2	−0.97	−0.30	−0.42	−0.45
CHO	−0.73	−0.23	−0.37	−0.35
COCl	−0.90	−0.23	−0.30	
$COOCH_3$	−0.93	−0.20	−0.27	
$COCH_3$	−0.63	−0.20	−0.27	
CN	−0.30	−0.30	−0.30	−0.32
COOH	−0.63	−0.10	−0.17	
CCl_3	−0.80	−0.17	−0.23	
$CHCl_2$	−0.13	−0.13	−0.13	
CH_2Cl	0	0	0	
CH_3	0.10	0.10	0.10	0.18
C_2H_5	0.07	0.07	0.07	
CH_2OH	0.07	0.07	0.07	
CH_2NH_2	0.03	0.03	0.03	
F	0.40	0.13	0	
Cl	0	0	0	−0.02
Br	0	0	0	−0.05
I	−0.30	0.17	0.10	0.05
OCH_3	0.23	0.23	0.23	0.40
OH	0.37	0.37	0.37	
NH_2	0.77	0.13	0.40	
$NH(CH_3)$	0.80	0.30	0.57	
$C(CH_3)_3$				0.05
$N(CH_3)_2$	0.50	0.20	0.50	

† Corio and Dailey[105] for solutions in cyclohexane (50 per cent by volume).
‡ Extrapolated values to infinite dilution in CCl_4 (due to Bothner-By and Glick[71]).

been deuterated in the para position.† Table 11-11 lists the results of Corio and Dailey, along with some other data[71,68] which were obtained by extrapolation to infinite dilution in CCl_4 to avoid association effects. The substituents listed in this table may be divided into three groups shown schematically in Fig. 11-15. In the first group are those which

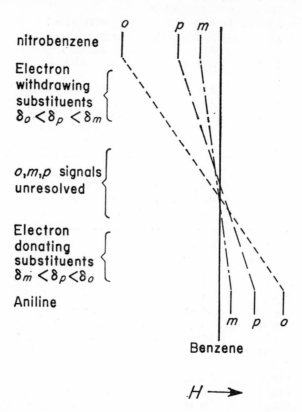

FIG. 11-15. Schematic representation of the correlation between ortho, meta, and para chemical shifts in monosubstituted benzenes for electron-donating and -withdrawing substituents.

give a pronounced shift of the whole spectrum to low field with respect to benzene (negative values of δ), which fall into the class of electron-withdrawing substituents. As first pointed out by Shoolery,[417] they would be expected to give rise to signals at lower field than benzene because of the contribution of mesomeric forms of the type $\langle\ +\ \rangle - X^-$, which result in less shielding of the ring protons. Another group of compounds is that in which the substituent donates electrons to the benzene ring (positive

† Unpublished results of the authors.

values of δ).   The whole spectrum is then shifted to the high-field side of benzene[417] corresponding to mesomeric structures of the type $\langle\ -\ \rangle\ -X^+$.

It is also evident, that, in most of the compounds of the first group, the order of the signals in the field is $o < p < m$, where the ortho signal is at lowest field.   For the second group (donor), on the other hand, the order of the signals in the field is $m < p < o$, with the ortho signal now appearing at highest applied field.   Finally, there are several compounds in which a donating or withdrawing substituent has little or no effect on the proton signal relative to benzene and for which there is no observable separation of the o, m, and p signals.   In this group, according to the results that have been published by Corio and Dailey,[105] the inductive effect of the substituent is partially compensated by the effect of conjugation.

Qualitatively, the order of the signals in the spectra of the monosubstituted benzenes with strong electron withdrawers and donors as substituents can be discussed in terms of the inductive and resonance effects.   For example, the ortho signal in nitrobenzene is expected to be at lowest field (smallest shielding) because of its proximity to the electron-withdrawing substituent, and at highest field in aniline, since the ortho proton is now more shielded than in benzene (Fig. 11-15).   The electron-withdrawing substituents are also meta-directing (more shielding at the meta protons), so that the signal of the meta proton in nitrobenzene is expected to be at highest field.   The electron-donating substituents are ortho-, para-directing, so the signals of the ortho and para protons are expected to be at higher field than the meta signal in aniline.   It seems that the different contributions from these effects might account for all the observed spectra.

Some correlation with Hammett's σ values of the position of the ortho, meta, and para signals of the compounds in Table 11-11 was attempted by Corio and Dailey[105] and Bothner-By and Glick.[68]   The chemical-shift data for the para proton obtained at infinite dilution correlated linearly with the Hammett σ values.[68]   An estimate of the quantitative nature of the inductive and resonance effects on the chemical shifts of the ortho, meta, and para protons can be made on the basis of inductive and resonance contributions (σ_I and σ_R, respectively) to the Hammett σ values. Taft[434] correlated the fluorine chemical-shift data[164] for meta and para substitution by considering the effect of meta substitution to be entirely inductive in nature, whereas the effect of para substitution is a linear combination of both inductive and resonance contributions.   (See Sec. 12-6 for a more detailed discussion.)   The effect of ortho substitution may be complicated by steric considerations, but in their absence might also depend only on inductive and resonance contributions.   Following

Taft, the ortho, meta, and para chemical shifts should be given by linear relations of the type

$$\delta_o \approx A\sigma_I - B\sigma_R$$
$$\delta_m = -A'\sigma_I$$
$$\delta_p = -A''\sigma_I - B''\sigma_R$$

where A, B, A', A'', and B'' are constants and in general different from one another. Using the σ_I and σ_R values given in Table 12-10, a linear relation may be obtained for the infinitely dilute chemical-shift data for the para proton, and presumably, if better data were available for the ortho and meta shifts, equally good correlations (of the type indicated by Taft) might be possible.

Batdorf[31] measured ring-proton chemical shifts in a number of polysubstituted benzenes under conditions of resolution of about 1 in 10^7. Under those conditions many of the compounds gave a single ring-proton signal. The ring-proton spectra of some para disubstituted benzenes were characteristic symmetrical four-line spectra consisting of two doublets, the outer pair being less intense than the inner pair. Under the conditions of resolution used, coupling of spins of protons on opposite sides of the benzene ring would not be resolved, and the spectra are essentially of the AB type.

In the work of Gutowsky et al.[164] on the fluorine magnetic resonances of substituted fluorobenzenes it was shown that the fluorine chemical shifts could be approximately represented in terms of additive contributions due to substituents in the ortho, meta, and para positions. This is also indicated for the proton chemical shifts in the spectra of 1,3-dimethyl-2-nitrobenzene and 2,4-dimethyl-1-nitrobenzene given by Corio and Dailey.[105] The kind of additivity scheme that seems suitable is the following: If in two monosubstituted benzenes, C_6H_5X and C_6H_5Y, the chemical shifts of the ortho, meta, and para protons are X_o, X_m, X_p and Y_o, Y_m, Y_p, respectively, referred to benzene, then in the disubstituted 1X,4Y benzene, the chemical shifts of the protons at the 2,3 positions are $X_o + Y_m$ and $X_m + Y_o$, respectively.

Methyl-substituted Benzenes. The spectra of the ring protons of the methyl-substituted benzenes consist essentially of one unresolved signal, the only compound in which pronounced separation of signals is apparent being *m*-xylene.† The position of the ring-hydrogen signal and methyl-group signal in the field does vary, however, with substitution. The chemical shifts extrapolated to infinite dilution in CCl_4 relative to water

---

† The ring proton signal in mesitylene was found by Hoffman [*Mol. Phys.*, **1**, 326 (1958)] to be broad, indicating coupling with the methyl protons. The methyl signal was a 1:3:3:1 quartet with about 0.6 cycle/sec spacing arising from equal spin coupling with the three-ring protons. The spin-spin coupling was ascribed to hyperconjugation between methyl-group orbitals and π-electron orbitals.

as an external reference are given in Table 11-12.   The effect of dilution on the chemical shift will be discussed in more detail in Sec. 16-2.   The values of the chemical shifts at infinite dilution in the same solvent do not require bulk-susceptibility corrections and are independent of dilution effects characteristic of aromatic molecules, and consequently are appropriate for discussing the effect of substitution.   All chemical shifts for

TABLE 11-12. OBSERVED CHEMICAL SHIFTS FOR METHYL BENZENES
(In ppm referred to water as external reference)

Molecule	Ring protons, infinite dilution in CCl_4	CH_3 protons, infinite dilution in CCl_4[†]
Benzene	−2.52	
Toluene	−2.35	2.45
o-Xylene	−2.25	2.56
m-Xylene	−2.12	2.50
p-Xylene	−2.20	2.52
1,2,4-Trimethylbenzene	−2.05	2.59 (1)
		2.62 (2)
1,3,5-Trimethylbenzene	−1.85	2.60
1,2,3,5-Tetramethylbenzene	−1.87	2.72 (1)
		2.62 (3)
1,2,4,5-Tetramethylbenzene	−1.97	2.65
Pentamethylbenzene	−1.87	2.67
Hexamethylbenzene		2.62

† The numbers in parentheses indicate relative intensities.

TABLE 11-13. CHEMICAL SHIFTS OF RING PROTONS AT INFINITE DILUTION IN CCl_4
(In cycles/sec referred to water as external reference at 40 Mc/sec)

Compound	Shift	Assignment
Benzene	−101	
Chlorobenzene	− 98	
o-Dichlorobenzene	−106	Proton A
	− 96	Proton B
m-Dichlorobenzene	− 97	
p-Dichlorobenzene	− 99	
1,2,3-Trichlorobenzene	−104	B_2
	− 95	A
1,3,5-Trichlorobenzene	− 99	
1,2,4-Trichlorobenzene	−109.4	C
	−107.1	A
	−100	B
1,2,3,4-Tetrachlorobenzene	−101.5	
1,2,4,5-Tetrachlorobenzene	−105	

the ring protons in these compounds are to high-field side of benzene, as would be expected for substituents which donate electrons to the ring. Increasing the number of methyl substituents tends to shift the ring-proton signal to higher field.   On the same basis, one might expect the

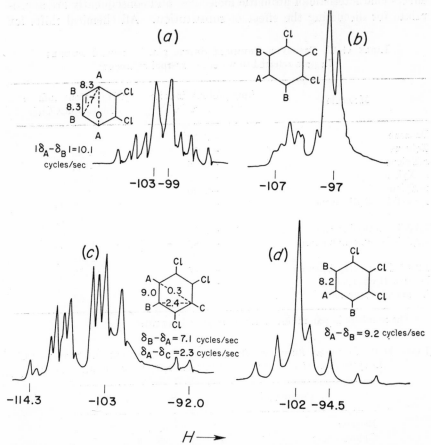

FIG. 11-16. Proton resonance spectra, in cycles per second, of some chlorobenzenes at 40 Mc/sec referred to an H_2O capillary.   The chemical shifts of the strongest bands were measured and extrapolated to infinitely dilute solution in CCl_4.   (a) o-Dichlorobenzene.   (b) m-Dichlorobenzene.   (c) 1,2,4-Trichlorobenzene.   (d) 1,2,3-Trichlorobenzene.

proton chemical shifts of the CH_3 groups to remain constant.   A small trend to high field is observed, however, with increasing substitution.

Chloro-substituted Benzenes.   The chemical shifts of the ring protons in the chlorobenzenes obtained at infinite dilution in CCl_4 with reference to an H_2O capillary are listed in Table 11-13.   All spectra for these compounds, except the ones shown in Fig. 11-16, consist of a single signal only, although some slight evidence of structure is observed for the signal of chlorobenzene. The spectra of three of these compounds, (*a*), (*c*), and (*d*), have been analyzed in detail, and the chemical shifts and spin coupling constants are shown in the figure. If $J_{36} \ll J_{35}$ in 1,2,4-trichlorobenzene (which may be reasonable because of the relative distances between protons), the signals can be assigned to the protons as indicated in Table 11-13. In *o*-dichlorobenzene only the magnitude of the chemical-shift difference between the type A and B protons is obtained from the analysis. However, by analogy with the 1,2,3- and 1,2,4-trichloro compounds, the lower-field signal is probably due to the A protons. The total spread in the chemical shifts of the protons in these compounds is very small, and the effects of substitution are not readily interpreted.

11-6. Heterocyclic Compounds

a. Saturated-ring Systems. A set of chemical-shift data obtained by Gutowsky, Rutledge, Tamres, and Searles[171] on three-, four-, five-, and six-membered rings containing oxygen, sulfur, and nitrogen is shown in Table 11-14. The chemical shift of the CH_2 protons α and β to the

TABLE 11-14. CHEMICAL SHIFTS OF α AND β PROTONS IN HETEROCYCLIC RINGS[171]
(In ppm from water)

Compound	αCH_2	βCH_2
$(CH_2)_2O$	2.6	
$(CH_2)_3O$	0.6	2.5
$(CH_2)_4O$	1.7	3.4
$(CH_2)_5O$	1.6	3.9
$(C_2H_5)_2O$	1.5	
$(CH_2)_2S$	2.3	
$(CH_2)_3S$	1.9	1.9
$(CH_2)_4S$	2.9	2.9
$(CH_2)_5S$	2.9	3.4
$(C_2H_5)_2S$	3.0	
$(CH_2)_2NH$	3.7	
$(CH_2)_3NH$	2.3	1.6
$(CH_2)_4NH$	1.9	3.0
$(CH_2)_5NH$	2.5	3.6
$(C_2H_5)_2NH$	3.0	

hetero atom are given with reference to water to an accuracy of ± 0.3 ppm. Comparing ring sizes, the αCH_2 shift in the cyclic oxides and sulfides is lowest for the four-membered ring, and in the cyclic imines for the five-membered ring.† The basicities of the cyclic imines toward tri-methylboron,[76] of cyclic ethers toward chloroform and methanol-d,[408,409] and of cyclic sulfides toward boron trifluoride[437] show that the basicity changes with ring size in the order four- > five- > six- > three-membered rings. According to Gutowsky, Rutledge, Tamres, and Searles,[171] the hetero atom has a low electron density in the three-membered ring and a high density in the four-membered rings, which agrees with the observed order of basicity. This conclusion is drawn from the position of the NMR signals of the αCH_2 protons in the applied field. A lower-field signal is believed to correspond to lower electron density on the CH_2 groups (lower shielding), which may be compensated for by a high electron density on the hetero atom.[171] Other saturated heterocyclic systems such as sugar acetates and paraldehydes will be discussed in Chap. 14.

The spectrum of morpholine, $\overline{OCH_2CH_2NHCH_2CH_2}$, consists of two equal, intense CH_2 signals at 1.1 and 2.3 ppm.[286] It is apparent from the signals of the αCH_2 groups in the six-membered ethers and imines that the signal at 1.1 ppm comes from the CH_2 groups in the α position with respect to the oxygen and the signal at 2.3 ppm comes from the CH_2 group α to the nitrogen.

b. Unsaturated Heterocyclic Compounds. *Pyridine.* The proton magnetic resonance spectrum of pyridine under high resolution has many lines and is quite complicated (Fig. 11-17). Since spin couplings with the nitrogen nucleus are eliminated by quadrupole relaxation (Sec. 10-3), the spectrum may be regarded as a prototype for monosubstituted benzenes. In the notation of Chap. 6 the protons in pyridine are grouped as AB_2X_2, where the α protons have been identified with X_2, the β protons with B_2, and the γ proton with A by comparison with spectra of pyridine substituted with deuterium in the appropriate positions.[401] Some simplifications in the A spectrum are noticeable at 60 Mc/sec (Fig. 11-17). The spectrum is still rather complicated for an unaided direct analysis, so the proton spectra of some partially deuterated pyridines were measured to obtain most of the spin coupling constants and chemical shifts required.[401] The complete analysis of the pyridine spectrum at 40 Mc/sec yields the following values of the chemical shifts and spin coupling constants[401,404] (assumed positive) in cycles per second:

$$\nu_0(\delta_4 - \delta_2) = 45.6 \qquad \nu_0(\delta_3 - \delta_4) = 15.0$$
$$J_{23} = 5.5 \qquad\qquad J_{34} = 7.5$$
$$J_{24} = 1.9 \qquad\qquad J_{35} = 1.6$$
$$J_{25} = 0.9 \qquad\qquad J_{26} = 0.4$$

† The trend in data for the cyclic imines may not be as reliable as for the other cyclic compounds because the imines are all hydrogen-bonded in the condensed phase. Differences in hydrogen-bond strength with ring size could also contribute to the observed difference in chemical shifts.

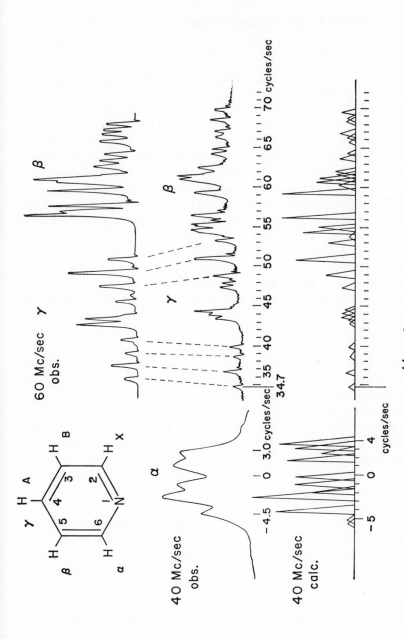

Fig. 11-17. The magnetic resonance spectrum of the γ and β protons of pyridine at 60 Mc/sec (*courtesy of Varian Associates*), and the complete proton spectrum of pyridine at 40 Mc/sec. (Schneider, Bernstein, and Pople.[404])

The spectrum calculated with these constants is compared with that observed at 40 Mc/sec in Fig. 11-17 and is quite satisfactory.

The chemical shifts at comparatively low resolution (about 1 in 10^7) for some substituted pyridines[38,26] have been reported. The assignments in the incompletely resolved region of the β- and γ-proton signals are not too accurate because the values of the quoted chemical shifts were usually measured for band centers or maxima and do not always correspond to the signal origins (chemical shifts). From the identification[38,26] made of the prominent features in the spectra of the monomethyl-substituted pyridines (picolines), one may evaluate changes in chemical shifts of the α, β, and γ protons relative to pyridine due to 2-, 3-, and 4-methyl substitution. It is interesting to note that the positions of the observed prominent features assigned[38,26] to α, β, and γ protons in the dimethylpyridines and trimethylpyridines can be calculated relative to pyridine to ± 0.15 ppm by simply adding the changes at these protons observed for the appropriate monomethyl pyridines. For example, the change in chemical shifts for the α, β, and γ protons in 2,3-dimethylpyridine relative to pyridine is very nearly the sum of the changes in 2- and 3-methylpyridine.

Quinoline. The spectrum of liquid quinoline is shown in Fig. 11-18. The quartets at lowest and highest fields are readily identified as the BX part of an ABX grouping expected for protons 2, 3, and 4. (See Fig. 11-18 for numbering.) The quartet expected for H_4 is located in the region indicated in the figure, and other tentative assignments are shown. The assignment of the H_8 signal is based on the spectrum of 8-methylquinoline, from which this signal is absent, and also can be identified from 4,7-dimethylquinoline (Fig. 11-18). From the spectrum, the following coupling constants, in cycles per second, can be evaluated for quinoline:

$$J_{34} = 7.3 \qquad J_{23} = 5.0 \qquad J_{78} \sim 7$$

The spectrum of 4,7-dimethylquinoline is readily interpreted on the basis of two sets of AB quartets from protons H_2, H_3 and H_5, H_6 and a single signal due to H_8. The width of the signals due to H_8, H_6, and H_3 is due to unresolved quartets arising from the spin interaction with the adjacent CH_3 group. From the spacings in the AB quartets, $J_{23} = 4.9$ cycles/sec and $J_{56} = 8.3$ cycles/sec.

Isoquinoline. The spectrum of liquid isoquinoline is shown in Fig. 11-18. The doublet at -3.2 ppm is part of the AB quartet from H_2 and H_3. By analogy with pyridine, H_2 is expected to be at lower field than H_3. Also the H_1 signal is expected at low field because of its proximity to the N atom, and it is readily identified. The coupling constant J_{23} is 6.0 cycles/sec.

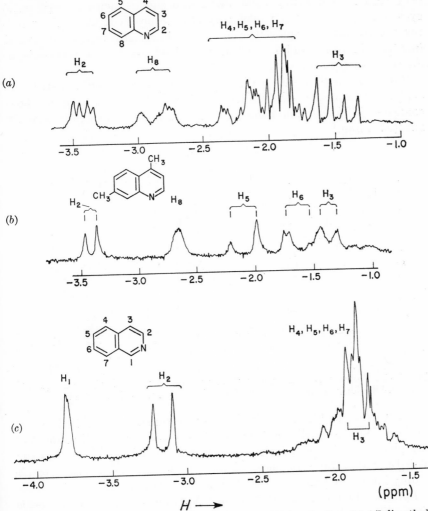

FIG. 11-18. Proton resonance spectra at 40 Mc/sec of (*a*) quinoline, (*b*) 4,7-dimethyl-quinoline, and (*c*) isoquinoline, referred to H_2O capillary.

Furan. The spectrum of liquid furan is shown in Fig. 11-19*a*. The triplet structure of the α and β protons which constitute an A_2X_2 grouping may be satisfactorily interpreted on the basis that the cross-ring coupling constant between α and β protons is equal to the $\alpha\beta$ coupling constant; that is, $J' = J$ in Fig. 11-19*a*. In the analysis of A_2X_2 spectra, $J' = J$ corresponds to $L = 0$ [Eq. (6-66)], which is a necessary and sufficient condition that the transition energies and intensities of Table

6-18 reduce to a 1:2:1 triplet with the equal spacing $J = J' = 1.5$ cycles/sec. However, a triplet may also be observed under the conditions of resolution employed even if $J \neq J'$ as long as $L \ll M$ and K (see Table 6-18). No information is obtained about the values of $J_{\alpha\alpha}$ or $J_{\beta\beta}$ from this spectrum.

Proton magnetic resonance has been used for detection and structure analysis of furans,[104,3] and the nature of the furan substitution has been confirmed in cafestol and columbin. Limonin was shown to be a β-substituted furan.[104]

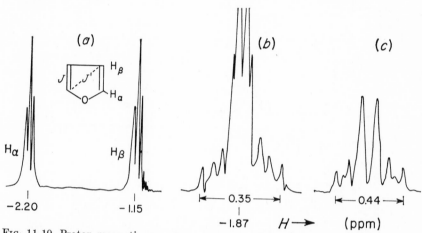

Fig. 11-19. Proton magnetic resonance spectra at 40 Mc/sec of (a) furan liquid, (b) thiophene liquid, (c) 20 per cent thiophene in CCl_4, referred to H_2O capillary.

Thiophene. In Fig. 11-19b and c the spectrum of liquid thiophene and a dilute solution are shown. The liquid spectrum is typical of the A_2B_2 grouping. The increased chemical shift in the dilute solution has simplified the appearance of the spectrum, but not sufficiently that it can be readily interpreted on the basis of an A_2X_2 situation.

Pyrrole. Liquid pyrrole[3] has the spectrum shown in Fig. 11-20a. Upon dilution in acetone, the two signals due to the α and β protons separate and appear as quartets with intensity distribution 1:3:3:1 (Fig. 11-20b). The NH signal is quadrupole broadened by N^{14} and appears at much lower field. The clue to the analysis of this spectrum comes from that of pyrrole-N-d (Fig. 11-20c), which consists of two triplets with equal spacing. It appears, then, that the A_2X_2 groupings in pyrrole and furan give similar spectra because $J = J'$ or $L \ll M$ and K. If $J = J'$, the spin coupling constant is found to be 2.1 cycles/sec. In order to explain the quartets in the spectrum of pyrrole (Fig. 11-20b), it is necessary to assume that the spin coupling from the NH proton with the α and β protons is the same and equal to $J_{\alpha\beta}$. The triplets in pyrrole-

N-d would then split into $1:3:3:1$ quartets with the same spacing as for the triplets.   The triplets observed for pyrrole-N-d are not well resolved $1:2:1$ triplets as in furan, since the spin coupling with deuterium ($\sim\frac{1}{3}$ cycle/sec) would lead to lines about $\frac{2}{3}$ cycle/sec broad which have not been too well resolved.   That the NH proton is coupling with the α and β protons is confirmed by the spectrum of 2,3-dimethylpyrrole (Fig. 11-20d).   The observed pair of triplets can be obtained from the expected

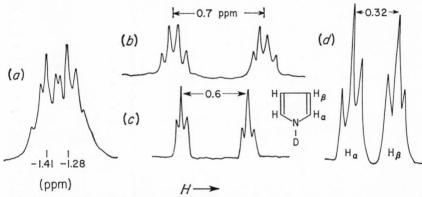

FIG. 11-20. Proton resonance spectra at 40 Mc/sec of (a) liquid pyrrole, (b) 20 per cent pyrrole in acetone, (c) 20 per cent pyrrole-N-d in acetone, and (d) 2,3-dimethylpyrrole (liquid), referred to H_2O capillary.[3]

quartet only if the spin couplings between the NH proton and H_α and H_β are the same and equal to $J_{\alpha\beta}$.   The broad NH signal is about 0.8 ppm to low field of the α- and β-proton signals.   From the spectrum of 2,5-dimethylpyrrole one may conclude that the α-proton signal appears at lower field than the signal due to the β protons.[3]

11-7. Characteristic Chemical Shifts of Proton Groups

The positions of proton signals in the applied field depend on the electronic environment around the proton, and this effect is less pronounced as the distance of the proton from a substituent increases.   It is convenient, therefore, to discuss separately the change in chemical shift with substitution for the following types of protons:

1. Those directly bonded to the substituent
2. Those which are two bonds removed from the substituent, that is, in the α position
3. Those which are three bonds removed from the substituent, that is, in the β position
4. All those which are four or more bonds away from the substituents

The chemical shifts of simple hydrides in the gas phase were given in Table 5-1. They were discussed in Sec. 7-5 in terms of the electronegativity of the atom bonded to hydrogen and the paramagnetic circulation around it. We recall that, the greater the electronegativity of the substituent, the less shielded is the proton, and the proton signal is shifted to low applied field. The paramagnetic effect, or magnetic anisotropy

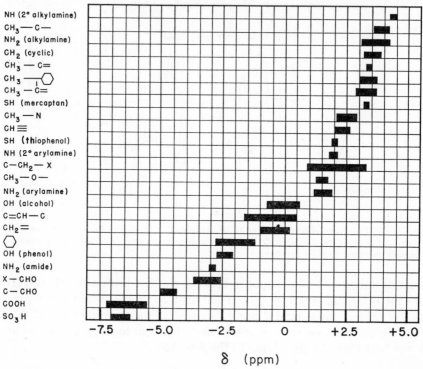

FIG. 11-21. Characteristic chemical shifts for some proton groupings relative to H_2O. (Meyer, Saika, and Gutowsky.[286])

of the substituent, on the other hand, usually shifts the proton signal to high field. The chemical shifts of protons directly bonded to different substituents are characteristic of the bond type, as indicated by the data shown in Table 5-1.

Some data on protons directly bonded to C, O, N, and S have been obtained by Meyer, Saika, and Gutowsky,[286] and Batdorf;[31] they are shown in Fig. 11-21 and Tables 11-15 and 11-16. The anomalous trend in CH chemical shifts with degree of hybridization of the carbon atoms in ethane, ethylene, and acetylene has been discussed previously in Sec. 7-5. The low-field shift of aromatic protons with respect to ethylene has been discussed in terms of aromatic ring currents in Sec. 7-5.

It is apparent that the OH signals in liquid alcohols, phenols, and acids are in very different spectral regions.   Even in infinitely dilute solutions in CCl$_4$, where the effect of hydrogen bonding has been removed, the phenol OH signal is about 3 ppm to low-field side of the alcohol signal† (Sec. 15-4).   Meyer, Saika, and Gutowsky[286] interpret this reduced

TABLE 11-15. CHEMICAL SHIFTS OF OH, NH$_2$, NH, AND SH GROUPS
(In ppm from water as external reference)

Proton group	Liquid compounds	Chemical-shift† range	Ref. and remarks
OH	Organic acids	−5.6 to −7.2	286
	Inorganic acids	−6.3 to −7.0	286
	Phenols	0.2 to −7.1	31, includes solutions
		−2.3	286
	Alcohols	−0.7 to 0.6	286
NH$_2$	Alkylamines	3.1 to 4.2	286
	Arylamines	1.2 to 1.9	286
		0.8 to 2.1	31
	Amide	−2.9	286, formamide
NH	Alkylamine	4.3 to 4.5	286
	Arylamine	1.9 to 2.0	286
SH	Mercaptan	3.3	286, benzyl mercaptan
	Thiophenol	2.0	286, thiophenol

† These data were obtained under relatively low conditions of resolution with an accuracy of 0.1 to 0.3 ppm.

shielding of the phenolic hydrogen in terms of resonance forms of the

type =O+—H.   Also, structures of the type

would cause the amino hydrogens to be less shielded than in alkylamines and account for the lower-field chemical shift (Table 11-15).   In the acid, the strong electron-withdrawing power of the COO group reduces the electronic shielding of the acid proton, giving rise to a very low field signal (Table 11-15).

In the case of hydrogen-bonded compounds such as phenols and amines the chemical shift of the protons capable of forming hydrogen bonds, namely OH and NH$_2$, respectively, can vary over a wide spectral region

† The ring current in phenol would account for only about 0.8 ppm of this shift to low field compared to alcohol, if it is assumed that the ring current is the same as in benzene and that phenol is coplanar (Sec. 11-5).

TABLE 11-16. APPROXIMATE PROTON CHEMICAL SHIFTS IN CH GROUPS
(Referred to water)

Proton group	Chemical shift	Remarks
H—C—C with C, C (paraffinic)	3.5	Liquid acyclic paraffins (Sec. 11-2)
H—C—C with C, N	1.0	Alkaloids, solutions in $CHCl_3$ (Sec. 11-8)
H—C—C with C, O	0	Sugar acetates, solutions in $CHCl_3$ (Chap. 14)
H—C—O with C, O	−1.0	Sugar acetates, solutions (Chap. 14)
Ethylene	0.1	Liquid, Table 11-3
Monoalkyl-substituted	−0.5 to 1.0	Liquids, Table 11-3
cis-Dialkyl-substituted	−0.1 to 0.5	Liquids, Table 11-3
trans-Dialkyl-substituted	−0.2 to 0.1	Liquids, Table 11-3
1,1-Dialkyl-substituted	0.4	Liquids, Table 11-3
Trialkyl-substituted	0.1	Liquids, Table 11-3
Aldehydes	−4.4 to −5.0	Liquids[286]
H—C(=O)—O	−2.6 to −3.1	Liquids[286]
H—C(=O)—N	−3.4 to −3.7	Liquids[286]
Benzene	−1.8	Liquids[286]
Substituted benzenes	−1.2 to −3.8	Liquids and solutions[31]
Acetylenic	3.1 to 3.5	Liquids, Table 11-6

(Chap. 15). In Table 11-17 the chemical shifts of the OH proton in liquid phenols as measured by Batdorf[31] are given. They have been arranged in order of decreasing field. It is apparent that the very strongly hydrogen-bonded liquid salicylates have chemical shifts −5.5 to −7.1 ppm to low-field side of H_2O, in keeping with the general result that association of this type shifts the signal to low field (Chap. 15). In liquid 2,6-diisopropylphenol the large isopropyl groups ortho to the OH interfere with intermolecular hydrogen-bond formation, so that the OH signal is at high field, corresponding to a very weak hydrogen bond being formed. It is interesting to compare the liquid spectra of the ortho-substituted phenols with the meta and para derivatives. Again steric hindrance of the ortho group is responsible for weaker intermolecular hydrogen bonds being formed, so that the OH signal is at higher field than in the meta and para compounds, where these bonds form more

TABLE 11-17. CHEMICAL SHIFTS[31] OF OH AND NH_2 GROUPS
IN SOME PHENOLS AND ARYL AMINES
(In ppm from water as external reference)

Compound	δ_{OH}	δ_{NH_2}
Phenols:		
2,6-Diisopropylphenol	0.2	
o-Cresol	−1.2	
o-Bromophenol	−1.4	
o-Chlorophenol	−1.5	
m-Cresol	−2.4	
m-Bromophenol	−2.1	
m-Chlorophenol	−2.5	
m-Isopropylphenol	−2.7	
Methyl salicylate	−5.6	
Benzyl salicylate	−5.7	
Salicyl aldehyde	−5.7	
Arylamines:		
2-Amino-1,3-dimethylbenzene		2.1
m-Chloroaniline		1.3
o-Chloroaniline		1.0
Hydrazine		0.8

freely. Of course, in the ortho-substituted molecules there is also competition between inter- and intramolecular hydrogen-bond formation.

In Table 11-17 the proton resonances of NH_2 in some aryl amines are listed (Batdorf[31]). Again, the NH_2 signal in the compound with two ortho substituents, 2-amino-1,3-dimethylbenzene, is at highest field corresponding to the situation in which the weakest intermolecular hydrogen bond is formed. In general the effect of dilution is to break some of the hydrogen bonds in the phenols and arylamines, shifting the signal in the direction of high applied field (Sec. 15-4).

The chemical shifts of protons not directly bonded to the substituent also depend on the nature of the substituent, and a comprehensive list of characteristic proton chemical shifts could be useful in identification of specific proton groups in a molecule. Many such data (for liquids) were obtained under low-resolution conditions; they are shown schematically in Fig. 11-21. Other data are reported with reference to benzene[111] and cyclohexane[72] as an internal standard; and some data at moderately high resolution with water as an external reference are available.[31] It is unfortunate that all measurements were not obtained under comparable

TABLE 11-18. PROTON CHEMICAL SHIFTS OF CH_3 GROUPS OF CH_3X COMPOUNDS[7]
(In ppm from water as external reference)

Compound	δ_{CH_3}, liquids†	0% in CCl_4
$C(CH_3)_4$	4.35	3.75
CH_3—C≡C	3.6‡	
$(CH_3)_3N$	3.18	
$(CH_3)_2CNOH$		2.98
CH_3CN	3.15	2.88
CH_3^*—$COOCH_3$	3.28	2.78
$(CH_3)_2CO$	3.33	2.70
CH_3COOH	3.19	2.69
$(CH_3CO)_2O$	3.04	2.60
CH_3I	2.00	2.60
CH_3CHO		2.59§
$CH_3C_6H_5$	3.25	2.47
$CH_3COC_6H_5$	3.00	2.24
CH_3NH_2		2.22§
CH_3Br	2.02	2.10
CH_3COBr	2.14	1.98
CH_3Cl	2.10	1.74
CH_3OCH_3	2.63	1.55
CH_3OH	1.85	1.39
$(CH_3O)_3B$	1.63	1.26
$(CH_3O)_4Si$	1.50	1.23
$(CH_3)_2SO_3$	1.48	1.21
$CH_3COO^*CH_3$	1.64	1.14
$CH_3OC_6H_5$	1.83	1.10
$(CH_3)_2CO_3$	1.36	1.02
$(CH_3)_2SO_4$	1.02	0.85
CH_3F	2.10	0.53
CH_3NO_2	1.19	0.48

† At room temperature.
‡ From Table 11-4, but uncorrected for bulk diamagnetic susceptibility.
§ Data of Dailey and Shoolery[111] converted to 0 per cent in CCl_4.

resolution and conditions to standardize the effects of bulk susceptibility and environmental interactions. In order to use such a list of characteristic shifts as Fig. 11-21, the NMR spectrum must be taken under the same experimental conditions as those used in constructing the figure or reference list.

a. Substitution Effects. The magnetic resonance spectra of protons in the α position with respect to a substituent have been measured in a wide variety of compounds.[111,72,7] The chemical shifts of the protons of the CH_3 groups in liquid CH_3X compounds have been measured by Allred and Rochow[7] with respect to water as an external reference and also at infinite dilution in CCl_4, and the results are given in Table 11-18. The

TABLE 11-19. CHEMICAL SHIFT OF PROTONS OF CH_2 GROUP
IN COMPOUNDS CH_3CH_2X[111]
(In ppm from benzene as internal reference)

Compound†	δ_{CH_2}	δ_{CH_3}
CH_3CH_2—C_3H_7	5.88	6.27
C_6H_{12} (cyclohexane)	5.68	
CH_3CH_2CN	5.18	6.33
CH_3CH_2CHO	5.08	6.37
$CH_3CH_2COCH_3$	5.03	6.33
CH_3CH_2SH	5.00	6.07
CH_3CH_2COOH	5.00	6.23
CH_3CH_2—$C≡C$	4.90‡	
$(CH_3CH_2)_2S$	4.80	6.13
$CH_3CH_2C_6H_5$	4.63	6.07
CH_3CH_2SCN	4.60	6.03
CH_3CH_2I	4.33	5.73
$CH_3CH_2NH_2$	4.33	6.17
CH_3CH_2Br	4.08	5.83
CH_3CH_2Cl	3.80	5.93
CH_3CH_2OH	3.48	6.03
$(CH_3CH_2)_2SO_3$	3.20	
$CH_3CH_2COOCH_3$	3.17	6.13
$(CH_3CH_2)_2SO_4$	3.13	6.17
$CH_3CH_2NO_3$	3.00	6.17
$CH_3CH_2NO_2$	2.97	6.00
CH_3CH_2F	2.87	6.07
CH_3CH_2N	3.0–3.5§	

† All compounds were made up in benzene solution (50 per cent benzene by volume).
‡ Results for substituted ethylenes (Table 11-3).
§ From results in alkaloids (Sec. 11-8).

position of the signal in the field is in somewhat different order in the liquids from that in CCl_4 solutions owing to the difference in bulk diamagnetic susceptibility and whatever association effects are present in the liquids. The authors point out that there is a general correlation of the position in the field (in CCl_4 solution) with the electronegativity of the first atom of the substituent X for analogous compounds (e.g., halogens). This relationship of the chemical shifts of protons in the α position with electronegativity was first observed by Shoolery[417] and investigated in more detail by Dailey and Shoolery.[111] The latter authors obtained the chemical shifts of the protons of the CH_2 (α position) and CH_3 groups (β position) in CH_3CH_2X compounds with respect to an internal benzene standard (Table 11-19). They found that the chemical-shift difference $\delta_{CH_3} - \delta_{CH_2}$ was approximately linearly dependent on the electronegativity of the atom in the substituent which was

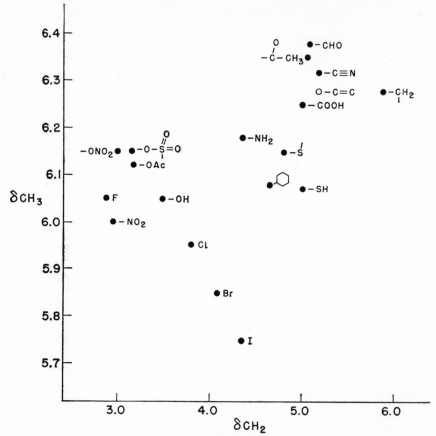

FIG. 11-22. δ_{CH_3} vs. δ_{CH_2} in CH_3CH_2X compounds, in parts per million from benzene. (Data from Dailey and Shoolery.[111])

directly bonded to the ethyl group, viz.:

$$\text{Electronegativity} = 0.695(\delta_{CH_3} - \delta_{CH_2}) + 1.71$$

where the chemical shifts are in parts per million. This relationship was established over a range of electronegativities from 2.6 to 3.9 but also applies for lower values. Thus, for example, Baker[27] observed $\delta_{CH_3} - \delta_{CH_2}$ to be zero and negative when X is Pb and Al respectively. It would seem that the difference $\delta_{CH_3} - \delta_{CH_2}$ is linearly dependent on electronegativity regardless of the fact that δ_{CH_3} and δ_{CH_2} separately may have different trends. This is indicated by the plot shown in Fig. 11-22. In the halides, for example, the CH_2 signals move to low field with increasing electronegativity, whereas the CH_3 signals in the same compounds move to high field. This reversal in trend for the β protons has also been observed[72] for the n-propyl, isopropyl, and *tert*-butyl halides.

Somewhat more disturbing is the fact that the chemical shifts of the α protons in cyclohexyl and isopropyl halides also show[72] a reversal in

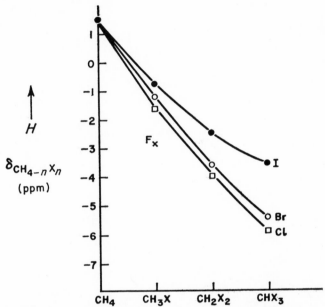

Fig. 11-23. The proton chemical shift in substituted methanes in parts per million from cyclohexane (internal). (Bothner-By and Naar-Colin.[72]) The value for CH_3F is from ref. 6 corrected to cyclohexane as reference; that for methane is from Table 11-1.

the trend expected solely on the basis of the electronegativity of the substituent. To explain these results, Bothner-By and Naar-Colin[72] invoke suitably chosen resonance structures. Although the effect of the anisotropy of the substituent (paramagnetic effect) might contribute in part to the position of the signal of the α protons in the field, it is unlikely that the effect at the β protons is large.† A correlation of the dipole moment with the chemical shift of the α protons accounts for the observed trend in the isopropyl, methyl, and ethyl halides.[72] The chemical shifts

---

† In CH_3F, CH_3Cl, CH_3Br, and CH_3I it has been shown by McConnell[269] that the chemical-shift changes due to the anisotropy of the halogen (taken as 20 per cent of its susceptibility) are 0.1, 0.3, 0.3, and 0.4 ppm, respectively. See also ref. 67.

of the γ and farther removed protons in monosubstituted halides were found to be practically independent of the substituent.

Increasing the number of halogen substitutions in methane produces a larger displacement of the proton signal to low field.[285] Meyer and Gutowsky[285] attributed this primarily to the inductive effect, which would decrease the proton shielding with increasing substitution. Opposing this, however, is the resonance effect, which increases the shielding at the proton[285] in the series CH_3X to CHX_3. The effect due to increasing halogen substitution has been investigated in greater detail by Bothner-By and Naar-Colin[72] (Fig. 11-23). Since iodine is the least ionic (electronegative) of the halogens, we might expect it to contribute the largest neighbor-anisotropy effect (Sec. 7-5) shifting the proton signal to high field. This is, of course, in the same sense as the electronegativity effect, which causes the proton signals to be at lowest field in the fluorine compounds and at the highest field in the iodine compounds. In these substituted methanes the opposing effect due to resonance seems of secondary importance, and the proton signals are observed in the expected order, those in the iodine compounds being at highest field and at progressively lower fields in the corresponding bromine, chlorine, and fluorine compounds.

11-8. Application to Structure Verification and Determination

Proton magnetic resonance spectroscopy has been applied to a wide variety of chemical compounds and has proved itself very useful in cases where two or more structural formulas can be written for a molecule and one is faced with the problem of selecting the correct one. It is also possible to make partial, and even complete, structure determinations from the NMR spectrum alone. Some illustrative examples of these applications are described below.

a. **Alkaloids.** Some applications of NMR spectroscopy to the elucidation of alkaloid structures have been possible. An alkaloid from *Lycopodium annotinum*, having the stoichiometric formula $C_{17}H_{24}N_2$, has been isolated.[17] This compound was known to have a substituted pyridine ring. The NMR spectrum gave three equally intense signals at low field, indicating by analogy with other substituted pyridines (Chap. 6) that the pyridine ring was disubstituted. Each of these signals under higher resolution consisted of three well-defined quartets corresponding to the three protons of the disubstituted pyridine ring. From the close similarity of the 12-line pattern with that of 2,3-lutidine (Fig. 6-10), one may deduce unambiguously that the saturated ring is joined to the pyridine ring at the 2,3 positions. Other applications to the identification of substitution in the pyridine ring have been made.[47]

In Fig. 11-24 the proton magnetic resonance spectrum of myosmine†
is shown.   Two structural formulas have been proposed for this molecule.
The low-field signals in Fig. 11-24 are from the four ring protons of the
pyridine nucleus, and it is apparent that the signal at lowest field with
the least number of spin-coupling components arises from $H_{\alpha'}$.   This is
a reasonable assumption, since the cross-ring coupling constants in
pyridine are small compared with the nearest-neighbor coupling constants (Sec. 6-8).   The quartet immediately to the right of this signal, by

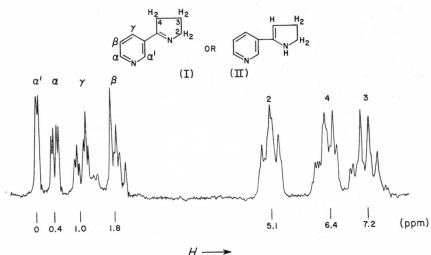

FIG. 11-24. The proton resonance spectrum of myosmine at 40 Mc/sec.

analogy with pyridine, is the H_α spectrum; and the octet to the right of
this is the quartet of the H_γ spectrum split into doublets by interaction
with $H_{\alpha'}$.   The last quartet of this group is then the H_β signal.   From
intensity considerations alone it is apparent that the three bands at
higher field in the aliphatic-hydrogen region are equal in intensity and
twice that of the area under any of the pyridine-proton signals.   Formula
I is therefore unambiguously indicated.   The fine structure of the bands
has not been analyzed, but it would appear that the band at lowest field
of these three should be assigned to the protons at carbon 2 of the five-
membered ring because of their proximity to the nitrogen atom.   Since
αCH_2 groups in substituted ethylenes are at lower field than those farther
removed from the double bond, the assignment of the bonds shown in
Fig. 11-24 seems reasonable.

The alkaloid gelsemine is known to have a CH_3—N group,[261] a
—CH_2—N group,[174] and a CH—N group.[174]   Further, a bridge oxygen

† The authors are indebted to L. Marion for this compound.

is known to be present, which indicates groups of the type CH—O and possibly —CH₂—O. The molecule also possesses a vinyl group.[262] The sharp spike in the spectrum (Fig. 11-25a) at 5.1 ppm to high-field side of

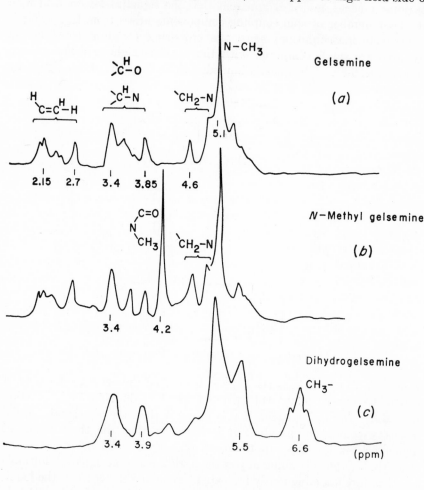

FIG. 11-25. The proton magnetic resonance spectra at 40 Mc/sec of (a) gelsemine in CHCl₃, (b) N-methylgelsemine in CHCl₃, and (c) dihydrogelsemine in CHCl₃. (CHCl₃ as internal standard.)

CHCl₃ (as an internal standard) is undoubtedly due to the CH₃—N group. One would expect the —CH₂—N group to have a signal at lower field, since substitution of CH₃ for H shifts the signal about 0.4 ppm (Sec. 11-7). The CH—N group should be at still lower field and in the neighborhood of the CH—O and —CH₂—O signals. The ethylenic protons are in the region 2.1 to 2.7 ppm by analogy with the substituted ethylenes. This assignment for the ethylenic protons is verified from the spectrum of dihydrogelsemine (Fig. 11-25c), in which the vinyl group has been hydrogenated to an ethyl group, by the absence of signals in this region of the spectrum. The spectrum of N-methylgelsemine (oxindole substitution) shows (Fig. 11-25b) the same principal features as that of gelsemine, as it should, with the addition of a sharp signal at 4.2 ppm due to the CH_3—N—C=O group. In the hydrogenated gelsemine the signal of the methyl protons of the ethyl group is at 6.6 ppm and is a triplet due to spin-spin coupling with the two equivalent hydrogens of the CH_2 group. This confirms the presence of the vinyl group in gelsemine. The CH_2 signal is presumably in the neighborhood of 5.5 ppm overlapped by other alkyl CH_2 and CH groups in the molecule. From the appearance of the spectrum in the 3.4 to 3.9 ppm region, intensity considerations support the assignment of the signal at 3.4 ppm to CH—O and possibly —CH_2—O groups, and that at 3.9 ppm to the CH—N group because there are more of the former than the latter. These assignments for the various protons neighboring a nitrogen atom are consistent with those made in connection with the spectrum of aspidospermine.[99]

b. Essential Oils. Many structural problems can be solved from the information in spectra which have not been taken under instrumental conditions for optimum resolution. In Fig. 11-26, for example, such proton resonance spectra of liquid eugenol, isoeugenol, methyl eugenol, and methyl isoeugenol are shown.† The chemical shifts have been referred to the methyl group of the CH_3O substituent. The range between 0 and 2.5 ppm to low-field side of the CH_3O signal is readily identified as the region in which to expect proton signals from ethylenic hydrogens, whereas in the region to high-field side of CH_3O the signals of CH_2 and CH_3 groups attached to carbon atoms are to be found. In Fig. 11-26a and b the OH signal is readily identified because it shifts to high field on dilution (Sec. 15-2).

The signals due to the benzene ring are at the lowest field in the spectra of these compounds. From the intensity distribution in the spectrum (Fig. 11-26a) it is readily seen that the ethylenic group labeled H_a, H_b, H_c represents three hydrogens and the CH_2 group has an intensity of 2. Further, the CH_2 group is split into a doublet, presumably by H_a; correspondingly, the signal due to H_a is more complex than that of H_b or H_c because of the triplet splitting due to the CH_2 group. The H_a, H_b, H_c signals can be identified by analogy with butene-1 (Sec. 11-3). In the conjugated compound isoeugenol, the disappearance of the CH_2 signal and appearance of the CH_3 signal are striking; also the ethylene-group intensity has dropped to two units. The resemblance of this spectrum

† The authors are indebted to L. Levi for the samples of essential oils.

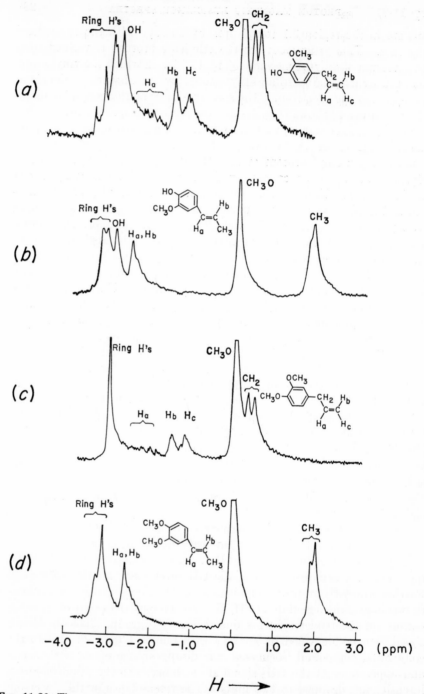

Fig. 11-26. The proton magnetic resonance spectra of some liquid essential oils at 40 Mc/sec: (a) eugenol, (b) isoeugenol, (c) methyl eugenol, and (d) methyl isoeugenol.

284

to that of *trans*-propenylbenzene in the ethylene-proton region and the lack of similarity with that of *cis*-propenylbenzene (Fig. 11-3) indicates that isoeugenol has a trans configuration. Corresponding changes in spectra are evident for methyl eugenol and methyl isoeugenol. It is of interest to note also that conjugation in the iso compounds has shifted the signals of the ethylenic protons H_a and H_b to low field by about 0.5 and 1.0 ppm, respectively, although part of this low-field shift is due to the effect of the benzene ring current.

c. Fatty Acids and Glyceride Oils. Even under conditions of non-optimal resolution, the proton resonance spectra of some fatty acids and glyceride oils provide interesting information. Some spectra of the acids are shown in Fig. 11-27, and the spectra of some oils in Fig. 11-28. From Fig. 11-27 it is apparent that the signal at −4.1 ppm in oleic acid[92] is due to the olefinic hydrogens and that at −0.75 ppm to the CH_2 group α to the carboxyl group. The CH_2 groups in the chain serve as internal reference on the chemical-shift scale, and at about 0.4 ppm to high field is the terminal CH_3 signal. The spectrum of 12,13-epoxy oleic acid[92] shows the features common to that of oleic acid and indicates that the HC—O—CH signal is at −1.55 ppm. The spectrum of methyl-9,12-linoleate shows the signal due to the CH_2 group in the diene structure C=C—CH_2—C=C at −1.55 ppm, whereas the conjugated ester shows the effect of conjugation on the ethylenic protons shifting the signal to low field, and also the absence of the diene CH_2 signal.

The proton resonance spectrum of sterculic acid has been obtained by Rinehart, Nilsson, and Whaley,[383] and no signal was observed in the region of −4.0 ppm (cf. Fig. 11-27) which would be characteristic of ethylenic-type protons. The authors concluded, therefore, that the structural formula was

$$CH_3(CH_2)_7—C{=\!=\!=}C—(CH_2)_7COOH$$
$$\diagdown\ \diagup$$
$$CH_2$$

rather than any of the proposed alternatives, each of which possessed olefinic protons. The proton resonance spectrum of dihydro sterculic acid[198] is very similar to that of sterculic acid except for the presence of a signal at 1.5 ppm to high-field side of the strong acyclic aliphatic CH_2 signal. This is characteristic of the CH_2 signal in a cyclopropane ring (Table 11-1). Further, in *trans*-1,2-dimethylcyclopropane, the ring-proton signal is at about 1.0 ppm to high-field side of the acyclic aliphatic CH_2 signal, whereas in *cis*-1,2-dimethylcyclopropane the signal is at about

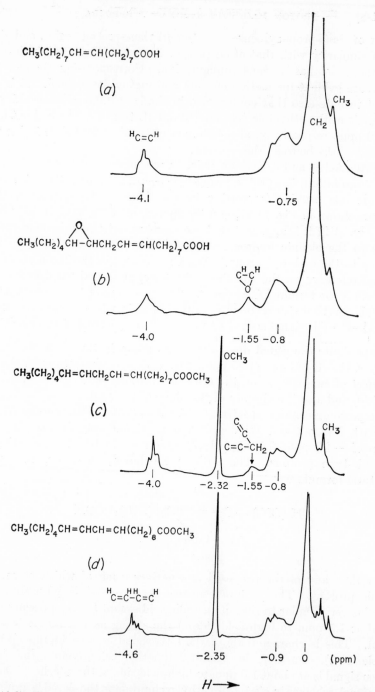

FIG. 11-27. The proton resonance spectra of some fatty acids and esters at 40 Mc/sec (the COOH signal is not shown): (*a*) oleic acid, (*b*) 12,13-epoxy oleic acid, (*c*) methyl linoleate, and (*d*) methyl-10,12-octadecadieneoate, all in $CHCl_3$.

286

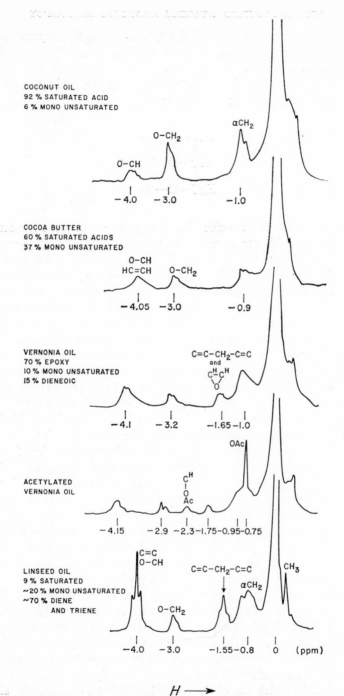

FIG. 11-28. The proton magnetic resonance spectra of some oils at 40 Mc/sec in CHCl₃.

287

1.6 ppm to high field.   The similarity in chemical shift suggests that the hydrogenated compound of sterculic acid is a cis 1,2-disubstituted cyclopropane.

Several oils have been investigated by the NMR technique;[198] all of them were glycerides of the general formula

$$
\begin{array}{c}
H_2C\!-\!O\!-\!R_1 \\
| \\
HC\!-\!O\!-\!R_2 \\
| \\
H_2C\!-\!O\!-\!R_3
\end{array}
$$

with various long-chain acids R_1, R_2, and R_3 as substituents.   In coconut oil the acids are essentially saturated.   From the spectrum of the oil (Fig. 11-28), the $O\!-\!CH_2$ signal appears at -3.0 ppm with intensity 4 and the $O\!-\!CH$ signal appears at -4.0 ppm with intensity 1. From Fig. 11-28 we see that the $O\!-\!CH$ signal coincides with the olefinic-hydrogen signals, so that in cocoa butter, in which the acids are essentially mono unsaturated and saturated, the signal at -4.05 ppm is due to $O\!-\!CH$ and $HC\!=\!CH$ protons.   In these glyceride oils there is a built-in reference standard for estimating the number of protons that are of the ethylenic or epoxy type, since the signal at -3.0 ppm comes from two $O\!-\!CH_2$ groups and represents four protons.   From the relative areas of the two signals at -4.05 and -3.0 ppm in cocoa butter, one can estimate the mono unsaturated acid content of the oil to be about one-third.   In linseed oil there are nonconjugated diene structures, mono unsaturated acids, and saturated acids, and the spectrum is readily assigned on this basis.   Vernonia oil contains a high percentage of epoxy acid but also some dieneoic acids as well as mono unsaturated acids.   The signal at -1.65 ppm is, then, a superposition of epoxy-group protons and CH_2 (diene) protons.   By acetylating the Vernonia oil the epoxy protons are removed and the methyl protons of the OAc group appear at -0.75 ppm. The remaining intensity at -1.75 ppm is due then to the $C\!=\!C\!-\!CH_2\!-\!C\!=\!C$ contribution.   In the acetylated Vernonia oil, the signal at -2.3 ppm is due to the two $H\!-\!C\!-\!OAc$ protons.

   d. **Substituted Three-, Four-, Five-, and Seven-membered Rings.** The proton spectrum of a 1,2,3-trisubstituted cyclopropane[420] is shown in Fig. 11-29.   The high-field region of the spectrum arises from the cyclopropane-ring protons.   If the molecule had the configuration in which all three substituents are on the same side of the cyclopropane ring, the three protons would be equivalent and give a single signal.   The only other configuration, in which one of the substituents is on the opposite side of the cyclopropane ring from the other two, has two types of protons, and the spectrum is expected to be of the type AB_2 or AX_2. From the

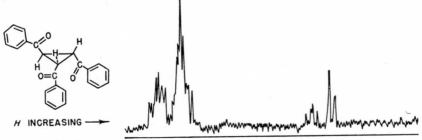

H INCREASING ———▶

FIG. 11-29. The proton magnetic resonance spectrum of a substituted cyclopropane at 40 Mc/sec. (After Shoolery.[420])

appearance of the spectrum it is evident that it corresponds to the five-line AX_2 case.

A further application has been made in deciding between two possible structures for Feist's acid.[218,73a] Evidence for I and II have been

$$ \text{I} \qquad\qquad \text{II} $$

reported in the literature.[66,133,251]   The NMR spectrum[218] in benzene solution of the compound which had been exchanged with D_2O to remove the signals of the acid protons from the spectrum gave two *equally intense* signals at 0.6 and 3.5 ppm to high field of the benzene-ring-proton signal.   This clearly supports structure II.   It is evident that the low-field signal corresponds to the two ethylene-type protons and the high-field signal to the protons in the three-membered ring.

An interesting application of NMR has been the identification of the structure of an isomer of distilbene† melting at 149°C.   The possible

† The authors are indebted to J. M. Morton for this sample.

configurations for distilbene are shown below. Compound (*b*) melts at 163°C, and its structure has been determined by X-ray analysis.[130] The isomer which melts at 149°C could in principle have structure (*c*), (*d*), or (*a*), although for steric reasons (*a*) might be considered unlikely. The

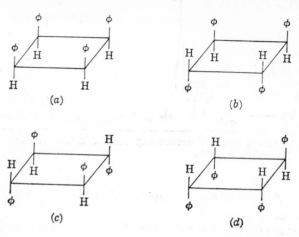

proton magnetic resonance spectrum in 3 per cent benzene solution is shown in Fig. 11-30, along with that of (*b*) for comparison. As expected, the four equivalent protons of (*b*) give a single signal at high field of the ring-proton signals. Also, structures (*a*) and (*c*) would give a single signal for the protons of the cyclobutane ring. The spectrum of (*d*), however, would arise from three different types of protons and could have the complicated pattern due to AB_2C. The observed spectrum, although not analyzed in detail, corresponds, then, to structure (*d*).

The determination of the structure of diketene[25] by NMR techniques showed it to be a heterocyclic four-membered ring. The spectrum in the liquid state consists of two signals of equal intensity. The proposed structures were those shown below. It is evident that V is the only

$$CH_3-\overset{\overset{\displaystyle O}{\|}}{C}-CH{=}C{=}O$$

I

$$\begin{array}{c} CH_3-C{=}CH \\ |\qquad\quad| \\ O{-}C{=}O \end{array}$$

IV

$$\begin{array}{c} O{=}C{-}CH \\ |\qquad\quad\| \\ H_2C{-}C{-}OH \end{array}$$

II

$$\begin{array}{c} O{=}C{-}CH_2 \\ |\qquad\quad| \\ H_2C{-}C{=}O \end{array}$$

III

$$\begin{array}{c} CH_2{=}C{-}CH_2 \\ |\qquad\quad| \\ O{-}C{=}O \end{array}$$

V

structure for which two main proton resonance signals of equal intensity are predicted.

Applications of proton magnetic resonance to the structure of seven-membered-ring acids have also been made.   It was shown from the NMR spectra that the α, β, and γ Buchner acids have heptadiene-like structures[122] and that thujic acid has a heptatriene structure.[149]   Nuclear magnetic

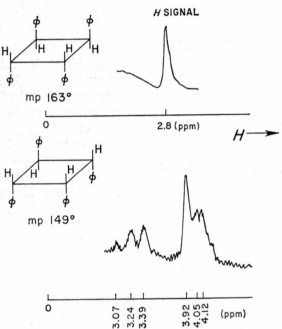

Fig. 11-30. The proton magnetic spectra of aliphatic hydrogens in distilbene at 40 Mc/sec, relative to phenyl hydrogen signal.

resonance has also been used to distinguish between bicycloheptadiene and cycloheptatriene structures.[103]

e. Steroids.   The basic hydrocarbons of some steroids† have been investigated by means of nuclear magnetic resonance.   The spectra in solutions of $CHCl_3$ are shown in Fig. 11-31.   From the spectrum of cis-methyldecalin it is evident that the lower-field CH_3 signal in the etiocholane series can be identified with the CH_3 group substituted at C_{10}.   When the A and B rings are trans, as in the androstane series, the CH_2 signal in the region 5.9 to 6.1 ppm is broader than in the etiocholane series, in which the A and B rings are cis.

A comprehensive study of the proton magnetic resonance spectra of steroids has been made by Shoolery[420] and Shoolery and Rogers.[424a]

† The authors are indebted to R. N. Jones for these compounds.

The compounds were studied in dilute solutions of carbon disulfide or heavy chloroform, concentrations ranging from about 0.1 to 0.5 molar. Some typical spectra are shown in Fig. 11-32. The spectra of 50-mg samples of testosterone and progesterone† are shown in Fig. 11-33. The assignment of some of the peaks is quite straightforward. In cortisone acetate, for example (Fig. 11-32), signals in order of increasing field are observed for the ethylenic proton (0.7 ppm), the CH_2 group in the side chain (1.47 ppm), the hydroxyl proton (2.85 ppm), the proton signals of the CH_3 group in the acetate group (4.23 ppm), the CH_3 group at C_{10} (5.00 ppm), and (by analogy with Fig. 11-31) the CH_3 group at C_{13} (5.75 ppm). According to Shoolery[420] the quartet due to the CH_2 group in the side chain arises from the different chemical shifts of these protons, since the spacing is field dependent. The different chemical shift of these hydrogens could arise from an internal hydrogen bond forming a ring which prevents free rotation of the CH_2 group.

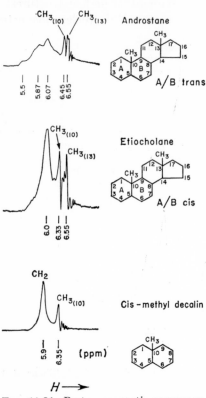

FIG. 11-31. Proton magnetic resonance spectra of androstane and etiocholane in CS_2 at 40 Mc/sec. Benzene is an internal reference.

Some useful correlations with structure have been derived[424a] from the spectra of 47 steroids. The identification of the signal due to the CH_3 groups at carbons 10 and 13 (protons at C_{19} and C_{18}, respectively) is unambiguous, and the assignment on the basis of the spectra of Figs. 11-31 and Fig. 11-32 is confirmed. One would expect the methyl-group resonance to be sensitive to the presence of an adjacent six- or five-membered ring. The signal positions of the protons in doubly bonded carbons were obtained for double bonds at the Δ^1, Δ^4, Δ^5, Δ^7, Δ^9, Δ^{16}, and Δ^{22} positions. For hydroxy-substituted steroids the signal of the tertiary hydrogen on the substituted carbon depends on the conformation. If the hydrogen is axial, the signal is about 20 cycles/sec at higher field than when it is equatorial in C_3 or C_{11} hydroxy-substituted compounds.

† *Ibid.*

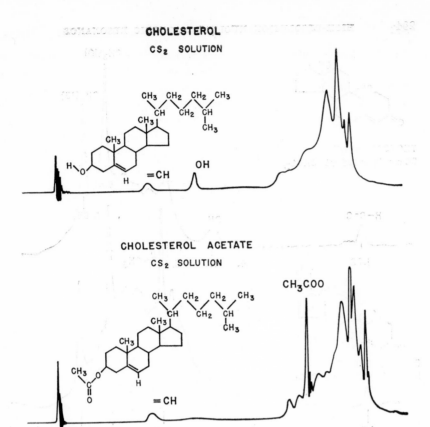

CHOLESTEROL

CS$_2$ SOLUTION

CHOLESTEROL ACETATE

CS$_2$ SOLUTION

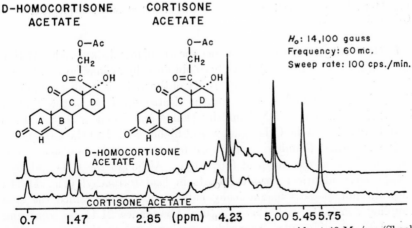

D-HOMOCORTISONE ACETATE

CORTISONE ACETATE

H_o: 14,100 gauss
Frequency: 60 mc.
Sweep rate: 100 cps./min.

FIG. 11-32. Proton magnetic resonance spectra of some steroids at 40 Mc/sec (Shoolery[420]) and at 60 Mc/sec (*courtesy of Varian Associates*).

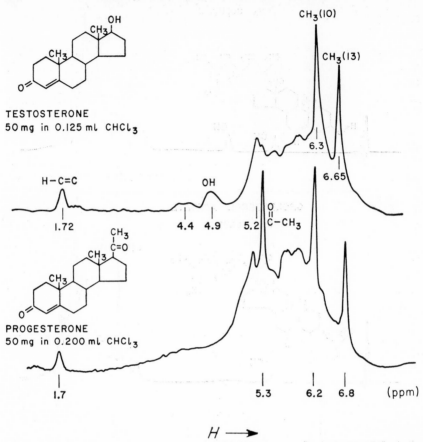

FIG. 11-33. Proton magnetic resonance spectra of testosterone and progesterone in CHCl₃ at 40 Mc/sec.

f. Metal Alkyls. Proton resonance spectra of metal alkyls, $AlCl(C_2H_5)_2$ and $Pb(C_2H_5)_4$ (Fig. 11-34), have been obtained by Baker[27] at 30 Mc/sec. In the metal alkyls the electronegativity of the metal is small enough that linear dependence of $\delta_{CH_3} - \delta_{CH_2}$ on the electronegativity of the X atom in the situation CH_3CH_2X found by Dailey and Shoolery[111] (Sec. 11-7) would predict that the CH_2 signal was at higher field than the CH_3 signal. This was indeed found to be the case for $AlCl(C_2H_5)_2$, and $\delta_{CH_3} - \delta_{CH_2}$ was found to be zero for lead tetraethyl. Although the CH_3 and CH_2 groups have identical chemical shifts in lead tetraethyl (Fig. 11-34), they do not possess magnetically equivalent protons, since the spin coupling constants with Pb^{207} (natural abundance 21.11 per cent and spin 1/2) are different. The wider spacing between the triplets (Fig. 11-34) leads to the surprising result that the coupling of CH_3 with

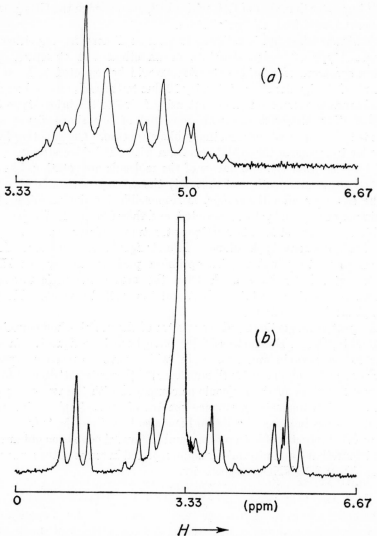

FIG. 11-34. (a) Proton spectrum of AlCl(C₂H₅)₂ at 30 Mc/sec relative to H₂O, in parts per million. Lines to high-field side of 4.3 ppm are due to CH₂; those to low field, to CH₃. (b) Proton spectrum of Pb(C₂H₅)₄ at 30 Mc/sec relative to H₂O. Unsplit C₂H₅ is centered at 3.2 ppm. Outer triplets are CH₃ split by Pb²⁰⁷. Inner quartets are CH₂. The extra lines in the high-field-side pattern are unexplained. (Baker.²⁷)

Pb^{207} is greater than that of CH_2 with Pb^{207}, even though the CH_3 group is farther removed from the metal atom.

Aluminum trimethyl is believed to exist as dimers, having either the diborane type of bridge structure or an ethane-like structure. The proton spectrum of a bridge structure would be expected to have two kinds of CH_3 signals: one of intensity 12 due to the CH_3 groups bound to the aluminum atoms and one of intensity 6 due to the bridge-type CH_3 groups. The observed spectrum consisted of one sharp signal only. This is to be expected for the ethane-like structure. On the other hand, in order to reconcile the NMR spectrum with the bridge structure, one could assume that the two halves of the molecule are rotating, like two meshed gears, sufficiently fast that only the average environment, which is the same for all CH_3 groups, is responsible for the chemical shift. Again only one signal is to be expected, and therefore the NMR spectrum in this case does not lead to a unique structural assignment.

g. Miscellaneous Applications. Two straightforward structure determinations that do not require optimum performance by the NMR spectrometer have been made from the proton magnetic resonance spectra of the vinyl acetate adduct and the methyl acrylate adduct of methyl dichlorosilane.[144]

The proton magnetic resonance spectra of the proteins hemocyanin,[205] ovalbumin,[144] and ribonuclease[395,207a] have been investigated. In contrast to hemocyanin and ovalbumin, which gave no resonance peaks, four peaks were observed for ribonuclease;[205] they were attributed to the internal flexibility of the molecule as compared with the two other proteins. Proton magnetic resonance spectra of some simple amino acids and dipeptides in aqueous solution have also been investigated.[435]

The NMR spectra of both protons and N^{14} nuclei have been obtained[370] for nitrourethane and nitramide and interpreted in terms of the structures $RNHNO_2$ and H_2NNO_2, respectively.

CHAPTER 12

NUCLEAR MAGNETIC RESONANCE SPECTRA OF
OTHER NUCLEI

12-1. Introduction

Of all magnetic nuclei, H^1 and F^{19} provide the widest application of the nuclear resonance technique, not only because of their importance chemically but also because of the favorable signal strengths of their resonance signals. Other magnetic nuclei whose resonances are of considerable interest from the chemical-structure and analytical standpoint are B^{11}, C^{13}, N^{14}, O^{17}, Si^{29}, P^{31}, S^{33}, and the halogens. Satisfactory high-resolution spectra of these nuclei in different compounds have been obtained for all but S^{33}. Measurements for the halogens Cl, Br, and I are somewhat limited. The special problems which arise to a greater or lesser degree in applying high-resolution techniques to measurements with all of these nuclei are due to (1) low signal strengths, which may be even further reduced by (2) low isotopic abundance of the particular magnetic nucleus, (3) a nuclear electric quadrupole moment which may cause excessive signal broadening, and (4) an unfavorably long spin-lattice relaxation time.

In most cases these situations, which vary with the different nuclear species, can be overcome by modifications in the measuring technique. A fortunate circumstance in this connection is the fact that for all of the heavier nuclei the chemical shifts are very much larger than proton shifts. Thus to obtain resolution comparable with proton spectra, much larger sample volumes can be employed, partly compensating for the reduced signal strength of the nuclei. In certain cases isotopic enrichment can be used to offset a low natural abundance of a particular nuclear species. Low signal strengths and long relaxation times in certain cases can also be successfully overcome by employing the dispersion mode (Sec. 3-5) and rapid-passage conditions.

Following the H^1 and F^{19} nuclei, the P^{31} nucleus (with spin 1/2) is the most favorable generally for the application of high-resolution NMR techniques. Nuclei with spin $\geqslant 1$ have electric quadrupole moments. This includes B^{11}, N^{14}, S^{33}, and the halogens Cl, Br, and I. Generally speaking, signal broadening due to quadrupole relaxation is more difficult to cope with. [The effect of such broadening on another nuclear species in the molecule can be overcome by double irradiation (Sec. 10-3).] Fortunately the effect of quadrupole broadening of B^{11} and N^{14} resonances in many compounds is not serious, although it may be prohibitively large in the magnetic isotopes of the halogens Cl, Br, and I. The low natural abundances of the magnetic nuclei C^{13} and O^{17} is in one sense an act of Providence. Because carbon and oxygen are present in a wide variety of hydrogen-containing compounds, the proton resonance spectra of such compounds would otherwise be greatly complicated. Resonances of both C^{13} and O^{17} in natural abundance have been successfully measured. The nuclei Li^7, Na^{23}, and Al^{27}, and those of a number of other metals, have favorable magnetic properties for NMR measurements, but as yet they have not been extensively employed.

12-2. Boron

The element boron has two naturally occurring isotopes: B^{10}, with natural abundance 18.83 per cent, and B^{11}, with 81.17 per cent. Both nuclei have magnetic moments (Appendix A); the spin of B^{10} is 3, and that of B^{11} is 3/2. B^{11} resonance measurements on a number of boron compounds, including several borohydrides, have been carried out by Ogg[304] and also by Shoolery[419] and Schaeffer, Shoolery, and Jones.[396] The resonances were observed at a fixed frequency of 9.6257 Mc/sec in a field of 7,050 gauss, as well as at 12.3 Mc/sec. Additional structural information was derived by examining the proton spectra of the same compounds. Because of the relatively large spin values of the boron nuclei, the proton spectra of hydrogens bonded to boron are complicated by the large number of fine-structure components of the signals. The proton spectra are accordingly greatly simplified by irradiating the B^{11} nuclei by the double-irradiation technique described in Sec. 10-3.

Boranes. Spectroscopic[346] and electron-diffraction[187] studies of diborane show that two of the hydrogen atoms (bridge hydrogens) are different from the remaining four (terminal) and that the molecule has the bridge-type rather than the ethane-type structure. The NMR spectra of boranes are of considerable interest in connection with the possibility of obtaining distinguishable signals for these two types of proton, and also for any structurally different boron nuclei. The proton resonance spectra of B_2H_6, B_4H_{10}, and B_5H_9, obtained by Kelly, Ray, and Ogg[217] and Shoolery,[419] indeed showed that the signal due to the bridge protons appeared at higher field than that due to the terminal protons. The principal features of these spectra are illustrated by that of diborane, B_2H_6 (Fig. 12-1a), which was reported by Ogg.[304] The asymmetric pattern immediately excludes the ethane-like structure for B_2H_6 and is in excellent agreement with the bridge model.   The spectrum is complicated by the splitting due to the $2I + 1 = 4$ spin orientations of B^{11} and the $2I + 1 = 7$ spin orientations of the less abundant isotope, B^{10}.   These

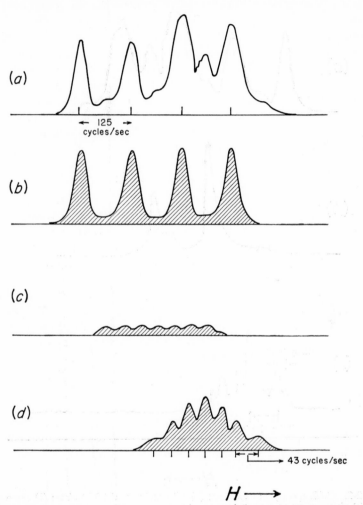

FIG. 12-1. (a) H^1 magnetic resonance spectrum of diborane at 30 Mc/sec; (b) protons directly bonded to B^{11}; (c) protons directly bonded to B^{10}; (d) bridge protons bonded to B^{11}.   (Ogg [304] and Shoolery.[419])

contributions to the proton spectrum are shown in Fig. 12-1b and c.   The spectrum arising from interaction of the bridge protons with the seven spin orientations due to *two* equivalent B^{11} nuclei is shown schematically in Fig. 12-1d.   This multiplet represents 65 per cent of the bridge-proton signals, the remainder being due to unresolved lines from B^{10}—B^{11} and B^{10}—B^{10} molecules. The spin coupling constant between the bridge protons and B^{11} was found to be 43 cycles/sec, whereas it is 125 cycles/sec for the directly bonded terminal protons.[304]

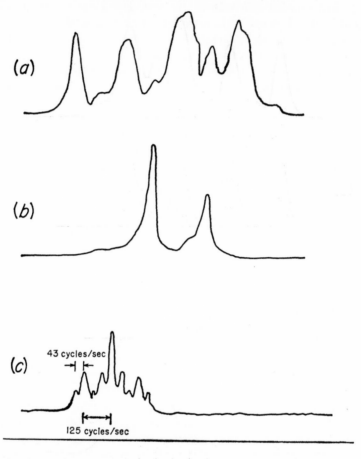

FIG. 12-2. NMR spectra of diborane: (a) H^1 spectrum at 30 Mc/sec; (b) same as (a) but with B^{11} excited at 9.6257 Mc/sec; (c) B^{11} magnetic resonance spectrum at 12.3 Mc/sec. (Shoolery.[419])

The above assignments were verified by applying the double-irradiation technique. Irradiation of the B^{11} nuclei at 9.6257 Mc/sec while the H^1 spectrum is measured at 30 Mc/sec yields the simple two-line spectrum[419] shown in Fig. 12-2b, in which the weak components due to the B^{10} splitting are, however, still detectable. This spectrum clearly illustrates the different chemical shift of the bridge protons and the nonbridging protons, the latter giving rise to a signal at a lower field with double intensity. A final confirmation is provided by the B^{11} spectrum[304,419] shown in Fig. 12-2c. This pattern arises from a strong spin coupling of two equivalent protons with each B^{11} nucleus, giving rise to a triplet each component of which is split into a triplet owing to a weaker coupling of each B^{11} nucleus with two other equivalent protons. This spectrum is therefore in agreement with the bridge model.

The NMR spectra of pentaborane-9, B_5H_9, which have been studied by Shoolery,[419] are reproduced in Fig. 12-3. The structure of pentaborane-9, as deduced from crystal analysis[129] and electron-diffraction data,[186] has a tetragonal configuration of boron nuclei. The four basal boron nuclei are equivalent, the nucleus at the apex of the pyramid being different. Each boron has a bonded proton (terminal proton), that of the apical boron being nonequivalent to the other four, and the basal boron atoms are also bonded by four bridge protons. The H^1 spectrum (Fig. 12-3a) shows four large lines due to the spin of each B^{11} nucleus coupling with the basal proton bonded to it. There are also four small shifted lines due to the apical proton and a large hump superimposed on the spectrum due to the bridge protons. Irradiation at the resonance frequency of the *basal* boron nuclei, 9.2576 Mc/sec, yields two lines of nearly equal intensity, indicating that the "basal" protons are evenly divided between directly bonded and bridge-bonded types. The different resonance frequency of the apical B^{11} atom prevents the apical proton spin multiplet from being more than partially collapsed. By slightly altering the B^{11} exciting frequency, the averaged-out signal of the apical proton can be "tuned in," and it appears approximately midway between the positions of the terminal- and bridge-proton signals arising from the basal hydrogens.[396] Under these conditions the latter signals are only partially collapsed to an averaged signal. The B^{11} spectrum (Fig. 12-3c) confirms the pyramidal structure in that it gives rise to two signals with intensity ratio 4:1, the weaker signal being due to the apical boron atom. Each of these signals is split into a doublet due to the proton directly bonded to each boron. Spin-multiplet components arising from the bridge protons or from spin-spin interactions between nonequivalent boron atoms were not detected.

The NMR spectra of pentaborane-11, B_5H_{11}, and decaborane, $B_{10}H_{14}$, have been investigated by Schaeffer, Shoolery, and Jones.[396] Saturation of the B^{11} spins in these compounds, as before, permitted observation of the separate proton signals of the bridged hydrogens and of the non-bridged hydrogens in each compound. For both compounds multiple signals were observed in the B^{11} spectra consistent with the molecular structures determined by X-ray analysis.[216,250]

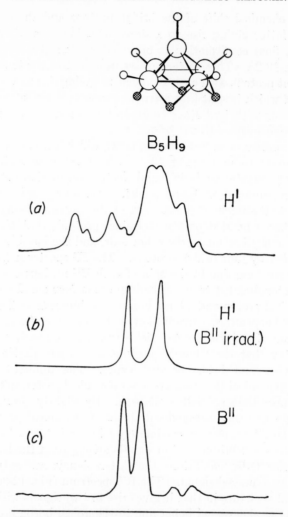

FIG. 12-3. The H^1 and B^{11} spectra of pentaborane-9: (a) H^1 spectrum at 30 Mc/sec; (b) same as (a) with B^{11} irradiated at 9.2576 Mc/sec; (c) B^{11} spectrum at 12.3 Mc/sec. (Shoolery.[419]) Molecular-structure diagram after Lipscomb.[250] Bridge hydrogens are shown shaded.

Sodium Borohydride, NaBH$_4$. The B^{11} resonance spectrum[304] of aqueous NaBH$_4$ gives rise to a quintuplet whose components have intensity ratios 1:4:6:4:1. This pattern of signals arises from spin coupling with four equivalent protons and is therefore consistent with a symmetrical structure for the BH$_4^-$ ion. The proton resonance consists of four strong lines due to spin coupling of the protons with B^{11} and seven weaker lines due to spin coupling with the B^{10} isotope. The values of

J_{HB} are approximately 82 cycles/sec for the B^{11} isotope and 27 cycles/sec for B^{10}.

Aluminum Borohydride, $Al(BH_4)_3$.   Electron-diffraction[32,426] and infrared-spectroscopic[347] studies have established that the aluminum nucleus in the aluminum borohydride molecule is located at the center of an equilateral triangle formed by the three boron nuclei.   The most probable arrangement of the protons is that of a tetrahedral configuration of four protons about each boron nucleus, with two protons in terminal position and two in bridge position between boron and aluminum nuclei.   Such a structure may be expected to give rise to NMR spectra somewhat similar to those observed for diborane (Fig. 12-1). The H^1 and B^{11} resonance spectra observed by Ogg and Ray[306] are shown in Fig. 12-4.   The proton resonance consists of a single broad signal, which is somewhat narrowed on simultaneous irradiation of the B^{11} nuclei.   The broadening of the spectra shown in Fig. 12-4a and b arises mainly from the electric quadrupole interaction (Sec. 10-3) of the Al^{27} nucleus, which has a spin of 5/2.   The broadening is eliminated by simultaneous irradiation of the Al^{27} nuclei, the proton spectrum then having a structure similar to that of the BH_4^- ion.[304] Thus all protons are directly bonded to the boron nuclei and are chemically equivalent.   This is confirmed

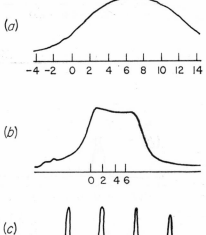

(a)

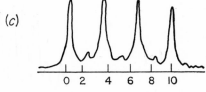

(b)

(c)

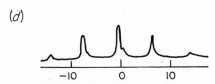

(d)

FIG. 12-4. The H^1 and B^{11} resonance spectra of $Al(BH_4)_3$: (a) H^1 resonance at 30 Mc/sec; (b) same as (a) with B^{11} irradiated at 9.6257 Mc/sec; (c) same as (a) with Al^{27} irradiated at 7.8177 Mc/sec; (d) B^{11} resonance at 12.3 Mc/sec. (Ogg and Ray.[306])

by the B^{11} resonance spectrum, which shows a quintuplet pattern similar to the B^{11} resonance of the BH_4^- ion.

The proton spectrum shown in Fig. 12-4b shows some structure and may be interpreted as a broadened multiplet arising from proton coupling with the Al^{27} spins, the magnitude of the spin coupling suggesting direct bonding between the two nuclei.   Thus it may be concluded that the

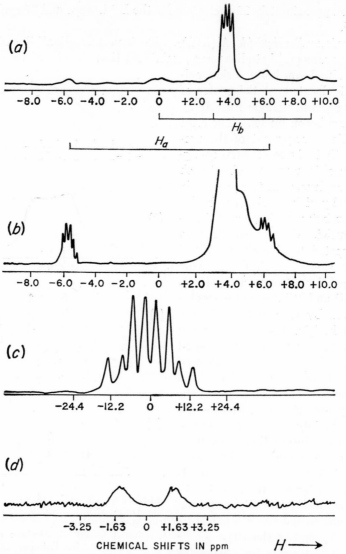

FIG. 12-5. NMR spectra of the molecule $(CH_3)_2PHBH_3$: (a) H^1 spectrum at 30 Mc/sec; (b) same as (a) with B^{11} excited at 9.6257 Mc/sec; (c) B^{11} spectrum at 12.3 Mc/sec; (d) P^{31} resonance spectrum at 12.3 Mc/sec. (Shoolery.[419])

protons are directly bonded to both aluminum and boron and all protons are equivalent. Accordingly, if both terminal hydrogens and bridge hydrogens are involved in the structure of aluminum borohydride, their different chemical environments must be averaged out by some dynamic process occurring within the molecule.

On the basis of proton and boron resonance measurements, Ogg and

Ray[306] showed that aluminum borohydride decomposes above 80°C into diborane, B_2H_6, and a compound of the composition $Al_2B_4H_{18}$. The latter also contains symmetrical BH_4 groups and may involve two hydrogen bridges between aluminum atoms.[306]

(CH₃)₂PHBH₃. The NMR spectra of this molecule measured by Shoolery[419] are of interest because they demonstrate rather clearly the wealth of information which can be gained by measuring the separate resonances of individual magnetic nuclei in a molecule and, where necessary, employing the double-irradiation technique to simplify the spectrum. Twelve of the fourteen nuclei in the molecule are magnetic. The H^1, B^{11}, and P^{31} resonance spectra are reproduced in Fig. 12-5. Inspection of the spectra leads to the following structure for the compound:

$$
\begin{array}{ccc}
 & CH_3 & H_b \\
 & | & | \\
H_a\!-\!P & \!\!-\!\!-\!\!-\!\! & B\!-\!H_b \\
 & | & | \\
 & CH_3 & H_b
\end{array}
$$

The proton spectrum contains an intense signal, due to the two equivalent methyl groups, which is split into four components by interaction with the spins of the phosphorus and H_a. The four signals at 0, 3.0, 6.0, and 9.0 ppm collapse on irradiating the B^{11} nucleus (Fig. 12-5b), and they are therefore assigned to the H_b protons. The H_a proton gives rise to two lines, at 6.0 and −5.7 ppm. This large doublet splitting indicates a direct bond to the P atom. The H_a signals become more intense on B^{11} irradiation, revealing a splitting by the six equivalent protons of the methyl groups. The B^{11} spectrum (Fig. 12-5c) contains a quartet with 1:3:3:1 intensity ratios, but each component of the quartet is doubled. The quartet arises from the three equivalent H_b protons and thus verifies the BH_3 group. The doubling of the quartet is due to interaction with the phosphorus spin of 1/2. Finally, the P^{31} spectrum consists of a doublet, confirming a direct bond of the phosphorus with H_a and the identification of the latter in the proton spectrum, where the same value of the coupling constant, J_{PH_a}, is observed. Table 12-1 summarizes the coupling constants derived from the above spectra.

TABLE 12-1. SPIN-SPIN COUPLING CONSTANTS[419] FOR THE
MOLECULE $(CH_3)_2PH_aB(H_b)_3$
(In cycles/sec)

Spectrum	J_{HP}	J_{HH_a}	J_{PH_a}	J_{BH_b}	J_{BP}	J_{PH_b}
H^1	12	6	350	90		12
B^{11}				90	50	
P^{31}			350			

TABLE 12-2. CHEMICAL SHIFTS OF C^{13}
(In compounds with more than one type of carbon atom, asterisk indicates nucleus measured)

Compound	δ, ppm		J_{CH}, cycles/sec, ref. 236
	Ref. 194	Ref. 236	
CH_2I_2	190		
CBr_4 (solid)		155	
CH_3I	153	148	151
$(CH_3)_4Sn$		137	126
C^*H_3CN		130	136
$(CH_3)_4Si$		129	120
CH_3Br	126	118	153
$CHBr_3$		115	208
CH_3NH_2	116		
C^*H_3COOH		108	131
$C_6H_3(C^*H_3)_3$ (mesitylene)		107	126
CH_2Br_2	111	106	185
$(CH_3S)_2$	109		
$(CH_3)_4C^*$		101	
CH_3Cl	107		
C_6H_{12} (cyclohexane)		100	140
$(C^*H_3)_2CO$		98	122
$(C^*H_3)_4C$		97	120
$(C^*H_3)_2NCHO$		93	139
CH_3OH	81	79	144
CH_2Cl_2	76	74	162
$(CH_3)_4NCl$ (aq. soln.)		73	146
CH_3NO_2	53	63	137
Dioxane	55	60	144
CCl_3Br		59	
$CHCl_3$	52	48	193
HCHO (38% aq. soln.)		40	172
$(H_2CO)_3$ (aq. soln.)		33	
$(CH_3O)_2C^*H_2$		33†	
CCl_4	35	26	
C^*F_3COOH		13	
CH_3C^*N		7	
$CHCl{=}CHCl$ (cis)		5	203
$C_6H_3(CH_3)_3$ (mesitylene, 2,4,6 positions)		1	160
C_6H_6	0	0	159
$C_{10}H_8$ (naphthalene)		0	157
$(C_2H_5O)_3C^*H$		0†	
$C_6H_3(CH_3)_3$ (mesitylene, 1,3,5 positions)		−10	
$(C_2H_5O)_4C^*$		−12†	
$(C_2H_5O)_2C^*O$		−27	
$(CH_3)(C_2H_5)C^*NOH$		−33	
$(CH_3)_2NC^*HO$		−36	198
CF_3C^*OOH		−37	

TABLE 12-2. CHEMICAL SHIFTS OF C^{13} (*Continued*)

| Compound | δ, ppm | | J_{CH}, cycles/sec, ref. 236 |
	Ref. 194	Ref. 236	
HCOOH	−37	−39	218
$(CH_3C*O)_2O$		−39	
K_2CO_3 (aq. soln.)		−43	
$CH_3C*OOCH_3$		−43	
CH_3C*OOH		−50	
KCN (aq. soln.)	−49		
CH_3C*OOK		−55	
CS_2		−65	
$(C_6H_5)(CH_3)C*O$		−70	
CH_3C*HO		−72	174
$(CH_3)_2C*O$		−78	

† Ref. 235.

12-3. Carbon

The only stable isotope of carbon with a nuclear magnetic moment is C^{13} ($I = 1/2$), which has a natural abundance of 1.1 per cent. The low abundance of this isotope, together with an associated long relaxation time T_1 (of the order of minutes in most carbon compounds), makes the direct measurement of the resonance absorption extremely difficult. However, by measuring the resonance signals in the dispersion mode (Sec. 4-3) under rapid-passage conditions, the NMR spectrum of C^{13} (in natural abundance) in a wide variety of compounds was successfully recorded by Lauterbur.[236] The resonances were observed at a fixed frequency of 8.5 Mc/sec in a magnetic field of about 7,940 gauss. In certain favorable compounds observations could also be made in absorption. C^{13} resonance measurements for a large number of compounds have also been carried out by Holm[194] at a field close to 10,000 gauss. The dispersion mode was employed in these measurements also. When chlorine or nitrogen is directly bonded to carbon, the signal strength is usually markedly reduced. Thus the resonance in CCl_4, for example, cannot be observed at all unless it is very rapidly traversed after allowing several minutes for relaxation.

Table 12-2 contains a summary of the measured C^{13} chemical shifts relative to the benzene signal. In compounds containing more than one type of equivalent carbon atom, the nucleus measured in any particular case is starred. Figure 12-6 shows some characteristic C^{13} resonance shifts for a number of different classes of compounds.[194] The largest shifts to high field occur when carbon is bonded to heavier atoms such as Br, I, and Sn, while predominantly low-field shifts are observed in molecules in which carbon is bonded to oxygen, as for example in the carbonyl and carboxyl groups. The carbon resonance of aliphatic hydrocarbons

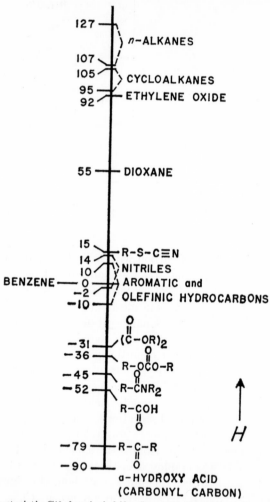

FIG. 12-6. Characteristic C^{13} chemical shifts (in parts per million) for various classes of compounds. (Holm.[194])

occurs at considerably higher fields than that of aromatic hydrocarbons. This may arise because the lower-lying excited states of the aromatic compounds lead to a larger paramagnetic contribution (Sec. 7-4).

The carbon chemical shifts, which are relatively large, appear to be rather sensitive to structural differences within the molecule. Thus the

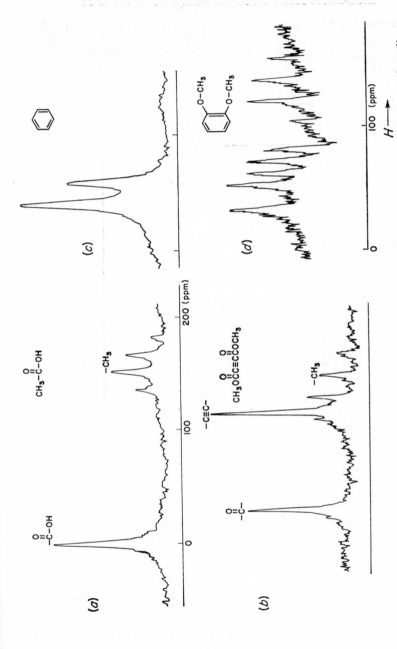

Fig. 12-7. C[13] (natural abundance) resonance spectra at 8.5 Mc/sec of (a) acetic acid, (b) dimethyl acetylene dicarboxylate, (c) benzene, and (d) o-dimethoxybenzene. Chemical shifts are shown relative to the carboxyl-carbon atom of acetic acid. (Lauterbur.[235])

resonances of the two nonequivalent groups of carbon atoms in the 2,4,6 positions and in the 1,3,5 positions in mesitylene differ by 11 ppm. Many of the compounds included in Table 12-2 give rise to relatively simple C^{13} spectra; other spectra, however, are more complex, owing to overlapping multiplets. Some interesting examples of C^{13} resonance spectra recorded by Lauterbur[235] are reproduced in Fig. 12-7. Fine-structure splitting due to the protons directly bonded to individual carbon atoms greatly

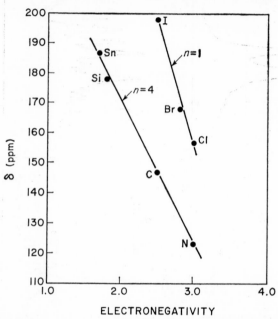

Fig. 12-8. C^{13} chemical shifts of $(CH_3)_nX$ compounds vs. the Pauling electronegativity. Chemical shifts are relative to the carboxyl-carbon resonance of acetic acid. (Lauterbur.[235])

facilitates the assignment of the spectra. Thus the signal of the carbon atom in a methyl group appears as a readily identifiable quartet. The C^{13} resonance of benzene is a doublet, because of splitting by the hydrogen atom directly bonded to each of the six equivalent carbon atoms.[†] Figure 12-7d shows the C^{13} spectrum of a disubstituted benzene, o-dimethoxybenzene. The chemical shifts between the three nonequivalent carbon atoms in the benzene ring (the five signals at low field in the figure) are comparatively large.

The C^{13} chemical shift of a methyl group shows a marked dependence

[†] The two components of the doublet are unequal in intensity because of saturation effects resulting from the shorter relaxation time of the proton spins coupled to the carbon nuclei. When the spectrum is traversed in the opposite direction, the high-field peak is more intense.

on the nature of the element to which the group is bonded. Figure 12-8 shows a plot of the methyl C^{13} chemical shifts of some methyl halides and certain tetramethyl compounds against the electronegativity of the bonded atom. [The point for N corresponds to the $N(CH_3)_4{}^+$ ion.] A simple linear correlation is apparent; increasing electronegativity shifts the C^{13} resonance to lower field. Additional effects, however, become operative with increasing substitution in the methyl group. Figure 12-9

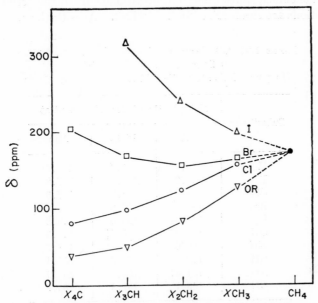

FIG. 12-9. Plot of C^{13} chemical shifts (referred to the carboxyl-carbon resonance of acetic acid) of substituted methanes. (Lauterbur.[235])

shows a plot of the C^{13} chemical shifts in a series of substituted methanes. (For the lower curve, R refers to methyl or ethyl groups.) Increasing chlorine substitution causes a progressive shift of the carbon resonance to lower field. This trend, however, appears to be arrested in the bromine-substituted compounds and is completely reversed in the iodine compounds. The curves appear to converge to a common point which may be expected to correspond to the position of the C^{13} resonance in CH_4. Crude extrapolation of the four curves yields a value of $\sim$190 to 200 ppm for the latter.

The above results thus demonstrate a dependence of the C^{13} shifts on electronegativity, together with some additional contribution which depends on the number and kind of halogen atom. These effects appear to be additive. Thus the successive replacement of chlorine atoms in CCl_4 by bromine atoms causes a linear variation of the C^{13} chemical shift.[235] A similar variation is found in several series of compounds of the type $XC^*H_{3-n}Me_n$ on successive replacement of Me groups by hydrogen atoms.

The C^{13} chemical shifts in aromatic compounds are of particular interest and may well hold considerable promise for a more detailed study of electron-charge distributions in aromatic rings. The methyl C^{13} chemical shift in a number of substituted toluenes has been measured.[235] The measured chemical shifts when the substituents are at the ortho, meta, or para positions are summarized in Table 12-3. As with the corresponding

TABLE 12-3. C^{13} CHEMICAL SHIFTS OF METHYL GROUP
IN SUBSTITUTED TOLUENES[235]
(In ppm relative to acetic acid carboxyl-carbon atom)

Substituent	Methyl C^{13} shift for substituent at		
	Ortho	Meta	Para
H	156.9	156.9	156.9
F	164.2	158.4	157.8
Cl	158.2	157.6	157.5
Br	156.1	157.6	157.6
I	147.6†	156.6	156.8
OH	162.0	156.5†	157.5
NH₂	160.6†	156.0†	157.7
CH₃	159.2	157.2†	157.4
NO₂	161.3†	157.8	156.9
CN	158.1	157.4	156.8

† The compound measured also contained a CH_3 group at the meta position.

proton chemical shifts (Sec. 11-5) or the fluorine chemical shifts (Sec. 12-6), a correlation with the Hammett σ constants may be anticipated. The experimental error of the C^{13} shifts is estimated[235] to be ± 0.3 ppm. In general the correlation of the C^{13} shifts with the corresponding fluorine shifts (Table 12-9) is better than that with the Hammett σ constants. The largest effects are observed for the substituents in the ortho position.

The proton-carbon spin coupling constant, values for which are included in Table 12-2, is relatively large and shows significant variations from compound to compound. The magnitude of this coupling constant tends to increase with decreasing magnetic shielding of the proton.[236] The coupling, however, attenuates rapidly with distance; no coupling with hydrogen separated from the carbon by more than one bond has been observed experimentally. There will, of course, be no observed coupling between carbon atoms because of the low C^{13} concentration.

12-4. Nitrogen

One of the first discoveries of chemical shifts arose out of measurements of N^{14} nuclear resonance signals by Proctor and Yu[354] in connection with the determination of the magnetic moment of N^{14}. It was observed that the frequency of the N^{14} resonance depended strongly on the chemical compound chosen. For a solution of NH_4NO_3 two resonances appeared, separated by 1.0 kc/sec in a field of 10,500 gauss ($\sim$300 ppm). Relative chemical shifts of N^{14} were measured for several compounds. The results are shown in the second column of Table 12-4. These results

TABLE 12-4. CHEMICAL SHIFTS OF N^{14} RELATIVE TO NO_3^- ION

Compound	δ, ppm		
	Proctor and Yu[354]	Masuda and Kanda[264]	Holder and Klein[192]
NH_4OH (28%)	364	372	
NH_4^+	303	346	348
$N_2H_4 \cdot H_2O$		346	
$(C_3H_7)_2NH, (C_2H_5)_3N$			321
N_2H_4			312
$(CH_3)_4NBr$			298
NH_3			290
$(NH_2)_2CO$	303	346	282
$NH_2OH \cdot HCl$			266
CH_3CONH_2			244
SCN^-		151	152
CH_3CN			131
CN^-	61	112	126
HNO_3 (100%)		52	
$C(NO_2)_4, C_2(NO_2)_6$			46
Pyridine			22
N_2			14
NO_3^-	0	0	0
CH_3NO_2		0	
$C_6H_5NO_2$			-2
$n\text{-}C_3H_7NO_2$			-26
NO_2^-			-254

were extended by Masuda and Kanda,[264] who employed a frequency of 1.92 Mc/sec with a field of 6,221 gauss. Their results are shown in the third column of Table 12-4 relative to the reference signal of the nitrate ion. More extensive N^{14} measurements have been carried out by Holder and Klein;[192] these results also are included in Table 12-4. The Holder and Klein results are in fair agreement with the Masuda and Kanda results, except for a marked discrepancy for urea.

The chemical shifts shown in Table 12-4 exhibit a general trend, although a complete interpretation in terms of electronic structure of the nitrogen compounds is not yet possible. The N^{14} resonance of NH_4^+ ion, as well as other compounds in which nitrogen is bonded to hydrogen, occurs at the highest field, while the resonances of compounds in which the nitrogen is bonded to oxygen atoms occur at the lowest field. The nitrogen chemical shifts for compounds in which nitrogen is bonded to carbon tend to occupy an intermediate position. This suggests that the electronegativity of neighboring atoms is an important factor determining the magnitude of the shifts. It has been further suggested[192] that the loss of ionic character and increase of covalency lead to asymmetries in the electronic structure, with consequent increased paramagnetic shifts to lower field. (See also Sec. 7-4.) In this connection it may be worth noting that the chemical shift of the covalently bonded N_2 molecule is close to that of the NO_3^- ion.

Except for certain compounds which are liquid at room temperature, the compounds listed in Table 12-4 were measured as aqueous solutions. It was observed that under these conditions the shifts of the nitrate, nitrite, and ammonium ions were both concentration and pH dependent.[264,192] This behavior has been made use of by Masuda and Kanda for determining the degree of dissociation of HNO_3 in aqueous solution (Sec. 18-1).

In most cases N^{14} magnetic resonance spectra have very broad lines. Since the N^{14} nucleus has a quadrupole moment, asymmetries of the electron charge distribution about the nucleus resulting from chemical-bond formation will accentuate signal broadening (Sec. 3-3). This behavior is clearly demonstrated by the N^{14} resonance measurements of Ogg and Ray[308] on ammonia and amines and their salts. The N^{14} resonance of pure dry NH_3, which is reproduced in Fig. 5-8b, consists of a very broad signal with four components arising from spin-spin splitting by the three protons. The NH_4^+ ion, in which the electron configuration about the nitrogen atom is symmetrical, gives rise to relatively sharp N^{14} signals. For example, the N^{14} spectrum of acidified† NH_4Cl (Fig. 5-8c) shows the expected five components resulting from spin coupling of four equivalent protons. Figure 12-10 shows N^{14} spectra for a series of methylammonium chlorides.[308] The line breadth of the $CH_3NH_3^+$ ion is less than that of ammonia but considerably greater than that of the NH_4^+ ion. No pronounced narrowing of the line width with increasing methyl substitution occurs until the $(CH_3)_4N^+$ ion is reached. The charge distribution in this ion is again symmetrical as in the NH_4^+ ion, and a sharp signal results.

The problem of quadrupole broadening of nitrogen NMR spectra can

† The addition of acid suppresses proton exchange with the solvent-water protons in these solutions.

in principle be overcome by making use of the N^{15} isotope, which has a spin $1/2$, instead of using the N^{14} resonance. However, because of the low signal strength (Appendix A) and the low natural abundance of N^{15},

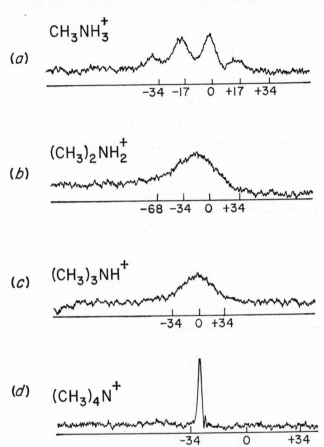

FIG. 12-10. N^{14} resonance spectra of methylammonium chlorides in acidified aqueous solutions measured at 3 Mc/sec. Reference scales are in parts per million relative to the N^{14} signal of a saturated aqueous solution of ammonium nitrate. (Ogg and Ray.[308])

isotopic enrichment is necessary. The use of N^{15} resonance measurements is therefore likely to be limited to certain specialized applications.

12-5. Oxygen

The relatively low abundance (~ 0.04 per cent) of O^{17}, the only isotope of oxygen possessing a magnetic moment, seriously limits nuclear resonance measurements of oxygen. Some measurements of O^{17} resonances in a variety of compounds have been successfully carried out, however, by Weaver, Tolbert, and LaForce.[458] With few exceptions, the natural thermal relaxation time T_1 of the O^{17} nucleus was found to be sufficiently short to provide the experimental conditions for slow-passage

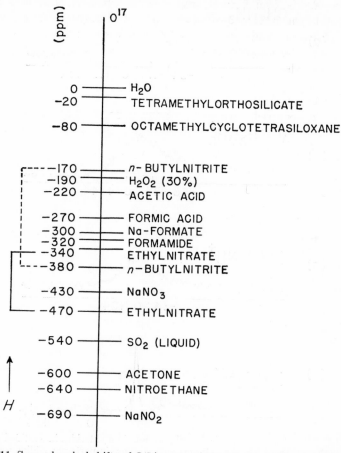

FIG. 12-11. Some chemical shifts of O^{17} in natural abundance relative to water. The brackets to the left indicate the compounds for which two separate resonance signals were observed. The dashed bracket indicates that this particular measurement was hampered by an unfavorable signal-to-noise ratio. (Weaver, Tolbert, and LaForce.[458])

observation of the resonance. The dispersion mode (Sec. 4-3) was employed in the measurements, since under these conditions the optimum value of the rf field H_1 required for maximum signal is less critical. The O^{17} resonance in water yielded a signal-to-noise ratio of 50. Under these conditions it was possible to measure O^{17} chemical shifts of the compounds shown in Fig. 12-11 (many of which have a relatively lower oxygen concentration than water), without isotopic enrichment. On the average the line width (for a field near 10,000 gauss) was observed to be of the order of 0.3 gauss.

Of all the compounds measured, the oxygen resonance in the water molecule occurs at the highest field. In this respect there is a close resemblance to the N^{14} chemical shifts (Sec. 12-4) in that chemical bonding with hydrogen atoms gives rise to resonances at highest field. The resemblance to the nitrogen chemical shifts also extends to other compounds. Thus the N^{14} and O^{17} chemical shifts of the NO_3^- and NO_2^- ions are in the same direction and of a similar order of magnitude. The two O^{17} resonance signals of ethyl nitrate are of some interest. These signals, which occurred with an intensity ratio of approximately 1:2, may be associated respectively with the oxygen in the C—O—N group

and the $N \overset{\nearrow O}{\underset{\searrow O}{}}$ group, the two oxygen atoms in the latter group being

equivalent. By analogy, multiple O^{17} resonance signals are to be expected in alkyl sulfates, sulfites, phosphates, and related compounds.

12-6. Fluorine

The F^{19} nucleus occupies an important position in NMR spectroscopy and in its application to chemistry. Like hydrogen, fluorine is monovalent and is capable of combining with many elements to form a wide variety of chemical compounds. The F^{19} nucleus, like the proton (Appendix A), gives rise to strong resonance signals, and, unlike most heavier nuclei, it has a favorable spin-lattice relaxation time T_1 in most compounds. It has, however, a definite advantage over the proton in that the range of chemical shifts of F^{19} in fluorine compounds is about an order of magnitude larger than the corresponding shifts in hydrogen-containing compounds. Accordingly the instrumental requirements for high resolution to obtain information comparable with proton measurements are usually not as demanding. Since the fluorine nucleus, like the proton, has a spin of 1/2, substitution of fluorine for hydrogen in a compound often yields NMR spectra which are very similar in appearance to the corresponding proton spectra, the larger fluorine chemical shifts being accompanied by larger spin coupling constants.

a. **Fluorine Chemical Shifts.** A general discussion of fluorine chemical shifts has been presented in Sec. 7-4. According to the theory of Saika and Slichter,[393] variations in the local paramagnetic circulations of the fluorine atom are the dominant cause of chemical shifts in fluorine compounds. This paramagnetic contribution, which represents a shift toward low field (low screening), is greatest in covalently bonded fluorine and is zero in the spherically symmetric F^- ion (Sec. 7-4). The magnitude of the paramagnetic contribution may thus be expected to depend on the amount of ionic character in the chemical bond. One would therefore expect a simple correlation of the chemical shift with the electronegativity of the atom or group to which fluorine is bonded. The

TABLE 12-5. F^{19} CHEMICAL SHIFTS IN SIMPLE FLUORIDES[159]
(Measured in field of 6,365 gauss)

Compound[†]	Chemical shift, ppm[‡]	Compound[†]	Chemical shift, ppm[‡]
F_2	0	CF_4	491.0
IF_7	261.5	PF_3	491.1 (m)
NF_3	285.0		436.3 (m)
BrF_5	290.5 (s)	SbF_3	507.9
	152.9 (w)	PF_5	520.3 (m)
ClF_3	343.4		483.9 (m)
SeF_6	372.7	SbF_5	537.3
SF_6	375.6	F^-	548.2
IF_5	418.2 (s)	BF_3	555.5
	368.9 (w)	SiF_4	598.9
BrF_3	461.1	BeF_2	599.1
AsF_3	469.1	GeF_4	608.8
TeF_6	485.9	HF	625.0

† F_2, which is chosen as the reference compound, was measured as a gas at 25 atm. F^- was measured as an aqueous solution of KF. SbF_3 was also measured as an aqueous solution. All other compounds were measured in the form of the pure liquids.

‡ The letters s, m, and w after components of complex lines refer to relative intensities as strong, medium, and weak.

rather extensive experimental data, summarized in the present section, lend support to this interpretation. It is also evident, however, that in some cases the measured chemical shifts are strongly influenced by other factors.

Simple Binary Fluorides. Measurement of F^{19} resonances in a number of fluorine compounds by Dickinson[118] resulted in one of the earliest discoveries of chemical shifts. A strong dependence of the fluorine shift on the nature of the chemical combination of the fluorine was observed. It was further demonstrated that these shifts could not be explained in terms of the calculated difference in diamagnetic shielding between a neutral fluorine atom and a fluorine ion.

Extensive fluorine resonance measurements on a wide variety of simple binary fluorides have been carried out by Gutowsky and Hoffman.[158,159] Their results are summarized in Table 12-5. In this series of compounds the F_2 resonance (arbitrarily chosen as the reference compound) occurs at the lowest field, whereas the HF resonance occurs at highest field. As indicated in the table, some compounds give rise to more than one resonance signal. In PF_3 and PF_5 the fluorine resonance signal is a symmetrical doublet, owing to spin-spin interaction with the P atom[166] (Fig. 5-3). BrF_5 and IF_5 each give rise to two signals of unequal intensity resulting from two sets of nonequivalent F atoms in these molecules. In BrF_5 and IF_5 the relative intensities of the two signals are in the ratio 4:1, in agreement with the tetragonal-pyramid structure[260] of the molecules. The weaker line, which occurs at a lower applied field in each compound, can be identified with the F atom at the apex of the pyramid. The compounds SbF_5 and IF_7 gave rise to broad signals indicative of multiple lines, but they were not resolved under the experimental conditions.

The chemical shifts of the fluorine compounds listed in Table 12-5 exhibit two general trends. The fluorine resonance is progressively displaced to lower field as the atomic number of the central atom of a *given* period of the periodic table increases. Thus, considering the first period, the resonance signal of BeF_2 occurs at highest field and that of F_2 at lowest field. A more general correlation is illustrated by Fig. 12-12, in which the fluorine chemical shifts are plotted against the Pauling electronegativity of the central atom to which the F atoms are bonded. The fluorine resonance tends to be displaced to low field with increasing electronegativity of the central atom. This implies that the more tightly electrons are held by the atom bound to fluorine, the less effective the electrons are in magnetically shielding the fluorine nucleus. Increasing electronegativity of the bonded atom destroys the symmetrical charge distribution, characteristic of the F^- ion, to a greater extent, thus increasing the paramagnetic contribution (Sec. 7-4) and causing the resonance to be displaced to lower field.

An unusually large shift to low field (-330 ppm relative to F_2) has been observed[418] for UF_6. The apparent paramagnetic contribution to the fluorine shift is nearly twice as large as that in F_2 (Sec. 7-4). The existence of low-lying excited states in uranium hexafluoride has been suggested as a possible explanation of this large shift.[426]

Halomethanes. Further support of the general correlation of fluorine chemical shifts with electronegativity of the atom or group of atoms to which the fluorine is bonded is provided by measurements on a series of halomethanes (Meyer and Gutowsky[285]). The data are summarized in Table 12-6. In the series CFH_3, CF_2H_2, CF_3H, and CF_4, successive replacement of the H atoms of methane by the more electronegative F atoms causes a progressive displacement of the fluorine resonance to lower field. Thus the effective group electronegativity influencing the fluorine

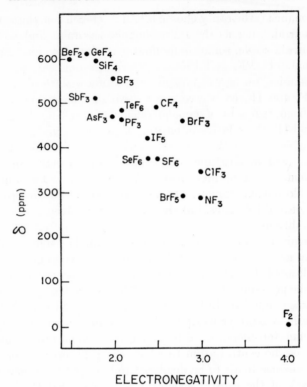

Fig. 12-12. The F^{19} chemical shifts of fluorine compounds plotted against the electronegativity of the central atom to which the fluorine is bonded. (Gutowsky and Hoffman.[159])

resonance in each compound may be expected to increase in the order $-CH_3 < -CH_2F < -CHF_2 < -CF_3$. This is consistent with the observed fluorine shifts. By the same reasoning a similar trend of the fluorine shifts would be expected in the compounds $CFCl_3$, CF_2Cl_2, CF_3Cl, and CF_4, corresponding to increasing group electronegativity in the order $-CCl_3 < -CFCl_2 < -CF_2Cl < -CF_3$. However, the observed chemical shifts (Table 12-6) are in the opposite direction, that is, to the low-field side of the CF_4 signal. Clearly, some additional factor

TABLE 12-6. F^{19} CHEMICAL SHIFTS IN HALOMETHANES[285]

Compound	δ_F, ppm	Compound	δ_F, ppm
CF_4†	0	CF_3Cl	−36.8
CF_3H	18.2	CF_2Cl_2	−60.4
CF_2H_2	80.9	$CFCl_3$	−76.7
CFH_3	210.0		

† Reference compound.

is operative.   It has been suggested[285] that, because of the greater tendency of fluorine to form partial double bonds as compared with chlorine, the structure I shown below is favored over structure II.   Accordingly,

$$Cl^-$$
$$Cl-C\!=\!F^+$$
$$\overset{|}{Cl}$$
$$I$$

$$Cl^+$$
$$\overset{\parallel}{Cl-C} \quad F^-$$
$$\overset{|}{Cl}$$
$$II$$

the F atom will tend to be less shielded and the resonance will appear at a lower field.   If this effect dominates the electronegativity difference between chlorine and fluorine, the net result would then be the CF bonds becoming less ionic in the series CH_3F, . . . , CF_4, . . . , $CFCl_3$, as shown by the progressive decrease in the measured δ values.

One further correlation of the observed chemical shifts in these compounds is worth noting.   The fluorine chemical shift in the series CFH_3, CF_2H_2, CF_3H, CF_4 decreases progressively with decreasing length of the CF bond in the respective compounds.[285]   If bond shortening is the result of increasing ionic character of the bond, the trend of the δ values with bond length would be expected to be in the opposite direction.   However if bond shortening results to a greater degree from double-bond character, as proposed by Pauling,[327] rather than from ionic character, the observed trend of the chemical shifts with bond length may be expected.

Fluorinated Organic Compounds.   Table 12-7 summarizes some typical F^{19} chemical shifts for a variety of fluorocarbons and fluorocarbon derivatives compiled from the measurements of Muller, Lauterbur,

TABLE 12-7. FLUORINE CHEMICAL SHIFTS IN FLUOROCARBONS
AND FLUOROCARBON DERIVATIVES[297,441]
(In ppm relative to CF_3COOH)

$CF_3-CF_2-CF_2-CF_3$
6   51

$CF_3-CF_2-CF_2-CF_2-CF_2-CF_3$
7   51   47   47

$CF_3-CF_2-CF_2-CF(CF_2-CF_3)_2$
5   47   34   107   37   3

$CF_3-CF_2-CF_2-CH_2Cl$
7   51   42

$CF_3-CF_2-CF_2-CH_2Br$
7   51   39

$CF_3-CF_2-CF_2-CH_2I$
7   51   33

$(CF_3)_4C$
−13.8

$(CF_3)_3C-F$
−1   112

$CF_2-(CF_2)_4-CF_2$
55

$CF_3-CF_2-CF_2-COCl$
7   51   39

$CF_3-CF_2-CF_2-CCl_3$
7   51   32

$CF_3-CF_2-CF_2-CF_2-CF_2H$
7   51   48   54   62

and Svatos[297] and of Tiers.[441]   The chemical shift, relative to that of CF_3COOH, is indicated for each structurally nonequivalent fluorine atom.   Contrary to the corresponding proton shifts in paraffin hydro-carbons, the fluorine shifts between primary, second, and tertiary fluorine atoms are relatively large.   Each type of fluorine atom is therefore readily identified in the NMR spectrum.   Moreover, whereas in the hydrocarbons the proton resonance of the methyl group appears at higher field than that of the methylene group, the corresponding fluorine shifts in the fluorocarbons are reversed, the CF_3 resonance appearing at lowest field.   These characteristic differences are a further manifestation of the much greater electronegativity of the fluorine atom relative to that of the proton.   The progressive displacement of the F^{19} resonance to lower field in the series CF, CF_2, and CF_3 suggests that the amount of charge which fluorine is able to draw from a carbon atom decreases as the number of competing fluorines bonded to that carbon increases.

Fluorine chemical shifts for a series of fluorocarbon derivatives are also shown in Table 12-7.   The fluorine shift of the CF_2 group adjacent to the substituent in each case is of some interest.   The "apparent electron-withdrawing power" of the substituents (as indicated by the δ values of the F atoms of the CF_2 group) is in the following order of effectiveness: CCl_3, CH_2I > COCl, CH_2Br > CH_2Cl > CF_3 > CF_2H.   Additional measurements of perfluoroalkyl halides[441] lead to the following evaluation of "apparent electron-withdrawing power": I > Br > Cl > F $\gg$ CF_2I > CF_2Br > CF_2Cl > CF_3.   Both series exhibit a trend opposite to that expected from group-electronegativity considerations.   A similar situation was encountered in the substituted methane series CF_4, $CClF_3$, CCl_2F_2, and CCl_3F, for which the explanation of the greater tendency of fluorine to form partial double bonds was advanced.[285]   In order to explain the effect of the above series of substituents on the fluorine shift of the CF_2 group, Tiers[441] has postulated a "repulsive unshielding" effect.   The bulkiness of groups such as CCl_3 and I was considered to give rise to steric interactions which compensate for their lesser electro-negativity in withdrawing electrons from a neighboring CF_2 group. There is at present no theoretical basis for determining whether or not steric interactions contribute significantly to the chemical shift.

Characteristic F^{19} chemical shifts for a wide variety of perfluoroorganic compounds have been measured by Muller, Lauterbur, and Svatos.[297] The data are collected in Table 12-8.   Tertiary fluorine atoms and fluorine atoms attached to alkyl groups give rise to resonances at highest fields, whereas those bonded to a carbonyl group or to nitrogen resonate at the lowest fields.   The complete spectral range is rather wide, and the resonances of fluorine atoms in different chemical environments are well separated.   Fluorine resonance measurements are thus ideally suited for molecular identification and structure determinations of fluorine compounds.

TABLE 12-8. CHARACTERISTIC F^{19} CHEMICAL SHIFTS IN FLUORINATED
ORGANIC COMPOUNDS[297]
(In ppm relative to CF$_3$COOH)

Group	No. of compounds	Range of δs observed
CH$_2$CH$_2$F	3	149.5 to 145.5
C$_3$CF	2	112.5, 107.0
C—CF$_2$—C	17	57.8 to 21.9
C—CF$_2$—N	10	51.1 to 8.6
C—NF—C	2	36.6, 36.0
C—CF$_2$—O	6	14.9 to −6.2
CF$_3^*$—CF$_2$—†	10	11.9 to 3.2
All other CF$_3$—C	10	0.0 to −19.7
C=CF—O	3	−9.4 to −11.8
CF$_3$—N	9	−18.8 to −36.2
O—CF$_2$—N	1	−20.6
CF$_2$=N	1	−25.2, −44.6
C—CF=N	1	−52.7
N—C(O)F	1	−81.0
C—NF$_2$	1	−92.0

† The asterisk identifies the fluorine group measured.

Substituted Fluorobenzenes. The effect of substitution on the fluorine resonance in monofluorobenzene has been studied by Gutowsky, McCall, McGarvey, and Meyer.[164] Their results are summarized in Table 12-9. The separate chemical shifts δ_o, δ_m, and δ_p refer to the F^{19} chemical shift in compounds in which the substituent is respectively ortho, meta, and para with respect to the fluorine atom. The reference compound throughout is unsubstituted monofluorobenzene. The results clearly demonstrate that the introduction of a substituent shifts the fluorine resonance by an amount and direction characteristic of the substituent and its position in the molecule. Substituents in benzene derivatives are known to alter the local electronic charge distribution at a given carbon atom, which affects the chemical reactivity, as well as certain other properties, in a specific way. These effects have been systematized empirically in terms of the well-known Hammett σ constants[181] defined by†

$$\sigma = \log K_i - \log K_i^0$$

where K_i and K_i^0 are the ionization constants for the substituted and unsubstituted benzoic acids. To the extent that the measured fluorine chemical shifts reflect the local electronic environment of the fluorine

† The symbol σ, as used here, follows accepted usage and is not to be confused with the nuclear magnetic screening constants σ used elsewhere in this book.

atom, a simple correlation of the δ values with the Hammett σ constants may be anticipated. Values of the latter for the meta- and para-substituted compounds are also listed in Table 12-9. A plot of the δ values against the σ constants yields separate straight lines for the meta- and

TABLE 12-9. FLUORINE CHEMICAL SHIFTS δ IN
MONOSUBSTITUTED FLUOROBENZENES[164]
(In ppm relative to fluorobenzene)

Substituent	Ortho	Meta		Para	
	δ_o	δ_m	σ	δ_p	σ
NO₂	5.6	−3.3	0.710	−10.8	0.778
CN	− 5.2	−3.0	0.608	− 9.6	0.656
COOH	− 3.5	−0.5	0.355	− 6.9	0.728
I	−19.3	−2.6	0.352	1.2	0.276
Br	− 5.5	−2.4	0.391	2.3	0.232
Cl	2.7	−2.1	0.373	2.4	0.227
F	25.9	−3.1	0.337	6.4	0.062
CH₃	5.0	0.9	−0.069	5.5	−0.170
CH₃CONH	12.8	−1.0		5.7	
OH	25.0	−0.9	0.10	10.6	−0.36
CH₃O	22.4			11.4	−0.268
C₂H₅O	21.7	−1.3	0.15	11.5	−0.25
NH₂	23.1	0.20	−0.161	14.6	−0.660

Substituent	δ_p	σ	Substituent	δ_m	σ
p-SO₂Cl	−12.6		m-CF₃	−2.8	0.41
p-CCl₃	− 2.6		m-CH(OH)CH₃	0.00	
p-Phenyl	2.7	0.009	m-O—C₆H₄—F	0.5	
p-O—C₆H₄—F	6.7				
p-NH—C₆H₅	9.4				
p-N(CH₃)₂	16.8	−0.720			

para-substituted compounds. The lines are fitted by the equations

$$\delta_m = -5.92\sigma_m \qquad (12\text{-}1)$$
$$\delta_p = -17.9\sigma_p + 4.84 \qquad (12\text{-}2)$$

although scatter of individual points from a straight line in many cases exceeds the experimental error (± 0.3 ppm). The different slopes for the two lines may be interpreted as a manifestation of the different character of the electronic effects arising from the meta and para substitution. A large body of indirect evidence[115,433] indicates that substituents influence the meta position mainly by the inductive mechanism, the para by resonance (mesomerism), and the ortho by a combination of inductive, resonance, and steric effects.   The observed δ values for the meta- and para-substituted compounds are in general consistent with these ascribed effects.   Thus, the more perturbing resonance effect causes a wider range of fluorine shifts in the para compounds than the shifts of the meta compounds caused by the less intense inductive effect.   Para substituents such as NO_2, CN, and CO_2H, which are capable of conjugating with the aromatic ring and which are strong electron-withdrawing groups, shift the fluorine resonance toward lower field.   Groups with unshared p orbitals, such as OH, CH_3O, and NH_2, which are electron-releasing groups, give rise to a high-field shift of the fluorine resonance.   A parallel but less pronounced shift of the para proton in benzenes monosubstituted with these groups is also observed (Sec. 11-5).

The δ values resulting from halogen substitution are of some interest. In general the δ_o values for these compounds (Table 12-9) cover a much wider range of chemical shifts than the corresponding δ_m and δ_p values. Moreover, the δ_o values become more negative (i.e., the resonance shifts to lower field) in the order F, Cl, Br, and I, the values for F and I being 25.9 and -19.3 ppm, respectively.   This trend in the δ_o values is opposite to that expected from electronegativity considerations.   The inductive effect depends on the electron affinity of the halogen and decreases in the order $F > Cl > Br > I$.   The resonance effect, on the other hand, depends on the ionization energy, and on this basis would be expected to decrease in magnitude in the order $I > Br > Cl > F$.   The latter effect may be expected to dominate the δ_p values.   It would also contribute to the δ_o values, but here the inductive effect would also be expected to be greater.   The large range of δ_o values thus appears to indicate some additional contribution at the ortho position which is not operative at the meta and para positions.   The nature of this additional interaction has not been satisfactorily interpreted.   It will be recalled that the fluorine chemical shifts in $CFCl_3$ relative to CF_4 (Table 12-6), and in the CF_2 group adjacent to groups such as CH_2I or CCl_3 (Table 12-7), are anomalous in that the shifts are in the opposite direction to that expected from electronegativity differences of the halogen substituents.   While this comparison is suggestive, it is at present not possible to draw a definite parallel with the ortho-substituted fluorobenzenes, or to invoke possible steric effects without further study.

In order to determine the extent to which substituent effects in fluorobenzene are additive, the fluorine chemical shifts in a number of polysubstituted fluorobenzenes were measured by Gutowsky, McCall, McGarvey, and Meyer.[164]   The differences between the measured values and those calculated with the aid of the values for the monosubstituted compounds, assuming additivity, are in most cases somewhat larger than the experimental error (± 0.3 ppm), but yet sufficiently small to demonstrate an approximate validity of the additivity principle.

The use of fluorine δ values of substituted benzenes for predicting Hammett σ constants has been suggested by Meyer and Gutowsky.[285] In this connection a modified interpretation of the measured δ values and their relation to the σ constants, which has been proposed by Taft,[434] leads to a better quantitative correlation of the two parameters than that given by Eqs. (12-1) and (12-2). It is based on a separation of the σ constants into independent inductive and resonance contributions according to the equation[433]

$$\sigma \equiv \sigma_I + \sigma_R \qquad (12\text{-}3)$$

The inductive contribution σ_I may be regarded as an electronic perturbation by the substituent acting through space or through sigma bonds of the benzene system. The resonance contribution σ_R, on the other hand, may be regarded as a perturbation acting solely through resonance interaction with the benzene π orbitals. Values of σ_I and σ_R for a number of substituents, as compiled by Taft,[434] are reproduced in Table 12-10. The

TABLE 12-10. INDUCTIVE (σ_I) AND RESONANCE (σ_R, σ_R^-)
PARAMETERS OF SUBSTITUENTS[434]

Substituent	σ_I	σ_R	Substituent	σ_I	σ_R	σ_R^-
NH_2	0.10	-0.76	H	0.00	0.00	0.00
OH	0.25	-0.61	$N(CH_3)_3^+$	0.86	0.00	
OCH_3	0.23	-0.50	CH_2Cl	0.17	0.01	
F	0.50	-0.44	CN	0.59	0.07	0.41
OC_6H_5	0.38	-0.41	$(CH_3)_3Si$	-0.12	0.11	
Cl	0.47	-0.24	CF_3	0.41	0.14	
Br	0.45	-0.22	CH_3SO_2	0.59	0.14	
CH_3	-0.05	-0.13	NO_2	0.63	0.15	0.64
I	0.38	-0.10	$C_2H_5CO_2C$	0.32	0.20	0.36
C_6H_5	0.10	-0.09	CH_3CO	0.27	0.25	0.60

σ_I values were derived from aliphatic-series reactivities,[433,387] in which resonance contributions are absent. The σ_R values were obtained as the difference of the Hammett σ constant for the para compound and σ_I. The additional constants σ_R^- shown in Table 12-10 are applicable to derivatives of aniline and phenol.[433] A plot of the measured δ_m values (Table 12-9) against $\Sigma\sigma_I$, where the summation is used to include polysubstituted benzenes† (assuming additivity of substituent effects), gives a good straight line represented by[434]

$$\delta_m = -5.83\Sigma\sigma_I + 0.20 \qquad (12\text{-}4)$$

† The δ values of polysubstituted benzenes of ref. 164 were employed.

The probable error of a single point (δ values) by this equation is 0.3 ppm, which is also the estimated experimental error.

The δ_p values, when plotted against σ_I in the same manner, scatter widely but systematically from the "meta line." Points for para substituents lying below the meta line are those for groups which are electron withdrawing by resonance interaction, whereas points above the line are for groups which are electron releasing by resonance interaction. The vertical deviations of the points from the meta line, that is, $\delta_p - (-5.83\Sigma\sigma_I + 0.20)$, which is essentially equivalent to $\delta_p - \delta_m$, are regarded as a measure of the resonance contribution σ_R. As shown by Fig. 12-13, a plot of these deviations against the σ_R values listed in Table 12-10 leads to an improved [Eq. (12-2)] linear correlation given by

$$\delta_p = -5.83\Sigma\sigma_I - 18.80\sigma_R + 0.80 \qquad (12\text{-}5)$$

The probable error of a single point is 0.7 ppm for a range of 20 ppm. For the substituents NO_2, CN, and CH_3CO, σ_R is used as a lower limit and σ_R^- as an upper limit. It is evident from Fig. 12-13 that an intermediate value is suggested by the proposed correlation.

The use of fluorine chemical shifts to study substituent effects in aromatic compounds appears rather promising. In principle, similar information should be obtainable from proton resonance measurements. However, since the proton shifts are very much smaller and the spectra are rather complex because of spin coupling from neighboring protons, extreme resolution and a complete analysis of the spectra are required to evaluate individual chemical shifts. Moreover, proton shifts are relatively more affected by solvent and dilution effects than are the much larger fluorine shifts. It is also conceivable that, since it has unshared p electrons capable of interacting with π electrons of the benzene system, fluorine may respond in a different way to resonance effects of substituents. Inductive effects may, however, be expected to cause proportionate shifts in the fluorine and proton resonances. Proton chemical-shift measurements in substituted benzenes (summarized in Sec. 11-5) are not yet sufficiently accurate or extensive to permit a correlation with τ values as quantitative as that obtained for F^{19} resonances in substituted benzenes.

b. Fluorine Spin Coupling Constants. The relatively greater interaction of the fluorine nucleus with spins of other magnetic nuclei compared to the interaction of protons has been mentioned earlier. Thus for example, the doublet splitting of the fluorine resonance in PF_3 (due to coupling with the phosphorus spin of 1/2) is 1,400 cycles/sec, compared with 183 cycles/sec for the proton splitting[166] in PH_3. As a result of the larger spin coupling, multiplet splitting of the fluorine resonance arising from a magnetic nucleus four or five bonds removed in the same molecule can often be detected. In contrast, spin interaction of protons separated by more than three bonds can usually not be observed experimentally.

The nature of fluorine electron-coupled spin-spin interactions has been

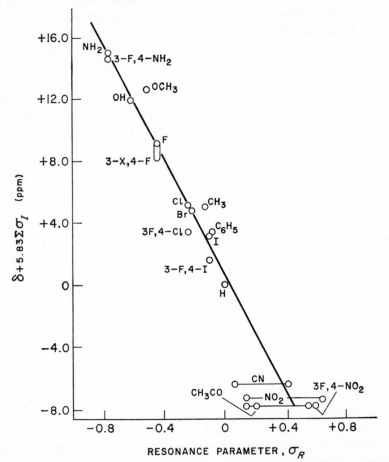

FIG. 12-13. Correlation plot of $\delta_p + 5.83\Sigma\sigma_I$ vs. the resonance parameter σ_R for substituted fluorobenzenes. (Taft.[434])

investigated in some detail by Gutowsky, McCall, and Slichter.[166,165] Their results provide an experimental basis for some of the theoretical interpretations discussed in Chap. 8. Some measurements of fluorine-phosphorus coupling constants are summarized in Table 12-11. In all the compounds listed, the fluorine atoms are directly bonded to phosphorus. The J_{PF} values in these compounds vary by a factor of two. The corresponding J_{PF} values measured from the splitting of the P^{31}

resonances, also shown in Table 12-11, agree with those derived from the F^{19} resonances to within the experimental error.

Fluorine chemical shifts for the compounds listed in Table 12-11 are given in the last column. There is no apparent direct over-all correlation between the measured J_{PF} values and the corresponding chemical shifts. In some cases, however, as for example in the closely related molecules $POCl_2F$, $POClF_2$, and POF_3, a simple linear relationship between these

TABLE 12-11. SPIN COUPLING CONSTANTS AND CHEMICAL SHIFTS
OF FLUORINE IN PHOSPHORUS COMPOUNDS[166]

Molecule	J_{PF}, cycles/sec†		Fluorine chemical shift, ppm‡
	F^{19} resonance	P^{31} resonance	
PF_3	1,400	1,410	−43.4
CH_3OPF_2	1,280	1,275	−25.0
$POCl_2F$	1,175	1,168	−69.0
$POClF_2$	1,120	1,137	−30.4
POF_3	1,055		15.8
$F_2PO(OH)$	978	984	9.0
$FPO(OH)_2$	954		− 2.5
PF_5	930		− 5.0
Na_2PO_3F (aq.)	781		26.8
HPF_6	713	707	− 5.5

† Derived from the multiplet splitting of F^{19} resonances and P^{31} resonances as shown.

‡ Measured relative to CF_3COOH at a field of 6,365 gauss.

parameters is indicated; the largest value of J_{PF} corresponds to the compound ($POCl_2F$) for which the fluorine resonance appears at lowest field. A similar correlation is found in the series CH_3F, CH_2F_2, and CHF_3, for which J_{HF} values are 44, 53, and 81 cycles/sec, respectively,[285] and F^{19} chemical shifts (Table 12-5) are 210.0, 80.9, and 18.2 ppm.

Compared to the relatively large coupling constants when the two interacting nuclei are directly bonded (Table 12-11), molecules such as BrF_5 and IF_5, in which the interacting nuclei are separated by two bonds, give rise to much smaller J values.[166] In each of these molecules there are two sets of nonequivalent fluorine nuclei (Table 12-5), the coupling constants being 76 cycles/sec in BrF_5 and 84 cycles/sec in IF_5.

Some representative J values for fluorine nuclei interacting with other magnetic nuclei in various states of chemical combination are given in Table 8-2. Of particular interest are the spin coupling interactions of fluorine nuclei with protons. The strongest interaction occurs in the molecule HF, in which the two nuclei are directly bonded. The value of

J_{HF} in anhydrous HF, derived by Solomon and Bloembergen,[430] is 615 cycles/sec. In the substituted methanes CH_xF_y, in which the interacting nuclei are two bonds removed, the J_{HF} values quoted above are in the range 40 to 80 cycles/sec. In ethyl fluoride,[169] CH_3CH_2F, the coupling between the methylene hydrogens and fluorine is 60 cycles/sec, and that between the methyl hydrogens and fluorine is 20 cycles/sec. Thus an additional CC bond causes an attenuation of the order of 1/3.

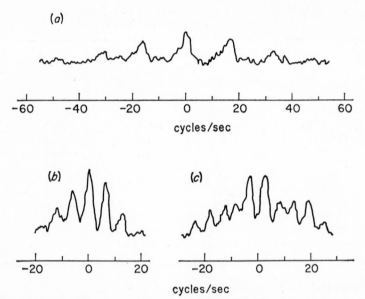

FIG. 12-14. Fluorine resonance spectrum of $(CF_3)_2NCF_2CF_3$: (a) CF_2 group, (b) CF_3 group, and (c) $N(CF_3)_2$ group. (Saika and Gutowsky.[392])

A somewhat unusual sequence of spin coupling constants has been observed[392] in the molecule $(CF_3)_2NCF_2CF_3$. The fluorine resonances of the groups $—CF_2—$, $—CF_3$, and $—N(CF_3)_2$, whose chemical shifts relative to trifluoroacetic acid are 19.9, 8.5, and -23.1 ppm, respectively, are reproduced in Fig. 12-14. The $—CF_2—$ signal (Fig. 12-14a) is a septet ($J \approx 16$ cycles/sec) arising from the coupling of the six fluorines in the $—N(CF_3)_2$ group. The $—CF_3$ group signal (Fig. 12-14b) is also a septet ($J \approx 6$ cycles/sec) which must also arise from coupling with the fluorines of the $—N(CF_3)_2$ group. The latter are five bonds removed, whereas the fluorines on the adjacent $—CF_2—$ group, which are only three bonds removed, produce no detectable splitting ($J \approx 1$ cycle/sec). A somewhat related situation is found[297] in the molecule $(CF_3)_2CHCF_2$-OCH_3, in which the strongest coupling ($J \approx 10.9$ cycles/sec) occurs between the fluorines of the CF_3 groups and those of the CF_2 group. The tertiary proton, though not as far removed, produces a smaller splitting ($J \approx 7.4$ cycles/sec) of the resonance signal of the CF_3 groups.

Fluorinated Cyclic Compounds. The fluorine spin coupling constants, as well as the fluorine chemical shifts, in substituted di- and tetrafluorocyclobutanes, studied by Shoolery[419] and by Phillips,[331] illustrate several features characteristic of cyclic molecules. Structure diagrams for a difluorocyclobutane and a tetrafluorocyclobutane are shown in Fig. 12-15. Since the cyclobutane ring is planar,† symmetrical substitution at each carbon atom preserves the plane of symmetry. Under these conditions two fluorine atoms bonded to a given carbon atom (indicated

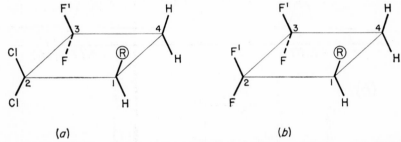

(a)   (b)

FIG. 12-15. Molecular diagrams of (<i>a</i>) substituted difluorocyclobutane and (<i>b</i>) substituted tetrafluorocyclobutane. Numbering of the carbon atoms is relative to the substituent R.

by F and F′ in Fig. 12-15) are magnetically equivalent. Thus the fluorine resonances of octafluorocyclobutane and of 1,1,2,2-tetrafluorocyclobutane‡ consist of a single signal.[331] A further example is provided by 1,1-dimethyl-2,2,3,3-tetrafluorocyclobutane, the fluorine resonance spectrum of which is shown in Fig. 12-16*a*. The peak at -2.87 ppm, which is a triplet due to spin coupling with the neighboring CH_2 group, can be assigned to the two equivalent fluorine atoms on carbon 3, and that at 9.77 ppm to the two equivalent fluorine atoms on carbon 2. A surprising feature of the spectrum is the apparent absence of spin coupling between the two sets of fluorine atoms on neighboring carbon atoms. Ordinarily such coupling might be expected to be greater than that between neighboring CF_2 and CH_2 groups.

Unsymmetrical substitution of the cyclobutane ring, as for example by

† Certain evidence from optical spectra and electron-diffraction analysis indicates the ring is somewhat puckered due to fluorine-atom repulsions.[240,131] The fluorine resonance of octafluorocyclobutane, however, consists of a single sharp line, indicating that any deviation from planarity is slight or that there exists a ring-inversion frequency sufficiently high to average the environments of the fluorine atoms.

‡ Spin coupling multiplets due to the protons on adjacent carbon atoms were not observed in the fluorine spectrum of this compound.

a single substituent R on carbon 1 (Fig. 12-15), destroys the plane of symmetry, causing the two fluorine atoms F and F' on a given carbon atom to become nonequivalent. The resulting fluorine resonance spectrum of substituted difluorocyclobutanes[419] (Fig. 12-15a) consists of four signals, as shown in Fig. 12-16b. This is a typical AB spectrum (Sec. 6-5) arising from two nonequivalent nuclei. The two signals on the high-field side exhibit a triplet splitting, presumably due to the neighboring

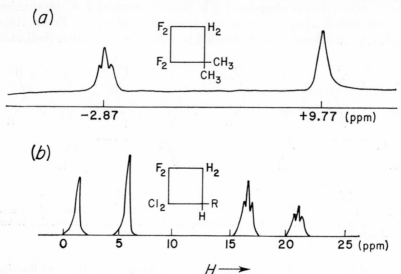

FIG. 12-16. (a) Fluorine spectrum of 1,1-dimethyl-2,2,3,3-tetrafluorocyclobutane at 30 Mc/sec. Chemical shifts shown are relative to 1,1,2,2-tetrafluorocyclobutane. (Phillips.[331]) (b) Fluorine spectrum of unsymmetrically substituted difluorocyclobutane at 40 Mc/sec. The substituted group R is $Si(OC_2H_5)_3$. (Shoolery.[419])

CH_2 group. This implies a much stronger coupling of the methylene-group protons with one of the two fluorine atoms than with the other. (The spectrum does not, of course, permit a definite assignment of signals to F and F'.) The fluorine resonance spectrum of 1-phenyl-2,2,3,3-tetrafluorocyclobutane, shown in Fig. 12-17, exhibits the maximum of eight lines to be expected for a compound containing two CF_2 groups, the two fluorine atoms of each CF_2 group being structurally nonequivalent. It has been established[331] from analysis of the NMR spectra of some unsymmetrically substituted 2,2- and 3,3-difluorocyclobutanes that in general the chemical shift between the two fluorine atoms on carbon 2 is greater than that between two fluorine atoms on carbon 3. On this basis the signals of the tetrafluoro compound can be assigned to the 2-fluorines and to the 3-fluorines, as shown in Fig. 12-17. Denoting the chemical shift and the spin coupling constants of the two nonequivalent fluorine atoms on carbon 2 by δ_2 and J_2, respectively, and the corresponding quantities for the two 3-fluorines by δ_3 and J_3, analysis of the spectrum yields

$$\delta_2 = 23.5 \text{ ppm} \qquad J_2 = 206 \text{ cycles/sec}$$
$$\delta_3 = 10.0 \text{ ppm} \qquad J_3 = 206 \text{ cycles/sec}$$

The chemical shift between the mean of the 2-fluorine signals and the

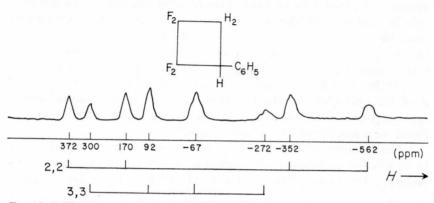

FIG. 12-17. Fluorine spectrum of 1-phenyl-2,2,3,3-tetrafluorocyclobutane at 30 Mc/sec. Chemical shifts indicated are relative to the fluorine signal of 1,1,2,2-tetrafluorocyclobutane. (Phillips.[331])

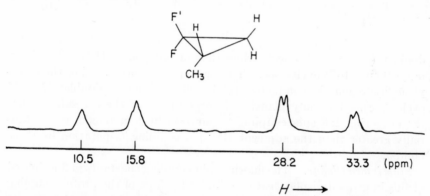

FIG. 12-18. Fluorine resonance spectrum of 1-methyl-2,2-difluorocyclopropane at 30 Mc/sec. Chemical shifts are relative to 1,1,2,2-tetrafluorocyclobutane. (Phillips.[331])

mean of the 3-fluorine signals is 3.4 ppm. Thus while there is a chemical shift between the fluorines on the neighboring carbon atoms, no spin-spin interaction between these fluorines is evident. Accordingly the spectrum is a superposition of two AB spectra rather than an ABCD spectrum.

The fluorine resonance spectrum of 1-methyl-2,2-difluorocyclopropane illustrates yet another remarkable angular dependence of the nuclear spin interaction observed in some cyclic systems in which nuclear configurations are fixed. The spectrum reproduced in Fig. 12-18 shows the familiar four-line pattern characteristic of two nonequivalent fluorine nuclei with $\delta = 16.8$ ppm and $J = 157$ cycles/sec. The signals arising from one of the two fluorine nuclei (at 28.2 and 33.3 ppm) are split into doublets, presumably by the single proton of the 1 position. The two signals at 10.5 and 15.8 ppm, arising from the other fluorine nucleus, appear to be split into unresolved triplets, presumably as the result of spin interaction with the two protons of the 3 position. This curious behavior is somewhat analogous to that observed in some difluorocyclobutanes (Fig. 12-16b) in which one of the two fluorine atoms on the same carbon atom is more strongly spin-coupled to a neighboring CH_2 group than is the other fluorine atom. It is also noteworthy that the value of J of 157 cycles/sec for the two fluorine nuclei in fluorinated methyl cyclopropane is significantly less than the average value of 211 cycles/sec found for a number of fluorocyclobutanes.[331]

A further apparent anomaly of fluorine spin coupling constants is found in fluorinated cyclobutenes,[412] typical of which are the following compounds. The proton signal of the vinyl hydrogen in compound I is a

F_2 —⌐—————⌐— H	F_2 —⌐—————⌐— H	F_2 —⌐—————⌐— F
F —⌞—————⌟— C_6H_5	Cl_2 —⌞—————⌟— C_6H_5	H_2 —⌞—————⌟— C_6H_5
Cl		
(I)	(II)	(III)

doublet ($J = 8$ cycles/sec), while that of compound II is not split by more than 1 to 2 cycles/sec. The proton resonance signal of the methylene hydrogens in compound III is split only into a doublet ($J = 12$ cycles/sec). The only plausible interpretation of these results is that the cross-ring HF spin coupling (separation by four bonds) is substantially greater than the adjacent HF spin coupling (separation by three bonds).

Fluorinated Olefins. The fluorine spin coupling constants in fluorinated olefins in general display features similar to those of the proton coupling constants (Sec. 11-3), in that the trans coupling constants are considerably larger than the cis coupling constants. Table 12-12 summarizes the nuclear spin coupling constants[275] of a variety of halogen-substituted ethylenes of the type

$$\begin{array}{ccc} X_1 & & X_3 \\ \diagdown & & \diagup \\ & C{=}C & \\ \diagup & & \diagdown \\ X_2 & & X_4 \end{array}$$

Except for $CH_2{=}CF_2$, $CH_2{=}CFCl$, and the perfluoromethyl compounds,

TABLE 12-12. NUCLEAR SPIN COUPLING CONSTANTS[275] IN HALOGENATED
OLEFINS $X_1X_2C{=}CX_3X_4$
(In cycles/sec)

X_1	X_2	X_3	X_4	J_{12}	J_{13}, cis	J_{23}, trans	J_{14}, trans	J_{24}, cis	J_{34}
H	F	Cl	Cl	81					
H	H	F	F	4	1	34	34	1	37
H	H	F	Cl	3	8	40			
F	F	H	Cl	41	3	13			
F	F	F	Cl	78	58	115			
F	F	F	Br	75	57	124			
F	F	F	CN	27	35	118			
F	F	F	H	87	33	119	12	3	72
F	F	F	CF_3	57	39	116	8	22	13
F	F	Cl	CF_3	†			12	21	
Cl	F	Cl	CF_3					20	

† The F^{19} resonance of the $={}CF_2$ group is complex and was not analyzed.

the simple first-order theory accounts for all the observed multiplets in the spectra of these compounds. An example[418] is the fluorine spectrum of the molecule $CF_2{=}CFCl$, which is reproduced in Fig. 12-19. The assignment of the three separate multiplets is indicated, the four components of the multiplet for any one fluorine atom arising from spin

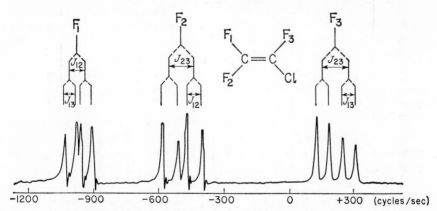

FIG. 12-19. Fluorine spectrum of $CF_2{=}CFCl$ at 30 Mc/sec. Chemical shifts, in cycles per second, are shown relative to perfluorocyclobutane. (Shoolery.[418])

interaction with each of the other two fluorine atoms. As can be seen from Table 12-12, the FF coupling constants for two fluorine atoms which are in trans positions are in the range 115 to 124 cycles/sec, while for

TABLE 12-13. PROTON AND FLUORINE SPIN COUPLING CONSTANTS† IN SUBSTITUTED BENZENES[161]
(In cycles/sec)

Compound	J_{HH}			J_{HF}			J_{FF}		
	Ortho	Meta	Para	Ortho	Meta	Para	Ortho	Meta	Para
2,3,5,6-Tetrachlorofluorobenzene						2.1			
2-Nitro-3-fluoro-5,6-dichlorobenzotrifluoride				8.4					
2,6-Dinitro-3,5-dichlorobenzene			<1						
2,4-Dimethyl-6-nitroaniline		1.2							
2,4-Difluoromesitylene					7.7				
2-Fluoromesitylene					7.0				
2,6-Dichloro-3,5-difluorobenzotrifluoride				7.8					
1,3,5-Trifluoro-2,6-dichlorobenzene				8.6		2.2		1.9	
2,4-Dinitro-6-chlorophenol		2.7							
2,6-Dibromophenol	7.9								
1,4-Difluoro-2,3,5-trichlorobenzene				8.4	6.3				12.0
2-Fluoro-4,6-dichlorophenol		2.3		9.6		−2.1			
2-Amino-3,5-difluoro-4-chloronitrobenzene				9.4		−2.2		3.1	
2-Fluoro-4,5-dichlorophenol			0.4	10.1	8.3				
2,6-Dichloro-3-fluorobenzotrifluoride				$\geqslant 6.2$	$\leqslant 6.2$				
2,3-Difluoro-5,6-dibromonitrobenzene				8.7	6.8		20.2		
2,4-Dichloro-3,5-difluoronitrobenzene				8.0		2.3		4.2	
2,4-Dichloro-3,6-difluoronitrobenzene				8.2	6.3				
2-Chloro-4,5-difluoronitrobenzene			<1	9.5	7.1		20.8		14.4

† Errors in the J values are estimated to be not greater than 0.4 cycle/sec.

those in cis positions the coupling constants range from 33 to 58 cycles/ sec. Nuclear couplings within the group, $=CF_2$ (gem fluorines), vary more widely: 27 to 87 cycles/sec.

An unusual multiplet structure in the F^{19} resonance spectrum of $CF_3CCl=CFCl$ has been observed by McConnell and Reilly.[274] Analysis of the spectrum, which is of the AB_3 type (Sec. 6-5), satisfactorily accounts for all signals, except for one relatively prominent signal in the B spectrum which remains to be interpreted.

Fluorobenzenes. Proton and fluorine spin coupling constants in a wide variety of substituted fluorobenzenes have been measured by Gutowsky, Holm, Saika, and Williams.[161] Values of the J_{HH}, J_{HF}, and J_{FF} coupling constants when the interacting nuclei are ortho, meta, or para with respect to each other are summarized in Table 12-13. While absolute signs of the spin coupling constants cannot be evaluated from the analysis of the observed spectra, in some cases, as indicated in the table, relative signs can be determined (Sec. 6-6). The magnitudes of J_{HH} and J_{HF} decrease in the order ortho > meta > para, following the expected attenuation with the number of bonds separating the interacting nuclei. The J_{FF} values differ in this respect in that the para coupling is larger than the meta coupling.

The first eight compounds listed in Table 12-13 give simple NMR spectra in which the multiplet splitting follows simple first-order theory (Sec. 5-2). The remaining compounds give rise to more complex spectra which are of the type ABX (Sec. 6-6). An interesting example of the first group, involving three sets of nonequivalent nuclei, is the spectrum of 1,3,5-trifluoro-2,6-dichlorobenzene,[161] which is reproduced in Fig. 12-20. The proton spectrum consists of a triplet arising from the two equivalent fluorine nuclei in the 3,5 positions, $J_{HF,ortho}$, each component of the triplet being split into doublets by the fluorine atom para to the proton, $J_{HF,para}$. The spectrum of the two equivalent fluorines is a doublet due to the adjacent proton, $J_{HF,ortho}$, each component of which is split into a doublet by the third fluorine atom, $J_{FF,meta}$. Finally the signal of the latter appears as a quartet resulting from a nearly equal coupling with the para proton and the 3,5 fluorine atoms.

c. Some Applications of Fluorine Resonance Measurements. *Halogen Fluorides.* The fluorine resonance spectrum[291] of ClF_3 at $-60°C$ (Sec. 5-2) shows two of the fluorine atoms in this molecule to be magnetically nonequivalent to the third fluorine, thus confirming a structure with C_{2v} symmetry. However, on raising the temperature, the spectrum undergoes a marked change in that the signals become broadened and eventually coalesce. Typical spectra measured[291] at four temperatures above $-60°C$ at a measuring frequency of 30 Mc/sec (to be compared with the spectrum shown in Fig. 5-6b) are reproduced in Fig. 12-21. The

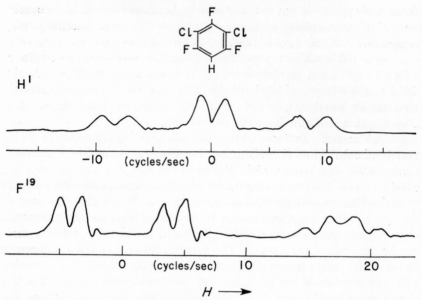

FIG. 12-20. Proton and fluorine resonance spectra of 1,3,5-trifluoro-2,6-dichloro-benzene.   (Gutowsky, Holm, Saika, and Williams.[161])

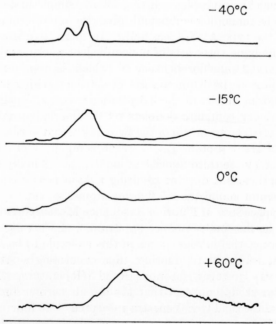

FIG. 12-21. Temperature dependence of F^{19} spectrum of ClF_3 at 30 Mc/sec.   (Muetterties and Phillips.[291])

spectra are typical of those for which an exchange of nuclei between different environments occurs (Sec. 10-2), the exchange becoming sufficiently rapid at the higher temperatures to coalesce the resonance signals. At $-15°C$, where the individual multiplets of spacing 403 cycles/sec become averaged, the lifetime τ of a fluorine atom at a given site is, from Eq. (10-30), equal to 5.6×10^{-4} sec. At $60°C$ the two signals, which at low temperatures are chemically shifted by 3,291 cycles/sec, coalesce. Hence at this temperature τ is equal to 6.6×10^{-5} sec. With these two values of τ and a relation of the form $\tau^{-1} = \tau_0^{-1} \exp(-E/RT)$, an approximate value of the activation energy of exchange of fluorine atoms in ClF_3 equal to 4.8 kcal/mole is obtained.[291]

The molecule BrF_3 may be expected to have a structure similar to that of ClF_3. The room-temperature spectrum of BrF_3 consists of a single sharp peak, which is not perceptibly broadened on cooling to the melting point ($8.8°C$). At these temperatures, therefore, rapid fluorine exchange is indicated, the exchange-activation energy being significantly lower than that for ClF_3.

The fluorine resonance spectrum of IF_5 consists of two signals with relative intensities 1 and 4 and with multiplet components 5 and 2, respectively. As mentioned previously (Sec. 12-6a), the spectrum confirms[159] the tetragonal-pyramid structure of IF_5, the apex fluorine atom being nonequivalent to the four basal fluorine atoms. Heating of the sample causes exchange of the fluorine atoms (possibly by way of dimer association[398]), as indicated by coalescence of signals in the spectrum. An exchange-activation energy of 13 kcal/mole was estimated.[291] The fluorine spectrum of the related molecule BrF_5 is similar to that of IF_5. However, heating to $180°C$ causes no significant exchange of fluorine atoms in BrF_5, from which it may be concluded that the activation energy involved is considerably greater than that in IF_5. Thus the observed relative rates of fluorine exchange in halogen fluorides is in the order $BrF_3 > ClF_3 > IF_5 > BrF_5$.

Perfluoroalkyl Derivatives of Sulfur Hexafluoride. Sulfur hexafluoride is a symmetrical molecule in which the six fluorine atoms occupy the corners of a regular octahedron. Accordingly, all six fluorine atoms are magnetically equivalent, the fluorine resonance spectrum consisting of a single sharp signal (Table 12-5). Replacement of one fluorine atom destroys the octahedral symmetry, causing the remaining fluorine atoms to become nonequivalent. This is demonstrated by the fluorine resonance spectra of the compounds R_FSF_5 (R_F is a perfluoro ethyl, propyl, or butyl group) measured by Muller, Lauterbur, and Svatos.[296] The positions of the signals in the spectra, together with their assignment, are shown in Table 12-14. The SF_5 group gives rise to two complex multiplets with a relative intensity ratio of 4:1. This therefore suggests

TABLE 12-14. FLUORINE CHEMICAL SHIFTS IN PERFLUOROALKYL
DERIVATIVES OF SULFUR HEXAFLUORIDE[296]
(In ppm relative to CF_3COOH)

Compound	Assignment					
	—SF$_5$	⟩SF$_4$⟨	—CF$_3$	C—CF$_2$—S	C—CF$_2$—C	O—CF$_2$—C
$C_2F_5SF_5$	−137.5† −118.7		5.3	15.5		
$C_3F_7SF_5$	‡		5.0	18.8	50.7	
$C_4F_9SF_5$	‡		5.2	18.0	46.5 49.5	
$(C_2F_5)_2SF_4$		−104	4.5	21.2		
$(C_3F_7)_2SF_4$		−106.1	5.0	16.5	50.0	
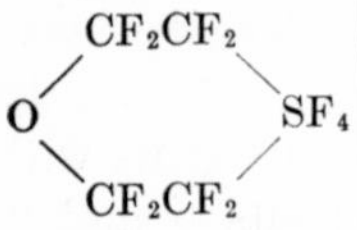 O⟨ CF$_2$CF$_2$ / CF$_2$CF$_2$ ⟩SF$_4$		−123.0§ − 94.8		22.2		2.4

† Derived from a complete spectral analysis.
‡ Essentially the same as $C_2F_5SF_5$, but a complete analysis was not made.
§ Taken as the centers of the two triplet resonances.

a tetragonal-pyramid structure for the five fluorine atoms, as shown in Fig. 12-22a. The structure is thus similar to that of IF_5, but whereas the fluorine resonance of the latter consists of two well-separated multiplets, the —SF$_5$ spectrum is of the type AB_4 rather than AX_4 (Sec. 6-5). Thus instead of a simple quintuplet, the apex fluorine atom F′ gives rise to nine distinguishable signals in the spectrum. Analysis of the spectrum[296] yields values of 18.8 ppm and 145 cycles/sec for the chemical-shift and spin coupling constants between apex and basal fluorine atoms, the signal of the apex fluorine appearing at lower field.

Disubstitution in sulfur hexafluoride, as in the compounds $(C_2F_5)_2SF_4$ and $(C_3F_7)_2SF_4$, gives rise to a single signal for the fluorine resonance of the SF$_4$ group. Accordingly, the four fluorine atoms are equivalent, suggesting that they lie in a plane as shown in Fig. 12-22b, the CSC angle formed by the two substituents being 180°. However, if disubstitution involves a cyclic structure, as in the molecule $OCF_2CF_2SF_4CF_2CF_2$, the

four fluorine atoms directly bonded to sulfur are no longer magnetically equivalent. The fluorine spectrum of the SF$_4$ group now consists of two signals of equal intensity, each of which is a triplet ($J = 93$ cycles/sec). Thus there are two sets of nonequivalent fluorine atoms with two atoms in each set. A plausible interpretation[296] is that the CSC angle in the molecule is in the neighborhood of 90°, the two fluorine atoms in the midplane (Fig. 12-22c) being equivalent to each other but nonequivalent to the two apex fluorine atoms F'.

Sulfur Tetrafluoride. The fluorine resonance spectrum of SF_4, measured at $-100°C$ by Cotton, George, and Waugh,[105a] consists of two equally intense triplet signals separated by 48 ppm. There are thus two pairs of structurally nonequivalent fluorine atoms in the molecule.

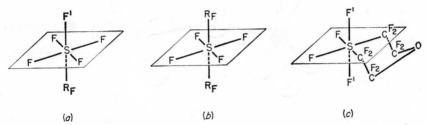

(a)   (b)   (c)

F<small>IG.</small> 12-22. Perfluoroalkyl derivatives of sulfur hexafluoride. (Muller, Lauterbur, and Svatos[296].)

(The spin coupling constant between the two types of fluorines is 78 cycles/sec.) The molecular symmetries D_{2d}, D_{2h}, C_{4h}, and T_d can thus be excluded, since each would correspond to a single-signal NMR spectrum. It was concluded[105a] that the nonplanar C_{2v} structure is the most likely one, in agreement with that suggested on the basis of infrared measurements.[121c] The structure may be regarded as derived from a trigonal bipyramid. One set of equivalent fluorine atoms occupies axial positions and the other set occupies two equatorial positions, the third equatorial position being occupied by a lone pair of electrons. The presence of this lone pair favors the formation of addition compounds of the type $SF_4 \cdot BF_3$ and also facilitates fluorine exchange in SF_4 itself. On raising the temperature of SF_4, the triplet structure of the F^{19} signals becomes averaged out at $-94°C$, and the two separate fluorine signals ultimately coalesce in the vicinity of $-20°C$ (Sec. 10-2). The derived activation energy of the fluorine-exchange process is of the order of 4 kcal/mole. Similar results from NMR measurements of SF_4 and SeF_4 have been obtained by Phillips and Muetterties.[333a]

Antimony Pentafluoride. Liquid antimony pentafluoride is an extremely viscous liquid at room temperature, suggesting a high degree of polymerization. The fluorine resonance spectrum[191] shown in Fig. 12-23b consists of three main peaks, A, B, and C, with relative intensities 1:2:2. The spectrum can be interpreted in terms of a polymeric structure of antimony pentafluoride (Fig. 12-23a) which contains three distinct groups of fluorine atoms, A, B, and C, each giving rise to a separate resonance signal (Fig. 12-23b).   Type A fluorine atoms may be regarded as shared or bridging fluorine atoms, type B are trans to type A fluorine atoms, and type C are trans to each other.   The spin-spin multiplets of the resonance signals, some of which are incompletely resolved, are consistent with the following coupling constants between nonequivalent

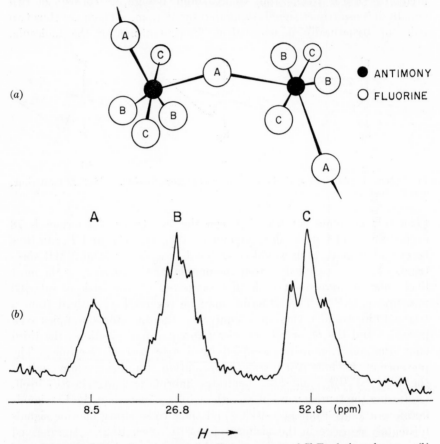

FIG. 12-23. (a) Schematic structure of a dimer segment of SbF_5 chain polymer.   (b) Fluorine resonance spectrum of SbF_5 at 40 Mc/sec and at $\sim -10°C$.   Chemical shifts are relative to trifluoroacetic acid.   (Hoffman, Holder, and Jolly.[191])

fluorine atoms: $J_{AB} = 70$, $J_{AC} < 30$, and $J_{BC} = 130$ cycles/sec. At higher temperatures the separate resonance signals become reduced to a single signal, suggesting an exchange of fluorine atoms.

   Fluorosulfonate Derivatives.   Additional evidence regarding the structure of fluorine fluorosulfonate, SO_3F_2, thionyl tetrafluoride, SOF_4, and pentafluorosulfur hypofluorite, SOF_6, has been obtained by Dudley, Shoolery, and Cady[128] from the fluorine spectra of these compounds.

From infrared spectra[126,127] it was concluded that the compounds SO_3F_2 and SOF_6 contain an OF group but SOF_4 does not. The spectrum of SO_3F_2 contains two peaks of equal intensity which, under higher resolution, show doublet splitting. This indicates two nonequivalent fluorine atoms, confirming that the structure is $SO_2F \cdot OF$. Thionyl tetrafluoride gives rise to a single fluorine resonance. Accordingly the four fluorine

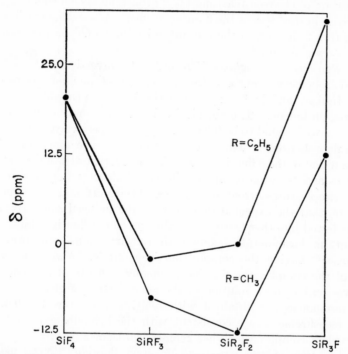

FIG. 12-24. Fluorine chemical shifts in methyl- and ethylfluorosilanes in parts per million relative to diethyldifluorosilane. (Schnell and Rochow.[406])

atoms are equivalent and the structure is F_4SO, rather than $SF_3 \cdot OF$ (provided that no exchange mechanism is operative). The fluorine spectrum of SOF_6 contains two signals with relative intensities 5:1. Thus the correct structure is $SF_5 \cdot OF$. Under higher resolution the SF_5 resonance is a doublet, while that of the OF group has six components. This suggests that all F nuclei in the SF_5 group in this molecule are magnetically equivalent, unlike the previous examples (Table 12-14).

Methyl- and Ethylfluorosilanes. Fluorine resonance measurements in methyl- and ethylfluorosilanes have been employed by Schnell and Rochow[406] to study the nature of the chemical bonding in these compounds. Figure 12-24 shows the measured fluorine chemical shifts plotted against the number of alkyl substituents in the compounds

Me_xSiF_{4-x} and Et_xSiF_{4-x}. The plot of the ethyl compounds lies above that of the methyl compounds, corresponding to a greater electron-releasing effect (with a resultant greater fluorine shielding) by substituting ethyl for methyl groups. Both plots exhibit a pronounced minimum, suggesting that two different effects are operative in modifying the fluorine chemical shifts. The most important of these is the inductive effect. Substitution of electron-releasing alkyl groups on silicon should result in an increase in shielding of the fluorine atoms. A possible opposing effect leading to a reduction in the fluoride shielding would be the occurrence of Si-F $d\pi$-$p\pi$ bonding.[406]

Miscellaneous Applications. In order to investigate the effect of induced aromatic-ring currents (Secs. 7-5 and 11-4) on fluorine resonances, Isobe, Inukai, and Ito[204a] measured the F^{19} chemical shifts in α- and β-fluoronaphthalene. The chemical shifts of the fluorines in the α and β positions were found to be 9.9 and 1.6 ppm, respectively, relative to the shift in fluorobenzene. Thus the α-fluorine resonance appears at a higher field than that of the β fluorine. This is the reverse order of that observed for the α- and β-proton resonances in naphthalene and of that predicted by the simple ring-current model (Sec. 11-4). It must be concluded, therefore, that the expected shifts due to the induced ring currents are overshadowed by other factors contributing to the fluorine shifts.

Tellurium hexafluoride reacts with tertiary amines to form stable complexes[292] having the composition $TeF_6 \cdot 2R_3N$. Above the melting point of the complex the fluorine resonance consists of a single signal. However on cooling a solution of the compound to a glass at $-180°C$, three resonances are obtained with relative intensities $1:1:0.4$. The NMR measurements are consistent with the behavior expected for an octacovalent complex which has geometrical isomers.

Confirmation of the structure of nitryl fluoride, FNO_2, has been obtained by Ogg and Ray[307] from fluorine resonance measurements. The fluorine spectrum consists of a triplet, each component having equal intensity. This, together with the observed magnitude of the multiplet splitting ($J = 113$ cycles/sec), which is similar to that observed in nitrogen trifluoride, leaves little doubt that the fluorine is directly bonded to nitrogen and not to oxygen.

Boron trifluoride, which is a strong electron-acceptor molecule, readily forms molecular complexes with electron-donor substances such as the oxygen-containing compounds water, alcohols, ethers, and ketones. Molecular complexes of this type have been studied by Diehl and Ogg[121a] by measuring the F^{19} chemical shift of known amounts of boron trifluoride in a given donor liquid. The chemical shift depends on the nature of the donor liquid, the concentration of boron trifluoride, and the temperature. The stability of the molecular complexes is such that, if boron trifluoride is added to a mixture of two donor liquids—methanol and ethanol, for example—two fluorine signals separated by approximately 2.0 ppm can be observed at sufficiently low temperatures. One signal arises from the boron trifluoride complex with methanol, the other from that with ethanol. On raising the temperature, the two signals broaden and ultimately coalesce, corresponding to rapid exchange of the boron trifluoride between the two types of donor molecules. Analysis of the signal shapes as a function of temperature by the methods of Sec. 10-2 yields information about the exchange rate and the exchange-activation energy. Measurement of the chemical shift and the relative intensity of the signals at lower temperatures permits a determination of the relative donor strength (basicity) of different donor liquids toward boron trifluoride, as well as the equilibrium constant for complex formation. Measurements at a series of different temperatures yield the corresponding enthalpy and entropy changes. For a series of hydroxy compounds the relative stability of the respective boron trifluoride complexes was found to be in the order water > methanol > ethanol > n-propanol > n-butanol. It is apparent from these, as well as other, results (Chap. 15) that NMR measurements provide a sensitive and generally fruitful method of studying molecular-complex formation. In the present systems it may be noted that the resonances measured (fluorine resonances) correspond to those of atoms one bond removed from the center of the molecular interaction, which is largely localized between the boron atom and the donor oxygen atom.

12-7. Silicon

The only magnetic isotope of silicon is Si^{29}, which has a spin of $1/2$ and a natural abundance of 4.70 per cent. Silicon chemical shifts in a variety of solid and liquid compounds have been measured by Holzman, Lauterbur, Anderson, and Koth[195] at a resonant frequency of 8 Mc/sec. Three methods were used to establish the resonant field:

1. For samples with a short T_1 the resonant magnetic field was obtained from the derivative of the absorption curve, using slow passage and low rf power.

2. For samples with a long T_1 the derivative of the dispersion curve was used to establish resonance on slow passage. Rapid passage and high rf field were also employed in some cases.

3. For nuclei with a very long T_1 the dispersion signal was used to locate resonance, using rapid scanning and high rf field intensity.

Compounds in which nitrogen, chlorine, bromine, or iodine are directly bonded to silicon give rise to much weaker and rather broad signals. When the number of such atoms bonded to silicon is increased, as in $SiCl_4$, $SiBr_4$, or $Si(NCO)_4$, the effect is more pronounced.

Some representative Si^{29} chemical shifts in various compounds[195] are listed in Table 12-15. The reference compound is a silicone (DC200) having a viscosity of 100 centipoises. The estimated error of the chemical shifts is of the order of 2 ppm.

TABLE 12-15. Si^{29} CHEMICAL SHIFTS IN VARIOUS COMPOUNDS[195]

Compound	δ, ppm	J_{SiH} or J_{SiF}, cycles/sec
Silica (fused)	92	
Quartz	88	
$[(CH_3)_3SiO]_4Si$†	80	
Multicomponent glass	72	
Silicon	64	
Sodium silicate (solution)	64	
$(C_2H_5O)_4Si$	59	
SiC (black)	48	
$C_6H_5SiH_3$	39	211
$(C_2H_5O)_3SiCH_3$	19	
$C_6H_5Si(CH_3)H_2$	16	194
$(CH_3SiHO)_4$	12	233
$(C_6H_5)_2SiH_2$	12	209
$[(CH_3)_2SiO]_x$ (DC200)	0	
SiC (green)	0	
$[(CH_3)_2SiO]_4$	− 2	
$C_6H_5Si(CH_3)_3$	−16	
$(CH_3)_4Si$	−21	
$[(CH_3)_3Si]_2CH_2$	−22	
$(CH_3)_3SiOC_2H_5$	−27	
$(CH_3)_3SiI$	−30	
$[(CH_3)_3SiO]_3PO$	−35	
$(CH_3)_3SiBr$	−45	
$(CH_3)_3SiF$	−48	268

† Nucleus measured.

Hydrogen or fluorine directly bonded to silicon gives rise to spin-multiplet splitting. Spin coupling constants derived from the spectra of several compounds are shown in Table 12-15. The value of J_{SiF} is only moderately larger than the corresponding J_{SiH} values.

12-8. Phosphorus

The only stable isotope of phosphorus is P^{31}, which has a spin of 1/2. Because of a smaller magnetic moment, the NMR sensitivity is about

7 per cent of that for H^1 or F^{19} nuclei. The P^{31} nucleus is nevertheless ideally suited for the application of high-resolution techniques because it gives rise to sharp signals, and since the chemical shifts are generally rather large, the reduced signal strength can be partially compensated by a larger sample size.

Phosphorus differs in an important respect from hydrogen or fluorine in that it is multivalent and exists in two stable valence states. This difference is reflected in the nature of the observed chemical shifts in

TABLE 12-16. P^{31} CHEMICAL SHIFTS IN INORGANIC PHOSPHORUS COMPOUNDS[163]
[In ppm referred to aqueous $(OH)_3PO$]

Trivalent compounds		Pentavalent compounds	
Compound	δ	Compound	δ
P_4 (in CS_2)	448	HPF_6	118
P_4	450	Br_3PS	111.8†
PH_3	241	Br_3PO	102.9†
P_4S_3	114	$F_2(OH)PO$	20.1
PF_3	− 97	ClF_2PO	14.8
CH_3F_2PO	−111	Cl_2FPO	0.0
P_2I_4 (in CS_2)	−170	$(OH)_3PO$	0.0
PI_3	−178	$H(OH)_2PO$	− 4.5
PCl_3	−215	Cl_3PO	− 5.4
PBr_3	−222	$Cl_2(C_2H_5O)PO$	− 6.4
		$H_2(OH)PO$	−13.8
		Cl_3PS	−30.8

† Data from ref. 295.

compounds of the three elements. Phosphorus forms covalent bonds to its neighboring atoms in all of its compounds, except perhaps for some metallic phosphides. In this respect it resembles carbon, and indeed the analogy is borne out by the vast variety of organophosphorus compounds, many of which are of biological significance.

a. **Phosphorus Chemical Shifts.** Shifts of the P^{31} resonance signal with chemical constitution were first observed by Knight[220] and later by Dickinson.[120] A more detailed study of phosphorus chemical shifts in a number of compounds has been carried out by Gutowsky and McCall.[163] Their results are summarized in Table 12-16. It may be noted that the pentavalent compounds exhibit a smaller range of chemical shifts than do the trivalent compounds. No simple or direct correlation of the shifts with the electronegativity of the atoms bonded to phosphorus is discernible from the data. Thus the P^{31} chemical shifts in the trihalides are in the order $PF_3 > PI_3 > PCl_3 > PBr_3$. In the compounds Cl_3PO, Cl_2FPO, ClF_2PO, and F_3PO the phosphorus shielding (chemical shift)

TABLE 12-17. P^{31} CHEMICAL SHIFTS OF ORGANOPHOSPHORUS COMPOUNDS
(In ppm relative to 85 per cent aqueous H_3PO_4)

Compound	δ	Ref.
Trivalent-phosphorus Compounds		
H_3P	238	449
$H_2(CH_3)P$	163.5	449
$H(CH_3)_2P$	98.5	449
$(CH_3)_3P$	61	449, 136
$F_2(C_2H_5)P$	30	449
$(C_2H_5)_3P$	20.4	295, 136
$ClF(C_2H_5)P$	20	449
$(C_6H_5)_3P$	5.9	295, 136
$(C_2H_5S)_3P$	−115.6	295
$[(CH_3)_2N]_3P$	−122	449
$(C_6H_5O)_3P$	−127	295, 449
$(C_2H_5O)_3P$	−138	295, 449
$(CH_3O)_3P$	−141	449
$Cl_2(C_6H_5)P$	−162	295, 136
$H(CH_3O)_2P$	−181	136
$Cl_2(CH_3O)P$	−181	136
$Cl_2(CH_3)P$	−191.2	136
Pentavalent-phosphorus Compounds		
$(C_6H_5O)_3PO$	17.3	295, 449
$(C_2H_5O)_3PO$	0.9	295, 449
$(C_2H_5O)Cl_2PO$	− 2.8	136
$(CH_3O)_2HPO$	− 11.0	449
$C_6H_5(OH)_2PO$	− 17.5	449
$(C_6H_5)_2(OH)PO$	− 20	449
$[(CH_3)_2N]_3PO$	− 23.4	295, 449
$(C_2H_5O)_2(SH)PO$	− 24.0	136
$(C_2H_5O)_2(C_2H_5S)PO$	− 26.4	295
$(CH_3)F_2PO$	− 27.4	136
$(CH_3)(C_2H_5O)(OH)PO$	− 28.5	136
$(CH_3)(OH)_2PO$	− 31.1	136
$(C_6H_5)Cl_2PO$	− 34.5	295
$(CH_3)(C_2H_5O)ClPO$	− 39.5	136
$(CH_3)Cl_2PO$	− 44.5	295, 136
$(C_2H_5)_3PSe$	− 45.8	295
$(C_2H_5)_3PO$	− 48.3	295
$(C_6H_5O)_3PS$	− 53.4	295
$(C_2H_5)_3PS$	− 54.5	295
$(C_2H_5S)_3PO$	− 61.3	295
$(C_2H_5O)_2ClPS$	− 68.1	136
$(C_2H_5O)_3PS$	− 68.1	295
$(C_6H_5)Cl_2PS$	− 74.8	295, 449
$(CH_3)Cl_2PS$	− 79.8	295, 136
$(C_2H_5O)_2(SH)PS$	− 85.7	136
$(C_2H_5S)_3PS$	− 92.9	295
$(C_2H_5)Cl_2PS$	− 94.3	295

increases with increasing fluorine substitution. Again, in the acids $H_2(OH)PO$, $H(OH)_2PO$, and $(OH)_3PO$ substitution of the hydrogen atoms directly bonded to phosphorus by OH groups *increases* the phosphorus shielding. Clearly, electronegativity differences are overshadowed by other factors arising out of the nature of the chemical bonds between phosphorus and other atoms.

Phosphorus chemical shifts for several hundred organophosphorus compounds have been measured (Muller, Lauterbur, and Goldenson;[295] Van Wazer, Callis, Shoolery, and Jones;[449] and Finegold[136]). Some representative values are listed in Table 12-17. As with the inorganic phosphorus compounds, the P^{31} chemical shifts of compounds in which phosphorus is trivalent extend over a wider range ($\sim$500 ppm) than for compounds in which phosphorus is pentavalent ($\sim$100 ppm). In each series of compounds, however, different substituents give rise to easily measurable differences in chemical shifts. The phosphorus resonances thus provide a convenient and valuable means of structure identification in these compounds.

In the trivalent-phosphorus compounds, while the effect of different substituents on the P^{31} resonance is not generally additive, useful correlation charts for the analysis of chemical-shift data can nevertheless be constructed. Such a chart[449] is reproduced in Fig. 12-25. Approximate individual contributions to the chemical shift by various substituents are shown schematically in Fig. 12-26. It is evident that these contributions show no over-all correlation with the electronegativity of the atom or group directly bonded to the phosphorus atom. In the pentavalent-phosphorus compounds, substituents can again be broadly classified according to their contribution to the chemical shift. In most cases the effect on the phosphorus chemical shift is opposite to that expected from electronegativity considerations. Thus, for example, the P^{31} resonance of R_3PS compounds generally appears at a *lower* field than that of the corresponding R_3PO compounds.

Attempts have been made to relate the phosphorus chemical shifts to bond properties, such as the degree of hybridization, and multiple-bond character, as well as ionic character (electronegativity differences). According to Gutowsky and McCall,[163] the "effective" electron density at the phosphorus atom results from a combination of the ionic character and partial double-bond character of the PX bond. An empirical correlation of the phosphorus shifts with bond properties has been developed by Muller, Lauterbur, and Goldenson[295] and extended by Parks.[320]

b. Phosphorus Spin Coupling Constants. Spin coupling interactions of atoms directly bonded to phosphorus are of considerable importance in structure determinations of phosphorus compounds by the NMR

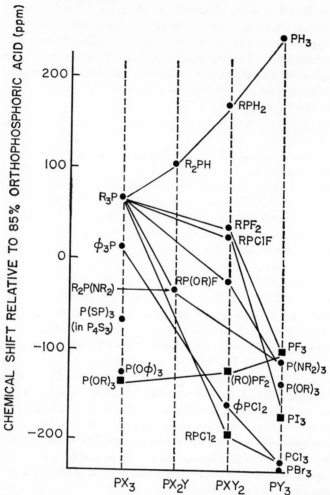

FIG. 12-25. P³¹ chemical-shift correlation chart for trivalent-phosphorus compounds. The group R represents an aliphatic radical. (Van Wazer, Callis, Shoolery, and Jones.[449])

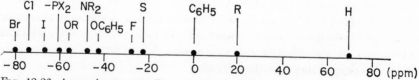

FIG. 12-26. Approximate contributions of substituents to the P³¹ chemical shift in trivalent-phosphorus compounds. (Van Wazer, Callis, Shoolery, and Jones.[449])

method.   Thus the large multiplet splitting of the P^{31} resonance by a directly bonded hydrogen atom permits a simple and unambiguous distinction between structures of the type $(RO)_2(OH)P$ and $(RO)_2HPO$. Some representative PH coupling constants observed in different compounds are listed in Table 12-18.   Values of coupling constants for phosphorus directly bonded to fluorine and other atoms may be found in Tables 12-11 and 8-2.

TABLE 12-18. PHOSPHORUS-PROTON SPIN COUPLING CONSTANTS

Compound	J_{PH}, cycles/sec	Ref.
H_3P	179	166
$H_2(CH_3)P$	205	84
$H(CH_3)_2P$	205	84
$H(OH)_2PO$	707	166
$H_2(OH)PO$	593, 561	166, 136
$H(CH_3O)PO$	710	84
$H(C_2H_5O)_2PO$	701	136
$H(C_2H_5O)_2PS$	645	136

In general, for related compounds the value of J_{PH}, where H is directly bonded to P in compounds having $P \rightarrow O$ linkages, is about 50 cycles/sec greater than in the corresponding compounds having $P \rightarrow S$ linkages.[136] This situation is reversed when the phosphorus and hydrogen atoms are two bonds removed.   Thus in a number of compounds measured,[136] J_{PH} was of the order of 15 to 20 cycles/sec for $P \rightarrow S$ compounds and about 10 cycles/sec for $P \rightarrow O$ compounds.   When the interacting nuclei are three bonds removed, as in the configuration P—S—C—H, P—O—C—H, and P—N—C—H, the value[295] of J_{PH} is generally of the order of 10 cycles/sec.   Owing to proton exchange, phosphorus-proton splittings for P—O—H configurations of compounds in aqueous solution are usually not observed.

Coupling constants in trivalent-phosphorus compounds are generally comparable in magnitude to those observed in pentavalent compounds with $P \rightarrow S$ linkages.[136]   Phosphorus-proton splitting of the P—O—C—H configuration is strikingly illustrated by the P^{31} spectrum[84] of $P(OCH_3)_3$, shown in Fig. 12-27.   Because the nine hydrogen atoms are magnetically equivalent, the P^{31} multiplet signal should consist of ten lines, eight of which can be identified in the spectrum.   The phosphorus-proton coupling constant is less than 20 cycles/sec.

c. Some Applications of P^{31} Resonances to Structure Determination. *Phosphorus Sulfides.*   The P^{31} resonance spectrum[84] of phosphorus sesquisulfide, P_4S_3, is shown in Fig. 12-28.   The spectrum is in accord with the structure determined by X-ray diffraction.[183]   One phosphorus atom is nonequivalent to the other three structurally equivalent phosphorus atoms, giving rise to the observed quadruplet and doublet signals, 1 and 2, respectively. The coupling constant, $J_{P_1P_2}$, is 86 cycles/sec.

Solutions of White Phosphorus. The P^{31} resonance of white phosphorus in CS_2 solution has been found to be concentration dependent.[329] Dilution causes the phosphorus resonance to shift to lower field. Extrapolation to infinite dilution yields a shift of 53 ± 7 ppm relative to the

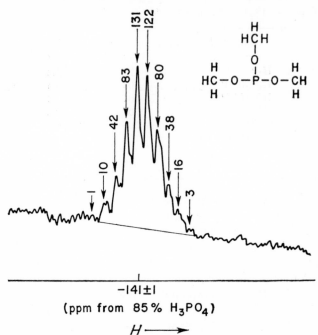

$$-141\pm1$$
(ppm from 85% H_3PO_4)

$H \longrightarrow$

FIG. 12-27. The P^{31} resonance multiplet of $P(OCH_3)_3$ at 12.3 Mc/sec. Approximate relative intensities of individual components are indicated by the numbers above each peak. (Callis, Van Wazer, Shoolery, and Anderson.[84])

resonance signal of pure white phosphorus. The observed effect is ascribed to an interaction of the dissolved phosphorus with the solvent.† Another possible effect is the chemical association of phosphorus molecules in solution.

Oxyacids Containing Two Phosphorus Atoms.[84] The known salts of the oxyacids containing two phosphorus atoms per anion are the (1) pyrophosphate, (2) hypophosphate, and (3) pyrophosphite. Two further anions, described by Blaser,[48] are the (4) "isohypophosphate"

---

† Shifts of P^{31} resonances in a number of phosphorus compounds owing to solvent interaction have been reported by Muller, Lauterbur, and Goldenson.[295] In these examples the observed shifts, which are relatively large, are attributable to hydrogen-bonding interactions with the solvent.

and (5) diphosphite. The structures of the anions of these five acids, as determined from chemical evidence, are

$$
\begin{bmatrix}
& O & & O & \\
O & P & O & P & O \\
& O & & O &
\end{bmatrix}^{4-}
\qquad
\begin{bmatrix}
& O & & O & \\
O & P & - & P & O \\
& O & & O &
\end{bmatrix}^{4-}
$$
$$
\text{I} \qquad\qquad\qquad \text{II}
$$

$$
\begin{bmatrix}
& O & & O & \\
O & P & O & P & O \\
& H & & H &
\end{bmatrix}^{=}
\qquad
\begin{bmatrix}
& O & & O & \\
O & P & O & P & O \\
& H & & O &
\end{bmatrix}^{3-}
\qquad
\begin{bmatrix}
& O & & O & \\
O & P & - & P & O \\
& H & & O &
\end{bmatrix}^{3-}
$$
$$
\text{III} \qquad\qquad \text{IV} \qquad\qquad \text{V}
$$

The P^{31} resonances of I and II consist of a single peak, confirming the symmetrical structures and the absence of hydrogen atoms directly

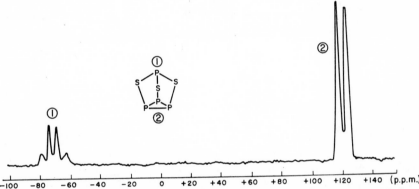

FIG. 12-28. P^{31} resonance spectrum of phosphorus sesquisulfide at 12.3 Mc/sec. Chemical shifts are shown relative to 85 per cent H_3PO_4. (Callis, Van Wazer, Shoolery, and Anderson.[84])

bonded to phosphorus. The spectrum of III contains two equal peaks separated by $\sim$685 cycles/sec. This separation was found to be field independent and must therefore be attributed to PH spin coupling. Thus the spectrum confirms a symmetrical structure with a hydrogen atom directly bonded to each phosphorus atom.

The spectra of the isohypophosphate anion IV and the diphosphite anion V, shown in Fig. 12-29, confirm the structures proposed by Blaser.[48] The spectrum of IV shows the resonance of the atom P_1 split into a doublet by the directly bonded proton ($J_{P_1H} = 620$ cycles/sec). Each signal in the spectrum shows a small splitting due to the P_1-P_2 inter-action ($J_{P_1P_2} = 17$ cycles/sec). The spectrum of V is of the type ABX (Sec. 6-6). Two of the possible eight phosphorus lines are too weak to be observed. Analysis[84] of the spectrum yields $\delta_{P_1P_2} = 15.8$ ppm, $J_{P_1H} = 444$ cycles/sec, $J_{P_2H} = 94$ cycles/sec, and $J_{P_1P_2} = 480$ cycles/sec.

Polyphosphates.[84]   The spectra of the pyro-, tripoly-, and tetrapoly-phosphate anions are shown in Fig. 12-30 on a common chemical-shift scale.   The phosphorus nuclei in the end and middle PO_4 groups are nonequivalent and resonate at different applied fields (labeled as E and

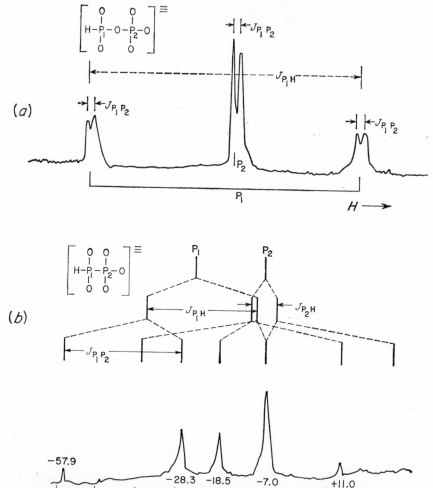

FIG. 12-29.   The P^{31} resonance spectra of (*a*) the isohypophosphate anion (in Na_3-HP_2O_6) at 12.3 Mc/sec and (*b*) the diphosphite anion at 16.3 Mc/sec.   Chemical shifts are relative to 85 per cent H_3PO_4.   (Callis, Van Wazer, Shoolery, and Anderson.[84])

M peaks in the figure).   The spin coupling constant between the two phosphorus atoms (corresponding to the POP configuration) is 17 cycles/sec.   The spectrum of the tetrapolyphosphate anion, which shows some fine structure, arises from an incompletely resolved A_2B_2 system (Sec.

6-7) having a plane of symmetry and two pairs of nonequivalent nuclei. The existence of spin-spin coupling in the polyphosphate anions indicates that the phosphorus and oxygen atoms are covalently bonded in these structures.

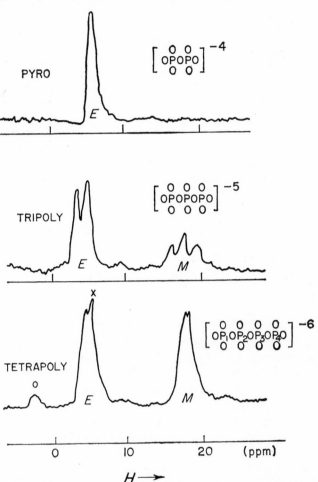

FIG. 12-30. The P^{31} resonance spectra of pyro-, tripoly-, and tetrapolyphosphate anions at 12.3 Mc/sec. The end and middle PO_4-group peaks are labeled E and M. The small peaks o and x are due to orthophosphate impurity. Chemical shifts are relative to 85 per cent H_3PO_4. (Callis, Van Wazer, Shoolery, and Anderson.[84])

Condensed Phosphates. In the condensed phosphates (phosphate chains) four types of PO_4 groups may be distinguished from structural considerations;[450] they are the isolated, end, middle, and branching-point groups. Each of the four gives separate and distinct signals in the P^{31} resonance spectra of condensed phosphates[448] (Fig. 12-30), thus providing a valuable analytical method for those compounds. Characteristic shifts are listed in Table 12-19. Spectra of solutions of the various phosphate glasses exhibit end- and middle-group peaks whose

TABLE 12-19. CHARACTERISTIC P^{31} SHIFTS OF PO_4 GROUPS
IN CONDENSED PHOSPHATES[448]

Type of PO_4 group	δ, ppm[†]
Orthophosphate ions (isolated groups):	
Trisubstituted (normal) salts	233
End groups:	
Doubly substituted	244
Middle groups:	
Short chains	256
Long chains	259
Branching points:	
Alkali-metal ultraphosphates	268
Azeotropic phosphoric acid	272

† Chemical shifts are relative to PBr_3.

intensities correspond to the average chain length. The tri- and tetra-metaphosphate rings show only one peak in solution; its position corresponds to that for middle groups.

12-9. Tin

Three isotopes of tin, Sn^{115}, Sn^{117}, and Sn^{119}, have nonzero magnetic moments (Appendix A). Of these isotopes, all of which have a spin of 1/2, Sn^{115} has a relatively low abundance (0.35 per cent). The two isotopes Sn^{117} and Sn^{119} have similar abundances (7.67 and 8.68 per cent, respectively) and only slightly different moments, Sn^{119} giving rise to somewhat stronger resonance signals.[237] The Sn^{119} resonances in a number of tin compounds have been measured by Lauterbur and Burke[237] at a fixed measuring frequency of 8.5 Mc/sec. Depending on the nuclear relaxation time in individual compounds, the resonances were recorded as rapid-passage signals or as slow-passage signals in the dispersion or absorption mode. Some typical Sn^{119} chemical shifts (relative to tin tetramethyl) in a variety of compounds are listed in Table 12-20. The shifts are remarkably large. A surprising feature of these results is the apparent lack of distinction between stannous and stannic compounds. Thus the shifts of $SnSO_4$ and $SnCl_2 \cdot 2H_2O$ are within the range of those observed for the stannic compounds. The resonances of some compounds exhibit an extremely large solvent dependence (Table 12-20) that is possibly due to the well-known tendency of tin compounds to coordinate strongly with many substances. The results suggest, in fact, that interactions of this type might profitably be studied by NMR techniques.

Redistribution reactions in mixtures of stannic halides have been demonstrated in a striking way by measurement of the Sn^{119} resonances in those systems.[237] Thus a mixture of $SnCl_4$ and $SnBr_4$ gives rise to a series of almost equally spaced resonance signals, intermediate between those of the parent compounds, corresponding to all the possible mixed

TABLE 12-20. Sn^{119} CHEMICAL SHIFTS IN TIN COMPOUNDS
RELATIVE TO TIN TETRAMETHYL[237]

Compound	Solvent	δ, ppm
SnI_4	CS_2	1,698
$SnSO_4$	H_2O	909
$SnBr_4$		638
$Na_2Sn(OH)_6$	H_2O	592
$SnCl_2 \cdot 2H_2O$	H_2O	420
$SnCl_2 \cdot 2H_2O$	$(CH_3)_2CO$	303
$SnCl_2 \cdot 2H_2O$	C_2H_5OH	282
$SnCl_4$		150
$(n\text{-}C_4H_9)_2Sn(C_6H_5)_2$		44
$(n\text{-}C_4H_9)SnCl_3$		14
$(n\text{-}C_4H_9)_4Sn$		8
$(CH_3)_4Sn$		0
$(CH_3)_2SnCl_2$	$(CH_3)_2CO$	-34
$(C_2H_5)_2SnCl_2$	$(CH_3)_2CO$	-50
$(n\text{-}C_4H_9)_2SnCl_2$	$(CH_3)_2CO$	-56
$(n\text{-}C_4H_9)_2SnCl_2$	CS_2	-112
$(n\text{-}C_4H_9)SnS$		-124
$(n\text{-}C_4H_9)_3SnCl$		-139
$(C_2H_5)_3SnCl$		-148

halides. Figure 12-31 shows part of the Sn^{119} resonance spectrum of a $2:1:1$ molar mixture of SnI_4, $SnBr_4$, and $SnCl_4$. The mixed halide peaks are identified. The position of individual signals is given fairly accurately by simple linear interpolation of the signals of the parent compounds, and the relative intensities are those to be expected for random halogen exchange. The average lifetimes of the halide molecules in the mixtures were found to be between 10^{-2} and 10 sec.

The proton-tin (Sn^{119}) spin coupling constant in tetramethyl tin is of the order of 54 cycles/sec. More distant protons in larger alkyl groups directly bonded to tin have coupling constants of the same order of magnitude. [A comparable effect has been observed in lead tetraethyl (Sec. 11-8).] The coupling constants between the methyl protons and tin have been found to depend on the nature of other substituents on the molecule and on the solvent used.[237]

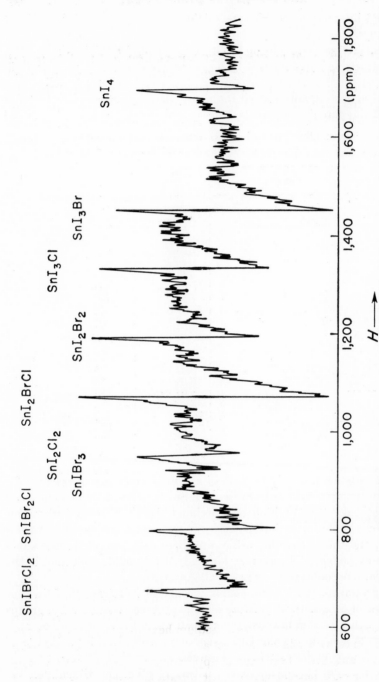

SnI$_4$

SnI$_3$Br

SnI$_3$Cl

SnI$_2$Br$_2$

SnI$_2$BrCl

SnI$_2$Cl$_2$

SnIBr$_3$

SnIBrCl$_2$ SnIBr$_2$Cl

$H \longrightarrow$

600   800   1,000   1,200   1,400   1,600   1,800   (ppm)

Fig. 12-31. Sn^{119} spectrum of a 2:1:1 molar mixture of SnI$_4$, SnBr$_4$, and SnCl$_4$ at 8.5 Mc/sec.   Chemical shifts are relative to tin tetramethyl.   (Lauterbur and Burke.[237])

12-10. Cobalt

Cobalt occurs in nature only as the isotope Co^{59}, which has a spin of 7/2. Nuclear resonances of Co^{59} were measured by Proctor and Yu[354] in their study of nuclear magnetic moments. It was observed that the resonance frequency of Co^{59} in a number of octahedral molecular complexes of cobalt showed surprisingly large variations amounting to as much as 1.3 per cent. The resonance shifts were attributed to an induced paramagnetism resulting from mixing by the magnetic field of low-lying electronic states with the ground state (Sec. 7-4).

TABLE 12-21. Co^{59} RESONANCE FREQUENCIES OF COBALT COMPLEXES[137]
(At 4,370.9 gauss)

Compound†	Resonance frequency, Mc/sec	Optical absorption maxima, mμ	
$K_3Co(CN)_6$	4.4171	311	259
$Li[Co(NO_2)_4(NH_3)_2]$	4.4478	426	347
$[Co(en)_2Cl_2]Cl$ (trans)	4.4485	505	
$[Co(CO_3)(en)_2]Br$	4.4486	512	358
$[Co(en)_3]Cl_3$	4.4488	470	340
$[Co(NO_2)_2(NH_3)_4]Cl$ (trans)	4.4489	445	
$[Co(pn)_3]Cl_3$	4.4490	470	340
$[Co(NO_2)_2(NH_3)_4]Cl$ (cis)	4.4493	450	
$Na_3[Co(NO_2)_6]$	4.4502 (strong) 4.4527 (weak) }	480	358
$[Co(NH_3)_6]Cl_3$	4.4534	475	338
$[Co(CO_3)(NH_3)_4]NO_3$	4.4575 4.4601 }	512	
$[Co(AA)_3]$ (in benzene)	4.4731	597	
$K_3[Co(C_2O_4)_3]$	4.4747	610	425
$[Co(CO_3)_3](NO_3)_3$	4.4795	645	444

† The abbreviations en, pn, and AA are used for ethylenediamine, propylenediamine, and acetylacetone, respectively.

The measurements of Proctor and Yu have been extended by Freeman, Murray, and Richards,[137] using a series of symmetrical and unsymmetrical cobalt complexes. The measured cobalt resonance frequencies, at a fixed applied field of 4,370.9 gauss, are listed in Table 12-21. All but one of the samples were measured in aqueous solution. Frequencies were measured to ± 50 cycles/sec. Sodium hexanitrocobaltate gave two resonance lines with relative intensities of 1:16, as previously observed by Proctor and Yu. Two lines of approximately equal intensity were observed for carbonatotetraminecobalt nitrate solution. The nature of these multiple resonances has not been established. Variations of up to

0.02 per cent were observed in the Co^{59} resonance frequency of cobalt acetylacetonate in different organic solvents. A linear temperature dependence of the resonance frequency was observed. The temperature coefficient of cobalt acetylacetonate in toluene and in chloroform solution is ~10.3 and ~13.3 cycles/(sec)(deg), respectively. Potassium hexacyanocobaltate in aqueous solution has a temperature coefficient of 6.2 cycles/(sec)(deg).

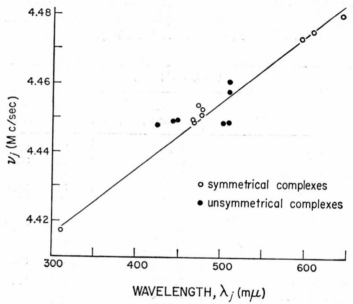

FIG. 12-32. Plot of the Co^{59} resonance frequency of a series of cobalt complexes vs. the wavelength of the lowest-frequency optical-absorption maximum. (Freeman, Murray, and Richards.[137])

A quantitative interpretation of the chemical shifts, based on crystal-field theory, has been given by Griffith and Orgel[148] (Sec. 7-4). Following Ramsey,[365] the shielding of the cobalt nuclei is given by

$$\sigma = A - \frac{B}{\Delta E} \qquad (12\text{-}6)$$

where A is the Lamb shielding term and the second term represents the paramagnetic term. According to Eq. (7-17) the latter is given by

$$\frac{B}{\Delta E} = \frac{8e^2\hbar^2}{mc^2\,\Delta E}\left\langle\frac{1}{r^3}\right\rangle_{\mathrm{av}} \qquad (12\text{-}7)$$

As pointed out by Griffith and Orgel,[148] the term A in Eq. (12-6) may be expected to be insensitive to the nature of the ligands, so that the measured frequencies should be linearly related to ΔE^{-1}, the electronic excitation energy characteristic of the ligand. Using measured values of ΔE, a good correspondence with the cobalt resonance frequencies reported by Proctor and Yu was obtained.[148] Figure 12-32 shows a plot of the cobalt resonance frequencies for the compounds listed in Table 12-21 against the wavelength of the first optical-absorption maximum for each compound. Points for symmetrical complexes give a somewhat better straight-line fit than those for unsymmetrical complexes. Nevertheless the plot amply confirms the basic assumptions of the theory. The temperature dependence of the chemical shift can be accounted for quantitatively by the variation of ΔE with temperature.[137]

12-11. Other Nuclei

Cl, Br, I. The halogen isotopes Cl^{35}, Cl^{37}, Br^{79}, Br^{81}, and I^{127} all possess spins greater than one. The nuclear resonance signals are accordingly substantially broadened by electric quadrupole relaxation. In certain cases, however, by virtue of molecular symmetry or spherical charge distributions, as in the halogen ions, the electric field gradient at the nucleus is small enough to permit satisfactory measurements of the resonance signals.

The Cl^{35} and Cl^{37} resonances in concentrated hydrochloric acid and in barium perchlorate and perchloric acid were measured by Proctor and Yu.[354] For both isotopes the resonances in perchloric acid were displaced to lower field by $\sim$900 ppm relative to the resonances in hydrochloric acid.

Chemical-shift measurements of Cl^{35}, Br^{81}, and I^{127} in aqueous solutions of HCl, HBr, and HI were carried out by Masuda and Kanda.[265] The results of these measurements are described in Sec. 18-1. Employing a magnetic field of 6,221 gauss, the observed line widths for the three nuclei showed a concentration dependence and varied over a range of 0.18 to 2.5 gauss, the order of increasing line width being $Cl^{35} < Br^{81} < I^{127}$.

Wertz[460] has investigated the Cl^{35} resonance in aqueous NaCl solutions on addition of paramagnetic ions in varying concentration. The line width of the chloride-ion signal, which is about 0.2 gauss in 3 M NaCl, may be increased or decreased, depending on the nature and concentration of the paramagnetic ions added. The Cl^{35} resonance shifted to lower applied fields on addition of Cr^{3+}, Co^{++}, Ni^{++}, and Cu^{++}, while Sm^{++} caused a high-field shift. The ions Ti^{3+}, Mn^{++}, Fe^{3+}, and Nd^{3+} had no effect.

The Cl^{35} chemical shifts of the pure liquid compounds $TiCl_4$, $VOCl_3$, CrO_2Cl_2, and $SiCl_4$ were measured by Masuda[263] in a magnetic field of 6,220 gauss. The chemical shifts, together with measured values of T_1

and line width, are listed in Table 12-22. The corresponding quadrupole coupling constants $\frac{1}{2}e^2qQ$, obtained by Dehmelt[114] from nuclear quadrupole resonance measurements of the solids at liquid-air temperatures, are included for comparison. The chemical-shift data can be interpreted

TABLE 12-22. Cl^{35} RESONANCES IN PURE LIQUID CHLORIDES[263]

Compound	δ, ppm†	T_1, msec	$\frac{1}{2}e^2qQ$, Mc/sec‡	Line width, gauss
$SiCl_4$	−180	0.043	20.35	9.3
CrO_2Cl_2	−580	0.077	15.68	4.5
$VOCl_3$	−770	0.12	11.54	3.1
$TiCl_4$	−820	0.3	6.05	1.2

† Relative to the reference signal of a dilute aqueous solution of NaCl.
‡ Ref. 114.

in terms of a substantial paramagnetic contribution of hybridized d orbitals.[263]

Na, Rb, Cs. Resonance signals of the alkali metals are usually sufficiently broadened by quadrupole relaxation to limit NMR measurements to ionic states. According to Wertz and Jardetzky,[462] the line width of the Na^{23} resonance in 3 M NaCl is about 32 milligauss. This compares with a line width of 200 milligauss of the Cl^{35} resonance in the same solution, although the two nuclei have quadrupole moments of similar magnitude. No shifts were observed in the Na^{23} resonances of a variety of sodium salts in aqueous solution. However, considerable variations in line width and amplitude are observed; they may be due to quadrupolar interactions.[462] Interactions of this type could result from ion-pair formation.

Chemical shifts of Rb^{87} and Cs^{133} resonances have been observed by Gutowsky and McGarvey[167] in solid polycrystalline rubidium and cesium halides. The results are summarized in Table 12-23. The resonances

TABLE 12-23. Rb^{87} AND Cs^{133} CHEMICAL SHIFTS IN SOLID HALIDES[167]

Salt	δ, ppm†	Salt	δ, ppm†
RbF	− 60	CsF	− 90
RbCl	− 89	CsCl	−163
RbBr	−129	CsBr	−208
RbI	−149	CsI	−252

† The reference is in each case a saturated solution of the chloride.

of the solids were much broader than those of the liquid (solution) reference, and those of the two fluorides were broader than those of the other halides. For both series of compounds the magnetic shielding of the alkali-metal nucleus decreases from the fluoride to the iodide, while the ion in solution has the largest shielding. If the salts in the crystalline state were completely ionic, the shielding should be the same as that in the free ion, and no chemical shift should be observed between different halides. The results can be interpreted[167] in terms of a partial covalent bonding in these salts, the extent of such bonding increasing as we go from the fluoride to the iodide. A similar interpretation has been used by Kanda[211] to explain the observed chemical shifts of chlorine, bromine, and iodine in solid metal halides.

Pb. The chemical shifts of Pb^{207} resonances in a number of lead compounds, measured by Piette and Weaver,[335a] are summarized in Table 12-24. The measurements were obtained at a frequency of 6.3208

TABLE 12-24. Pb^{207} CHEMICAL SHIFTS IN LEAD COMPOUNDS[335a]

Compound	δ, ppm	Compound	δ, ppm
Pb (metal)	0	$Pb(NO_3)_2$ (solid)	14,540
PbO_2	6,250	$Pb(NO_3)_2$ (solution)	14,050
PbO (yellow)	7,370	$Pb(ClO_4)_2$ (solution)	14,050
Pb (zirconate)(solid)	12,460	PbO (solid)(red)	11,180
$Pb(Ac)_2$ (solution)	12,540	$Pb(C_2O_4)_2$ (solid)	12,300
$PbSO_4$ (solid)	14,700	$PbCl_2$ (solid)	12,300

Mc/sec ($H_0 = 7,040$ gauss). The resonance of metallic lead (used as the reference substance) appears at the lowest field. In lead compounds the chemical shift is very large, amounting to as much as 1.4 per cent. In ionic compounds, such as $Pb(NO_3)_2$ in solution, the resonance is greatly displaced to high field, owing to the symmetry of the charge distribution about the lead ion. In other compounds involving some covalent bonding there is a contribution due to the second-order paramagnetic term, the Pb^{207} resonance appearing at somewhat lower fields. In PbO_2, which is a conductor, the shielding arises almost entirely from conduction electrons. This is confirmed by the relatively short T_1 observed in this compound.

Se. A few measurements of magnetic resonances of Se^{77}, which has a natural abundance of 7.5 per cent, have been reported by Walchli.[452] Measurements were made on liquid H_2Se and on aqueous H_2SeO_3 and H_2SeO_4. The resonance of H_2Se was shifted to higher field by $\sim$1,500 ppm relative to that of aqueous H_2SeO_3.

Cu, Tl. The nuclear resonance of Cu^{63} in concentrated hydrochloric acid solutions containing both cuprous and cupric chloride was measured by McConnell and Weaver.[276] The measured line width was shown to be rather sensitive to the relative concentrations of the two species of ion. The line width depends on the rate of the electron-transfer process

$$Cu^{++} + Cu^+ \rightarrow Cu^+ + Cu^{++}$$

Measurements of the resonance line widths thus permit an evaluation of the rate constant for this process.[276,271]

An example of a chemical shift between the nuclear resonance of metallic ions in two different oxidation states is provided by the Tl^{3+} and Tl^+ ions of thallium salts. Gutowsky and McGarvey[168] measured the Tl^{205} resonance of thallous acetate and thallous and thallic nitrates in aqueous solution. The resonance of the Tl^+ ion was shifted to higher field by about 1,900 ppm relative to that of the Tl^{3+} ion. The measured shift is more than a hundred times larger than the shift obtained from the difference of the calculated diamagnetic (Lamb) shielding (Sec. 7-1) for the two ions. In view of this large discrepancy, the ions cannot be regarded as monatomic, and additional shielding effects arising from ion hydration or complex formation must be involved. This interpretation is supported by the additional observation[168] that the resonances of both thallous and thallic ions showed a marked dependence on the degree of dilution and on the nature and concentration of anions present.

CHAPTER 13

HINDERED INTERNAL ROTATION

13-1. Introduction

We have seen in Chaps. 11 and 12 how the screening of nuclei may depend on subtle changes of environment. It is to be expected, therefore, that NMR spectroscopy could make significant contributions to the problem of structural isomerism involving restricted rotation. When the barrier hindering internal rotation is very high (as in isomers which are cis and trans with respect to a double bond), the rotamers can usually be isolated and have distinguishable NMR spectra. In other cases, where isolation is not possible, the resonance spectrum may consist of a superposition of the spectra due to the forms in equilibrium.

According to resonance theory,[326] the CN bond in amides, for example, can assume double-bond character owing to resonance forms of the type

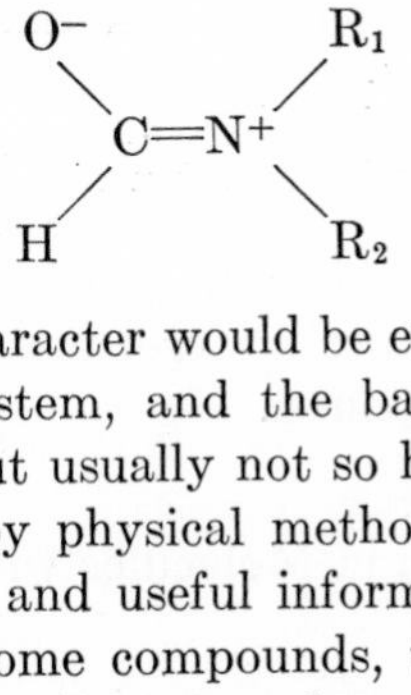

$$\underset{H}{\overset{O^-}{\diagdown}} C = N^+ \underset{R_2}{\overset{R_1}{\diagup}}$$

The partial double-bond character would be expected to impart a planar configuration to such a system, and the barrier to hindered rotation might well be quite high but usually not so high that the cis and trans isomers can be separated by physical methods. The NMR technique has given some interesting and useful information for isomers of compounds of this type. In some compounds, the interconversion of one isomer into the other may be slow enough to allow two separate spectra to be obtained. This requires the rate of interconversion to be less than the chemical shifts, in cycles per second, between signals from the two isomers.

In this chapter we shall discuss some of the NMR results obtained for the isomers of four classes of compounds, namely, those in which isomerism is due to a double bond, partial double-bond character, restricted rotation about a single bond, and restricted inversion at a nitrogen atom.

365

13-2. Cis-Trans Isomerism about a CC Double Bond

The high barrier associated with the double bond gives rise to two physically distinguishable isomers in substituted ethylenes which might be expected to have different screening constants for the ethylenic hydrogens. Cis and trans isomers of this kind have been encountered in Sec. 11-3 for butene-2 and propenylbenzene. As can be seen from Table 11-3, the signal of the ethylenic hydrogens in *cis*-butene-2 is at slightly lower field than in the trans compound. The signal for the ethylenic proton nearest the benzene ring is also at slightly lower field in *cis*-propenylbenzene than in *trans*-propenylbenzene (Table 11-2). Some other cis-trans shifts are given in Table 13-1. The difference for stilbene

TABLE 13-1. RELATIVE CHEMICAL SHIFTS[†] OF THE ETHYLENIC HYDROGENS
IN CIS AND TRANS ISOMERS
(In ppm)

Compounds	$\delta_{trans} - \delta_{cis}$	Ring-current effect[‡]
Butene-2 (liquid)	0.1	
1,2-Dichloroethylene	0.05[§]	
Fumaric-maleic acids	−0.5[¶]	
Stilbene	−0.5[§]	−0.5

[†] Bulk-susceptibility corrections have been made where necessary.

[‡] Calculated for a coplanar trans structure and a cis structure having benzene rings at right angles to the plane.

[§] Extrapolated to infinite dilution in CCl_4.

[¶] Extrapolated to infinite dilution in dioxane.

may be due to the fact that the induced moments of the coplanar benzene rings in *trans*-stilbene produce a larger low-field shift than do the nonplanar rings in the cis compound.

13-3. Cis-Trans Isomerism in Molecules with Partial Double-bond Character

a. Amides. The proton magnetic resonance spectrum at 30 Mc/sec of liquid N,N-dimethylformamide[330] at room temperature (Fig. 13-1) consists of a CH signal at −2.95 ppm from H_2O and two methyl-group signals separated by 6 cycles/sec. The two CH_3 signals are not the components of a spin multiplet because, at 40 Mc/sec, the separation increases to 9 cycles/sec. A similar splitting in N,N-dimethylacetamide was also observed. The chemical shift between the methyl groups is due to their different environments in the planar structure.[330,155,160] The magnitude of the shift, 6 cycles/sec, places an upper limit on the average rate of rotation about the CN bond at room temperature of about 36 sec^{-1}.

The basis for a quantitative study of the rates of hindered internal rotation has been developed by Gutowsky, McCall, and Slichter;[166] Gutowsky and Saika;[172] and Gutowsky and Holm[160] (Sec. 10.2). In Fig. 10-1 the NMR signals are shown for two interchanging species A and B when the populations are equal.

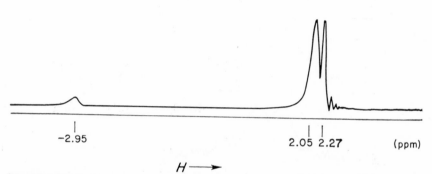

Fig. 13-1. The proton magnetic resonance spectrum at 30 Mc/sec of N,N-dimethyl-formamide referred to H_2O.   (Phillips.[330])

If the interchange from one isomer to the other is treated as a typical rate process, the temperature dependence of the rate constant k for the interchange may be expressed by[160]

$$k = k_0 e^{-E_a/RT} \tag{13-1}$$

where k_0 is the frequency factor and E_a is the potential barrier hindering the internal rotation.   From Eq. (10-26) the rate constant is $1/2\tau$, so Eq. (13-1) can be rewritten

$$\log_{10}\frac{1}{2\pi\tau(\nu_A - \nu_B)} = \log_{10}\frac{k_0}{\pi(\nu_A - \nu_B)} - \frac{E_a}{2.3RT} \tag{13-2}$$

Thus an examination of a spectrum at different temperatures provides values of τ which can be used in Eq. (13-2) to give values for the height of the potential barrier hindering rotation and the frequency factor k_0.   The spectrum of the N-methyl groups in N,N-dimethylacetamide at several temperatures is shown in Fig. 13-2; it resembles qualitatively the theoretical curves shown in Fig. 10-1. The simple Eq. (10-31) cannot be used to evaluate $2\pi\tau(\nu_A - \nu_B)$ accurately because the resonance line width and chemical shift $\nu_A - \nu_B$ are of the same order of magnitude.

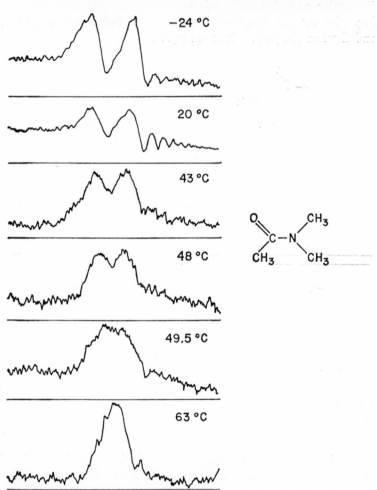

Fig. 13-2. The proton magnetic resonance spectrum of the N-methyl groups in N,N-dimethylacetamide at several temperatures at 17.735 Mc/sec. (Gutowsky and Holm.[160])

Gutowsky and Holm[160] have given methods for dealing with such a case. The plots of $1/2\pi\tau(\nu_A - \nu_B)$ vs. $1/T$ for N,N-dimethylacetamide and N,N-dimethylformamide are shown in Fig. 13-3. The barrier heights obtained from the slopes of the lines in this figure are 7 ± 3 kcal and 12 ± 2 kcal for N,N-dimethylformamide and N,N-dimethylacetamide, respectively, and the frequency factors are 10^3 to 10^7 and 10^7 to 10^{10}, respectively. In general, the errors in the final results of this type of experiment are quite large, mainly because of the small value of the observed separation of the signals.

As pointed out by Gutowsky and Holm, k_0 is the internal torsional frequency in Eq. (13-1), which could be expected to be greater by a factor

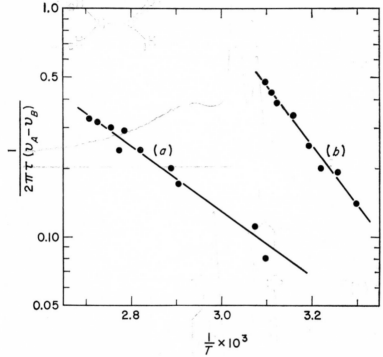

FIG. 13-3. Temperature dependence of the interconversion rate for (a) N,N-dimethylformamide and (b) N,N-dimethylacetamide. (Gutowsky and Holm.[160])

of about 2 for N,N-dimethylacetamide than for N,N-dimethylformamide. The observed ratio, however, is about 10^4. Similar effects have been found[123] for cis-trans isomerization reactions which involve double bonds, and the discussion of these may also apply to molecules with partial double-bond character.

Spectra of N-methylformamide and N-methylacetamide appear to arise from only one of the two possible rotational isomers.[330,160] This result is consistent with the infrared and Raman spectra of N-methylacetamide, from which it was concluded[288] that almost all of the molecules are in the configuration in which the NH is trans to the C=O bond. It would be difficult to decide the configuration on the basis of the NMR spectra, but it is probable that, whatever form N-methylacetamide takes, that for N-methylformamide will be the same, since the positions of the N-methyl signals in the field are the same for both. The NMR spectra of N-methylformanilide and N-methylacetanilide also can be interpreted in terms of the presence of only one isomeric form.[160]

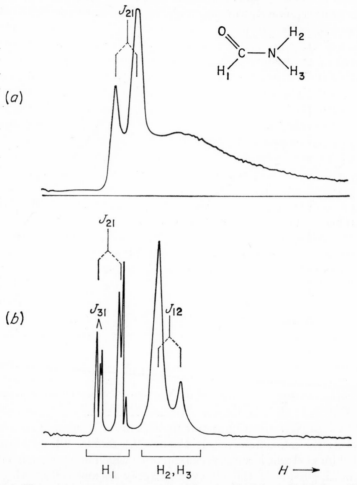

FIG. 13-4. The proton resonance spectra of formamide (a) at 40 Mc/sec, N^{14} not decoupled, and (b) doubly irradiated, H^1 at 40 Mc/sec and N^{14} at 2.8904 Mc/sec. (Piette, Ray, and Ogg.[335])

By analogy with N,N-dimethylformamide, one might expect the two protons bonded to nitrogen in formamide itself to be nonequivalent. Due to the quadrupole broadening by N^{14}, the proton spectrum of formamide (Fig. 13-4a) is of no help in providing such information. However, the spectrum obtained by Piette, Ray, and Ogg,[335] in which the

N^{14} coupling to the protons has been averaged out by the application of a strong rf field at the N^{14} resonant frequency (Fig. 13-4b), does reveal the nonequivalence of these protons. If the rotation about the CN bond were sufficiently rapid, the coupling constants of H_2 and H_3 with H_1 (see Fig. 13-4) would be equal on the average, and H_2 and H_3 would also have the same average screening constant. The spectrum would then be of the AB_2 type. However, the spacing in the observed spectrum shown in Fig. 13-4b cannot be interpreted in this way, but it may readily be assigned on the basis of three nonequivalent protons corresponding to hindered rotation about the CN bond. The quartet at low field arises from proton H_1, which has a large doublet spacing attributed to the trans coupling with H_2 ($J_{12} = 13$ cycles/sec) and a small cis coupling with H_3 ($J_{13} = 2.1$ cycles/sec). This is consistent with large trans and smaller cis proton coupling constants obtained for a CC double bond (Sec. 11-3). The signal of the proton H_2 shows the large spacing due to the trans coupling and is superimposed on the H_3 signal, which is unresolved.

b. Alkyl Nitrites. The existence of cis and trans isomers about the NO single bond in alkyl nitrites was first demonstrated by Tarte[438] from the doubling of the $N\!=\!O$ stretching and $O\!-\!N\!=\!O$ bending frequencies in their infrared spectra. Due to resonance, the $N\!-\!O$ single bond takes on partial double-bond character. The resultant barrier hindering free rotation about this bond leads to two planar isomers of the type

$$\begin{array}{ccc} \text{R}\!-\!\text{O} & \qquad & \text{R}\!-\!\text{O} \\ | & & | \\ \text{O}\!=\!\text{N} & & \text{N}\!=\!\text{O} \\ \text{cis} & & \text{trans} \end{array}$$

The proton resonance spectra of methyl, ethyl, and n-propyl nitrites at room temperature show no evidence of the presence of both rotational isomers (Fig. 13-5a). In order that the proton resonances of separate spectra be observed, it is necessary to slow down the rate at which the isomers interconvert. This was accomplished by Piette, Ray, and Ogg[334] by lowering the temperature (Fig. 13-5b). A dilution study on methyl nitrite eliminated the possibility of dimerization being responsible for the extra signals.

Phillips, Looney, and Spaeth[333] assigned the high-field triplet B in n-propyl nitrite at low temperature (Fig. 13-5b) to the CH_2 signal of the trans form by analogy with the chemical shift of the OCH_2 group in alcohols and ethers, which appears at about the same position. In the cis position the perturbing influence of the $N\!=\!O$ group might be expected to give rise to a displaced CH_2 signal. The low-field triplet A is therefore assigned to the cis form. A similar identification was made by Piette, Ray, and Ogg[334] from arguments based on the effect of hydrogen

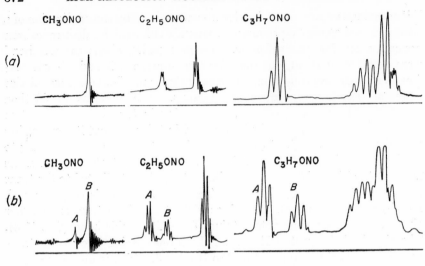

$H \longrightarrow$

FIG. 13-5. The proton resonance spectra at 30 Mc/sec of methyl, ethyl, and n-propyl nitrite (a) at 21°C and (b) at −60°C. (Piette, Ray, and Ogg.[334]) *A* is the cis form, and *B* the trans form.

bonding. From the relative intensities of the signals, Piette et al. concluded that at −60°C the trans form is the more stable in methyl nitrite, while in ethyl and n-propyl nitrite the cis form is the more stable. On the basis of these assignments the relative amounts of cis and trans isomers in these and other alkyl nitrites are shown in Table 13-2. The steric

TABLE 13-2. CIS/TRANS ISOMER RATIOS IN SOME NITRITES

Compound	Ref.	Cis/trans ratio at	
		$\sim -60°$	$20°$
Methyl nitrite	334	0.3	
n-Propyl nitrite	333	1.8	1.7
Isobutyl nitrite	333	2.3	2.2
1,4-Butylene dinitrite	333	1.6	1.2
Isoamyl nitrite	333	1.7	1.3
Benzyl nitrite	332	2.0	
Isopropyl nitrite	333	0.1	0.1
tert-Butyl nitrite	332	0	

requirements of the isopropyl and tertiary-butyl groups would account for the predominance of the trans form. It is difficult to see, however, why the trans form is the more stable in methyl nitrite. The cis/trans ratios at the two temperatures given in Table 13-2 show that the relative concentrations are only slightly temperature dependent. An average value for the energy difference of about 130 cal/mole for all nitrites would account for the change in the observed ratio with temperature. It should be pointed out that there are two discrepancies between the NMR data and the results obtained from vibrational spectroscopic measurements. From the temperature dependence of the infrared doublets,

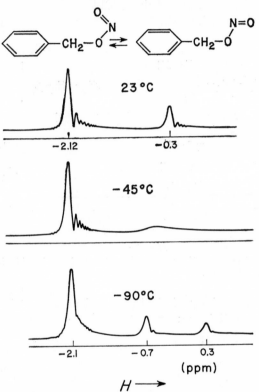

FIG. 13-6. Proton resonance spectrum of benzyl nitrite at different temperatures referred to H_2O. (Phillips.[332])

Tarte[438] concluded that the cis form was more stable for methyl nitrite. For other nitrites, the cis/trans isomer ratios obtained from optical densities are not in good agreement with the NMR results.[333]

The temperature dependence of the proton magnetic resonance spectrum of benzyl nitrite dissolved in CS_2 (Phillips[332]) is shown in Fig. 13-6. The peak at -2.12 ppm in the spectrum taken at 23°C is due to the benzene-ring protons, and that at -0.3 ppm to the protons of the CH_2 group. This latter signal broadens at $-45°$ and finally at $-90°C$ gives rise to two sharp signals at -0.7 and 0.3 ppm. The signal at lower field (-0.7 ppm) is assigned to the cis form and that at 0.3 ppm to the trans form by analogy with the other alkyl nitrites. The single OCH_2 resonance of benzyl nitrite at 23°C is of course an average of the two low-temperature cis and trans resonances weighted by the mole fractions of the two isomers. Thus the −0.3-ppm resonance at 23°C is approximately the average of the resonances at −0.7 and 0.3 ppm for a cis/trans ratio of 1.6:1. The temperature dependence of the isomer ratio[332] from −60 to 23°C yields a value of about 0.3 kcal/mole for the energy difference between the two isomers.

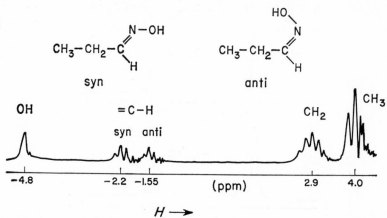

FIG. 13-7. The proton magnetic resonance spectrum of propionaldoxime at 40 Mc/sec referred to H_2O. (Phillips.[332])

c. Aldoximes. Oximes of aldehydes and unsymmetrical ketones can exist in syn and anti forms:

$$N—OH \qquad\qquad N—OH$$
$$\parallel \qquad\qquad\qquad \parallel$$
$$R—C—H \qquad\qquad H—C—R$$
$$\text{Syn} \qquad\qquad\qquad \text{Anti}$$

The magnetic resonance spectrum of propionaldoxime[332] is shown in Fig. 13-7. The structures of the CH_2 and CH_3 resonances can be accounted for by mutual spin-spin coupling between protons of the $=CH$, CH_2, and CH_3 groups. The $=CH$ signals consist of two triplets of equal intensity which arise from spin coupling with the protons of the CH_2 group. By analogy with the nitrites, the low-field signal at −2.2 ppm was assigned to the syn form and that at −1.55 ppm to the anti form. The syn/anti isomer ratios for some aldoximes estimated from signal intensities are given in Table 13-3. This order of isomer ratios would be anticipated from steric considerations.

d. Nitrosamines. Looney, Phillips, and Reilly[259] found the room-temperature proton magnetic resonance spectrum of N,N-dimethyl-

TABLE 13-3. SYN/ANTI RATIOS FOR SOME ALDOXIMES[332]

Aldoxime	Syn/anti isomer ratios
Acetaldoxime	0.6
Propionaldoxime	1.0
Isobutyraldoxime	2.1
n-Heptaldoxime	1.0

nitrosamine to consist of two peaks of equal intensity separated by 26 cycles/sec at fixed radio frequency of 40 Mc/sec (Fig. 13-8). The peaks arise from the methyl groups in this molecule, which has been stabi-

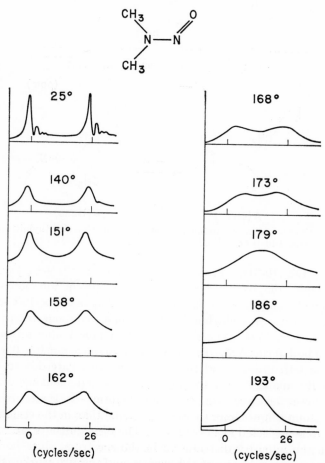

FIG. 13-8. Temperature dependence of the proton signals of N,N-dimethylnitrosamine at 40 Mc/sec. (Looney, Phillips, and Reilly.[259])

lized in the planar form by resonance forms of the type

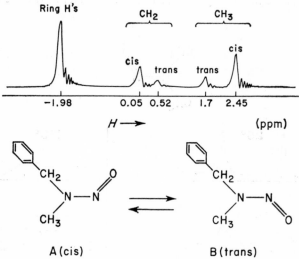

Since the number of protons is identical in the two nonequivalent environments and the chemical shift is large compared with the line widths of the signals, the product of the lifetime and the chemical shift, $2\pi\tau(\nu_A - \nu_B)$,

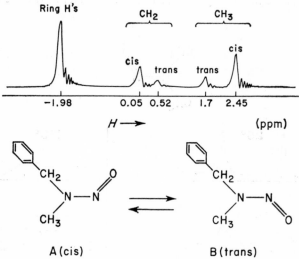

FIG. 13-9. Proton magnetic resonance spectrum of benzylmethylnitrosamine at 40 Mc/sec referred to H_2O. (Phillips.[332])

is given by Eq. (10-31). From a plot of $\log_{10}\left[1/2\pi\tau(\nu_A - \nu_B)\right]$ vs. $1/T$ for this molecule, the barrier height for methyl-group interconversion is found to be 23 kcal, and the frequency factor $k_0 = 0.7 \times 10^{13}$ sec^{-1}.

The spectrum of benzylmethylnitrosamine at room temperature[332] is shown in Fig. 13-9. The signal at -1.98 ppm is due to the phenyl protons of both forms A and B. The signals in the region 0 to 0.5 ppm are due to the CH_2 groups, and those at highest field are due to the CH_3 groups. By analogy with the alkyl nitrites and aldoximes, the CH_2 signal at lower field was assigned to the cis form. In the trans molecule the CH_3 group is now closer to the $N\!\!=\!\!O$ bond than in the cis form, so its signal is to be expected at lower field. These assignments are consistent also with the intensity distribution in the spectrum, since both strong signals are assigned to one of the isomers and the two weaker signals to the other. The cis/trans isomer ratio is 3.1 at 23°C and is not appreciably altered[332] over the temperature range 0 to 125°C, indicating that the energy difference between the two isomers is very small.

The proton magnetic resonance spectrum of phenylmethylnitrosamine shows only a single methyl signal.[332] This was interpreted on the basis of one form of the two possible isomers for this molecule.

13-4. Restricted Rotation about a Single Bond

Hindered rotation about a single bond in saturated compounds has been investigated[288] by a variety of physical techniques including Raman and infrared spectroscopy, microwave spectroscopy, and electron-diffraction and dipole-moment measurements. In these compounds the barrier to internal rotation is usually considerably lower than for compounds having double-bond character. This means that interconversion of the rotational isomers in dynamic equilibrium is usually much faster, so that the possibility of observing chemical shifts corresponding to the various isomers is considerably reduced. By lowering the temperature, however, it may be possible to reduce the rate of interconversion sufficiently that the resonance spectrum of more than one isomer is obtained.

a. Classification of Spectra. The NMR spectra of substituted ethanes can be classified according to the following possibilities:[339]

1. The energy difference between the isomers of long lifetime may be so large that only the most stable is present.

2. There may be a mixture of isomers in equilibrium, each sufficiently long-lived and abundant to give its own NMR spectrum. The observed spectrum will then be a superposition of these components.

3. Internal rotation may be occurring at a sufficiently rapid rate for the effective chemical shifts (screening) and spin coupling constants to be averaged.

Other intermediate cases could arise. For example, interconversion could be rapid between two isomers while a third is stable for a longer period.

If the form of the spectrum appropriate to rapid internal rotation differs from that of the individual rotational isomers, the NMR spectrum may be used to place an approximate lower limit on the rate of rotation (if the spectrum is of type 3), or an upper limit (if the spectrum is of type 1 or 2). It is possible then to classify the NMR spectra of substituted ethanes according to whether the rotation is slow (case 1 or 2) or rapid (case 3). As an example, we may consider the spectrum of the ethyl group in the monosubstituted ethanes CH_3CH_2R. Without loss of generality we may take R to be magnetically inactive. This molecule has three rotational isomers of equal energy and population. They are shown in Fig. 13-10 on the assumption that "staggered" configurations are more stable[288] than "eclipsed" ones. If the rotation is slow, the proton resonance will be typical of one structure. Thus in form I, the proton H_2 will have a different screening constant than the pair H_1,H_3, and the pair H_4,H_5 will have the same screening constant. Consequently, if the chemical shifts are large enough, the spectrum should show three types of protons (H_2; H_1,H_3; and H_4,H_5) and be of the type AB_2X_2, in the notation of Chap. 6. Since there will be a considerable number of distinct coupling constants involved, the spectrum may be complex.

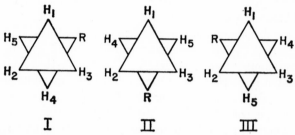

Fig. 13-10. The rotational configurations of CH_3CH_2R. The hydrogens of the methyl group are H_1, H_2, and H_3; those of the methylene group are H_4 and H_5.

If the rotation is rapid, on the other hand, the environment of any given proton has to be averaged over the three configurations I, II, and III with equal weights. The screening constants of the three protons H_1, H_2, and H_3 then become identical. Further, the spin coupling constants between any hydrogen on the CH_3 group (e.g., H_1) and the two protons of the CH_2 group become equal, that is, $J_{H_1H_4} = J_{H_1H_5}$ (average). This may be seen quite readily if, for convenience, we call the coupling constant between two hydrogens in the trans configuration (i.e., with an azimuthal angle of 180°) J_T and that between two hydrogens for which the azimuthal angle is 60° J_G. The average values of $J_{H_1H_4}$ and $J_{H_1H_5}$ over the configurations I, II, and III, respectively, are then

$$J_{H_1H_4} = \tfrac{1}{3}(J_T + J_G + J_G)$$
$$J_{H_1H_5} = \tfrac{1}{3}(J_G + J_G + J_T) \tag{13-3}$$

and equal to one another. Hence, for rapid rotation the spectrum will become of type A_2B_3 with all AB coupling constants equal. If the chemical shift between the CH_3 and CH_2 protons is sufficiently large, the spectrum will consist of a 1:2:1 triplet and a 1:3:3:1 quartet (see Fig. 5-4). If the chemical shift is of the same order as the spin coupling constants, the spectrum is more complicated but still of the A_2B_3 pattern. Thus, from the appearance and analysis of the proton resonance spectrum of a molecule CH_3CH_2R, some qualitative information about the rate of internal rotation may be obtained. The spectra observed for monosubstituted ethanes can all be interpreted on the basis of rapid internal rotation with a coupling constant of about 7 cycles/sec (Glick and Bothner-By[143]). No spectrum has been obtained as yet, which indicates that slow rotation is taking place.

Drysdale and Phillips[125] first applied NMR techniques to the investigation of hindered rotation in substituted ethanes. They found the fluorine spectrum in compounds of the type CF_2R-$CHPQ$ to be two quartets

TABLE 13-4. PROTON RESONANCE SPECTRA OF SUBSTITUTED ETHANES[339]

Compound†	Form of spectrum	
	Slow rotation	Rapid rotation
CH_3—$CH_2'R$	AB_2C_2	A_2B_3 (all $J_{HH'}$ equal)
CH_3—$CH'RR$	ABC_2	AB_3 (all $J_{HH'}$ equal)
CH_3—$CH'RS$	$ABCD$	AB_3 (all $J_{HH'}$ equal)
CH_2R—CH_2R	A_4 (trans) and A_2B_2 (gauche)	A_4
CH_2R—$CH_2'S$	A_2B_2 (trans) and $ABCD$ (gauche)	A_2B_2 (all $J_{HH'}$ not equal)
CH_3—$CRRR$	A_3	A_3
CH_3—$CRRS$	AB_2	A_3
CH_3—$CPQR$	ABC	A_3
CH_2R—$CHSS$	AB_2 and ABC	AB_2
CH_2R—$CHPS$	Three ABC	ABC
CH_2R—$CSSS$	A_2	A_2
CH_2R—$CSSP$	A_2 and AB	A_2
CH_2R—$CSPQ$	Three AB	AB
$CHRR$—$CHRR$	Two A_2	A_2
$CHRR$—$CHSS$	Two AB	AB
$CHRR$—$CHPS$	Three AB	AB
$CHRS$—$CHRS$ (meso)	A_2 and AB	A_2
$CHRS$—$CHRS$ (dl)	Three A_2	A_2
$CHPQ$—$CHRS$	Six AB	Two AB (mixture of two isomers)

† P, Q, R, and S are substituents which show no spin coupling with the protons.

and the proton spectrum to be a single quartet. The complete spectrum is of the type ABX with nonequivalent fluorine nuclei. If the two fluorines were equivalent, the spectrum would be of the type A_2X and the fluorine signal would appear as a doublet. Even at temperatures up to 200°C, at which the internal rotation is rapid, the pattern of the spectrum remained of the ABX type. It was pointed out by Nair and Roberts[299] that the fluorines in the three rotational isomers

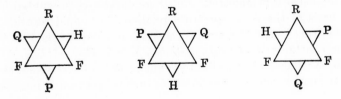

are not equivalent, even after averaging, so that an ABX-type spectrum is obtained for rapid internal rotation.   Under conditions of slow internal rotation, the three physically distinct isomers may have different populations and the spectrum would be a superposition of three ABX-type spectra.

The NMR spectra of other types of substituted ethanes can be discussed in a similar manner, and a systematic tabulation of the predicted types of spectra for slow and rapid rotation is given in Table 13-4.   The actual form of the spectrum can be used as direct evidence for or against rapid rotation only if the predicted spectrum for rapid rotation differs from that corresponding to any one of the individual isomers.   The

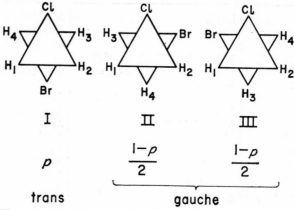

Fig. 13-11. The rotational isomers of 1-chloro-2-bromoethane and their relative weights.

table has been constructed for proton spectra, but it is clear that similar conclusions apply to other nuclei, particularly fluorine.

A clear-cut example of rapid rotation in a disubstituted ethane has been obtained for 1-chloro-2-bromoethane by Pople, Schneider, and Bernstein[342] (Sec. 6-7).   As may be seen from Fig. 13-11, its spectrum should be the superposition of A_2B_2 (trans) and ABCD (gauche) if both isomers were sufficiently prevalent and if rotation were slow enough. It is known from spectroscopic data[23,466] that the energy difference between the two isomers in the liquid is about 440 cal/mole, with the trans more stable, so that the Boltzmann distribution of the isomers is about two trans to one gauche at room temperature.   The observed spectrum (Fig. 6-18) is symmetrical and therefore can be accounted for only on the basis of the A_2B_2 spectrum predicted for rapid rotation.   The analysis of this (Sec. 6-7) provides the average values of the two *different* coupling constants $J = \frac{1}{2}(J_{H_2H_3} + J_{H_1H_4})$ and $J' = \frac{1}{2}(J_{H_1H_3} + J_{H_2H_4})$. From these values it is possible to evaluate the trans coupling constant J_T and the gauche coupling constant J_G (defined previously in connection with the discussion of the spectrum of the ethyl group). If the concentration of the trans isomer I is p, then forms II and III (Fig. 13-11) are each present to the extent $\frac{1}{2}(1 - p)$. From this figure it is apparent that the average of J_{23} and J_{14} over all configurations is

$$J = pJ_G + \frac{1}{2}(1 - p)(J_T + J_G) \qquad (13\text{-}4)$$

Similarly, the average of J_{13} and J_{24} is

$$J' = pJ_T + (1 - p)J_G \qquad (13\text{-}5)$$

This result for the average values of the coupling constants was derived independently by Graham and Waugh.[147] Using the values of 6 and 9 cycles/sec obtained at room temperature for J and J', respectively (Sec. 6-7), and the approximate value of $p = \frac{2}{3}$ (indicated by the energy difference of the isomers), we find $J_G = 5$ and $J_T = 11$ cycles/sec. By substituting these values in Eq. (13-3), one may estimate the mean coupling constant in CH_3CH_2X compounds to be 7 cycles/sec, in agreement with the observed values.[143] We shall see in Sec. 14-4 that trans coupling constants in six-membered rings are about two to three times greater than equatorial (gauche) constants, so that the alternative choice of 9 and 6 cycles/sec for J and J', which gives $J_T < J_G$, may be excluded. Similar examples of 1,2-disubstituted ethane spectra have been obtained by Shoolery and Crawford[422] and Graham and Waugh[147] and interpreted independently by those authors.

b. Temperature Dependence of Spectra. As can be seen from Table 13-4, in certain cases any single measurement of the nuclear resonance spectrum of a substituted ethane does not necessarily distinguish between slow and rapid rotation. The variation of the spectrum with temperature, however, may provide significant additional evidence. Thus if rotation is rapid, the chemical shifts will be averaged over the three configurations

$$\delta = p_1\delta_1 + p_2\delta_2 + p_3\delta_3 \qquad (13\text{-}6)$$

where p_1, p_2, and p_3 are the fractional populations. If the isomers have different energies, the ratio $p_1:p_2:p_3$ will be given by

$$p_1:p_2:p_3 = a_1e^{-E_1/kT}:a_2e^{-E_2/kT}:a_3e^{-E_3/kT} \qquad (13\text{-}7)$$

where a_1, a_2, and a_3 are in general different for each isomer and will be only slightly temperature dependent. The spin coupling constants are to be averaged in a similar manner.

If the apparent chemical shifts and coupling constants are temperature dependent, rapid rotation is indicated. However, if the spectrum is independent of temperature (and the molecule is such that the form of the spectrum for the rotating molecule is the same as that for one of the isomers), there are three main possibilities:

1. The molecules exist almost entirely as one isomer, rotation being highly hindered.

2. The molecules may be rotating rapidly but the energy difference between the isomeric forms may be so large that one of the weighting factors p_1, p_2, or p_3 is much larger than the other two.

3. The energy differences may all be small, so that temperature will not change appreciably the relative populations.

The temperature dependencies of the spectra of several substituted ethanes have been measured. Drysdale and Phillips[125] obtained the

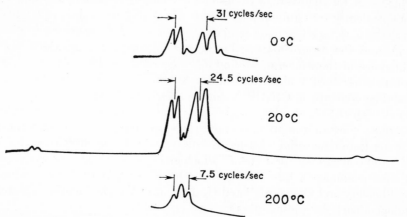

Fig. 13-12. The F^{19} resonance spectrum at 30 Mc/sec of CF_2Cl—$CHCl\phi$. Only the strong central pair of doublets is shown at 0 and 200°C. (Drysdale and Phillips.[125])

fluorine resonance spectrum of CF_2Cl—$CHCl\phi$ (at 30 Mc/sec) over the range 0 to 200°C (Fig. 13-12). It is characteristic of an ABX type and is temperature dependent, suggesting that rapid rotation is taking place. The spectrum at 20°C is essentially an AB quartet each component of which is split by coupling with the proton. Using the value of the FF spin coupling constant determined from this spectrum, the chemical shift between the two gem fluorines can be calculated to be approximately 101, 90, and 46 cycles/sec at the temperatures 0, 20, and 200°C, respectively. As expected, the chemical shift decreases with increasing temperature.

Nair and Roberts[299] measured the fluorine resonance spectra of CF_2Br—CBr_2Cl (I) and CF_2Br—$CBr_2\phi$ (II) in CS_2 solution over a range of temperatures. Down to −30°C only one signal was observed. At −80°, however, I appears to freeze to about a 1.4:1 mixture of the symmetrical isomer (which may be identified by its single resonance) and the d,l pair (identified by its quartet). For compound II the symmetrical isomer is present only to the extent of about 10 per cent at −80°C. Another spectrum of the same type is that of CF_2Br—CBr_2CN in chloroform, which has been obtained at various temperatures by Phillips[332] and is shown in Fig. 13-13. The spectrum at 23°C corresponds to rapid rotation and is of the type A_2. At $-98°C$ the rotation is slow and the quartet (432, 272, -272, -432 cycles/sec) of the d,l forms is observed as well as the single signal (-78 cycles/sec) due to the symmetrical isomer. At $-98°C$ the symmetrical isomer is present to the extent of about 22 per cent. The transition from fast to slow rotation takes place at about $-70°C$.

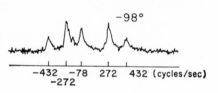

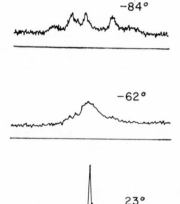

FIG. 13-13. F^{19} resonance spectrum of CF_2Br—CBr_2CN (at 40 Mc/sec) in chloroform. (Phillips.[332])

The proton resonance spectrum of 1,2-dibromo-1,1-difluoroethane has been measured over the temperature range of -54 to 104°C by Graham and Waugh.[147] Owing to rapid rotation, the spectrum is of the A_2X_2 type, which results in this case in a quartet for the proton signals with closely spaced central components. This spacing was found to decrease with increasing temperature.

Spectra of CF_2Br—$CBr(CN)$-(CH_3) have been obtained at various temperatures by Phillips[332] (Fig. 13-14). The molecule is of the type CF_2R—$CPQS$, and as may be seen from Table 13-4 should consist of three AB-type spectra for slow rotation and a single AB type for rapid rotation. At 23°C the spectrum is consistent with the four-line AB type expected for rapid rotation. Between -60 and $-100°$, a "freezing-in" of at least one of the isomers and possibly all three seems to be taking place. The dependence of the chemical shift (obtained by analyzing the four-line AB spectrum) on temperature was investigated in detail by Phillips; the results are shown in Fig. 13-15. The 220-cycle/sec room-temperature value of the chemical shift decreases with increasing temperature and appears to be approaching an asymptotic value of about 120 cycles/sec. Similarly it increases smoothly to a value of 291 cycles/sec at a temperature of $-50°C$. Between -60 and $-100°$, however, there is a rapid increase from 302 to 576 cycles/sec corresponding to the

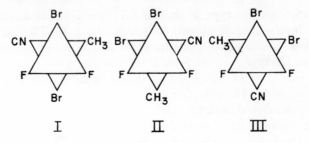

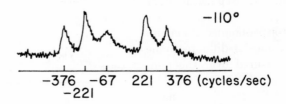

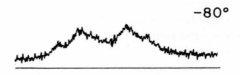

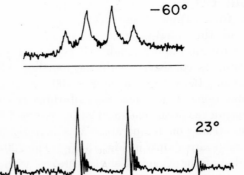

FIG. 13-14. Temperature dependence of fluorine resonance spectra of CF_2Br—CBr-$(CN)(CH_3)$ at 40 Mc/sec. The rotational isomers are also shown. (Phillips.[332])

"freezing-in" of one or all of the isomers. From the observed chemical shift as a function of temperature, a value of about 700 cal/mole was estimated[332] for the energy difference between II or III and I.

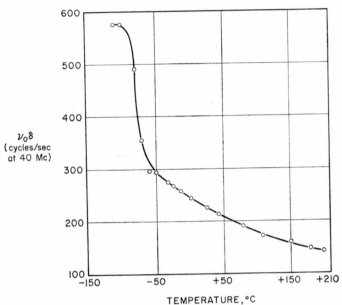

FIG. 13-15. Temperature dependence of chemical shift between fluorines in $CF_2Br-CBr(CN)(CH_3)$. Below 40°C, solutions in $CHCl_3$ were used. (Phillips.[332])

13-5. Restricted Inversion at a Nitrogen Atom

Cyclic Imines. The rapid rate of inversion of the ammonia molecule[189] is slowed down drastically by introducing heavy substituents in place of the hydrogen atoms. Suitably substituted ethylenimines might be expected to have structural isomers due to the restricted inversion at the N atom, but successful resolution of such molecules into stable optically active antipodes has not yet been achieved. The NMR spectra of N-ethylethylenimine (I) and N-ethylallenimine (II) obtained by Bottini and Roberts[73] (Fig. 13-16) indicate that the inversion rate for these compounds is too fast at room temperature to enable a successful resolution into the optical antipodes to be accomplished. At room temperature, I shows the characteristic bands of the ethyl group and two slightly split triplet-band systems. According to Bottini and Roberts,[73] these bands, indicated by the vertical arrows in Fig. 13-16, are due to the two groups of ring protons, which are either cis or trans to the ethyl group bonded to the pyramidal nitrogen atom. The bands are separated by about 27 cycles/sec at 40 Mc/sec, so the mean lifetime of such a molecule before the nitrogen inverts is of the order of 0.01 sec. On heating I to 120 to 130°C, the ring hydrogens appear to lose their identity with respect to the position of the ethyl group and one signal only is

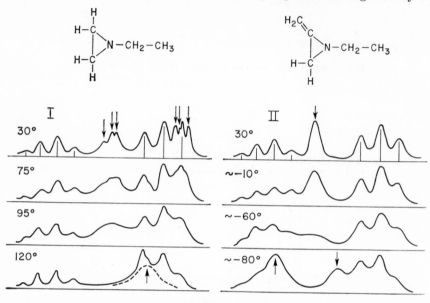

FIG. 13-16. Proton magnetic resonance of N-ethylethylenimine (I) and N-ethyl-allenimine (II) at 40 Mc/sec. Vertical lines mark characteristic bands of ethyl group, while vertical arrows indicate absorption of ring hydrogens. The temperature-invariant absorption of the double-bond methylene protons of II is off scale on the left. (Bottini and Roberts.[73])

observed at high field (see dashed lines in Fig. 13-16). Thus, the isomers are inverting considerably faster than 27 times per second. Similarly in II, there are two signals for the cis and trans pairs of hydrogens at −80°C but only one at 30°C. The separation between the ring-hydrogen signals at −80°C is about 30 cycles/sec at 40 Mc/sec, so that the inversion rate is about 200 times per second.

CHAPTER 14

INVESTIGATION OF MOLECULAR CONFORMATION
BY PROTON MAGNETIC RESONANCE

14-1. Introduction

The term "conformation" was introduced by Haworth[185] to denote the different spatial arrangements of the atoms in a classical organic structure (configuration). The different arrangements of the atoms are produced solely by rotation about bonds without any bonds being broken. A classical example is provided by the chair and boat conformations of cyclohexane. In the chair form the C atoms lie roughly in a plane, and

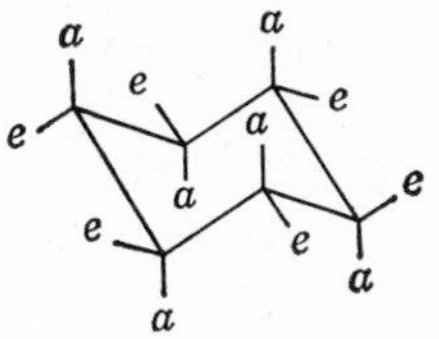

(chair) 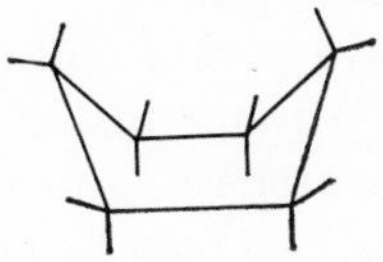   (boat)

the CH bonds which are approximately in this "plane" are called equatorial bonds. They are marked e in the figure. The CH bonds nearly perpendicular to the plane are known as axial bonds; they are marked a in the figure. Another example of two conformations is to be found in the chair form of the ring system of monosaccharides designated $C1$ and $1C$ by Reeves.[377] The difference between these conformations is that all

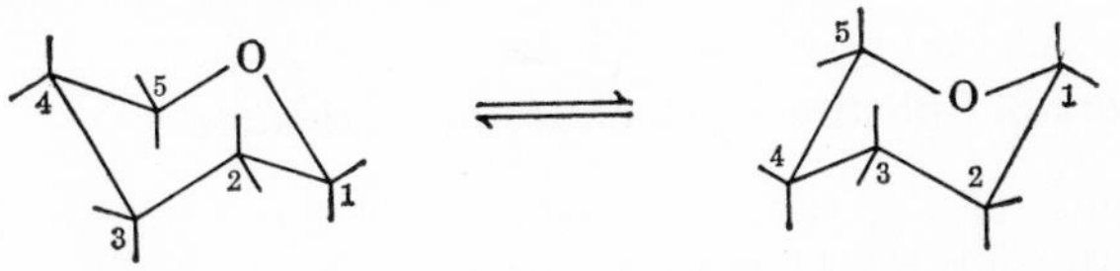

C1   1C

equatorial and axial situations in the $C1$ form have become axial and equatorial, respectively, in the $1C$ conformation. Cyclohexane in the chair form has two conformations, corresponding to the $C1$ and $1C$ forms of the cyclic ether shown above, in which a and e situations have become e and a, respectively. From symmetry considerations cyclohexane in

387

the chair form has six identical equatorially substituted protons and six identical axial protons. It is possible for the local magnetic field at these axial and equatorial protons to be different, so that there would be a chemical shift between axial and equatorial hydrogens. However, in the case of cyclohexane, in which inversion from one conformation to the other takes place rapidly, the equatorial and axial protons experience the average local field, and only one signal is observed. This requires that the rate at which the change from one conformation to the other takes place must be faster than the inverse of the chemical-shift difference between axial and equatorial protons (measured in cycles per second). This inversion rate depends on the height of the potential barrier that must be surmounted when one conformation changes into the other, and it has been shown that substitution of hydrogen by larger atoms or groups can reduce the rate drastically.[203] Frequently only one conformation occurs, because the other is energetically relatively unstable. From considerations[219,112] of the nonbonded interactions involved in various conformations, it seems that equatorially substituted chair forms are more stable than axially substituted ones primarily because of the strong repulsion existing between axial substituents in the 1,3,5 positions. For comprehensive reviews on conformations in ring systems the reader is referred to Barton,[30] Hassel,[182] Klyne,[219] and Dauben and Pitzer.[112]

In this chapter we shall be concerned with the NMR spectra of conformations of compounds having one or two six-membered rings in the chair form and usually for molecules in which only one conformation is obtained. However, a few cases in which the system contains a high concentration of both conformations in dynamic equilibrium have been investigated. No measurements on boat forms have been made, and in fact there seems to be little evidence that they exist to any appreciable extent in saturated six-membered rings (for references see Raphael[369]). In cyclohexane-1,4-dione, however, where the substituents are small, the dipole moment[238] suggests that the boat form may be present to the extent of 10 per cent.

14-2. Isomers of Substituted Symmetrical Trioxane

Two isomers of the trichloro analogue of paraldehyde with melting points of 116 and 152°C have been prepared.[89] An investigation by Novak and Whalley[302] of the infrared and proton resonance spectra and electric moments showed that both isomers are in the chair form. The proton magnetic resonance spectra of these compounds in CCl_4 are shown in Fig. 14-1. The isomer that melts at 152°C undoubtedly has three equatorially substituted CCl_3 groups, since the spectrum consists of one signal only, corresponding to the three equivalent axial protons. The other possible configuration, with three axial CCl_3 groups, is excluded on grounds of the large axial-axial repulsions.   The spectrum of the isomer melting at 116°C has two signals with relative intensity of 1:2.   The structure with two equatorial and one axial CCl_3 groups would give this type of spectrum, owing to the two equivalent axial protons and the single equatorial proton.   The protons are evidently so far away from each

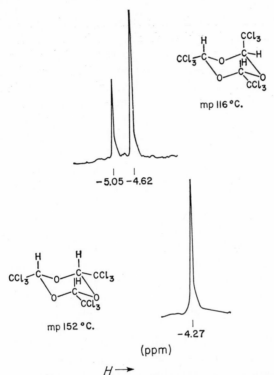

mp 116 °C.

−5.05 −4.62

mp 152 °C.

−4.27

(ppm)

H →

Fig. 14-1. Proton magnetic resonance spectra (40 Mc/sec) of substituted isomeric trioxanes in CCl_4.   Reference compound is cyclohexane in a capillary tube.

other that there is negligible spin coupling.   The structure with two axial CCl_3 groups and one equatorial CCl_3 group, which would also give rise to a spectrum consisting of two signals in the ratio 1:2, can be excluded because of the large repulsion between two axial CCl_3 groups in the 1,3 positions.   It is difficult to see how the observed chemical shift between axial and equatorial hydrogens could be due to changes in electron density at the protons.   Very likely it is due to magnetic effects of the other atoms in the molecule.   In particular, the small fields due to the anisotropy of the neighboring groups (Sec. 7-5) may be significantly different for the two structures.   Another possibility is that the chemical shift may be due to a small ring current (Sec. 7-5).

14-3. Substituted Cyclohexanes

The Isomeric 1,2,3,4,5,6-*Hexachlorocyclohexanes.* The hexachlorocyclohexanes provide an interesting series of isomers whose structure and proton magnetic resonance spectra bear a 1:1 correspondence.[242] The spectra of the α, β, γ, δ, and ε isomers shown in Fig. 14-2 were obtained in dioxane solution.

In the β isomer all chlorine atoms are equatorially substituted. The other conformation, in which all six chlorine atoms are axial, would possess so much strain energy due to the repulsion between the 1,3,5 axially disposed substituents that for energetic reasons alone it would be extremely unstable. The six equivalent axial hydrogens in this molecule give rise to the single signal observed at −0.63 ppm. The δ compound has one axial-chlorine and five equatorial-chlorine substituents. Again, the conformation with five chlorines axial and one equatorial is not considered likely because of energy considerations. The spectrum is exactly what would be expected from five equivalent axial hydrogens and one equatorial hydrogen, namely, two signals with intensity ratio 1:5. It is interesting to note that the axial hydrogens in the β and δ compound are very nearly at the same position in the field in the two molecules. In the ε compound there are two axial chlorines in the 1,4 positions and four equatorial chlorines. Again the conformation with four axial chlorines and two equatorial chlorines in the 1,4 positions is unlikely because of steric hindrance due to the two 3,5 diaxial substitutions. The spectrum, which consists of two lines with intensity ratio 2:4, is consistent with the structure of the ε compound. In both the δ and ε isomers the signal due to the equatorial hydrogens is at lower field than that for the axial hydrogens. Note, however, that the chemical shift of the axial hydrogens in the ε isomer is no longer the same as for the β and δ compounds. The γ isomer is known[447] to have chlorines axially substituted at the 1,2,6 positions, with three others equatorially substituted at the 3,4,5 positions. By analogy with the spectra of the β, δ, and ε compounds, one might have expected two signals of equal intensity corresponding to the three axial and three equatorial hydrogens. However, the other conformation of this isomer has axial substituents at the 3,4,5 positions and three equatorial substituents at 1,2,6, so that both conformations have exactly the same spatial configuration and equal energies. This suggests that the observed NMR spectrum corresponds to that of an equal mixture of the two conformations, which invert at a rate sufficiently fast that only an averaged signal of axial and equatorial protons is obtained.

The spectrum of the α isomer differs from the others in two respects. First, it is the only spectrum of these isomers which exhibits a multiplicity of lines due to spin-spin coupling. Second, with chlorines substituted

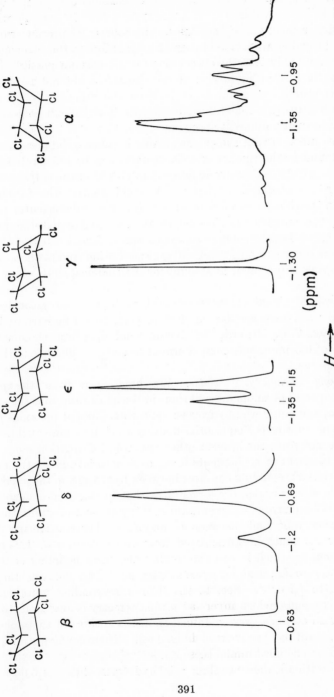

Fig. 14-2. Proton resonance spectra of the 1,2,3,4,5,6-hexachlorocyclohexanes (40 Mc/sec) in dioxane as internal reference. (Lemieux et al.[242])

axially at carbons 1,2 and equatorially at carbons 3,4,5,6, it would be expected to have two lines with intensity 2:4, and by analogy with the β, δ, and ϵ isomers the signal due to the four axial protons would be expected at higher applied field than the signal due to the two equatorial protons. An analysis of the observed spectrum was not possible, so that chemical shifts (that is, origins of the signals) could not be assigned. Since this isomer differs in structure from the others only by having diaxial substitution at the 1,2 carbon atoms, it is difficult to see why it should have such a different spectrum.

It seems unlikely that the chemical shift between axial and equatorial protons found in the spectra of these isomers can be interpreted on the basis of the neighbor-anisotropy effect [Eq. (7-26)] of the chlorine atoms. According to a calculation of McConnell,[269] this contribution is about 0.3 ppm when the chlorine atom is bonded to the same carbon as the proton. However, the magnetic environments at axial and equatorial protons differ in these isomers only because of the different positions of the chlorines at other carbon atoms. The contribution due to these remote chlorine atoms is too small to account for the chemical shifts observed in the spectra.

The low-field signal of the equatorial protons in all saturated six-membered rings may possibly be due, in part, to a ring current in the skeleton (Sec. 7-5). In order to give an axial-equatorial chemical-shift difference of 0.5 ppm, this current would have to be about one-third of that in benzene.

Dimethoxy Cyclohexyl Acetates. We have seen from the proton resonance spectra of six-membered rings in the chair form that the signals of the axial and equatorial hydrogens appear at different positions in the applied field, that of the equatorial hydrogen being at lower field. It is possible to get from the spectra other valuable information concerning the orientation of the substituents (axial or equatorial), given the knowledge that the spin coupling constant between hydrogens in the axial-axial orientation aa is considerably larger than that in the axial-equatorial ae or equatorial-equatorial ee orientations. (In these molecules there is no distinction to be made between J_{ae} and J_{ee}.) The relative size of J_{aa} and J_{ae} or J_{ee} could be anticipated from the spectrum of 1,2-chloro-bromoethane, in which it was shown that the trans coupling constant, corresponding to J_{aa}, is about twice as large as the gauche constant, corresponding to J_{ae} or J_{ee} (Sec. 13-4). The corresponding coupling constants in six-membered rings (in which the geometry is analogous to that in substituted ethanes) were obtained from the spectra of the molecules whose configurations are shown in Fig. 14-3. Their configurations were established by chemical methods.[243]

In configuration I, there are three axial hydrogens at the 2,1,6 positions,

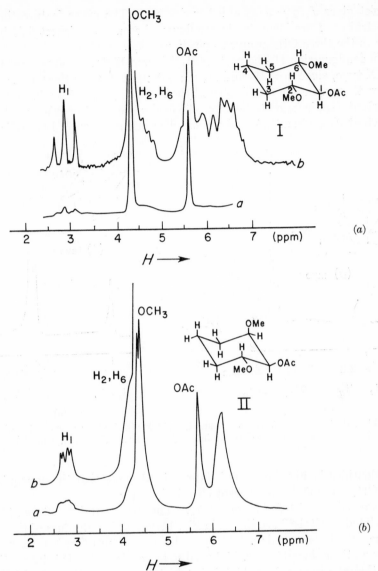

FIG. 14-3. Proton magnetic resonance spectra (40 Mc/sec) at (a) low gain and (b) high gain, in chloroform as internal reference.   (Lemieux et al.[242])

whereas in II the configuration is $2a,1a,6e$.   The lowest-field signal in the spectra of both I and II (Fig. 14-3) is readily identified with the 1 hydrogen.   In I, the protons H_1, H_2, and H_6 form a grouping which is approximately of the AX_2 type, since the H_2 and H_6 signals are located about 60 cycles/sec to high field of the H_1 triplet.   The spacing in this triplet gives $J_{1a2a} = J_{1a6a} = 9.2$ cycles/sec. The other features in the spectrum of I are identified in the figure, the band at highest field being due to the three CH_2 groups at positions 3,4,5.

In configuration II, the protons H_1, H_2, and H_6 form a grouping of the ABX type, since now H_2 and H_6 are not equivalent as they were for I. From the spacings in the X quartet (the H_1 signal) the axial-axial coupling constant J_{1a2a} is found to be about 6.5 cycles/sec and the axial-equatorial constant J_{1a6e} about 2.4 cycles/sec. The other spectral features for II

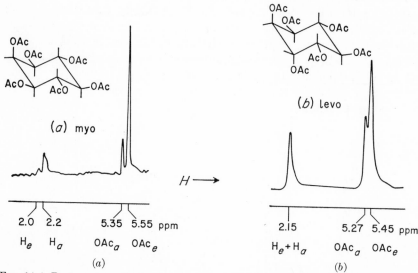

FIG. 14-4. Proton magnetic resonance spectra (40 Mc/sec) of (a) myo- and (b) levo-inositol hexaacetates in chloroform as internal reference. (Lemieux, Kullnig, Bernstein, and Schneider.[241])

are identified in Fig. 14-3. It is interesting to note that the nonequivalent CH_3O groups have different chemical shifts.

Myo- and Levo-inositol Hexaacetates. The spectra and structure of two acetylated inositols[241] are shown in Fig. 14-4a and b. Because of the size of the substituents and instability of 1,3 diaxial substitution, only the conformations shown in Fig. 14-4 need to be considered. It is interesting that the myo isomer (Fig. 14-4a), in which there are five equatorial OAc groups and one axial OAc group, has two proton signals due to the CH_3 groups of OAc with relative intensity of 1:5. Also, the levo isomer has two such signals with relative intensity of 2:4, corresponding to the two axial and four equatorial OAc groups. The ring-proton signal due to five axial and one equatorial hydrogens in the myo compound is analogous to the spectrum of the δ isomer of hexachlorocyclohexane (page 390) in which the intensity distribution is also 1:5 with the signal due to the equatorial hydrogen at lower field than that due to the five axial hydrogens.   The separation of 0.2 ppm (Fig. 14-4a) seems to be the chemical shift between these axial and equatorial protons and is not due to spin coupling because, as seen above, the *ae* coupling constant is considerably smaller than 8 cycles/sec (which is 0.2 ppm at 40 Mc/sec).

14-4. Acetylated Sugars

The proton resonance spectra of some anomeric pentacetates in solution with chloroform have been measured.[243]   Anomers differ only by the nature (equatorial or axial) of the substitution at carbon 1.   (See Fig. 14-5 for numbering.)   The pentaacetates differ among themselves by having OAc groups substituted in different axial or equatorial positions, but in all compounds the substituent at C_5 is always —CH_2—OAc in

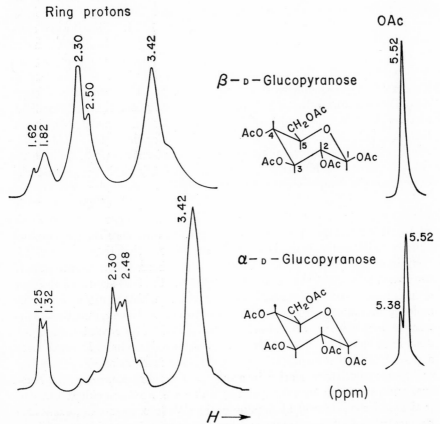

FIG. 14-5. Proton magnetic resonance spectra of some sugar pentaacetates (40 Mc/sec) in chloroform as internal reference.   (Lemieux, Kullnig, Bernstein, and Schneider.[241])

the equatorial position. The spectra of two of these compounds are shown in Fig. 14-5. In β-D-glucopyranose pentaacetate the signal of the anomeric hydrogen H_{1a} is expected at lowest field because the hydrogen is bound to a carbon having two bonded oxygen atoms. Further, the signal should be a doublet with fairly large spacing because of axial-axial spin coupling with H_{2a}. From the spectrum, J_{1a2a} is found to be 8 cycles/sec. This assignment was confirmed from the spectra of the compound deuterated in this position, from which the signal at about 1.75 ppm was absent. The relative intensities of the signals in the region of 1.7, 2.4, and 3.4 ppm are 1:3:3, respectively. A reasonable assignment for the other protons is that the nearly equivalent $2a$, $3a$, and $4a$ protons are at 2.4 ppm, while the CH_2 group and $5a$ proton are at 3.4 ppm. The five equatorial OAc groups give one signal, due to the five equivalent CH_3 groups.

Deuteration of the proton H_{1e} confirmed that the low-field signal in the anomer of the above compound, namely, α-D-glucopyranose pentaacetate, was the lowest-field signal in the spectrum (Fig. 14-5). Since in this compound the spin coupling of this proton is of the ea type, the doublet due to H_{2a} has a small separation and is measured to be $J_{1e2a} = 3.5$ cycles/sec. It is worth noting also that the H_{1e} chemical shift is about 0.44 ppm to lower field than that due to H_{1a} in the β anomer. This is again consistent with the equatorial-proton signals being found generally at lower field, as in all the other ring compounds so far investigated with the exception of levo-inositol. Again a reasonable assignment for the signals of H_{2a}, H_{3a}, and H_{4a} is the band at 2.4 ppm, and CH_2 and H_{5a} at 3.4 ppm. There are two CH_3 signals with relative intensity about 4:1 from the four equatorial OAc groups and one axial OAc group.

An internally consistent assignment for the signals of the spectra in Fig. 14-5, as well as some other sugar pentaacetates, is presented in Table 14-1. Whenever possible, spin coupling constants have been estimated; where the symbol $<$ is used, it is to be understood that the estimated J is less than the observed bandwidth and has been taken as one-half of the bandwidth. As can be seen in Table 14-1, the CH_3 signals of the OAc groups have very nearly a 1:1 correspondence with the number of axial and equatorial OAc groups. It is also evident that the α and β anomers may be readily identified from the chemical shift of the lowest-field signal. This is of considerable interest, since these anomers have hitherto been assigned only on the basis of Hudson's rule of isorotation.[199]

The measured chemical shifts and spin coupling constants for some sugar tetraacetates are also listed in Table 14-1. It is evident that the position of the lowest-field signal identifies the α or β anomer, except for the acetylated riboses. The number and relative intensity of CH_3 signals of the OAc groups are in most cases indicative of the relative number

TABLE 14-1. CHEMICAL SHIFTS OF RING PROTONS IN SOME ACETYLATED SUGARS

(In ppm from CHCl₃ as internal reference)

Compound	Proton										Side chain at C₅	CH₃ signals of OAc groups†		Spin coupling constants, cycles/sec
	1a	1e	2a	2e	3a	3e	4a	4e	5a	5e	CH₂	Axial	Equatorial	
Pentaacetates:														
β-D-glucopyranose	1.72		2.40		2.30		2.30		3.42		3.42		5.52	$J_{1a2a} = 8$
α-D-glucopyranose		1.28	2.45		2.30		2.30		3.42		3.42	5.37 (1)	5.52 (4)	$J_{1e2a} = 3.2$
β-D-galactopyranose	1.80		2.35		2.3			~2.1	3.42		3.42	~5.26 (1)	~5.40 (4)	$J_{1a2a} = 6$
α-D-galactopyranose		1.18	2.25		2.3			~2.1	3.42		3.42	5.37 (2)	5.58 (3)	$J_{1ea} < 3$
β-D-mannopyranose	1.60			~2.15	2.4		~2.4		3.45		3.45	~5.40 (1)	~5.52 (5)	$J_{1a2e} < 3$
α-D-mannopyranose		1.30		~2.0	2.12		2.12		3.25		3.25	5.30 (2)	~5.42 (3)	$J_{1e2e} < 3$
β-D-allopyranose	1.50		~2.5			1.81	2.5		3.30		3.30	~5.45 (1)	~5.50 (4)	$J_{1a2a} = 8$ $J_{3e4a} \approx 2.5$
Tetraacetates:														
β-D-xylopyranose	1.88		2.60		2.60		2.60		~4.13	~3.53			5.47	$J_{1a2a} = 6$ $J_{5a5e} = 12$ $J_{5a4a} = 8$ $J_{5e4a} = 3.2$
α-D-xylopyranose		1.24	2.4		2.4		2.4		~3.6	~3.6		5.36 (1)	5.50 (3)	$J_{1e2a} = 3$
α-L-arabinopyranose	1.83		~2.3		~2.3			2.3	~3.6	~3.6		5.5–5.6	5.5–5.6	$J_{1a2a} \approx 8$
β-L-arabinopyranose		1.14	2.05		2.05			2.05	3.52	3.52		5.22 (2)	5.35 (2)	$J_{1e2e} < 3$
β-D-ribopyranose	1.55		2.45			2.1	2.45		3.52	3.52		5.40 (1)	5.46 (3)	$J_{1a2a} = 5$ $J_{3e4a} \approx 3$
α-D-ribopyranose		1.49	2.37			2.0	2.37		3.65	3.65		5.38 (2)	5.48 (2)	$J_{1e2a} = 2$ $J_{3e4a} = 3$
α-D-lyxopyranose‡		1.59		2.33	2.33		2.33			3.73		5.40 (2)	5.48 (2)	$J_{1e2e} = 3$

† The numbers in parentheses indicate relative intensities.

‡ The two conformations of this molecule have about equal energy, so the spectrum is probably the result of rapid interconversion between the two conformations.

397

of equatorial and axial OAc substituents.   The spectrum of β-D-xylopyra-nose tetraacetate, shown in Fig. 14-6, is of particular interest.   The low-field signal is from H_{1a} and is a doublet owing to spin coupling with the H_{2a} proton.   Again the spin coupling constant for this aa situation is quite large and is found to be $J_{1a2a} = 6.0$ cycles/sec.   The two quartets in the region 3.3 to 4.4 ppm are very similar to the pattern obtained for an ABX-type spectrum (Fig. 6-9) with the X quartet overlapped by the

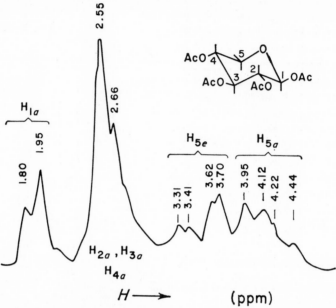

FIG. 14-6. Proton resonance spectrum (40 Mc/sec) of β-D-xylopyranose tetraacetate in chloroform as internal reference.   (Lemieux et al.[242])

signals from H_{2a} and H_{3a} in the region around 2.6 ppm.   This is consistent with the observed relative intensities of 1:3:1:1 as we proceed from the lowest-field ring-hydrogen signal to the highest.   Analysis of the eight-line spectrum (Sec. 6-6) gives 24 cycles/sec for the chemical shift between the H_{5e} and H_{5a} protons, and

$$J_{5a5e} = 12.0 \text{ cycles/sec} \quad J_{5a4a} = 8.0 \text{ cycles/sec} \quad J_{5e4a} = 3.2 \text{ cycles/sec}$$

for the coupling constants.   From this analysis the quartet due to H_{4a} should have 3.5-cycle/sec spacing in the outer doublets, and the inner pair of lines should be separated by 4.2 cycles/sec.   Thus the whole quartet that extends 0.28 ppm could lie under the band at about 2.6 ppm.   Again the equatorial hydrogen is at lower field than the axial hydrogen at C_5, and the aa spin coupling constant is considerably larger than the ea coupling constant.   Further, the spin-spin coupling constant between axial and equatorial protons on the same carbon atom is found to be $J_{5a5e} = 12.0$ cycles/sec, which may be compared with the value of 12.4 cycles/sec found for methane by Gutowsky, Meyer, and McClure[170] (using CH_3D). The anomer of this compound, α-D-xylopyranose tetraacetate, shows the anomeric chemical-shift difference of about 0.6 ppm for the equatorial and axial hydrogen at the C_1 position (Table 14-1).

Inspection of the spin-spin coupling constants in Table 14-1 shows that the *aa* constants vary between 5 and 8 cycles/sec with an average value of 7 cycles/sec, whereas the *ae*, *ea*, and *ee* spin coupling constants (which are not expected to be different from one another) vary between 2 and 3.5 cycles/sec with an average value of about 3 cycles/sec. These may be compared with the values of 9.4 cycles/sec for *aa* and 2.7 cycles/sec for *ae* and *ee* coupling constants, estimated by Cohen, Sheppard, and Turner[95] from the spectrum of dioxane containing C^{13} (Sec. 6-9).

14-5. cis- and trans-Decalin

The rather different proton resonance spectra of *cis*- and *trans*-decalin are of some interest (Fig. 14-7). The *trans* configuration is rigid, so that the difference in chemical shifts between axial and equatorial protons may give rise to the broad signal observed. In the case of *cis*-decalin, on the other hand, one of the rings is bent away from the plane of the other

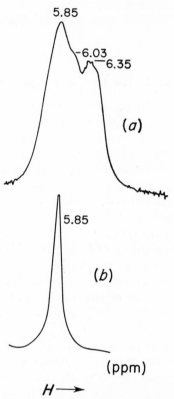

FIG. 14-7. Proton resonance spectra of (a) *trans*- and (b) *cis*-decalin at 40 Mc/sec. Methylene chloride is the external reference compound.

(both still being in the chair form), and it is recognized[112] that the configuration is flexible with respect to internal rotation about CC bonds. If this interchange from one conformation to the other is fast enough, the chemical shifts for axial and equatorial hydrogens would average out (just as in cyclohexane for example) and give the sharper signal observed.

CHAPTER 15

HYDROGEN BONDING

15-1. The Hydrogen-bond Shift

The possibility of applying proton resonance measurements to studies of hydrogen bonding became apparent following the observation of Arnold and Packard[22] that the chemical shift of the proton signal of the ethanol OH group was temperature dependent. Under the conditions of resolution employed in the experiment, no temperature dependence of the CH_2 and CH_3 proton signals was observed. The measured shift of the OH proton signal relative to the CH_2 signal as a function of temperature is shown in Fig. 15-1. According to these results an increase of temperature from 160 to 350°K causes the OH proton signal to shift toward that of the CH_2 group, i.e., to higher field, by approximately 1.6 ppm. It was further observed that dilution of the alcohol by solvents had an effect similar to raising its temperature. Thus for a 10 per cent solution of ethanol in carbon tetrachloride the chemical shift between the OH and CH_2 signals was very nearly that of pure alcohol at its boiling point.

An interpretation of these results was put forward by Liddel and Ramsey.[247] The existence of a temperature dependence of the resonance signal can be understood if there are alternative molecular states whose energy separation is of the order of kT. Since alcohol forms hydrogen bonds involving the hydrogen in the OH group, this hydrogen should experience a different magnetic shielding in the associated and unassociated states. If the correlation time related to the lifetimes of the two states is sufficiently small (less than a millisecond), the hydrogen resonance will be observed at the frequency corresponding to the average shielding for the two states. Since changes of temperature will alter the populations of the associated and unassociated states, the resonance frequency will be temperature dependent. Solvent dilution, because it also causes dissociation of the hydrogen bonds, will have an effect equivalent to that of raising the temperature.†

† For a detailed treatment of the general subject of hydrogen bonds the reader is referred to the book by Pimentel and McClellan,[335b] "The Hydrogen Bond," W. H. Freeman and Co., San Francisco, 1959.

Subsequent studies, to be described in the following sections, have shown the temperature- and dilution-dependent proton-signal shifts to be quite general for hydrogen-bonded systems.   Proton magnetic resonance measurements, in fact, have become a valuable new technique for studying hydrogen bonding and other molecular interactions.   The method is a rather sensitive one, and with present-day techniques even relatively weak interactions can be detected.   In some instances shifts can be observed for other protons within the molecule which are several bonds

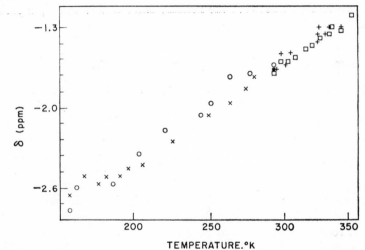

FIG. 15-1. Chemical shift of ethanol OH signal relative to CH_2 signal (measured at 7,600 gauss) vs. temperature.   The different symbols represent results obtained in different runs.   (Arnold and Packard.[22])

removed from the center of interaction.   The method appears to be superior in sensitivity to optical frequency-shift measurements in the infrared.   For certain weak interactions or hydrogen bonds, infrared frequency shifts are sometimes not detectable, although under these circumstances band-intensity measurements[200] may compare more favorably in sensitivity with the NMR method.   For stronger hydrogen bonds, the information derived from proton resonance measurements is largely complementary to that obtained from infrared absorption measurements.   A further consideration, however, by way of comparison, is the relative simplicity of the NMR spectrum for the large number of molecules of interest, as well as the simplicity of carrying out proton resonance shift measurements.   Because of the time scale involved in the NMR measurements, one may sometimes obtain the lifetime of the hydrogen-bonded state, or indicate its limits.

In applying the proton resonance technique to investigations of molecular interactions, we are interested in the chemical shift of the proton for the associated and nonassociated states. The difference between these two shifts (which really represents a "shift" of a chemical shift) may be called the association shift, or *hydrogen-bond shift*. Since in the present chapter we shall be concerned only with association by hydrogen bonds, the latter term will be used throughout, and it will be taken to apply specifically to the signal shifts of the hydrogen atom involved in the hydrogen bond. Although sometimes used less explicitly, the term "hydrogen-bond shift" in the general sense applies to the extreme shift of the proton signal between the nonassociated and *completely* associated states.

15-2. Some Measurements of Hydrogen-bond Shifts

In practice the chemical shift of the hydrogen signal for the nonassociated state can be obtained either by successively diluting with an inert solvent and extrapolating the results to infinite dilution or by direct measurement in the gaseous state at temperatures sufficiently high to ensure complete dissociation. Strictly speaking, the completely hydrogen-bonded state can be realized only in the crystalline solid. Since, however, high-resolution NMR techniques cannot be applied to solids, the nearest practical approach to this state is the liquid just above the melting point. For some purposes, however, the chemical shift of the liquid at room temperature has been used.

Hydrogen-bond shifts in ammonia and water were first demonstrated by Ogg[303,305] by measuring the proton shifts in the liquid and gaseous states. For both substances the proton signal of the gaseous state appeared at a substantially higher field. Values of the hydrogen-bond shifts of a series of simple hydride molecules have since been measured by Schneider, Bernstein, and Pople.[402] The results are summarized in Table 15-1. The liquid temperatures were dictated by the availability of density data required for applying bulk-susceptibility corrections. Thus the hydrogen-bond shifts in some cases do not refer to the maximum value.

Of all the compounds listed in Table 15-1, the measured hydrogen-bond shift is zero only for the saturated hydrocarbons, methane and ethane. For the remaining compounds surprisingly large shifts are observed. Association in all cases shifts the proton signal to low field. Molecules such as ammonia, water, hydrogen fluoride, and hydrogen chloride, normally regarded as hydrogen-bonded in the liquid state, show shifts which are approximately in the relative order of their hydrogen-bond strengths.

The comparatively large shifts observed for acetylene and ethylene are perhaps somewhat surprising.   The acetylene shift is larger than that for ammonia.   While molecules such as acetylene are not normally regarded as hydrogen-bonded in the liquid state, there is in fact evidence that weak bonds are formed, the π bond functioning as a donor center. The ability of acetylenic and olefinic molecules to act as π-electron donors with acceptor molecules such as hydrogen chloride and chloroform has been demonstrated by infrared absorption measurements[210] and by

TABLE 15-1. HYDROGEN-BOND SHIFTS OF SIMPLE HYDRIDE MOLECULES[402]

Compound	Mp, °C	Temperature of liquid measurements, °C	Chemical shift relative to CH_4 (gas), ppm		Hydrogen-bond shift, ppm
			Liquid†	Gas	
CH_4	−184	−98	0	0	0
C_2H_6	−172	−88	−0.73	−0.75	0
C_2H_4	−170	−60	−5.61	−5.18	0.43
C_2H_2	− 82	−82	−2.65	−1.35	1.30
NH_3	− 77	−77	−1.00	0.05	1.05
H_2O	0	0	−5.18	−0.60	4.58
HF	− 92	−60	−9.15	−2.50	6.65
PH_3	−133	−90	−2.26	−1.48	0.78
H_2S	− 83	−61	−1.58	−0.08	1.50
HCl	−112	−86	−1.60	0.45	2.05
HBr	− 88	−67	2.57	4.35	1.78
HI	− 50	− 5	10.70	13.25	2.55
HCN	− 14	−13	−4.48	−2.83	1.65

† Measured relative to cyclopentane and corrected for the chemical shift between liquid cyclopentane and CH_4 (gas) and for the bulk-susceptibility differences.

thermal analysis,[101] as well as by proton magnetic resonance measurements[374] (Sec. 16-3).   The "acidic" nature of the hydrogen atoms in acetylene is consistent with the fact that they are replaceable by metals, and also the large solubility of acetylene in donor solvents such as ether and acetone.   Thus the observed hydrogen-bond shifts in ethylene and acetylene can be interpreted as due to self-association in which the hydrogen atom of one molecule interacts with the π electrons of a neighboring molecule.

The observed hydrogen-bond shifts of the hydrogen halides are also of some interest, particularly the comparatively large value for hydrogen iodide.   Iodine atoms are normally regarded as being rather weak donors, and hence hydrogen bonding in hydrogen iodide might be expected to give rise to smaller hydrogen-bond shifts compared with, say, hydrogen chloride.

If the observed hydrogen-bond shifts are directly related in each case to the hydrogen-bond strength, one might also expect a correlation with the corresponding frequency shift of the HX-stretching vibration frequency. The latter may be taken as the difference of the HX frequency measured in the liquid and gaseous states. Using available data in the

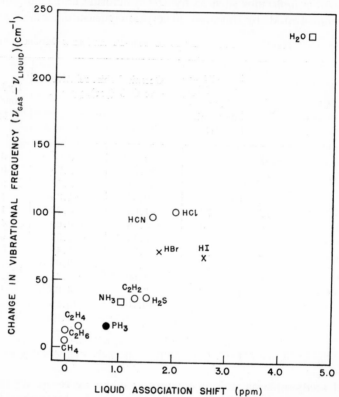

FIG. 15-2. Correlation of the vibration-frequency difference between liquid and gaseous states with NMR hydrogen-bond shifts.[402] The infrared data were derived from the following sources: ×, ref. 220a; ○, ref. 189; □, ref. 73b; ●, ref. 266a.

literature for these frequency shifts together with the NMR measurements, the correlation chart shown in Fig. 15-2 is obtained.† Although a rough correlation is apparent, there is a fair amount of scatter of the individual points.

Hydrogen-bond shifts in the systems chloroform-acetone and chloroform-triethylamine have been measured by Huggins, Pimentel, and

† It should be noted that the available infrared data for the liquids were not obtained for the same temperatures as the NMR data, nor do all the NMR hydrogen-bond shifts correspond to the maximum shifts characteristic of the liquids just above their melting points.

Shoolery[201] by observing the shift of the chloroform-proton signal as a function of concentration. Some doubt had previously persisted about whether the molecular interaction in the acetone-chloroform system was due to hydrogen bonding. This stemmed from the fact that a vibrational-frequency shift of the chloroform CH-stretching mode had not been observed, and moreover, hydrogen attached to carbon was sometimes regarded as being incapable of hydrogen-bond formation. The proton resonance shifts in this system, together with infrared band-intensity measurements,[200] are strong evidence that the interaction is due to hydrogen bonding. By making use of the chloroform-proton shifts in the donor solvents extrapolated to infinite dilution, Huggins, Pimentel, and Shoolery derived equilibrium constants for the association equilibria. No corrections were made, however, for the self-association of chloroform. From the temperature dependence of the equilibrium constants the heats of formation found for the chloroform-acetone and chloroform-triethylamine complexes were −2.5 and −4.0 kcal/mole, respectively.

The question of whether the NMR hydrogen-bond shifts may give a relative measure of hydrogen-bond strength is an important one, and it would provide a valuable aid to hydrogen-bond studies if it turned out to be so. The alternative possibility is that a simple correlation of this kind is upset by anomalous secondary magnetic effects peculiar to individual donor atoms or molecules. To investigate this question, Korinek and Schneider[221] measured the proton shift of chloroform, chosen as a common acceptor molecule, as a function of concentration in a series of different donor liquids. In this manner hydrogen bonds of different energy can be formed, and the hydrogen-bond shift in each case is measured under comparable conditions. Ideally, however, for this experiment both the acceptor molecules and the individual donor molecules D should themselves be nonassociated, since otherwise on mixing one measures differences in hydrogen-bond strengths rather than the true hydrogen-bond strength of the simple 1:1 complex, D · · · HX. Chloroform is weakly self-associating, but adequate correction for this can be made.

The results are shown in Fig. 15-3, where the chemical shift of the proton signal is plotted as a function of chloroform concentration in each of a number of nonassociated and inert donor solvents. Dilution of chloroform with the inert solvents cyclopentane, n-hexane, and cyclohexane causes the chloroform-proton signal to shift to higher field, as shown in the uppermost curve. This is due to the dissociation of chloroform on dilution. Extrapolating the curve to infinite dilution yields a shift of 0.30 ppm relative to pure chloroform, which represents the true chemical shift of an unassociated chloroform molecule. On the other hand, dilution of chloroform with triethylamine, which is a stronger donor molecule than chloroform itself, causes a shift to lower field.   At infinite dilution each chloroform molecule is surrounded by a large excess of donor molecules, and hence the measured shift is characteristic of chloroform hydrogen-bonded to triethylamine.   The chemical shift under these conditions is -0.90 ppm.   When combined with the shift for the unassociated chloroform molecule, the resulting hydrogen-bond shift is 1.20 ppm.

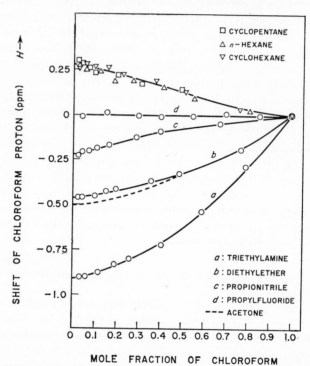

FIG. 15-3. Shift of the chloroform proton signal (corrected for bulk-susceptibility differences) in inert solvents and in donor solvents.   (Korinek and Schneider.[221])

Hydrogen-bond shifts for the other donor liquids are evaluated in a similar manner; they are shown in Table 15-2.

Since all measurements were made at room temperature, the observed values do not correspond to the maximum hydrogen-bond shifts that would be obtained at lower temperatures.   However this is not a serious consideration for the present comparison because each system is measured under closely similar conditions.   Unfortunately, no values of the actual hydrogen-bond strengths for these systems are available for comparison, so it is only possible to compare with other relevant properties of the donor molecules.   The observed shifts are compared with ionization potentials, lone-pair dipole moments, and infrared data in Table 15-2.

While it is not possible to demonstrate a quantitative correlation of the NMR hydrogen-bond shifts with hydrogen-bond strength, the trend of

TABLE 15-2. SUMMARY OF CHLOROFORM-SOLUTION DATA[221]

Donor liquid	Hydrogen-bond shift, ppm	Ionization potential,[†] ev	Lone-pair dipole,[‡] esu × 10^{18}	Infrared data[§]	
				CD frequency shift, cm^{-1}	Half-band width, cm^{-1}
Triethylamine	1.20	9.0	3.25	84	42
Acetone	0.81	9.69	3.03	0	16
Diethyl ether	0.76	9.54	2.78	10	15
Propionitrile	0.55	11.9	3.74		
Propyl fluoride	0.32	12	2.44		

† The values of the ionization potentials are those of Morrison and Nicholson, *J. Chem. Phys.*, **20**, 1021 (1952); Price, *Chem. Revs.*, **41**, 257 (1947); and Watanabe, *J. Chem. Phys.*, **26**, 542 (1957).

‡ Refs. 399 and 107.

§ Ref. 200.

the results is encouraging. At any rate, there appear to be no anomalous magnetic effects arising in these systems sufficiently serious to discourage correlations of this kind.

15-3. Theoretical Interpretation of Hydrogen-bond Shifts

As described above, proton magnetic resonance signals are usually displaced to lower field by the formation of a hydrogen bond, the only exceptions to this behavior being connected with association to some aromatic molecules (Sec. 16-3). There are several possible interpretations of this low-field shift, and they will now be considered.[402]

The chemical shift of the proton in an isolated molecule XH is determined by the intramolecular electronic circulations in the manner described in Chap. 7. The hydrogen-bond shift arises because the magnetic field experienced by the proton is modified when a hydrogen bond XH · · · Y is formed, where Y is a donor atom of a second molecule. If we ignore the possibility of currents flowing from one molecule to another, there are two general effects which may be considered separately:

1. The proton in XH will experience a magnetic field due directly to the currents induced in the Y atom on the second molecule, and if this has a nonzero average over all directions, there will be a net contribution to the proton chemical shift.

2. The presence of the Y system will disturb the electronic structure of the XH bond and consequently modify its magnetic susceptibility. This

will lead to a change in the currents in the XH bond and consequently to an altered shielding constant.

A theory of effect (1) is very similar to the neighbor-anisotropy effect for free molecules (Sec. 7-5). The secondary magnetic field at the proton due to the Y currents will be nonzero (to a first approximation) only if the local susceptibility of the Y atom is anisotropic. We may then use Eq. (7-26), the internuclear axis being along the Y · · · H direction and R being the corresponding distance. Since the distance is usually longer than intramolecular-bond lengths, and since it occurs as an inverse cube in the formula, the contribution is not expected to be very large. Either sign is possible according to the nature of Y, but for linear molecules forming linear hydrogen bonds it should be toward high field (as for the corresponding intramolecular neighbor-anisotropy effect). A quantitative estimate can be made for linear FH · · · F bonds by using the same F anisotropy as for the intramolecular HF calculation (Sec. 7-5) and $R = 1.7$ A. This gives a positive contribution to the shielding constant of 0.6 ppm, which is smaller than the observed shifts for strong hydrogen bonds and is in any case in the wrong direction. Actually HF probably forms nonlinear hydrogen bonds, but even for HCN, in which the bonds may be linear, a low-field shift is observed. It does not seem likely, therefore, that this type of contribution can be the main feature leading to the low-field shift in strong hydrogen bonds.

Turning now to effect (2), the effect of association on the magnetic properties of the XH bond itself, we note that normal hydrogen bonds are usually interpreted as being primarily electrostatic in character. We are therefore led to ask whether the observed shifts can be interpreted if the primary function of Y is to provide a strong electric field in the vicinity of the XH bond. Qualitatively, this can be interpreted[421] by noting that the field tends to draw the proton away from the bonding electrons and consequently reduces the electron density immediately around it. Also the diamagnetic circulations within the hydrogen atom would tend to be inhibited by the presence of a strong electric field. Both of these effects predict a reduction in screening and a shift to low field.

A very crude model for the chemical shift due to distortion in an intermolecular electric field is the calculation of the chemical shift of a free hydrogen atom when it is placed in an electric field E. This problem is exactly soluble[79,262a] and gives a shift

$$\delta = -\frac{881}{216}\frac{a^3 E^2}{mc^2} \tag{15-1}$$

where a is the Bohr radius. According to this equation, a shift of 4 ppm would be produced by an electric field of 0.14 atomic unit.   Such a field would arise from a single electronic charge at a distance of about 1.4 A.

In addition to its primarily electrostatic character, it has often been suggested that the hydrogen bond has some covalent character corresponding to structures such as

$$X^- \cdots H{-}Y^+$$

It is difficult to make any estimate of the effect structures of this type would have on the chemical shift.   In so far as they involve donation of electrons from the Y molecule into the XH bond, they might be expected to lead to increased electron density on the hydrogen atom and a shift to high field.   But it is likely that any such contribution is masked by the more important electrostatic effect.

One other possible contribution to the association shift that should be mentioned is the quenching of the intramolecular paramagnetic effect. As discussed previously (Sec. 7-5), the appearance of the signal of protons in linear molecules at higher fields than expected is ascribed to the anisotropy of paramagnetic terms on neighboring atoms, diamagnetic circulation being able to occur more easily about the molecular axis which has electrical axial symmetry.   If now the XH molecule acts as a donor to a second molecule, with the molecular axes of the two molecules at some angle (or some similar association),

this axial symmetry will be partially removed, and the paramagnetic high-field shift will be reduced.   This will appear as a shift to low field on association.   Such an effect may well be important in acetylene, which probably self-associates by a proton of one molecule attaching itself to the π electrons of another.   On the other hand, it would not be important for HCN, which probably forms a linear hydrogen-bonded system.   This is consistent with the observation that the association shifts of these two molecules are comparable in spite of the fact that HCN forms much stronger bonds according to the vibrational criterion.

This quenching effect can also be invoked to explain the anomalously large association shift of hydrogen iodide.   The appearance of the free-molecule signal far to high field was interpreted earlier (Sec. 7-5) in terms of a large anisotropic paramagnetic effect.   It follows that such molecules are more susceptible to having this contribution quenched by intermolecular association.

15-4. Alcohols and Phenols

Alcohols. Following the first experiments by Arnold and Packard[22] on proton resonance shifts in methyl and ethyl alcohol, further studies of hydrogen-bond shifts of OH groups in alcohols and phenols have been carried out. Cohen and Reid[94] used the solvent-dilution method to obtain the hydrogen-bond shift for CH_3OH and C_2H_5OH in a number of

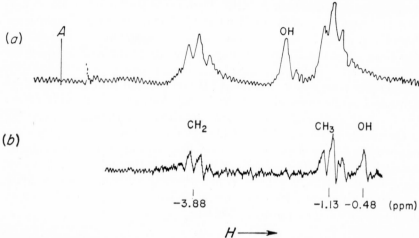

FIG. 15-4. (*a*) NMR trace of a dilute solution of ethanol in CCl_4. The signal of the OH proton has moved from A, its position in pure ethanol at room temperature. (Cohen and Reid.[94])   (*b*) Proton resonance spectrum of gaseous ethanol.   (Pressure, 10 atm; temperature, 220°C.)   Chemical shifts are shown relative to gaseous methane. (Schneider.[400])

solvents. The shifts were found to be about 5 ppm. On extreme dilution the hydroxyl-proton signal appears at higher field than the signal of the methyl group. The spectrum at intermediate dilution is shown in Fig. 15-4a. A similar behavior following dilution of ethanol in benzene was reported by Diehl.[121]

Becker, Liddel, and Shoolery[33] have carried out a detailed study of the ethanol OH dilution shift in carbon tetrachloride solution, with particular attention to the behavior at low concentrations of ethanol. A plot of their measurements is shown in Fig. 15-5. The general shape of the dilution curve, including the reversal of curvature at x near 0.015, is of the form to be expected for a system of monomers, dimers, and higher polymers. The value of δ_M, the OH shift corresponding to the monomer, obtained by extrapolation to $x = 0$, is 0.41 ppm. The value of δ_P, corresponding to polymeric alcohol ($x = 1$), is -4.16. Thus at room temperature the total hydrogen-bond shift, $\delta_M - \delta_P$, is 4.57 ppm.

At very low concentrations of ethanol, the OH proton shift is influenced almost entirely by the monomer-dimer equilibrium. The limiting slope of the dilution curve can be used to obtain the equilibrium constant from the equation[33]

$$\left(\frac{\partial \delta}{\partial x}\right)_{x=0} = 2K\,\Delta_D \tag{15-2}$$

where Δ_D is the monomer-dimer shift, $\delta_D - \delta_M$. The value of Δ_D is

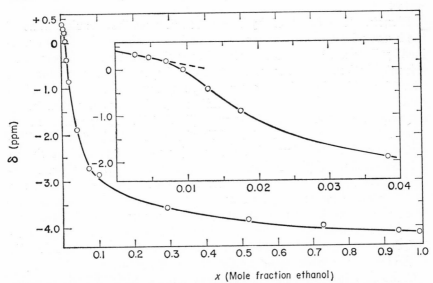

Fig. 15-5. Chemical shift of hydroxyl-proton resonance vs. ethanol concentration in carbon tetrachloride at room temperature. The chemical-shift reference point is the methyl-group resonance of ethanol. (Becker, Liddel, and Shoolery.[33])

different depending on whether "open" dimers, involving one hydrogen bond, or "cyclic" dimers, involving two nonlinear hydrogen bonds, are formed. Making use of infrared data,[33,246] Becker, Liddel, and Shoolery estimate Δ_D to be about 2.3 ppm for a cyclic dimer and 1.2 ppm for an open dimer. With these values the equilibrium constants derived from Eq. (15-2) are 13 and 6.5 for open and cyclic dimers, respectively. The results suggest that the dimer is structurally different from higher polymers.

The true chemical shift of the OH signal for the *isolated* ethanol molecule is more satisfactorily obtained from measurements in the gas phase.[400] Figure 15-4b shows a reproduction of the spectrum obtained for gaseous ethanol at a pressure of 10 atm and a temperature of 220°C, which is well above the saturation temperature. The chemical shift of the OH signal relative to methane is -0.48 ppm, which may be compared with the corresponding chemical shift of gaseous H_2O of -0.60 ppm (Table 5-1). The chemical shift of the OH group in liquid ethanol at $-114°C$, which is close to the melting point, was also measured. When combined with the gas data, this leads to a value of the hydrogen-bond shift for ethanol of 6.15 ppm, somewhat larger than the dilution shift shown in Fig. 15-5. Again by way of comparison, the corresponding hydrogen-bond shift of water is 4.58 ppm (Table 15-1). The hydrogen-bond energy in ethanol is known to be somewhat greater than that in water.

Phenols. The effect of hydrogen bonding on the chemical shift of the hydroxyl-group proton signal in a variety of phenols has been examined by Batdorf.[31] Large variations in the signal shift were observed on solvent dilution. Some representative dilution curves are reproduced in Fig. 15-6. Dilution with benzene (curve *a*) causes a pronounced high-field shift of the OH signal. This shift can be largely accounted for by the ring effect of the aromatic solvent (Sec. 16-3). Inert solvents such as cyclohexane cause but a slight shift of the phenol OH signal on dilution (curve *b*). Dilution with acetone (curve *c*) at first gives rise to a low-field shift of the OH signal which extends down to phenol concentrations of approximately 60 mole per cent. This implies that the hydrogen bond formed by the phenol OH group with the donor oxygen atom of acetone is stronger than the bond between phenol molecules. A molecular addition compound† with the composition $2C_6H_5OH \cdot CH_3COCH_3$ is known.[397] On further dilution with acetone a small shift of the hydroxyl-proton signal to high field is apparent.

Ortho-substituted phenols are of particular interest. When the ortho substituent, as for example a methyl group, cannot form an intramolecular hydrogen bond with the OH group, the OH signal in the pure compound occurs at higher field than the signal of phenol itself, but the dilution shift in acetone was found to be larger than that of phenol. These effects, which are illustrated by curves *d* and *e* in Fig. 15-6 for *o*-cresol and *o*-bromophenol, were attributed to a weaker hydrogen bond in the pure compound (compared to that of phenol) resulting from steric hindrance by the ortho substituent. In agreement with this interpretation, the hydroxyl-proton signal of 2,6-diisopropylphenol, in which steric hindrance may be expected to be very pronounced, occurred at higher field than that of any of the other substituted phenols measured. Ortho substituents, which contain carbonyl or nitro groups, give rise to a different behavior. In the pure compounds the OH signal occurs at considerably lower field than the signal of phenol itself. These compounds are capable of form-

† The possibility that this compound involves acetal formation cannot be definitely ruled out.

ing strong *intramolecular* hydrogen bonds. Accordingly, on dilution in solvents only a very small OH shift can be observed.[31]

A further study of the hydrogen bonding in phenols by proton resonance techniques has been carried out by Huggins, Pimentel, and

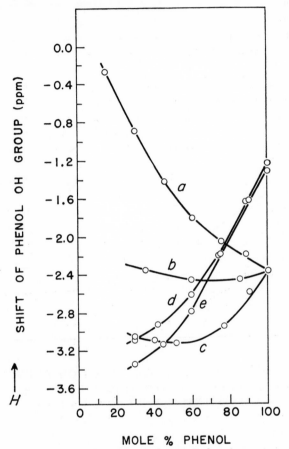

FIG. 15-6. Shift of the hydroxyl-proton resonance signal of phenols on dilution with solvent. Chemical shifts are referred to the proton signal of an external water reference. Curve *a*, phenol in benzene; *b*, phenol in cyclohexane; *c*, phenol in acetone; *d*, *o*-cresol in acetone; *e*, *o*-bromophenol in acetone. (Batdorf.[31])

Shoolery.[202] Dilution curves in carbon tetrachloride were measured for phenol, *o*-cresol, *p*-chlorophenol, *m*-chlorophenol, and *o*-chlorophenol (Fig. 15-7). The insert in Fig. 15-7, plotted on a larger scale, shows the low-concentration measurements extrapolated to infinite dilution. The intercepts δ_0 and δ_1 at $x = 0$ and $x = 1$, respectively, and the limiting slopes at $x = 0$, $(\partial\delta/\partial x)_0$ are listed in Table 15-3.

The most striking feature of the dilution measurements in Fig. 15-7 is the distinctive curve for *o*-chlorophenol. This has a zero slope at $x = 0$, which is undoubtedly due to an intramolecular hydrogen bond in this compound. Accordingly, monomeric *o*-chlorophenol is stabilized relative

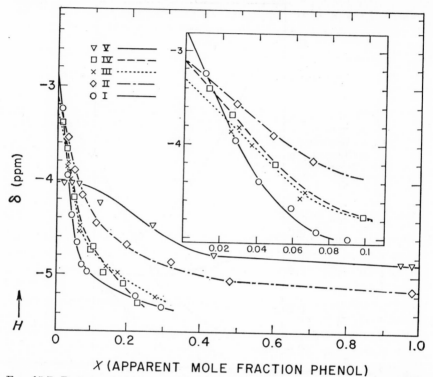

X (APPARENT MOLE FRACTION PHENOL)

FIG. 15-7. Proton resonance measurements of the OH group of phenols in carbon tetrachloride with cyclohexane as internal reference: I, phenol; II, *o*-cresol; III, *p*-chlorophenol; IV, *m*-chlorophenol; V, *o*-chlorophenol. (Huggins, Pimentel, and Shoolery.[202])

to polymeric intermolecularly hydrogen-bonded species, and at concentrations $x < 0.06$ substantially all of the molecules are present as monomer. Moreover since in this case the proton signal at infinite dilution refers to a molecule which has an internal hydrogen bond, the signal occurs at lower field than the corresponding signals for the other phenols. At very low concentration the latter exist largely as non-hydrogen-bonded monomers, as indicated by the δ_0 values of Table 15-3.

The limiting slopes, $(\partial\delta/\partial x)_0$, for the compounds II, III, and IV are distinctly lower than the slope for phenol itself. Equation (15-2) can again be employed to evaluate the equilibrium constant K for dimerization in these compounds. On the basis of infrared measurements, the value of Δ_D is estimated[202] to lie within the limits $\frac{1}{2}(\delta_1 - \delta_0) > \Delta_D > \frac{1}{4}(\delta_1 - \delta_0)$. Selecting $\Delta_D = \frac{1}{2}(\delta_1 - \delta_0) \pm \frac{1}{4}\Delta_D$, the equilibrium constants shown in Table 15-3 were derived. These show a satisfactory correlation with the mean association energy obtained by Mecke.[281]

TABLE 15-3. PARAMETERS OF DILUTION CURVES AND EQUILIBRIUM CONSTANTS
FOR DIMERIZATION OF PHENOLS IN CCl_4[202]
(In ppm)

Compound	δ_0	$\left(\dfrac{\partial \delta}{\partial x}\right)_0$	δ_1	K
I. Phenol	-2.8	42	-5.6	13 ± 7
II. o-Cresol	-3.1	16	-5.15	8 ± 4
III. p-Chlorophenol	-3.3	20	-5.6	9 ± 4
IV. m-Chlorophenol	-3.1	22	-5.6	9 ± 4
V. o-Chlorophenol	-4.1	0.0	-4.87	0

15-5. Carboxylic Acids

Several studies of proton resonance shifts of the carboxylic acid OH group accompanying solvent dilution have been carried out. Dilution curves with water as a solvent have been measured by Gutowsky and Saika[172] and by Bhar and Lindström.[45] The curves in Fig. 15-8 show the results obtained by Bhar and Lindström for solutions of acetic and propionic acids in water. There is a "hump" in the dilution curve at a concentration at which the volume fractions of water and acid are equal. This feature has so far not been explained. The measurements of Gutowsky and Saika for acetic acid yielded a linear dependence of the hydroxyl-group shift on concentration.

In moderately concentrated solutions of acetic acid in CS_2 no pronounced chemical shift of the OH signal relative to that of the pure substance is observed.[202] However, acetone, which has a carbonyl group with which the acid OH group can form hydrogen bonds, gives rise to pronounced dilution shifts.[202,41]

Figure 15-9 shows the proton-signal shifts for the acetic acid OH group as a function of acid concentration in the solvents cyclohexane, carbon tetrachloride, and 1,1-dichloroethane.[376] It is evident that dilution with cyclohexane causes the OH signal to shift to low field, which is in the opposite direction to that expected if hydrogen bonds are being disrupted. Carbon tetrachloride behaves similarly, but at an acid concentration of 0.10 mole per cent there is a minimum in the curve, and at lower concentrations a shift toward *high* field sets in. This behavior is even more pronounced with the polar solvent 1,1-dichloroethane. The behavior at low concentrations can be explained in terms of a monomer-dimer equilibrium, the OH signal of the monomer being at much higher field than that of the hydrogen-bonded dimer.   The relative concentration of the more polar monomer is favored by a solvent with high dielectric constant.   The dielectric constants of the solvents used are in the

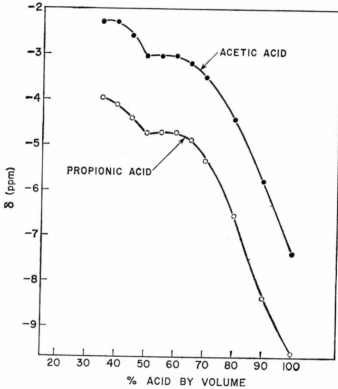

FIG. 15-8. Proton resonance shifts of the OH groups of acetic and propionic acids as functions of concentration in water.   The shifts are relative to the methyl-group signals for the acids.   (Bhar and Lindström.[45])

order, cyclohexane < carbon tetrachloride < 1,1-dichloroethane.   Extrapolation of the cyclohexane dilution curve to zero concentration may be expected to yield an approximate value of the OH chemical shift characteristic of the dimer.   The value is −0.65 ppm relative to pure liquid acetic acid.   To obtain the corresponding OH chemical shift of the monomer, measurements of gaseous acetic acid were made.[376]   At a temperature of 300°C the hydroxyl-proton signal still varied with temperature, indicating incomplete dimer dissociation.   The true chemical shift of the OH signal of the monomer could therefore not be definitely established; its position is beyond 5.65 ppm to the high-field side of the dimer signal.

The fact that the dimer chemical shift is to low field by 0.65 ppm (relative to undiluted acetic acid) suggests that the strongest hydrogen bonds in acetic acid occur in the dimer and that, whatever the form of association is in the pure liquid, it is not purely dimeric. Very likely some form

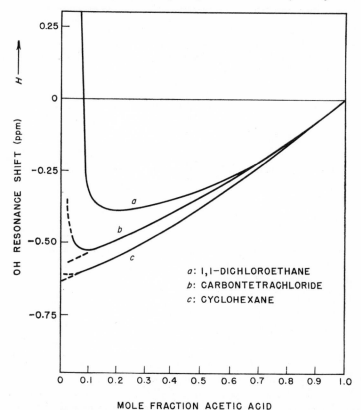

FIG. 15-9. Solvent-dilution shift of the hydroxyl-proton resonance signal of acetic acid. The chemical shifts δ are relative to pure acetic acid. (Reeves and Schneider.[376])

of disordered chain association occurs, one involving somewhat weaker hydrogen bonds.

15-6. The Mean Lifetime of Hydrogen Bonds and Proton-exchange Effects

In infrared measurements of hydrogen-bonded systems, it is frequently possible to observe vibrational bands for both the associated (hydrogen-bond) state and the nonassociated (monomer) state simultaneously in the same medium. This is not possible in NMR measurements, because of the large difference in the frequencies involved in the two techniques. To observe both the associated and nonassociated states in the same medium by NMR measurement requires the lifetime of each state to be longer than the reciprocal of the hydrogen-bond shift (expressed in frequency units). The reciprocal of the shift may have values of 10^{-2} to 10^{-3} sec. Since only one sharp signal is observed, the lifetime of the hydrogen-bonded state must be considerably shorter than this. Thus in a time of this order of magnitude, the hydrogen bond will break up and re-form many times, and the hydrogen atom will bond with several different neighboring donor molecules. Accordingly, at each concentration, a given hydrogen will experience an averaged-out environment depending on the number and kind of donor species present.

In certain systems in which the molecules are associated by relatively strong hydrogen bonds, proton-exchange effects may be observed. The proton may be regarded as alternating between the structures XH $\cdots$ Y and X $\cdots$ HY. When this exchange occurs relatively infrequently, two separate signals are observed in the NMR spectrum; they correspond to the different environment of the proton at the two different donor sites X and Y (Sec. 10-2). Under certain conditions, as for example by increasing the temperature, the two separate signals due to these states can be made to coalesce into a single sharp signal. Analysis of these effects provides valuable information about the rate and mechanism of the exchange process (Sec. 18-4).

Proton exchange has been found to be greatly accelerated in the presence of strong acids or bases. In aqueous solutions of mineral acids, which are discussed in Chap. 18, a very rapid exchange occurs between the hydrogens of the acid and those of the solvent-water molecules, resulting in a single sharp proton signal. The proton exchange induced in ethyl alcohol by the addition of a small amount of acid or base, first observed by Arnold,[20] has been mentioned in Sec. 5-4. The proton resonance spectra of ethyl alcohol before and after addition of hydrogen chloride are shown in Fig. 5-7. It will be noted that rapid exchange of the hydrogen of the hydroxyl group reduces the triplet structure of the OH signal to a single sharp line, and the splitting of the methylene signal by the OH proton also becomes averaged out. If τ is the exchange time (or the mean lifetime of a proton in one of its alternate sites), the spin-multiplet components become averaged out when $\tau \leqslant \sqrt{2}/2\pi\,\Delta\nu$, where $\Delta\nu$ is the separation of the multiplet components in cycles per second. Using methods of analysis described in Sec. 10-2, Arnold evaluated τ from the observed shape of the hydroxyl-proton signals resulting from the addition of varying amounts of acid or base. The results, which are summarized in Table 15-4, show that relatively small concentrations of acid or base, of the order of 10^{-5} normal, are sufficient to induce rapid exchange of the hydroxyl protons.

TABLE 15-4. HYDROXYL-PROTON-EXCHANGE TIME τ IN ETHYL ALCOHOL
AS FUNCTION OF ADDED ACID OR BASE[20]

Concentration of added acid or base	τ, sec	Concentration of added acid or base	τ, sec
$1.9 \times 10^{-6} N$ HCl	1.2	$1 \times 10^{-5} N$ HCl	0.012
$5 \times 10^{-6} N$ HCl	0.8	$3.8 \times 10^{-6} N$ NaOH	0.3
$9 \times 10^{-6} N$ HCl	0.025	$12.5 \times 10^{-5} N$ NaOH	0.006

Since proton exchange is a rate process, a characteristic temperature dependence should be observable. Figure 15-10 shows a series of NMR traces of the proton spectrum of pure ethanol at various temperatures. The gradual "washing out" of the spin-spin multiplets due to enhanced exchange of the hydroxyl hydrogen with increasing temperature is apparent. At a temperature of 80°, where the OH triplet structure is

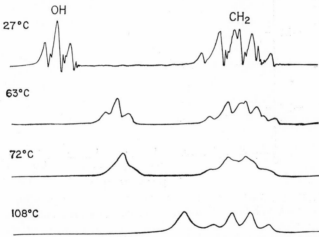

FIG. 15-10. NMR traces of pure ethanol (OH and CH_2 signals only) at different temperatures recorded at the same sweep rate, showing the gradual coalescence of spin multiplets with increasing temperature. There is also a progressive shift of the hydroxyl-group signal toward higher field.

completely collapsed, τ is of the order of 0.03 sec. At still higher temperatures, the exchange rate is further increased, and the hydroxyl- and methylene-proton signals again become sharper.

Measurements of water-ethanol mixtures have demonstrated a further type of proton-exchange behavior. When small amounts of water are added to pure alcohol, a separate signal is observed for both the water and alcohol OH groups. As the concentration of water is increased, a point is reached at which the two signals suddenly coalesce; this corresponds to the onset of rapid proton exchange. The OH chemical shifts as a function of concentration, which are rather striking, are shown in Fig. 15-11, reproduced from the work of Weinberg and Zimmerman.[459] The relative molecular concentrations when the signals coalesce are approximately 1:1. At higher concentrations the chemical shift of the coalesced signal remains almost constant. As the concentration is varied through

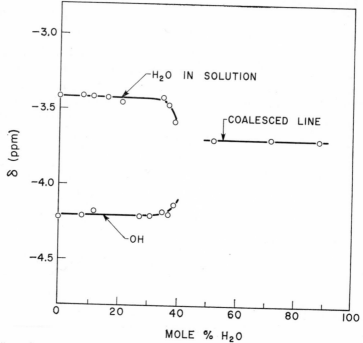

FIG. 15-11. Chemical shifts of water and ethanol OH groups (relative to methyl-group signal of ethanol) as a function of concentration. (Weinberg and Zimmerman.[459])

the transition range, changes in the spin-multiplet structure of the methylene-group signal similar to those shown in Fig. 15-10 are observed.

The transition from slow to fast exchange can also be observed by varying the temperature.[405] Figure 15-12 shows a series of NMR traces of an ethanol-water mixture, with molar ratio 2:1, taken at different temperatures. At the lowest temperature ($-32°C$) the proton signal of the OH group of the alcohol shows a triplet structure indicating that at this temperature τ is considerably greater than 0.03 sec. As the temperature is raised, the increased rate of proton exchange is demonstrated by the gradual coalescence of the OH signals, which is complete at 72°C.

In the present example the protons may be thought of as exchanging between the oxygen atoms of the water and alcohol molecules. By

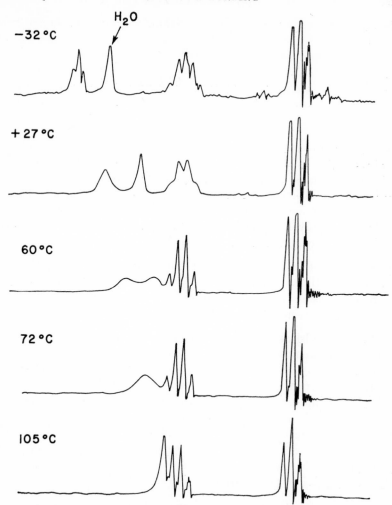

FIG. 15-12. NMR traces of ethanol-water (2:1) mixture at different temperatures, showing the gradual coalescence of the hydroxyl-group signals due to proton exchange. All traces are at a constant sweep rate. The OH signals progressively shift to higher magnetic field because of increased hydrogen-bond dissociation at the higher temperature. (Schneider and Reeves.[405])

applying Eq. (10-31) to the data obtained at a series of temperatures, values for the exchange lifetime τ can be derived. The value of τ at 72°C, at which the two OH signals coalesce, is 7.3×10^{-3} sec. From the values of τ at different temperatures, a rough activation energy for the exchange process of about 7.6 kcal/mole is obtained.

CHAPTER 16

SOLVENT EFFECTS

The position of a nuclear resonance line of a particular molecule in a liquid is affected by the surrounding molecules, which may be of the same or different species, as in the pure liquid or a solvent respectively. In solutions the position of the resonance signal is often found to be concentration dependent. By extrapolating to infinite dilution, the effect of neighboring solvent molecules can be observed separately. In general two different effects can be distinguished:

1. Shifts due to a difference in the bulk diamagnetic susceptibility of the solute and the solvent
2. Shifts arising from intermolecular interactions between solute molecules or between solute and solvent molecules

For two cylindrical samples (in this case the solute and the solvent) differing in volume susceptibility by $\Delta\chi_v$, the bulk-susceptibility shift is given by $\frac{2}{3}\pi \Delta\chi_v$ (Sec. 4-9). Shifts observed in excess of this amount must then be attributed to intermolecular-interaction effects. A specific interaction of this kind is that of hydrogen bonding, which, as described in the previous chapter, gives rise to pronounced proton chemical shifts. Intermolecular effects having a rather different origin are found with aromatic molecules (Sec. 16-2). In certain other systems involving highly polarizable molecules, resonance shifts may arise from intermolecular dispersion, polarization, or electrostatic forces.

16-1. Solvent Effects for Proton and Fluorine Resonances

The position of the proton resonance signal of several solutes in different solvent media has been studied by Bothner-By and Glick.[70] The results, summarized in Table 16-1, are expressed in terms of the dilution shift $\delta_1 - \delta_0$, where δ_1 is the chemical shift of the pure solute and δ_0 the solute shift (extrapolated to infinite dilution) in a particular solvent. The calculated shifts arising from the difference in bulk susceptibility of solute and solvent are shown in the second last column. As indicated by the differences listed in the last column, this does not account for the whole of the observed dilution shifts. The excess shifts, which must be attributed to intermolecular effects, are generally greater when the solute

422

contains large halogen atoms such as iodine. Moreover, the excess shifts are approximately proportional to the bulk-susceptibility shifts. This led Bothner-By and Glick[70] to suggest that for aliphatic compounds a good estimate of the over-all dilution shift could be obtained by replacing the factor $2\pi/3$ in the bulk-susceptibility-correction formula (4-6) by a mean factor 2.6. A related observation is that of Evans,[133a] who found that

TABLE 16-1. COMPARISON OF OBSERVED PROTON RESONANCE DILUTION
SHIFTS IN ALIPHATIC COMPOUNDS WITH SHIFT DUE TO
BULK-SUSCEPTIBILITY DIFFERENCES[70]
(In ppm)

Solute	Solvent	$\Delta\chi_v$†	$\delta_1 - \delta_0$	$\dfrac{2\pi}{3}\Delta\chi_v$	Difference
CH_2I_2	CCl_4	-0.47	-1.23	-0.98	-0.25
CH_2I_2	CH_2Cl_2	-0.43	-1.22	-0.90	-0.32
CH_3I	CCl_4	-0.23	-0.60	-0.48	-0.12
CH_3I	Acetone	-0.46	-1.25	-0.96	-0.29
CH_3I	Dioxane	-0.33	-0.84	-0.69	-0.15
CH_2Cl_2	CCl_4	-0.04	-0.10	-0.08	-0.02
CH_2Cl_2	CH_2Br_2	0.21	0.56	0.45	0.11
CH_3Cl	CCl_4	0.12	0.36	0.25	0.11
$CHCl_3$	CCl_4	-0.04	-0.10	-0.08	-0.02
CH_2Br_2	CCl_4	-0.25	-0.60	-0.52	-0.08
CH_3Br	CCl_4	-0.04	-0.10	-0.08	-0.02
$CHBr_3$	CCl_4	-0.25	-0.62	-0.52	-0.10
Acetone	CCl_4	0.23	0.64	0.48	0.16
Dioxane	CCl_4	0.10	0.25	0.21	0.04
$ClCH_2CH_2Cl$	$BrCH_2CH_2Br$	0.16	0.41	0.33	0.08

† Difference between the volume susceptibility of solute and solvent.

the proton shift of methane at infinite dilution in CCl_4 (corrected for the bulk susceptibility of the solvent) differed by 0.5 ppm from that of gaseous methane, the signal of the latter appearing at higher field.

Somewhat larger solvent effects have been observed in fluorine resonances. Thus the shift of carbon tetrafluoride at infinite dilution in CCl_4 (corrected for the bulk susceptibility of the solvent) appears to lower field by 7.8 ppm relative to gaseous carbon tetrafluoride. Similar effects have been found for other fluorine compounds. Table 16-2 summarizes some measurements, obtained by Evans,[133a] of the fluorine resonance dilution shifts of benzotrifluoride in various solvents. These large shifts clearly cannot be accounted for by the bulk-susceptibility differences between the solute and the various solvents, and must be attributed to intermolecular effects. Again the largest excess shifts appear with solvents containing heavy halogen atoms. If the fluorine chemical shifts are determined mainly by the paramagnetic shielding term (Sec. 7-4), it is estimated that a decrease of ΔE (the electronic excitation energy of the solute molecule) of the order of 1 per cent could account for the magnitude of the observed shifts. A decrease of this order could arise from polarizations by solvent molecules.[133a]

A further study of solvent effects on fluorine resonances has been carried out by Glick and Ehrenson,[143a] who measured the dilution shifts of 1,2-dibromotetrafluoroethane in various halogenated solvents. After correcting for the bulk susceptibility, fairly large excess shifts were again

TABLE 16-2. DILUTION SHIFT $\delta_1 - \delta_0$ OF FLUORINE RESONANCE
OF BENZOTRIFLUORIDE IN VARIOUS SOLVENTS[133a]

Solvent	$\delta_1 - \delta_0$, ppm†	Solvent	$\delta_1 - \delta_0$, ppm†
Methylene iodide	-5.5	Benzene	-1.1
Bromoform	-3.8	Ethanol	0.06
Carbon disulfide	-2.1	n-Heptane	0.22
Carbon tetrachloride	-1.5	Ether	0.30
Methylene chloride	-1.2	Perfluoroheptane	2.68

† The shifts are taken relative to benzotrifluoride, negative shifts indicating a displacement to low field.

found. These could be approximately correlated with the molecular polarizability of the solvent molecules.

16-2. Solvent-dilution Effects Involving Aromatic Compounds

The proton chemical shift of aromatic compounds when dissolved in nonaromatic solvents has been found to be strongly concentration dependent. Related to this effect is the further observation that the proton chemical shifts of nonaromatic compounds, when dissolved in aromatic solvents, as for example benzene, are also concentration dependent. When the solute molecules, either aliphatic or aromatic, are capable of a specific molecular interaction with the aromatic-solvent molecules, the proton signals of the solute show an even more pronounced concentration dependence as well as a temperature dependence. All of these effects have a common origin, namely, the large diamagnetic anisotropy of the aromatic molecule resulting from the circulation of the mobile π electrons induced by the magnetic field.[474,71,374]

a. **Aromatic Solutes in Nonaromatic Solvents.** A simple system consisting of an aromatic compound in a noninteracting aliphatic solvent is that of benzene dissolved in n-hexane. The chemical shift of the benzene-proton signal, measured by Zimmerman and Foster[474] as a function of concentration, is shown in Fig. 16-1. It will be noted that dilution by

n-hexane causes the benzene-proton signal to shift to lower field. The extreme shift to low field of the benzene signal at infinite dilution is 0.34 ppm.   Since n-hexane may be regarded as a relatively inert solvent, this shift of the "isolated" benzene molecule relative to that of benzene molecules in pure liquid benzene cannot be attributed to interactions with the solvent and must be accounted for in terms of the characteristic magnetic properties of the aromatic solute.

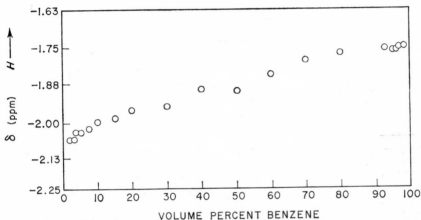

FIG. 16-1. The chemical shift of benzene (corrected for bulk susceptibility) as a function of concentration in n-hexane.   (Zimmerman and Foster.[474])

According to the ring-current model, described in Sec. 7-5, the benzene molecule in a magnetic field may be regarded as a simple current loop resulting from the induced circulation of the mobile π electrons in the carbon ring.   Since this circulation of electrons is diamagnetic in origin, the resultant magnetic moment, which may be regarded as centered in the ring, will be opposed to the applied field, as illustrated in Fig. 7-3. The magnetic field due to this moment will have lines of force approximately as shown, and hence the component of this field at a proton in the plane of the carbon ring will reinforce the applied field.   It is evident from Fig. 7-3 that the field at a point directly *above* or *below* the plane of the carbon ring is opposed to the externally applied field.   Hence in liquid benzene, if a proton in a neighboring benzene molecule finds itself in either one of these positions, its resonance signal will be displaced to high field.   Aromatic molecules are somewhat disk-shaped, and hence there is a greater probability for a neighboring molecule to be above or below the molecular plane of a given molecule rather than in the plane. Moreover, in these positions a neighboring molecule is able to approach much closer to the center of the carbon ring, where the induced magnetic field is large.   Thus after averaging over all possible molecular orientations, there is a net shift of the proton signal of benzene to high field. Dilution of pure benzene with an inert solvent causes the benzene molecules to be further apart on the average, thus reducing this effect. The benzene signal is accordingly shifted to lower field, in the limit approaching the resonance position of the "isolated" molecule. It is worth noting that apart from these magnetic effects, no specific molecular association between neighboring benzene molecules need be assumed to account for the observed dilution shifts. A quantitative calculation of this shift

TABLE 16-3. DILUTION SHIFTS OF METHYL BENZENES IN CARBON TETRACHLORIDE

Compound	Chemical shift, ppm†		Dilution shift, ppm, $\delta_1 - \delta_0$	Molecular volume V_1, cm³/mole	$V_1(\delta_1 - \delta_0)$
	Pure liquid, δ_1	Infinite dilution, δ_0			
Benzene	-1.90	-2.60	0.70	88.8	62.2
Toluene	-1.80	-2.43	0.63	106.2	67.0
o-Xylene	-1.85	-2.33	0.48	120.6	58.0
m-Xylene	-1.70	-2.20	0.50	123.0	61.5
p-Xylene	-1.75	-2.28	0.53	123.3	65.4
Mesitylene	-1.50	-1.93	0.43	139.0	59.8
1,2,4-Trimethylbenzene	-1.65	-2.13	0.48	137.2	65.8
1,2,3,5-Tetramethylbenzene	-1.48	-1.95	0.48	150.0	72.0

† The chemical shifts (corrected for bulk susceptibility) are for the protons bonded to the aromatic ring and are referred to water.

based on a cylindrical-disk model was made by Bothner-By and Glick.[71] The secondary magnetic field due to a neighboring molecule falls off inversely as the cube of the distance of separation.

The chemical shift is rather sensitive to dilution, which increases the mean separation of the aromatic molecules. Addition of substituent groups to the benzene ring, which increases the effective molecular volume, also increases the mean separation of aromatic rings, and therefore the substituted compounds may be expected to give rise to correspondingly smaller over-all dilution shifts. This behavior is illustrated by the chemical-shift measurements of the ring-proton signals of a series of methyl-substituted benzenes (Table 16-3). The dilution shift $\delta_1 - \delta_0$ is nearly inversely proportional to the molar volume V_1.

An extensive study of the shift of proton resonance signals of aromatic compounds in different aliphatic solvents has been carried out by Bothner-By and Glick.[71] In Fig. 16-2 a plot is shown of the dilution shifts $\delta_1 - \delta_0$ against the difference in volume susceptibility between

solute and solvent, $\chi_{v,\text{solute}} - \chi_{v,\text{solvent}}$. The solid line shown in the figure
corresponds to the theoretical bulk-susceptibility shifts (Sec. 4-9). The
measured dilution shifts of the aromatic solutes, however, are greater
and fall roughly on a line which is displaced from the theoretical line by

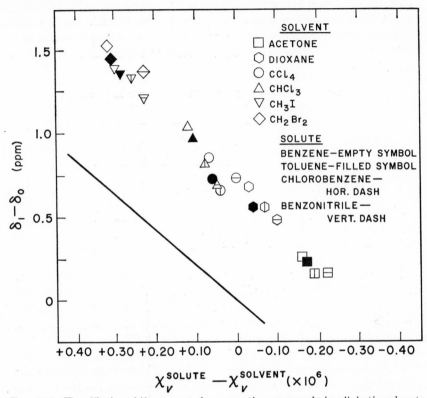

FIG. 16-2. The dilution shifts $\delta_1 - \delta_0$ for aromatic compounds in aliphatic solvents
as a function of the volume-susceptibility difference. The solid line corresponds to
the theoretical bulk-susceptibility shift. (Bothner-By and Glick.[71])

about 0.65 ppm. This displacement corresponds to the characteristic
dilution shifts of the aromatic compounds.

For polynuclear aromatic compounds the solvent-dilution effects are
more pronounced, since electron circulations induced by the external
field in neighboring fused rings will also contribute to the over-all magnetic interaction with the proton of a neighboring molecule. Table 16-4
shows some measured dilution shifts (corrected for bulk-susceptibility
differences) for polynuclear aromatic hydrocarbons.

b. Dilution Shifts of Solutes in Aromatic Solvents. When an aromatic
compound is used as a solvent for an aliphatic solute, the latter exhibits
anomalously large dilution shifts.[71] Progressive dilution of the solute

by the aromatic solvent causes the proton signal of the solute to shift progressively to *higher* field.   This is in the opposite direction to the dilution shifts described above for aromatic solutes.   This difference in behavior also follows from the ring-current model; protons of solute molecules above and below the plane of the aromatic rings of neighboring solvent molecules will resonate at a higher applied field.   Addition of more solvent brings more solute molecules in close contact with aromatic molecules, causing an increased shift of the resonance signal to high field.

TABLE 16-4. DILUTION SHIFTS OF SOME AROMATIC HYDROCARBONS
(Corrected for bulk-susceptibility differences)

Compound	Dilution shift, $\delta_1 - \delta_0$, ppm	Solvent
Benzene	0.70	CCl_4
Naphthalene	0.93†	Dioxane
Pyrene	1.6‡	Dioxane

† Dilution to 5 mole per cent of naphthalene.
‡ Dilution to 3.8 mole per cent of pyrene.

The general behavior of these systems is likewise not predictable on the basis of the bulk-susceptibility correction.   This is illustrated by the plot shown in Fig. 16-3, where the dilution shift of aliphatic *solute* protons $\delta_1 - \delta_0$ is plotted against the volume-susceptibility difference between the solute and the aromatic solvents.   The observed dilution shifts, in contrast to the behavior indicated in Fig. 16-2 for aromatic solutes, now fall *below* the line corresponding to the bulk-susceptibility shift.   The points corresponding to different aliphatic solutes approximate a linear dependence on susceptibility difference only very roughly.   The rather large deviations, as for example those for the solute chloroform, are attributable to a specific molecular interaction (molecular association) which modifies the effects due to intermolecular magnetic interactions.

16-3. Association Involving Aromatic Compounds

a. Association Effects with HX Acceptor Groups.   Chloroform is typical of the considerable number of acceptor molecules capable of forming weak molecular complexes with aromatic molecules.   The interaction with aromatic molecules gives rise to pronounced shifts of the chloroform-proton signal, measurements of which provide a fruitful means of studying the molecular interactions in these systems.   The self-association of chloroform is not large, and the observed chemical shifts can be corrected by the methods discussed in Sec. 15-2. Figure 16-4 shows a plot of the shift of the chloroform-proton signal as a function of concentration in mesitylene, 1,2-dichlorobenzene, nitrobenzene, and 1,3-cyclohexadiene.[374,400] In mesitylene the chloroform-proton signal shows a pronounced shift to high field which, at infinite dilution, amounts to

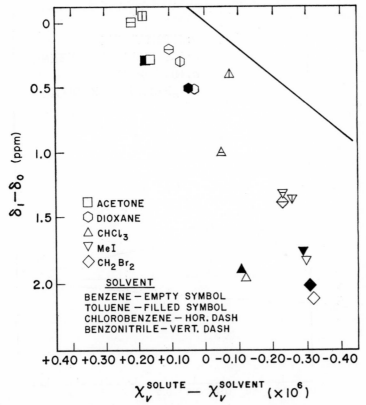

FIG. 16-3. Plot of the dilution shifts of some aliphatic compounds in aromatic solvents. Solid line corresponds to the theoretical bulk-susceptibility shift.   (Bothner-By and Glick.[71])

1.40 ppm. The corresponding shifts in benzene and toluene are of a similar order of magnitude.[374,31]

The proton resonance measurements in these systems provide some evidence of the nature of the molecular complex formed between chloroform and benzene (or mesitylene).† The fact that a pronounced shift to *high* field is observed suggests that in the complex the chloroform proton is drawn closely to the benzene ring in an orientation in which it experi-

† Further evidence for complex formation in these systems comes from freezing-point diagrams[374] and infrared data.[200]

ences a large high-field shift due to the secondary magnetic field resulting
from the induced ring current. It is evident from Fig. 7-3 that this
orientation must be one in which the chloroform proton is directed approximately at right angles to the plane of the aromatic ring and in the vicinity
of the hexagonal axis.

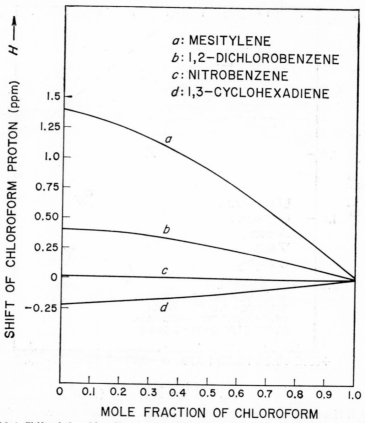

FIG. 16-4. Shift of the chloroform-proton resonance signal as a function of concentration in different solvents relative to liquid chloroform. (Reeves and Schneider.[374])

The shift of the chloroform proton in solutions of 1,2-dichlorobenzene,
as shown in Fig. 16-4, is also toward higher field but very much less than
that of mesitylene. Nitrobenzene, on the other hand, causes no appreciable shift (curve c, Fig. 16-4). It is known that the introduction of electron-withdrawing substituents reduces the π-donor capacity of the aromatic carbon ring. However, the induced ring diamagnetism should
still be operative. The small chloroform shifts in these solvents must be
interpreted in terms of another type of competing association in which
the halogen atoms and the oxygen atoms of the nitro group of the solvent

molecules act as n-donors for the chloroform hydrogen. As discussed in Sec. 15-2, association of this type (hydrogen bonding) causes a shift of the chloroform proton to *low* field, and it would therefore partially cancel the shift to high field arising from the induced ring current of the aromatic molecule.

In 1,3-cyclohexadiene, which has two olefinic bonds, no large induced ring circulation is possible. The observed chloroform-proton shift in this solvent (curve d, Fig. 16-4) is to low field. This shift, which is small but nonetheless real, must be attributed to a significant interaction of the chloroform proton with the π electrons of the olefinic bonds.[101,75,210]

TABLE 16-5. DILUTION SHIFTS IN DIOXANE OF PROTON SIGNALS
OF FIVE- AND SEVEN-MEMBERED RINGS OF AZULENE[403]
(Corrected for bulk-susceptibility differences)

Signal	Concentration of azulene, mole %			$\delta_1 - \delta_0$,† ppm
	100	20	3	
Five-ring signal‡	−3.52	−4.23	−4.33	0.81
Seven-ring signal‡	−3.67	−4.65	−4.90	1.23

† The dilution shifts shown refer to a dilution to 3 mole per cent and not to infinite dilution.

‡ The measured shifts in each case are in ppm relative to dioxane and refer to signal b of the five-ring spectrum and signal A of the seven-ring spectrum as denoted in Fig. 11-11.

The dilution shifts of the hydroxyl-proton signal of phenol as a function of concentration in benzene,[31] which are reproduced in Fig. 15-6, curve a, are of some interest. Dilution of phenol with benzene down to a phenol concentration of 14.6 mole per cent causes a shift of the OH proton to high field by approximately 2.0 ppm. This shift, which is much larger than the corresponding shifts in other (nonaromatic) solvents,[31] arises from the combined effect of the aromatic solvent and a partial dissociation of the phenol-phenol hydrogen bonds.

b. Azulene. Dilution of alternant aromatic hydrocarbons that give rise to more than one proton signal in the NMR spectrum causes each proton signal in the spectrum to be shifted to low field by nearly an equal amount. In contrast, solvent dilution of the nonalternant hydrocarbon azulene gives rise to significantly different dilution shifts for some proton signals in the spectrum than for others.[403] This is illustrated by the proton spectra of azulene reproduced in Fig. 11-11. It is evident from this figure that the AB₂ group of signals from the five-membered ring has a different dilution shift from the remaining seven-membered-ring signals. The dilution shifts of the five-membered-ring and the seven-membered-ring protons can be measured separately; they are summarized in Table 16-5. Thus on dilution to 3 mole per cent, the seven-ring spectrum is shifted to low field by 1.23 ppm, while the five-ring spectrum has the smaller dilution shift of 0.81 ppm. Similar results were obtained for acepleiadylene,[403] in which the dilution shifts are 1.4 ppm for the five-membered ring and 1.8 ppm for both the six- and seven-membered rings.

To account for the different dilution shifts of the five- and seven-membered ring spectra requires some specific molecular-interaction effect not present in alternant aromatic hydrocarbons. It is probable that there is a preferred mutual orientation of neighboring molecules in which the long molecular axes tend to be parallel. This arrangement appears to be supported by the crystal-structure analysis of azulene.[385,436]

CHAPTER 17

KETO-ENOL TAUTOMERISM

17-1. Nuclear Magnetic Resonance Measurements of Keto-Enol Tautomerism

By applying high-resolution NMR techniques to the study of keto-enol tautomerism, valuable new information can be gained in a rather simple and direct way. This application of NMR methods has not yet been extensively explored, but sufficient measurements, mainly on 2,4-pentanedione (acetylacetone), have been carried out to indicate its usefulness.

The nature of keto-enol equilibria in β-diketones and β-keto esters was established by Meyer's bromine-titration method.[283,96] This is essentially a chemical method, and the detailed procedures involved may raise some doubts whether the equilibrium in the system is perturbed to some extent. Various optical methods based on infrared[239,345] and ultraviolet[151,74] absorption spectra and on refractive-index measurements[284] have been used. Depending on the nature of the spectrum for the particular compound being studied, which in some cases may be rather complex, these techniques are not always applicable or sufficiently quantitative. In common with the NMR method, however, they have the advantage that they are physical methods and hence cannot disturb the tautomeric equilibrium being measured.

The tautomeric equilibrium of acetylacetone can be written

$$CH_3-\underset{\underset{O}{\|}}{C}-CH_2-\underset{\underset{O}{\|}}{C}-CH_3 \rightleftharpoons CH_3-\underset{\underset{O-H\,\cdots\,O}{|}}{C}=CH----\underset{}{C}-CH_3$$

I, keto   II, enol

where the enol form may be internally hydrogen-bonded. The proton magnetic resonance spectrum of pure liquid acetylacetone has been studied by Jarret, Sadler, and Shoolery,[208] by Bhar,[42] and by Reeves.[373] A representative spectrum is reproduced in Fig. 17-1. The relative chemical shifts and assignments shown are due to Reeves.[373] The two signals at -13.6 and -3.6 ppm, which have equal intensities, are assigned respectively to the OH and $=$CH$-$ groups of the enol form. The hydroxyl-group signal is somewhat broadened. The signals at the

433

extreme right (high field) are due to the methyl groups, the signal for the enol form, CH₃ (II), which was used as a reference for the chemical-shift measurements, being at slightly higher field than that for the keto form,

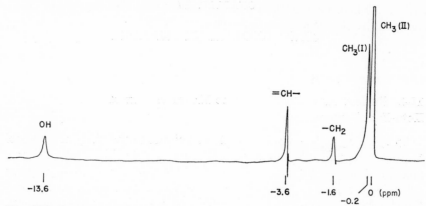

Fɪɢ. 17-1. Proton resonance spectrum (40 Mc/sec) of pure 2,4-pentanedione (acetylacetone) at room temperature, showing separate signals of the keto (I) and enol (II) tautomers.

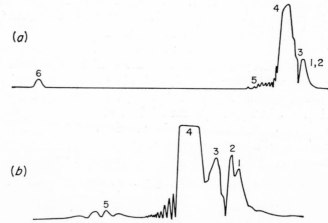

Fɪɢ. 17-2. NMR spectrum of 3-methyl-2,4-pentanedione (30 Mc/sec, magnetic field swept from right to left). (a) Complete spectrum. (b) High-field portion of spectrum (a) under higher resolution. (Jarret, Sadler, and Shoolery.[208])

CH₃ (I). The remaining signal in the spectrum is due to the —CH₂— group of the keto form.

Since the various signals in this simple spectrum are well separated, the relative intensities of the individual signals are readily measured to yield values for the keto-enol ratio. The unusually large chemical shift for the OH group of the enol form II is somewhat surprising. It represents the largest shift to low field of any OH group (including that of carboxylic acids) yet observed. This is no doubt partly due to an internal hydrogen bond.

The spectrum of 3-methyl-2,4-pentanedione measured by Jarret, Sadler, and Shoolery[208] is shown in Fig. 17-2. The two tautomers are represented by the following equilibrium:

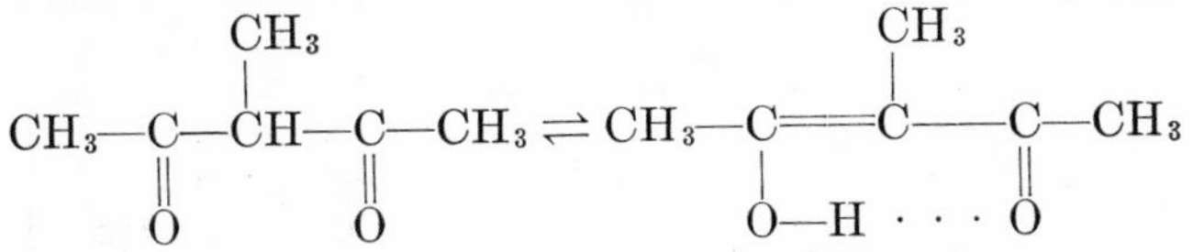

$$
\underset{\text{III, keto}}{
\begin{array}{c}
\text{CH}_3 \\
| \\
\text{CH}_3-\text{C}-\text{CH}-\text{C}-\text{CH}_3 \\
\parallel \quad\quad \parallel \\
\text{O} \quad\quad\quad \text{O}
\end{array}}
\rightleftharpoons
\underset{\text{IV, enol}}{
\begin{array}{c}
\text{CH}_3 \\
| \\
\text{CH}_3-\text{C}=\text{C}-\text{C}-\text{CH}_3 \\
| \quad\quad\quad \parallel \\
\text{O}-\text{H} \cdots \text{O}
\end{array}}
$$

The assignment of the spectrum is straightforward. Peaks 1 and 2 arise from the protons of the 3-methyl group in the keto form III. The signal is a doublet due to spin-spin coupling with the single tertiary hydrogen. In the enol form IV this proton is not present, and hence the signal due to the 3-methyl-group protons will be single. This is identified with peak 3 (Fig. 17-2b). Peak 4 is identified with the terminal methyl groups of both forms, and region 5 with the —CH— group of the keto form III. The latter is a quartet due to spin-spin coupling with the adjacent methyl-group protons. As in acetylacetone, the signal due to the OH group of the enol form, peak 6, is shifted well out to low field.

17-2. Keto-Enol Equilibrium

The relative concentrations of the keto and enol tautomers in pure liquid acetylacetone at room temperature, as deduced from the NMR intensities, were measured by Jarret, Sadler, and Shoolery,[208] Bhar,[42] and Reeves.[373] The results are shown in Table 17-1. The measurements obtained by Bhar have not been included because they were based on a rather low-resolution spectrum. The later, more extensive, measure-

TABLE 17-1. KETO-ENOL EQUILIBRIUM MEASUREMENTS
(At 25°C)

Compound	Per cent of keto tautomer		
	Bromine titration[283]	NMR method	
		Ref. 208	Ref. 373
2,4-Pentanedione	24	15	18.6 ± 0.6
3-Methyl-2,4-pentanedione	68.5	70	

ments of Reeves[373] are probably more reliable and were obtained from spectra under conditions of somewhat higher resolution and at a higher radio frequency (40 Mc/sec). The relative intensities (areas) of the —CH$_2$— and =CH— peaks were used to obtain the relative concentrations of the keto and enol tautomers, although excellent agreement was also found when the OH peak was used. For comparison, the equilibrium values of the keto-enol ratio obtained from the bromine-titration

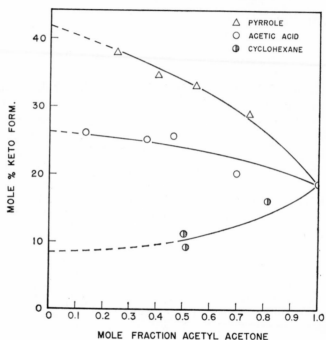

FIG. 17-3. Effect of solvents on the keto-enol equilibrium of acetylacetone from NMR measurements. (Reeves.[373])

method are included in Table 17-1. The equilibrium concentrations of keto and enol forms in 3-methyl-2,4-pentanedione obtained by Jarret, Sadler, and Shoolery[208] are also shown.

The effect of temperature on the keto-enol equilibrium has also been studied.[373] Proton resonance measurements were made over the temperature range −16 to 116°C. From the slope of a plot of $\log_{10} (C_2/C_1)$ vs. $1/T$, where C_1 and C_2 are respectively the mole fractions of keto and enol forms in the equilibrium system at each temperature, the enthalpy of keto-enol conversion ΔH was found to be $2{,}700 \pm 100$ cal/mole. This is significantly higher than the corresponding values found in dilute solution or in the gas phase from infrared measurements.[345]

Effect of Solvents.   Solvents may alter the keto-enol equilibrium either by altering the dielectric constant of the system or by preferential hydrogen bonding between solvent molecules and one of the tautomers.   Figure 17-3 illustrates the effect of varying concentrations of cyclohexane, acetic acid, and pyrrole on the keto-enol equilibrium of acetylacetone.[373] The inert solvent cyclohexane has a dielectric constant which is lower than that of acetylacetone, thus favoring the less polar (enol) of the two

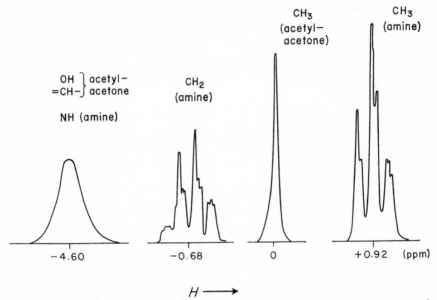

FIG. 17-4. Proton resonance spectrum of the equimolar mixture of acetylacetone and diethylamine.   All signals were recorded at the same sweep rate but at different receiver gain.   (Reeves and Schneider.[375])

tautomers.   Acetic acid may be expected to form strong hydrogen bonds with the enol form, which, like acetic acid, has a carbonyl group and a hydroxyl group.   However, addition of acetic acid to acetylacetone does not appreciably affect the keto-enol equilibrium.   It must be concluded, therefore, that acetic acid molecules behave largely as an inert medium by virtue of self-association, mainly in the form of dimers. Addition of pyrrole shifts the equilibrium toward higher concentrations of the keto tautomer.

The strongly basic solvents triethylamine and diethylamine have a profound effect on the keto-enol equilibrium.   At all concentrations of acetylacetone in triethylamine (up to 87 mole per cent) the NMR spectrum indicates a complete conversion to the enol tautomer.[373]   This implies a strong hydrogen-bonding interaction of the nitrogen atom of the amine with the enolic OH group.   Confirmation of this is to be found in the extraordinarily large dilution shift (greater than 7 ppm) of the hydroxyl-proton signal to high field in triethylamine solutions.

A strong interaction between diethylamine and acetylacetone is indicated by the formation of a molecular complex, with evolution of heat, when the two compounds are mixed in equimolar amounts.[375] The proton resonance spectrum of the complex just above its melting point (41.5°C) is shown in Fig. 17-4. The acetylacetone gives rise to only two signals; one is due to the methyl groups, and the other is a broad coalesced signal that arises from the resonances of the OH and =CH— groups and also the resonance of the NH group of the amine.

17-3. Proton-exchange Effects in Acidic and Basic Solvents

Two types of proton exchanges have been revealed by NMR measurements of acetylacetone systems.[375,405] The first involves only the hydroxyl group of the enol tautomer, while the second type is more extensive and involves the over-all keto-enol conversion process. Under certain conditions the rates of these proton exchanges can be studied.

Exchange of the enol OH proton in pure acetylacetone is indicated by the fact that the NMR spectrum shows the methyl groups of the enol tautomer to be equivalent (Fig. 17-1). This equivalence could arise from a rapid exchange of the proton between the two oxygen atoms of the enol tautomer. At room temperature the proton resonance spectrum of acetylacetone in acetic acid shows a separate signal for the enolic OH group and for the acetic acid OH group.[405] Both signals, however, are broadened, indicating that a proton-exchange process involving both groups is taking place. Raising the temperature increases the rate of proton exchange, and as shown by the traces reproduced in Fig. 17-5, the separate OH signals coalesce to a single signal. This occurs at a temperature in the neighborhood of 64°C. At this temperature τ the lifetime of the proton at either of its alternative sites is, from Eq. (10-30), equal to 1.5×10^{-3} sec. At lower temperatures the exchange is slow, presumably because of a preferred self-association of the solution components, the enol tautomer forming a strong intramolecular hydrogen bond and the acetic acid being strongly associated in the form of dimers.

The keto-enol conversion process itself may be regarded as a proton-exchange process in the sense that a proton is transferred from a carbon atom to an oxygen atom, and vice versa. At room temperature this process is evidently comparatively slow, since the NMR spectrum of acetylacetone (Fig. 17-1) shows separate sharp line spectra for the individual tautomers. If the keto-enol conversion rate could be sufficiently accelerated, the separate signals of the two tautomers would coalesce to give a single "averaged" spectrum. This would require τ to be of the

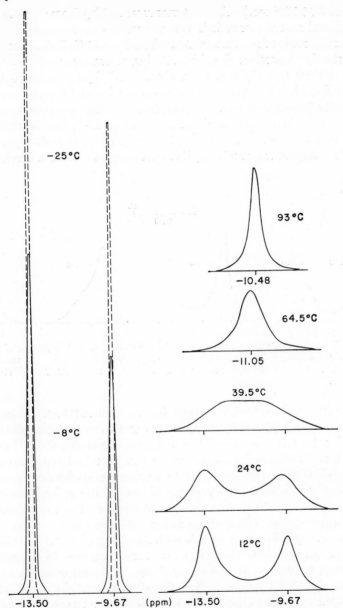

FIG. 17-5. Effect of temperature on the proton-exchange behavior between acetic acid and the enol tautomer of acetylacetone. Only the OH signals of the proton resonance spectrum of the solution are shown. Chemical shifts shown are relative to the methyl-group signal of the enol tautomer. The concentration of acetylacetone in the solution is 58 mole per cent. (Schneider and Reeves.[405])

order of 5×10^{-4} sec.† A direct measurement by Bhar[41] of the conversion rate of acetylacetone indicates the value of τ at room temperature to be of the order of several minutes. Heating to 150°C does not decrease τ sufficiently to produce signal broadening or coalescence.[375]

In solutions of acetylacetone in di- or in triethylamine not only is the keto-enol equilibrium greatly perturbed, but in addition the tautomeric conversion rate is apparently accelerated.[375] Thus the proton spectrum of acetylacetone in diethylamine, shown in Fig. 17-4, may be regarded as an "averaged" spectrum resulting from rapid proton exchanges. However, to interpret the spectrum, it is necessary to assume a much shorter

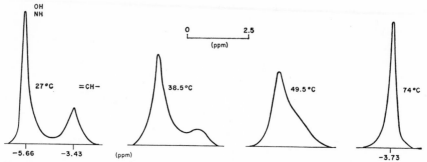

FIG. 17-6. Proton resonance signals of the OH, =CH—, and NH groups of an equimolar mixture of acetylacetone and diethylamine dissolved in CCl₄. Chemical shifts are relative to the methyl-group signal of the enol tautomer. (Reeves and Schneider.[375])

lifetime for the keto tautomer than for the enol tautomer. The rather broad signal at low field in the spectrum of Fig. 17-4 can be assigned to the OH and =CH— groups of the enol tautomer and to the NH group of the amine. The broad, structureless nature of this signal suggests that the protons of these three groups are simultaneously exchanging. This is confirmed by the resonance spectrum of the 1:1 diethylamine-acetylacetone complex dissolved in carbon tetrachloride at a concentration of 15 mole per cent. The corresponding low-field signal, shown in Fig. 17-6, is now split into two signals with intensity ratio 2:1. This signal must accordingly arise from at least three protons. The signal with intensity 1 appearing at −3.43 ppm can be assigned to the =CH— group of the enol tautomer. The signal at lower field (with intensity 2) must then be due to the enol OH group and the amine NH group, the two groups undergoing rapid proton exchange. As shown by the NMR traces taken at various temperatures (Fig. 17-6), heating the solution

† This value follows from Eq. (10-30), together with the separation of the enol OH signal and the keto —CH₂— signal of ∼480 cycles/sec, measured at 40 Mc/sec (Fig. 17-1).

causes a coalescence of the two signals. This implies a proton exchange of the enol =CH— group with the OH and NH groups, but the exchange is not as rapid as that between the latter two groups.

Rapid proton exchange between NH and OH groups in the above system may be expected, but the involvement of the =CH— group of the enol tautomer in the over-all exchange process is rather surprising. A possible interpretation is that this exchange takes place via the keto tautomer as a short-lived intermediate state. Assuming that all proton exchanges take place by way of hydrogen-bonded structures (Sec. 15-6), so that the proton transfers to lone-pair-electron or π-electron donor sites,[405] the following exchanges can occur:

1. $O—H \cdots N \rightleftharpoons O \cdots H—N$

2. $H_{II}—C$
    $\quad \| \quad \cdots \quad H_I—N \rightleftharpoons$
    $\quad C$

    Enol

    $H_{II}—C—H_I \cdots N$
    $\quad \quad \quad |$
    $\quad \quad \quad C$

    Keto

3. $H_{II}—C$
    $\quad \| \quad \cdots \quad H_I—O \rightleftharpoons$
    $\quad C$

    Enol

    $H_{II}—C—H_I \cdots O$
    $\quad \quad \quad |$
    $\quad \quad \quad C$

    Keto

Process (3) represents the ordinary keto-enol conversion, and both (2) and (3) involve the keto tautomer as an intermediate "exchange" state. This permits the protons H_I and H_{II} to become equivalent, and accordingly both can take part in the exchange process.

According to the above interpretation, diethylamine accelerates the keto-enol conversion rate by virtue of strong hydrogen-bond interactions with the enol tautomer, thus facilitating rapid proton exchanges. In this respect triethylamine is somewhat less effective, presumably because it lacks an exchangeable proton of its own. The proton spectrum of acetylacetone in triethylamine shows rather broad OH group and =CH— group signals of the enol tautomer.[375] Heating the solution causes further broadening, but the rate of proton exchanges is not sufficiently rapid to cause the signals to collapse to an averaged spectrum.

CHAPTER 18

AQUEOUS ELECTROLYTES

18-1. Dissociation Equilibria of Acids and Bases

One of the earliest chemical applications of nuclear magnetic resonance was to the study of dissociation equilibria in aqueous solutions of electrolytes yielding hydrogen-containing ions. The proton resonances of some common strong acids and bases were first investigated by Gutowsky and Saika.[172] Simultaneously, Masuda and Kanda[264,265] examined the corresponding spectra of other nuclei involved in the solutions.

The proton resonance spectrum of all acids investigated consists of a single line with a chemical shift depending on concentration. Since there are several species present, this is an indication of rapid exchange of protons. If the dissociation equilibrium is written

$$HA + H_2O \rightleftharpoons H_3O^+ + A^- \tag{18-1}$$

any given proton will divide its time between undissociated molecules HA, solvent-water molecules, and hydronium ions H_3O^+ (and possibly also A^- if it still contains protons). From the general considerations outlined in Chap. 10, therefore, it follows that the frequency of exchange between these species must be considerably greater than the separation, measured in cycles per second, between the signals the individual species would have if exchange did not occur. This places a lower limit of 10^2 to 10^3 sec^{-1} for the rate of such processes.

The position of the single line itself is a number average of the resonant frequencies of the individual species, and the variation of the line with concentration is therefore dependent on the degree of dissociation of the acid. The same applies to the resonant frequencies of nuclei other than protons which are present (as for example Cl^{35} in HCl solutions).

a. Monobasic Acids. To investigate the concentration shift quantitatively, we begin by assuming complete dissociation. If x is the stoichiometric mole fraction of the acid, the number of hydronium ions H_3O^+ will be Nx per mole, leaving $N(1 - 2x)$ water molecules per mole. Thus the fraction of protons on hydronium ions will be

$$p = \frac{3x}{3x + 2(1 - 2x)} = \frac{3x}{2 - x} \tag{18-2}$$

If we can treat the chemical shift δ as an appropriate mean of the chemical shifts $\delta_{H_3O^+}$ and δ_{H_2O} for the hydronium ion and the water molecule separately, then

$$\delta = p\delta_{H_3O^+} + (1 - p)\delta_{H_2O} \qquad (18\text{-}3)$$

It is convenient to measure chemical shifts relative to pure water in these

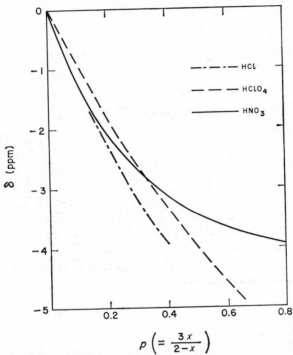

$$p\left(= \frac{3x}{2-x}\right)$$

FIG. 18-1. Proton resonance shifts for aqueous solutions of some strong monobasic acids. (Hood, Redlich, and Reilly.[196])

applications, so δ should be proportional to the hydronium-ion proton fraction

$$\delta = p\delta_{H_3O^+} \qquad (18\text{-}4)$$

Observed values of δ are plotted against p for moderate concentrations in Fig. 18-1, which is based on the work of Hood, Redlich, and Reilly.[196] These authors revised and extended the original work of Gutowsky and Saika and included bulk-susceptibility corrections. For values of p up to about 0.2 (corresponding to a mole fraction of 0.12), the values fall approximately on straight lines, from the slope of which we obtain $\delta_{H_3O^+}$ according to Eq. (18-4). If the simple interpretation given above were valid, this would give the chemical shift for the hydronium ion and would be the same for all acids. The actual values obtained by Hood,

Redlich, and Reilly were -11.8, -11.4, and -9.2 ppm for nitric, hydrochloric, and perchloric acids, respectively. The difference between the value for perchloric acid and the others shows the limitation of this picture and has to be attributed to an effect of the negative ion on the proton resonance of water molecules in its vicinity.

The deviations from straight-line behavior at higher concentrations are also attributed to some form of interaction between the protons and the anions. The deviations can be analyzed in terms of a model involving incomplete dissociation. If the mole fraction of hydronium ions is αx, where $\alpha < 1$ and the mole fraction of undissociated acid molecules is $(1 - \alpha)x$, then α is the degree of dissociation. The chemical-shift expression (18-4) can be replaced by

$$\delta = \alpha p \delta_{H_3O^+} + \tfrac{1}{3}(1 - \alpha) p \delta_{HA} \qquad (18\text{-}5)$$

and, $\delta_{H_3O^+}$ being known, it can be used to estimate α. It should be emphasized, however, that this model is oversimplified, because at higher concentrations, other forms of ionic interaction may be playing a part.

Another estimate of the apparent degree of dissociation α can be obtained from the magnetic resonance shift of other nuclei. Such investigations have been carried out by Masuda and Kanda.[264,265] For the N^{14} resonance of nitric acid, for example, they choose the solvated NO_3^- ion as the reference and then compare the shift δ with that for anhydrous HNO_3. By similar arguments, if the degree of dissociation is α and other interionic effects are neglected,

$$\delta = \delta_{HNO_3}(1 - \alpha) \qquad (18\text{-}6)$$

The N^{14} shifts are rather larger than those for protons, the signal for anhydrous HNO_3 being displaced 52 ppm to high field from the dilute-solution signal of NO_3^-.

The degrees of dissociation of nitric acid found in these ways are illustrated in Fig. 18-2, where a comparison is also made with a corresponding curve obtained from Raman-line intensities.[372] Values obtained by nuclear resonance techniques are seen to be rather higher than those by the other method.

The variation of α with concentration can be used to get a rough value of the thermodynamic dissociation constant K. By extrapolating the logarithm of

$$K\beta = \frac{a}{c(1 - \alpha)} \qquad (18\text{-}7)$$

(where a = activity of nitric acid
$\quad c$ = concentration, moles/liter
$\quad \beta$ = activity coefficient of undissociated molecule)

to zero concentration, Hood, Redlich, and Reilly[196] obtained $K = 22$. The close agreement with the value $K = 21$ from the Raman measurements is largely fortuitous.   By similar measurements, the same authors[196] obtained $K = 38$ for perchloric acid, $K = 1.8$ for trifluoroacetic acid, and $K = 1.1$ for heptafluorobutyric acid.

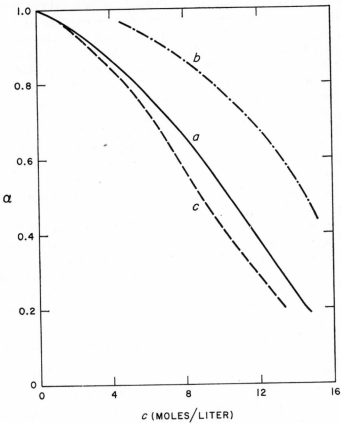

FIG. 18-2. Degree of dissociation of nitric acid estimated (*a*) by proton resonance,[172] (*b*) by N^{14} resonance,[265] and (*c*) by Raman intensities.[372]

Masuda and Kanda[265] also investigated the Cl^{35}, Br^{81}, and I^{127} shifts in aqueous hydrochloric, hydrobromic, and hydroiodic acids as a function of concentration.   These signals were all found to shift to lower fields as the concentration was increased, indicating the presence of undissociated species or some kind of ion pairs.   The direction of the shift implies that the screening constant for the Cl^- ion is larger than for Cl in the HCl molecule.   This agrees with the general theory of chemical shifts; for the hydrated Cl^- ion will have a more nearly spherical distribution of electrons.

The same authors[265] also made some interesting observations of line widths in these acidic systems. The line width of the Cl^{35} resonance signal in perchloric acid rises from 0.12 gauss in dilute solution to 0.67 gauss in the anhydrous material. This can be understood in terms of the electric quadrupole relaxation mechanism for the Cl^{35} nuclei. In the dissociated ClO_4^- ions, the chlorine nuclei are in a field of tetrahedral symmetry and cannot experience an electric field gradient, so that quadrupole relaxation will be relatively small. In an undissociated molecule $HClO_4$, however, this symmetry is destroyed and the spin-lattice relaxation time is shortened, leading to signal broadening. Similar results were found for the line widths of the Cl^{35}, Br^{81}, and I^{127} signals in the halogen acids. Here the spherical symmetry of the ions is destroyed when molecules or ion pairs are formed.

b. Sulfuric Acid. The only dibasic acid which has been investigated by these methods is sulfuric acid, which was studied by Gutowsky and Saika,[172] by Morin, Paulett, and Hobbs,[290] and by Hood and Reilly.[197] The proton chemical shift (as parts per million relative to pure water after correction for bulk susceptibility) is shown as a function of mole fraction H_2SO_4 in Fig. 18-3.

The theoretical interpretation is complicated by the possibility of a second dissociation. If the mole fraction of sulfuric acid is x, and if the degree of dissociation of H_2SO_4 to HSO_4^- and H_3O^+ is α_1 and that of HSO_4^- to $SO_4^=$ and H_3O^+ is α_2, we can obtain an expression for the shift along lines similar to those used for monobasic acids. Consider one mole of solution containing $2N$ protons. If we allow only for dissociation into HSO_4^- and H_3O^+, the composition will be

$$Nx(1 - \alpha_1) H_2SO_4 + Nx\alpha_1 HSO_4^- + Nx\alpha_1 H_3O^+ + N(1 - x - x\alpha_1) H_2O$$

If we also allow for the second dissociation, the composition becomes

$$Nx(1 - \alpha_1) H_2SO_4 + Nx\alpha_1(1 - \alpha_2) HSO_4^- + Nx\alpha_1\alpha_2 SO_4^=$$
$$+ Nx\alpha_1(1 + \alpha_2) H_3O^+ + N(1 - x - x\alpha_1 - x\alpha_1\alpha_2) H_2O$$

Consequently the resultant chemical shift is given by

$$\frac{\delta}{x} = (1 - \alpha_1)\delta_{H_2SO_4} + \tfrac{1}{2}\alpha_1(1 - \alpha_2)\delta_{HSO_4^-} + \tfrac{3}{2}\alpha_1(1 + \alpha_2)\delta_{H_3O^+} \quad (18\text{-}8)$$

Hood and Reilly assumed that $\delta_{H_2SO_4}$ was the shift for 100 per cent H_2SO_4, namely, -6.15 ppm. For the calculation of the degrees of dissociation α_1 and α_2, they used

$$\frac{\delta}{x} = -6.15 - 8.10\alpha_1 - 25\alpha_1\alpha_2 \quad (18\text{-}9)$$

The value -8.10 was obtained from the behavior at $x = 1$, assuming that

$H_2SO_4 + H_2O \rightleftharpoons H_3O^+ + HSO_4^-$ approaches completion in this limit. The value -25 was chosen to give the best over-all agreement with the Raman-intensity work of Young.[472]　This corresponds to $\delta_{H_3O^+} = -13.1$, to be compared with the values of -11.8, -11.4, and -9.2 obtained from monobasic acids.　Values of α_1 and α_2 were found by assuming a small

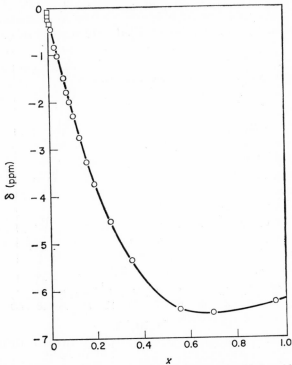

Fig. 18-3. Proton resonance shifts for aqueous solutions of sulfuric acid.　$\bigcirc$, data of Hood and Reilly;[197] $\square$, data of Morin, Paulett, and Hobbs.[290]

intermediate-concentration range where dissociation of HSO_4^- is significant ($\alpha_2 > 0$) but that of H_2SO_4 is incomplete ($\alpha_1 < 1$).　The results are shown in Fig. 18-4, together with other points obtained from the Raman work of Young.[472]

c. Sodium and Potassium Hydroxide.　Proton resonances in aqueous solutions of NaOH and KOH were observed by Gutowsky and Saika.[172] Although the range of observation was limited by the solubility, it was established that the signal shifted to low field with increasing concentration.　Further, the limiting slopes in dilute solutions were the same within experimental error.　Just as measurements on acids give information of the proton resonance of H_3O^+, so this slope gives the chemical shift of the hydroxide ion OH^-.

If x is the mole fraction of NaOH or KOH, then if complete dissociation is assumed, the fraction of protons present as OH⁻ is

$$p = \frac{x}{2 - x} \tag{18-10}$$

and the chemical shift will be

$$\delta = p\delta_{\text{OH}^-} \tag{18-11}$$

The limiting slope gives a value of about -10 ppm for δ_{OH^-}.

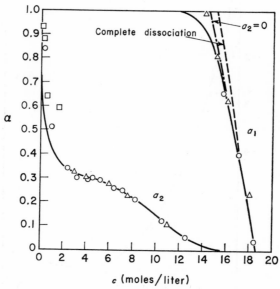

FIG. 18-4. Degrees of dissociation of sulfuric acid. ○, data of Hood and Reilly;[197] □, data of Morin, Paulett, and Hobbs;[290] △, data of Young.[472]

For higher concentrations, Gutowsky and Saika found that the shift to low field was substantially smaller for NaOH solutions than for KOH solutions, implying the formation of Na⁺OH⁻ ion pairs. They suggested that this was due to stronger interionic forces with Na⁺ ions because of their smaller size.

d. Hydronium and Hydroxide Ions. If the chemical shifts in dilute solutions of acids and bases are interpreted in the simple manner described above, we are led to the conclusion that the ions H_3O^+ and OH⁻ both have proton resonance frequencies displaced about 10 ppm to low field from liquid water at room temperature. The fact that both the positive and negative ions are displaced to low field is difficult to explain in terms of any picture of the isolated systems. By comparison with the bare proton shift (27 ppm to the low-field side of water), Gutowsky and Saika[172] suggested that the shift of H_3O^+ may represent about one-third ionic character in the bonds, with the hydrogen positive. However this cannot account for the displacement of the OH^- signal.

It seems likely that these large apparent shifts to low field can be understood only in relation to the environment of the ions. In the first place, the effective shift measured arises not only from the proton or protons on the ion, but also from any extra effect on neighboring water molecules. Secondly, the ions are certainly strongly hydrated, and it is clear from other studies of hydrogen bonding (Chap. 15) that this type of association leads to strong shifts to low fields; so it may not be valid to draw conclusions about the electronic structure of ions from their chemical shifts.

18-2. Diamagnetic-salt Solutions

The effect of a considerable number of diamagnetic salts on the proton resonance of water was examined by Shoolery and Alder.[421] In all cases only a single line was observed and, apart from a few exceptions mentioned below, the line widths were not significantly broader than the line width for pure water. Both high- and low-field shifts from pure water were observed (Fig. 18-5).

Since only a single signal is observed, the proton chemical shift in any solution is an average over that appropriate to the various possible positions of a water molecule, such as the normal "pure liquid" positions and those in the immediate vicinity of positive and negative ions. Clearly it should be possible to separate the effects of the two kinds of ions at sufficiently low concentrations and so introduce a shift per mole of ion. This is analogous to the separation of heats and entropies of solvation of individual ions from data on various salts. It is only necessary to select one value arbitrarily to establish a relative scale. Thus Shoolery and Alder were able to fit all their data (uncorrected for bulk susceptibility) within the limitations of extrapolation and experimental error by a formula

$$\delta = m(n^+\delta^+ + n^-\delta^-) \tag{18-12}$$

where δ^+ and δ^- = relative molar shifts caused by positive and negative ions

n^+ and n^- = number of moles of cations and anions formed in dissociation of 1 mole of salt

m = concentration, moles/1,000 g water

The values for δ^+ and δ^- based on an arbitrary value for ClO_4^- are given in Table 18-1.

The data were interpreted by Shoolery and Alder in terms of the combined effect of a low-field shift for the protons of water molecules strongly bonded to ions, together with a high-field shift due to the tendency of the

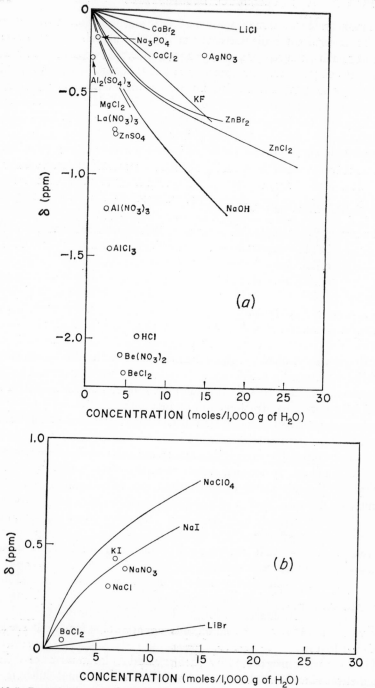

FIG. 18-5. Proton chemical shifts (*a*) to low field and (*b*) to high field in aqueous electrolyte solutions. (Shoolery and Alder.[421])

450

ion to break up the hydrogen-bonded structure of the water itself. This
is consistent with the observed fact that uni-univalent electrolytes consisting of relatively large ions mainly break down the structure and lead
to high-field shifts. Also, the smaller the ion and the higher its charge
the greater is the tendency for the shift to be to low field corresponding to
the effect of strong hydration. This is well illustrated by the series of
halide ions and the large low-field shifts of trivalent ions of both types.

TABLE 18-1. RELATIVE MOLAR SHIFTS OF PROTON RESONANCE FOR EACH ION†
(In ppm)

Ion	Shift	Ion	Shift	Ion	Shift
I^-	0.035	K^+	0.071	Ba^{++}	0.023
Br^-	0.021	Na^+	0.057	Ca^{++}	−0.045
Cl^-	0.001	Li^+	−0.009	Mg^{++}	−0.208
F^-	−0.120	Ag^+	−0.028	Be^{++}	−0.489
ClO_4^-	0.085‡			Zn^{++}	−0.124
NO_3^-	0.009			La^{3+}	−0.239
$SO_4^=$	−0.117			Al^{3+}	−0.519
PO_4^{3-}	−0.383				

† After Shoolery and Alder.[421]
‡ Assumed as standard.

Three systems studied by Shoolery and Alder showed line broadening
compared with pure water. These were $AlCl_3$, $ZnCl_2$, and $BeCl_2$. In
concentrated zinc and beryllium dichloride, the broadening, in cycles per
second, is practically unaltered by changing the frequency from 30 to
3 Mc/sec. This can be mainly attributed to the effect of viscosity, which
is considerable for these solutions. In the case of aluminum trichloride,
on the other hand, the broadening is substantially reduced on going to
lower frequencies. It was suggested that this was because the water
molecules in the Al^{3+} hydration shell are so strongly bound that the time
of exchange between hydrated and other positions was long enough to
give an incompletely collapsed spectrum. Shoolery and Alder estimated
from the observed effect that the exchange time was about 8 msec. It is
possible, of course, that this may represent a proton intermolecular
exchange time rather than an exchange of whole water molecules.

18-3. Chemical Shifts Due to Paramagnetic Ions

In solutions of salts containing paramagnetic ions, rather large signal
shifts of the order of 10 ppm are observed.[58,120] Some of this is due to
the bulk-susceptibility effect, the paramagnetic solutions having a much
higher susceptibility, but shifts are found even for spherical samples.
Further, the shifts depend markedly on the nucleus involved.

The most satisfactory explanation of these shifts, suggested by Bloembergen,[56] is that the unpaired electrons interact with the protons through the Fermi-type Hamiltonian (contact term), which also leads to hyperfine structure in electron resonance. If S is the electron spin, the corresponding energy takes the form $A\mathbf{I} \cdot \mathbf{S}$. Bloembergen gives the quantitative expression

$$\sigma = -\frac{8\pi}{3} |\psi(0)|^2 \chi_v z n^{-1} \tag{18-13}$$

for the corresponding shift. Here $|\psi(0)|^2$ is the probability of the paramagnetic electrons being at a neighboring proton (the odd electron density being partly delocalized from the ion onto the solvation shell), χ_v is the volume susceptibility, z the coordination number, and n is the number of water molecules per cubic centimeter. This expression is very similar to the Knight shift in metals, which is also due to unpaired electrons.

18-4. Aqueous Solutions of Ammonia and Related Substances

A number of investigations have been carried out on solutions involving the ammonium ion and various methylated derivatives. Frequently conditions are such that exchange is rapid and only a combined signal is observed for the water protons and the protons bonded to nitrogen. Ogg,[303] for example, found that minute traces of water in liquid ammonia are sufficient to induce proton exchange and collapse the triplet proton spectrum (N^{14} having spin 1) to a single signal. It was suggested that exchange takes place by the mechanism

$$NH_3 + H_2O \rightleftharpoons NH_4^+ + OH^- \tag{18-14}$$

In other cases, separate signals can sometimes be observed and their collapse can be used to investigate the rates and mechanisms of the processes involved. Some studies of the protolysis of methylated ammonium ions are described below in Sec. b.

a. Acid-Base Equilibria. Proton chemical shifts of aqueous solutions of ammonia over a range of concentrations have been measured by Gutowsky and Fujiwara[157] at room temperature. At all concentrations the resonance was found to be a single sharp signal, so its position is determined as a number average of the separate positions for the nuclei in the absence of exchange. The results for aqueous ammonia and some ammonium salts are shown in Fig. 18-6.

If p_1 is the fraction of protons in NH_3, the simplest theory, assuming no dissociation or other effect, would give

$$\delta = p_1 \delta_{NH_3} \tag{18-15}$$

if the chemical shift is referred to pure water ($\delta_{H_2O} = 0$). Here δ_{NH_3} is just the shift of pure ammonia, so Eq. (18-15) predicts the dashed line in the figure for water-ammonia mixtures. The observed results are all displaced to low field from this. This deviation may be partly due to somewhat stronger interactions between unlike molecules, but the similarity to the shifts produced by ammonium acetate and ammonium

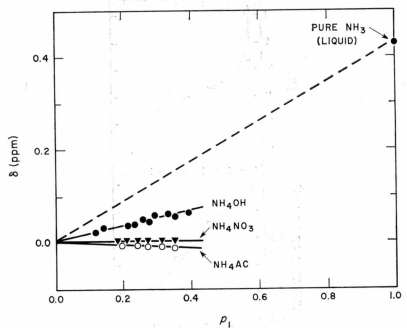

FIG. 18-6. Proton resonance shifts in aqueous solutions of ammonia and ammonium salts at room temperature. Values of δ are referred to pure water, and p_1 is the stoichiometric fraction of protons as NH_3. (Gutowsky and Fujiwara.[157])

nitrate suggest that a considerable amount of ionization to NH_4^+ and OH^- is present.

Grunwald, Loewenstein, and Meiboom[153] have studied acid-base equilibria in aqueous solutions of methylamine, dimethylamine, and trimethylamine. These equilibria can be represented schematically by

$$R_3NH^+ \rightleftharpoons R_3N + H^+ \qquad (18\text{-}16)$$

where R represents either a methyl group or hydrogen. Under conditions in which both components are present, the spectra consist of two sharp signals, one for the methyl protons and the other for the protons exchanging between water, hydronium ions, hydroxide ions, and the ionizable positions on nitrogen. Grunwald, Loewenstein, and Meiboom investigated the chemical shift of the methyl signal as a function of acid/base ratio as measured by titration. They found that the shift, measured relative to the tetramethylammonium ion as reference, was a linear function of the concentration ratio of acid to base plus acid for all three systems. Figure 18-7 shows their results for the methylamine system.

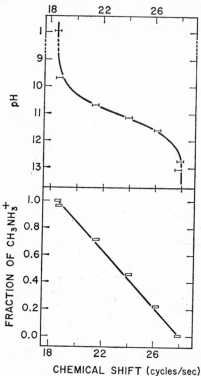

FIG. 18-7. Chemical shift of methyl protons (cycles per second at 7,430 gauss) relative to $(CH_3)_4N^+$ in CH_3NH_2-$CH_3NH_3^+$ equilibrium mixture as a function of pH (upper part) and concentration ratio of acid to base plus acid. (Grunwald, Loewenstein, and Meiboom.[153])

b. Rate Studies of Protolysis. In addition to the equilibrium studies described in the previous section, nuclear resonance has been used by Grunwald, Loewenstein, and Meiboom[152] to investigate the kinetics of protolysis of methylammonium ions. Their general results can be described qualitatively in terms of Fig. 18-8, which shows the proton spectra of aqueous methylammonium chloride at a series of pH values. At pH = 0.96, the methyl signal shows a sharp 1:3:3:1 quadruplet structure due to coupling with the NH_3^+ protons, so that the rate of protolysis is slow. As the pH value is increased, the methyl quadruplet collapses into a single line, while the NH_3^+ triplet (due to coupling with

N¹⁴) diminishes in intensity and ultimately disappears.   The water signal broadens and then narrows again.

These changes provide quantitative information about the protolysis rate and mechanism.   The collapse of the methyl-multiplet structure

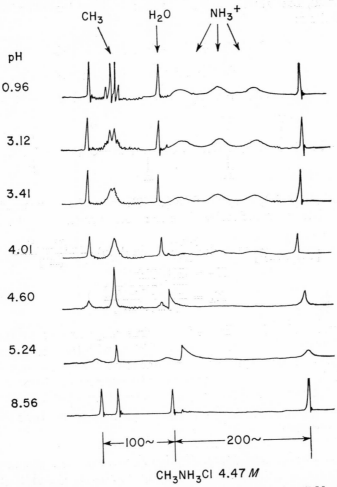

Fɪɢ. 18-8. Proton magnetic resonance spectra at 31.65 Mc/sec of 4.47 M solutions of methylammonium chloride in water at various pH.   The lines at extreme left and right are repetitions of the water line.   Different groups were recorded at different amplifications.   (Grunwald, Loewenstein, and Meiboom.[152])

arises because the protons on the NH_3^+ group are being more frequently replaced than others.   The broadening of the water line at intermediate pH indicates that water molecules play some part in this process, and at high pH there is a single line for H_2O and NH_3^+ protons.   Since the amount of methylamine present was small under conditions examined, the rate-determining step is

$$CH_3NH_3^+ + B \rightarrow CH_3NH_2 + BH \qquad (18\text{-}17)$$

Grunwald, Loewenstein, and Meiboom considered the following possible mechanisms:

$$CH_3NH_3^+ + H_2O \xrightarrow{k_1} CH_3NH_2 + H_3O^+ \qquad (18\text{-}18)$$

$$CH_3NH_3^+ + OH^- \xrightarrow{k_2} CH_3NH_2 + H_2O \qquad (18\text{-}19)$$

$$CH_3NH_3^+ + NH_2CH_3 \xrightarrow{k_3} CH_3NH_2 + NH_3CH_3^+ \qquad (18\text{-}20)$$

$$CH_3\overset{H}{\underset{H}{N}}-H^+ + \overset{H}{O}-H + \overset{H}{\underset{H}{N}}CH_3 \xrightarrow{k_4} CH_3\overset{H}{\underset{H}{N}} + H-\overset{H}{O} + H^+-\overset{H}{\underset{H}{N}}CH_3 \quad (18\text{-}21)$$

In reaction (18-21), as opposed to (18-20), the exchange proceeds via an intermediate water molecule. The complete expression for the rate is

$$\frac{\text{Rate}}{[CH_3NH_3^+]} = k_1 + \frac{k_2 K_W}{[H^+]} + (k_3 + k_4)\frac{[CH_3NH_3^+]K_A}{[H^+]} \qquad (18\text{-}22)$$

where
$$K_W = [H^+][OH^-] \qquad (18\text{-}23)$$

$$K_A = \frac{[H^+][CH_3NH_2]}{[CH_3NH_3^+]} \qquad (18\text{-}24)$$

The value of k_1 is negligible in the time range covered by the NMR method (0.2 to 0.002 sec). This is consistent with the fact that the CH$_3$ quadruplet is not collapsed at low pH and low concentration of $CH_3NH_3^+$ (Fig. 18-8), where Eq. (18-18) would be the only mechanism. An upper limit of 0.2 sec^{-1} was placed on k_1. Under other conditions the rate of protolysis was measured by observing the shape of the partially collapsed CH$_3$ quadruplet, using a theory similar to that of Gutowsky, McCall, and Slichter (Sec. 10-3a). To allow for field-inhomogeneity broadening in the absence of exchange, an effective T_2 was included. By measuring the rate as a function of the concentrations $[CH_3NH_3^+]$ and $[H^+]$, it was possible to obtain information about the constants k_2 and $k_3 + k_4$. In fact $k_2 K_W$ was found to be zero within experimental error, so that a rate measurement directly gives $k_3 + k_4$.

Grunwald, Loewenstein, and Meiboom[152] were also able to estimate the relative importance of processes (18-20) and (18-21) by examining the broadening of the water line, since this could be caused by (18-21) but not by (18-20). As we have seen [Eq. (10-17)], extra broadening here can be used to measure the mean time a proton spends on a water molecule before returning to nitrogen. Combined with the over-all rate measurement, this enables one to make an estimate of the fraction of protolysis that proceeds by transfer of a proton to a water molecule, and so to distinguish between the two mechanisms. For 4 M methylammonium chloride, a value of 0.58 was found for $k_3/(k_3 + k_4)$.

An exactly parallel investigation of di- and trimethylammonium ions was carried out by Loewenstein and Meiboom.[253] The complete results for all systems are summarized in Table 18-2. They show that the impor-

TABLE 18-2. PROTOLYSIS-RATE CONSTANTS OF MONO-, DI-
AND TRIMETHYLAMMONIUM IONS[253]
(Measured by proton resonance in sec^{-1} mole^{-1}, $T = 22 \pm 1°$C)

Compound	k_1†	k_2‡	k_3§	k_4¶
$CH_3NH_3^+$	0.4×10^{-2}	10^{11}	2.5×10^8	3.4×10^8
$(CH_3)_2NH_2^+$	0.4×10^{-2}	10^{11}	0.4×10^8	5.6×10^8
$(CH_3)_3NH^+$	5.5×10^{-2}	10^{11}	0.0×10^8	3.1×10^8

† Reaction with H_2O [Eq. (18-18)].
‡ Reaction with OH$^-$ [Eq. (18-19)].
§ Reaction with free amine [Eq. (18-20)].
¶ Reaction with free amine via solvent [Eq. (18-21)].

tance of exchange via the solvent increases with methyl substitution. Also, the rate constant k_1 (direct exchange with water molecules) becomes detectable in trimethylammonium ion. This may be connected with its greater basicity.[134]

CHAPTER 19

QUANTITATIVE ANALYSIS

The application of the NMR technique to problems of quantitative analysis has not been extensively investigated. This may be due to the fact that other techniques are often considered to be more suitable for specific analytical applications than the NMR technique in its present stage of instrumental development. Nevertheless, nuclear resonance has an important role to play in quantitative analysis and should prove increasingly useful in the field.

19-1. Signal-intensity Measurements

The underlying principle permitting use of magnetic resonance absorption as a quantitative measure of a particular substance is that the signal strength is proportional to the number of magnetic nuclei (Sec. 3-5). The dependence of signal strength on H_1, T_1, and T_2 for peaks and areas obtained in either absorption or dispersion has been discussed in Sec. 3-5 and in the literature.[156,380,465a] Here we shall be concerned primarily with the practical aspects of using signal intensities as a measure of concentration.

In practice, the intensity information required may be either:

1. The relative intensities of signals in the same spectrum
2. The comparison of intensities from different spectra (for example, a signal from solutions of different concentrations)

As discussed in Sec. 4-7, it is generally preferable to use area measurements in both these applications. By comparison of Eqs. (3-80a) and (3-80b) it is apparent that at low rf power (low H_1) the area of the absorption signal is independent of T_2, whereas the peak height is proportional to T_2. When weak signals are observed, it is necessary to increase H_1 in order to obtain a better intensity measurement. Under these conditions it is even more important to use areas rather than peak heights, since the area is less critically dependent on H_1. Indeed as H_1 is increased, the area tends to become constant, whereas the peak height diminishes to zero [cf. Eqs. (3-80a) and (3-80b)]. At high power, however, the area is a good measure of relative intensity only if the product T_1T_2 is the same for all signals. As pointed out in Chap. 9, T_1 and T_2 may be unequal, so that intensities evaluated on this basis may not always be accurate. To circumvent this difficulty, one usually constructs a standard calibration curve of signal strength as a function of the known concentration of standard samples. When a calibration curve is not available, one resorts to the less accurate procedure of assuming a direct proportionality of the signal intensity with the number of nuclei present. The above considerations are valid, of course, only for the same apparatus and experimental conditions.

Some general instrumental conditions affecting the accuracy of signal-intensity measurements (areas) have been investigated in detail by Williams.[465a] In addition to the problems of magnet stability and inhomogeneity and saturation effects, the effects of circuit loading and distortion as well as the leakage-voltage level were considered. It was demonstrated that, for quantitative absorption signal-intensity measurements, the ratio of maximum signal voltage to leakage voltage should be much smaller than unity. This requirement is unimportant when peak-height measurements are used.

As may be seen from comparison of Eqs. (3-80d) and (3-80b), use of the peak of the dispersion signal is preferable to using the peak-absorption signal because the dispersion signal depends less critically on the strength of the H_1 field. The area of the dispersion-mode signal between peaks is independent of T_1 and T_2 and therefore gives a good estimate of the intensity [Eq. (3-80e)]. This is particularly useful for measuring the intensity of weak signals.

The above considerations were concerned with signal intensity in static samples. Mitchell and Phillips[287] have described NMR techniques for analysis of H_2O in H_2O/D_2O mixtures in flowing samples. The effect of flowing motion on signal strength has been investigated by Bloom and Shoolery[62] and Suryan.[432] For liquids or solutions having relaxation times between 0.1 and 0.05 sec flowing at such a rate that the contents of the receiver coil are replaced about every hundredth of a second, Suryan found the signal from the flowing sample to be greater than that obtained from a static sample with rf power close to saturation.

Several applications of NMR techniques involving quantitative analysis have already been discussed in previous chapters. They include equilibrium and dissociation constants, protolysis, keto-enol tautomerism, and rotational isomerism (Chaps. 13, 15, 17, and 18). In this chapter we shall deal with some other applications chiefly concerned with the increase or decrease of a signal intensity as a measure of the number of magnetic nuclei. Methods[190,78] which rely on measurements of T_1 and T_2 to give concentration information are not discussed.

19-2. Moisture Analysis

One of the more highly developed applications of NMR techniques to chemical analysis involves the determination of water content in a wide variety of materials and products. Conventional methods of moisture

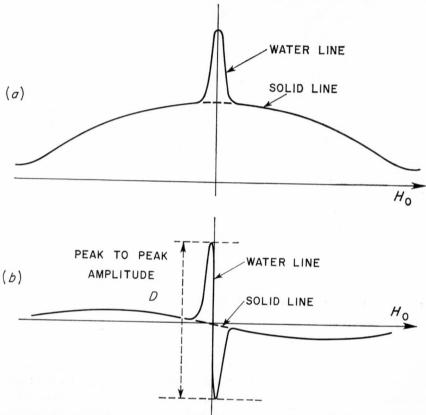

FIG. 19-1. Proton resonance signals (schematic) of sorbed water in biological materials. (a) Absorption curve. (b) Derivative curve. (*Courtesy of Schlumberger Well Surveying Corp.*)

determination in agricultural materials, food products, and pulp and paper products are often time consuming and sometimes unsatisfactory for other reasons. The successful development of the NMR method followed the extensive exploratory work of Shaw and Elsken and coworkers[413-415] and of Rollwitz[388] and Conway, Cohee, and Smith.[100]

The principle underlying the NMR method is based on the fact that the water molecules contained in many substances are relatively mobile compared to those of the hydrogen-containing host substance, which is usually in the form of a crystalline or amorphous solid or a highly viscous liquid. The proton resonance of such systems therefore appears as a greatly broadened signal superimposed on which is a narrow line arising from the sorbed water. This is schematically illustrated by Fig. 19-1. The upper curve shows the absorption curve. In most cases the water

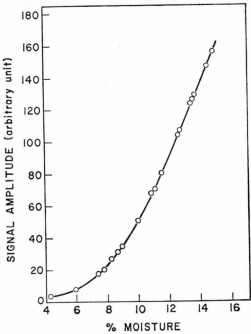

Fig. 19-2. Calibration curve for pearl starch. (*Courtesy of Corn Products Refining Co.*)

line has a width about two or three times that of pure liquid water, whereas the width of the line of the host material may be 10 to 100 times greater. Thus the absorption due to protons in the nonaqueous constituents of the sample is essentially constant over the narrow frequency region occupied by the water signal, and accordingly the intensity of the latter can be used for a quantitative measure of water content. In practice, it is more convenient to use the derivative curve (Fig. 19-1b) and to measure the peak-to-peak amplitude. The procedure is standardized by constructing a calibration curve for the substance to be analyzed, using samples of known moisture content. A typical curve of this kind is shown in Fig. 19-2.

The NMR method offers a rapid, nondestructive analysis, and since the result is in the form of an electrical signal, automatic control of drying and blending operations is possible.[5] The method is not affected by particle size and can be applied to a very large number of materials varying in water content from a few to 100 per cent.   Instruments specially designed for moisture analysis are commercially available.† The precision of the moisture analysis is of the order of ± 0.1 per cent or better. The absolute accuracy is of course only as good as that of the calibration curve.   The instrument employs a permanent magnet with a field strength of 1,750 gauss.   In order to reduce sampling error and increase signal strength, a relatively large sample volume (40 cm³) is employed. Greater sensitivity is also achieved by use of a narrow-band recording system.   The derivative of the absorption mode is obtained by field-modulation techniques,[344] together with phase-sensitive detection.

It may be noted that the calibration curve shown in Fig. 19-2 becomes nonlinear at low moisture content.   This behavior is typical of many materials and results from a greater (averaged) interaction of the sorbed water with the host material when only small amounts of water are present.   As a result the water line becomes broader and the signal amplitude is no longer a linear function of water content.   For starch containing about 15 per cent water, the line width of the water signal is about two times that of pure liquid.   As the water content of the starch is decreased, the line width of the absorption increases rapidly.   The measurement of line width of the water signal has been suggested by Shaw, Elsken, and Kunsman[415] as an alternative method for moisture analysis. The method is limited to relatively low moisture contents, but it has the advantage that spectrometer adjustments and other factors, such as sample packing, are less critical.

19-3. Miscellaneous Applications

   a. **Reaction Mixtures.**   Since the NMR technique is nondestructive, it is particularly suited to following changes of concentration in reaction mixtures.   An example of this type of application is the thermal isomerization of substituted 5-aminotetrazoles described by Whittaker, Moore, Shoolery and Jones.[463]   The reaction proceeds according to

For the ethyl compound ($R = C_2H_5$), spectra obtained from 150 to 160° at intervals of 30 and 60 min were obtained.   The typical quartet for CH_2

† Schlumberger Well Surveying Corporation, Ridgefield, Conn.

and triplet for CH_3 were observed at the start of the reaction corresponding to I. As the reaction progressed, a new CH_3CH_2 signal pattern appeared at lower field corresponding to the ethyl group in II and increased in intensity as time went on. Quantitative measurements were not made, but it was noted that at 200°C the equilibrium concentration of II was 96 per cent.

A semiquantitative investigation of the proton resonance in the B_2D_6—B_5H_5 exchange reaction has been carried out by Koske, Kaufman, and Lauterbur.[222] From measurements of the ratios of the heights of the appropriate peaks corresponding to the terminal and bridge-type protons of pentaborane, the relative rates of exchange were found to be the same (within the experimental error of ±10 per cent) for the two types of protons.

The kinetics of isomerization of the insecticide β-ethyl-mercapto-ethyl-diethyl-thionophosphate (III) to the thioisomer (IV)

$$EtO \diagdown \underset{\diagup}{P} \diagup \overset{S}{\diagdown} \qquad \rightleftharpoons \qquad EtO \diagdown \underset{\diagup}{P} \diagup \overset{O}{\diagdown}$$

EtO	OC₂H₄SC₂H₅	EtO	SC₂H₄SC₂H₅
	III		IV

has been investigated quantitatively by Muller and Goldenson.[294] The magnetic resonance of the P^{31} nucleus was a single line for each isomer, the two being separated by about 40 ppm. The rate data could be represented by the equation $-dc/dt = k_1c/(k_2 + c)$, in which c is the concentration in mole per cent and t is in hours. At 100 and 115°C the NMR data gave $k_1 = 0.074$ and $k_2 = 0.55$, and $k_1 = 0.255$ and $k_2 = 0.45$, respectively.

The kinetics of the hydrolysis of acetic anhydride to acetic acid was studied by Bhar and Forsling.[43] The proton of the carboxyl group and the protons of the water give a single signal by virtue of rapid exchange. The separation of this signal from that of the CH_3 groups [which appeared as a single signal under the conditions of resolution (10^{-6} to 10^{-7})] was related to the concentration as described in Chap. 18. Analysis of the data gave the specific rate constant for a first-order reaction equal to 6×10^{-5} sec^{-1} at 27°C. These results agree well with those obtained by chemical analysis up to 0.5 mole fraction of acetic acid formed. The lack of agreement at higher yields of acetic acid was attributed to molecular association and complex formation in the reacting liquid system and also to the approximate validity of the theory of Gutowsky and Saika (Sec. 10-2) relating the position of the signal in the field to the concentration. A similar investigation of the reaction between methanol and acetic anhydride was carried out by Bhar,[41] and the proton magnetic resonance data were found to correspond with a second-order reaction.

b. Isotopes. Isotopic-abundance ratios have been measured for H^2/H^1 and Li^6/Li^7 in aqueous solution by adding a paramagnetic substance to the sample.[193] This shortens T_1 and makes the T_2/T_1 ratio essentially unity. Proton resonance has been used to measure[287] the water content of H_2O/D_2O mixtures in both static and flowing samples covering the range 0.2 to 100 per cent H_2O in D_2O. The plot of resonance absorption vs. per cent H_2O in D_2O was found to be linear over the range 0 to 0.4 per cent H_2O in D_2O, but is not linear for higher concentrations, presumably because of the change of T_1 with concentration. The accuracy of the analyses in the low-concentration range is limited by the signal-to-noise ratio (about 20:1 for 0.3 per cent H_2O in D_2O). When enough sample is available, and small amounts of H_2O are to be detected, it has been found convenient[156] to make up known mixtures of the sample with pure H_2O. Extrapolation of the intensity of the proton signal to 0 per cent H_2O enables the concentration of H_2O in the original sample to be obtained from the intercept on the intensity axis. Both narrow-band phase-sensitive systems and high-resolution methods have been employed for these experiments.

c. Phosphates. The P resonances of the anions of various oxy acids of phosphorus have been measured.[83] The data are collected in Table 19-1. (See also Table 12-19.) In actual mixtures the relative amounts

TABLE 19-1. PHOSPHORUS RESONANCES OF ANIONS OF VARIOUS OXY ACIDS[83]

Compound	δ, ppm†	Relative intensity
Hypophosphite	133	1/4
	87	1/2
	42	1/4
Phosphate:		
Middle groups	120	1
End groups	109	1
Orthophosphate	100	1
Hypophosphate	91	1
Ortho- and pyrophosphites	120	1/2
	64	1/2

† The chemical shift is defined as

$$\delta = 100 + 10^6[(H - H_{H_3PO_4})/H_{H_3PO_4}]$$

where $H_{H_3PO_4}$ is the resonant field of 85 per cent orthophosphoric acid.

of these phosphorus compounds have been measured from areas under the absorption signal with an accuracy of 2 to 10 per cent. At present the analysis by NMR is applicable to relatively concentrated solutions and thus is suitable only for acids and alkali-metal and ammonium salts.

d. Other Applications. There is no question that NMR techniques can be adapted for quantitative measurements in other areas, such as compounds of biological importance, provided concentrations are adequate or dilute solutions can be concentrated sufficiently before investigation. Direct determination of magnetic nuclei in solid samples, such as soils and ores, might also be practical with broad-band techniques.

GENERAL REVIEWS

Andrew, E. R.: "Nuclear Magnetic Resonance," Cambridge University Press, New York, 1955.

Castells, J.: *Rev. cienc. apl. (Madrid)*, **9**, 499 (1957).

Dailey, B. P.: *Ann. Rev. Phys. Chem.*, **4**, 425 (1953).

Darrow, K. K.: *Bell System Tech. J.*, **32**, 74, 384 (1953).

Gordy, W.: "Techniques of Organic Chemistry," vol. 9, chap. 2, Interscience Publishers, Inc., New York, 1956.

Gutowsky, H. S.: Analytical Applications of NMR, in W. G. Berl (ed.): "Physical Methods in Chemical Analysis," vol. 3, Academic Press, Inc., New York, 1956.

——: *Ann. Rev. Phys. Chem.*, **5**, 333 (1954).

Hauser, K. H.: *Angew. Chem.*, **68**, 729 (1956).

Hutchison, C. A.: *Ann. Rev. Phys. Chem.*, **7**, 359 (1956).

McConnell, H. M.: *Ann. Rev. Phys. Chem.*, **8**, 105 (1957).

Pake, G. E.: *Am. J. Phys.*, **18**, 438, 473 (1950).

——: *Ann. Rev. Nuclear Sci.*, **4**, 33 (1954).

——: Nuclear Magnetic Resonance, in "Solid State Physics," vol. 2, Academic Press, Inc., New York, 1956.

Shoolery, J. N., and H. E. Weaver: *Ann. Rev. Phys. Chem.*, **6**, 433 (1955).

Smith, J. A. S.: *Quart. Revs. (London)*, **7**, 279 (1953).

Wertz, J. E.: *Chem. Revs.*, **5**, 829 (1955).

BIBLIOGRAPHY

1 Abragam, A., and W. G. Proctor: *Phys. Rev.*, **106**, 160(L), (1957).

2 Abragam, A., and M. H. L. Pryce: *Proc. Roy. Soc. (London)*, **A205**, 135 (1951).

3 Abraham, R. J., and H. J. Bernstein: *Can. J. Chem.*, **37**, no. 6 (1959).

4 Abraham, R. J., J. Pople, and H. J. Bernstein: *Can. J. Chem.*, **36**, 1302 (1958).

5 Aikman, A. R., R. K. Codrington, and F. F. Kirchner: *Control Eng.*, June, 1957.

6 Alexander, S.: *J. Chem. Phys.*, **28**, 358 (1958).

7 Allred, A. L., and E. G. Rochow: *J. Am. Chem. Soc.*, **79**, 5361 (1957).

8 Anderson, H. L.: *Phys. Rev.*, **76**, 1460 (1949).

9 Anderson, P. W.: *J. Phys. Soc. Japan*, **9**, 316 (1954).

10 Anderson, W. A.: *Phys. Rev.*, **102**, 151 (1956).

11 Anderson, W. A.: *Phys. Rev.*, **104**, 850 (1956).
12 Anderson, W. A., and J. T. Arnold: *Phys. Rev.*, **94**, 497 (1954).
13 Anderson, W. A., and J. T. Arnold: *Phys. Rev.*, **101**, 511 (1956).
14 Anderson, W. A., and H. M. McConnell: *J. Chem. Phys.*, **26**, 1496 (1957).
15 Andrew, E. R.: "Nuclear Magnetic Resonance," Cambridge University Press, New York, 1955.
16 Andrew, E. R.: *Phys. Rev.*, **82**, 443 (1951).
17 Anet, F. A. L., and C. R. Eves: *Can. J. Chem.*, **36**, 902 (1958).
18 Angus, W. R., and D. V. Tilston: *Trans. Faraday Soc.*, **43**, 221 (1947).
19 Arnold, J. T.: Ph.D. thesis, Stanford University, 1954.
20 Arnold, J. T.: *Phys. Rev.*, **102**, 136 (1956).
21 Arnold, J. T., S. S. Dharmatti, and M. E. Packard: *J. Chem. Phys.*, **19**, 507 (1951).
22 Arnold, J. T., and M. E. Packard: *J. Chem. Phys.*, **19**, 1608 (1951).
23 Aronov, O. L., V. M. Tatevski, and A. V. Frost: *Doklady Akad. Nauk SSSR*, **60**, 387 (1948).
24 Auer, H.: *Ann. Physik*, **18**, 593 (1933).
25 Bader, A. R., H. S. Gutowsky, G. A. Williams, and P. E. Yankwitch: *J. Am. Chem. Soc.*, **78**, 2385 (1956).
26 Baker, E. B.: *J. Chem. Phys.*, **23**, 1981 (1955).
27 Baker, E. B.: *J. Chem. Phys.*, **26**, 960 (1957).
28 Baker, E. B., and L. W. Burd: *Rev. Sci. Instr.*, **28**, 313 (1957).
29 Bannerjee, N. K., T. P. Das, and A. K. Saha: *Proc. Roy. Soc. (London)*, **A226**, 490 (1954).
30 Barton, D. H. R.: *J. Chem. Soc.*, 1027 (1953).
31 Batdorf, R. L.: Ph.D. thesis, University of Minnesota, 1955.
32 Beach, J. Y., and S. H. Bauer: *J. Am. Chem. Soc.*, **62**, 3440 (1940).
33 Becker, E. D., U. Liddel, and J. N. Shoolery: *J. Mol. Spectroscopy*, **2**, 1 (1958).
34 Belgers, H. G., L. van der Kint, and J. S. van Wieringen: *Phys. Rev.*, **95**, 1683 (1954).
35 Bené, G. J., P. M. Denis, and R. C. Extermann: *Physica*, **17**, 308 (1951).
36 Benedek, G. B., and E. M. Purcell: *J. Chem. Phys.*, **22**, 2003 (1954).
37 Bernstein, H. J., J. A. Pople, and W. G. Schneider: *Can. J. Chem.*, **35**, 65 (1957).
38 Bernstein, H. J., and W. G. Schneider: *J. Chem. Phys.*, **24**, 469 (1956).
39 Bernstein, H. J., W. G. Schneider, and J. A. Pople: *Proc. Roy. Soc. (London)*, **A236**, 515 (1956).
40 Bhagavantam, S.: *Indian J. Phys.*, **4**, 1 (1929).
41 Bhar, B. N.: *Arkiv Fysik*, **12**, 171 (1957).
42 Bhar, B. N.: *Arkiv Kemi*, **10**, 223 (1956).
43 Bhar, B. N., and W. Forsling: *Arkiv Fysik*, **11**, 405 (1957).
44 Bhar, B. N., W. Forsling, and G. Lindström: *Arkiv Fysik*, **10**, 59 (1956).
45 Bhar, B. N., and G. Lindström: *J. Chem. Phys.*, **23**, 1958 (1955).
46 Bhatnagar, S. S., and K. N. Mathur: "Physical Principles and Applications of Magnetochemistry," Macmillan & Co., Ltd., London, 1935.
47 Biemann, K., G. Buchi, and B. H. Walker: *J. Am. Chem. Soc.*, **79**, 5558 (1957).
48 Blaser, B.: *Ber.*, **68**, 1670 (1935); **86**, 563 (1953).
49 Bloch, F.: *Phys. Rev.*, **70**, 460 (1946).
50 Bloch, F.: *Phys. Rev.*, **93**, 944 (1954).
51 Bloch, F.: *Phys. Rev.*, **94**, 496 (1954).
52 Bloch, F.: *Phys. Rev.*, **102**, 104 (1956).
53 Bloch, F., W. W. Hansen, and M. E. Packard: *Phys. Rev.*, **69**, 127 (1946).

54   Bloch, F., W. W. Hansen, and M. E. Packard: *Phys. Rev.*, **70**, 474 (1946).
55   Bloembergen, N.: *J. Chem. Phys.*, **27**, 572 (1957).
56   Bloembergen, N.: *J. Chem. Phys.*, **27**, 595 (1957).
57   Bloembergen, N.: "Nuclear Magnetic Relaxation," Nijhoff, The Hague, 1948.
58   Bloembergen, N., and W. C. Dickinson: *Phys. Rev.*, **79**, 179 (1950).
59   Bloembergen, N., E. M. Purcell, and R. V. Pound: *Phys. Rev.*, **73**, 679 (1948).
60   Bloom, A. L.: *J. Chem. Phys.*, **25**, 793 (1956).
61   Bloom, A. L.: *Phys. Rev.*, **98**, 1105 (1955).
62   Bloom, A. L., and J. N. Shoolery: *Phys. Rev.*, **90**, 358(A) (1953).
63   Bloom, A. L., and J. N. Shoolery: *Phys. Rev.*, **97**, 1261 (1955).
64   Bloom, M.: *Physica*, **23**, 237 (1957).
65   Bonet, G. V., and A. V. Bushkovitch: *J. Chem. Phys.*, **21**, 1299 (1953).
66   Boreham, G. R., F. R. Goss, and G. J. Minkoff: *Chem. & Ind. (London)*, 1954 (1955).
67   Bothner-By, A. A., and C. Naar-Colin: *Ann. N.Y. Acad. Sci.*, **70**, 833 (1958).
68   Bothner-By, A. A., and R. E. Glick: *J. Am. Chem. Soc.*, **78**, 1071 (1956).
69   Bothner-By, A. A., and R. E. Glick: *J. Chem. Phys.*, **25**, 362 (1956).
70   Bothner-By, A. A., and R. E. Glick: *J. Chem. Phys.*, **26**, 1647 (1957).
71   Bothner-By, A. A., and R. E. Glick: *J. Chem. Phys.*, **26**, 1651 (1957).
72   Bothner-By, A. A., and C. Naar-Colin: *J. Am. Chem. Soc.*, **80**, 1728 (1958).
73   Bottini, A. T., and J. D. Roberts: *J. Am. Chem. Soc.*, **78**, 5126 (1956).
73a   Bottini, A. T., and J. D. Roberts: *J. Org. Chem.*, **21**, 1169 (1956); *J. Am. Chem. Soc.*, **80**, 5203 (1958).
73b   Briegleb, G.: "Zwischenmolekular Kräfte und Molekülstruktur," J. W. Edwards, Publisher, Inc., Ann Arbor, Mich., 1944.
74   Briegleb, G., and W. Strohmeier: *Z. Naturforsch.*, **6b**, 6 (1951).
75   Brown, H. C., and J. D. Brady: *J. Am. Chem. Soc.*, **74**, 3570 (1952).
76   Brown, H. C., and M. Gerstein: *J. Am. Chem. Soc.*, **72**, 2926 (1950).
77   Brown, R. M.: *Phys. Rev.*, **78**, 530 (1950).
78   Bruce, C. R., R. E. Norberg, and S. I. Weissman: *J. Chem. Phys.*, **24**, 473 (1956).
79   Buckingham, A. D., and J. A. Pople: *Proc. Cambridge Phil. Soc.*, **53**, 262 (1957).
80   Buckingham, R. A., H. S. W. Massey, and S. R. Tibbs: *Proc. Roy. Soc. (London)*, **A178**, 119 (1941).
81   Burbank, R. D., and F. N. Bensey: *J. Chem. Phys.*, **21**, 602 (1953).
82   Burgess, J. H., and R. M. Brown: *Rev. Sci. Instr.*, **23**, 334 (1952).
83   Callis, C. F., J. R. Van Wazer, and J. N. Shoolery: *Anal. Chem.*, **28**, 269 (1956).
84   Callis, C. F., J. R. Van Wazer, J. N. Shoolery, and W. A. Anderson: *J. Am. Chem. Soc.*, **79**, 2719 (1957).
85   Carr, H. Y., and E. M. Purcell: *Phys. Rev.*, **88**, 415 (1952).
86   Carr, H. Y., and E. M. Purcell: *Phys. Rev.*, **94**, 630 (1954).
87   Carter, C.: *Proc. Roy. Soc. (London)*, **A235**, 321 (1956).
88   Carver, T. R., and C. P. Slichter: *Phys. Rev.*, **92**, 212 (1953).
89   Chattaway, F. D., and E. G. Kellett: *J. Chem. Soc.*, 2709 (1928).
90   Chiarotti, G., G. Cristiani, L. Giulotto, and G. Lanzi: *Nuovo cimento*, **12**, 519 (1954).
91   Chiarotti, G., and L. Giulotto: *Phys. Rev.*, **93**, 1241 (1954).
92   Chisholm, M. J., and C. Y. Hopkins: *Can. J. Chem.*, **35**, 358 (1957).
93   Clapp, J. K.: *Proc. IRE*, **36**, 356 (1948); **42**, 1295 (1954).
94   Cohen, A. D., and C. Reid: *J. Chem. Phys.*, **25**, 790 (1956).
95   Cohen, A. D., N. Sheppard, and J. J. Turner: *Proc. Chem. Soc. (London)*, **118** (1958).

96 Conant, J. B., and A. F. Thompson: *J. Am. Chem. Soc.*, **54**, 4039 (1932).
97 Condon, E. U., and G. H. Shortley: "Theory of Atomic Spectra," Cambridge University Press, New York, 1953.
98 Conger, R. L., and P. W. Selwood: *J. Chem. Phys.*, **20**, 383 (1952).
99 Conroy, H., P. R. Brook, M. K. Ront, and N. Silverman: *J. Am. Chem. Soc.*, **79**, 1763 (1957).
100 Conway, T. F., R. F. Cohee, and R. J. Smith: *Food Eng.*, June, 1957.
101 Cook, D., Y. Lupien, and W. G. Schneider: *Can. J. Chem.*, **34**, 957 (1956).
102 Cook, D., Y. Lupien, and W. G. Schneider: *Can. J. Chem.*, **34**, 964 (1956).
103 Corey, E. J., H. J. Burke, and W. A. Remers: *J. Am. Chem. Soc.*, **77**, 4941 (1955).
104 Corey, E. J., G. Slomp, S. Dev, S. Tobinga, and E. R. Glazier: *J. Am. Chem. Soc.*, **80**, 1204 (1958).
105 Corio, P. L., and B. P. Dailey: *J. Am. Chem. Soc.*, **78**, 3043 (1956).
105*a* Cotton, F. A., J. W. George, and J. S. Waugh: *J. Chem. Phys.*, **28**, 994 (1958).
106 Cotton, A., and H. Mouton: *Compt. rend.*, **141**, 317, 349 (1905).
107 Coulson, C. A.: "Valence," p. 207, Clarendon Press, Oxford, 1952.
108 Coulson, C. A., and H. C. Longuet-Higgins: *Proc. Roy. Soc. (London)*, **A191**, 39 (1947).
109 Das, T. P., and R. Bersohn: *Phys. Rev.*, **104**, 476 (1956).
110 Das, T. P., and D. K. Roy: *Phys. Rev.*, **98**, 525 (1955).
111 Dailey, B. P., and J. N. Shoolery: *J. Am. Chem. Soc.*, **77**, 3977 (1955).
112 Dauben, W. G., and K. S. Pitzer: "Steric Effects in Organic Chemistry," chap. 1, John Wiley & Sons, Inc., New York, 1956.
113 Debye, P.: "Polar Molecules," Dover Publications, New York, 1945.
114 Dehmelt, H. G.: *J. Chem. Phys.*, **21**, 380 (1953).
115 Dewar, M. J. S.: "The Electronic Theory of Organic Chemistry," Clarendon Press, Oxford, 1949.
116 Dharmatti, S. S., and H. E. Weaver: *Phys. Rev.*, **87**, 675 (1952).
117 Dicke, R. H.: *Rev. Sci. Instr.*, **17**, 268 (1946).
118 Dickinson, W. C.: *Phys. Rev.*, **77**, 736 (1950).
119 Dickinson, W. C.: *Phys. Rev.*, **80**, 563 (1950).
120 Dickinson, W. C.: *Phys. Rev.*, **81**, 717 (1951).
121 Diehl, P.: *Helv. Phys. Acta*, **30**, 91 (1957).
121*a* Diehl, P., and R. A. Ogg: *Nature*, **180**, 1114 (1957).
121*b* Dirac, P. A. M.: "Principles of Quantum Mechanics," Oxford University Press, New York, 1935.
121*c* Dodd, R. E., L. A. Woodward, and H. L. Roberts: *Trans. Faraday Soc.*, **52**, 1052 (1956).
122 Doering, W. Von E., G. Laber, R. Vonderwohl, N. F. Chamberlain, and R. B. Williams: *J. Am. Chem. Soc.*, **78**, 5448 (1956).
123 Douglas, J. E., B. S. Rabinovitch, and F. S. Looney: *J. Chem. Phys.*, **23**, 315 (1955).
124 Drain, L. E.: *Proc. Phys. Soc. (London)*, **62A**, 301 (1949).
125 Drysdale, J. J., and W. D. Phillips: *J. Am. Chem. Soc.*, **79**, 319 (1957).
126 Dudley, F. B., G. H. Cady, and D. F. Eggers: *J. Am. Chem. Soc.*, **78**, 290 (1956).
127 Dudley, F. B., G. H. Cady, and D. F. Eggers: *J. Am. Chem. Soc.*, **78**, 1553 (1956).
128 Dudley, F. B., and J. N. Shoolery, and G. H. Cady: *J. Am. Chem. Soc.*, **78**, 568 (1956).
129 Dulmadge, W. J., and W. N. Lipscomb: *J. Am. Chem. Soc.*, **73**, 3539 (1951).
130 Dunitz, J. D.: *Acta Cryst.*, **2**, 1 (1949).

131   Edgell, W. F., and D. C. Weiblen: *J. Chem. Phys.*, **18**, 571 (1950).
132   Eggleston, B. C., D. F. Evans, and R. E. Richards: *J. Chem. Soc.*, 941 (1954).
133   Ettinger, M. T.: *J. Am. Chem. Soc.*, **74**, 5805 (1952).
133a   Evans, D. F.: *Proc. Chem. Soc. (London)*, 115 (1958).
134   Everett, D. H., and W. F. K. Wynne-Jones: *Proc. Roy. Soc. (London)*, **A177**, 499 (1941).
135   Fermi, E.: *Z. Physik*, **60**, 320 (1930).
135a   Fessenden, R. W., and J. S. Waugh: *Abstracts, Am. Chem. Soc. Meeting*, New York, 1957.
136   Finegold, H.: *Ann. N.Y. Acad. Sci.*, **70**, 875 (1958).
137   Freeman, R., G. R. Murray, and R. E. Richards: *Proc. Roy. Soc. (London)*, **A242**, 455 (1957).
138   Frey, H. M.: *J. Chem. Phys.*, **25**, 600 (1956).
139   Gabillard, R.: *Compt. rend.*, **232**, 1551 (1951).
140   Gabillard, R.: *Compt. rend.*, **233**, 39 (1951).
141   Gabillard, R.: *Phys. Rev.*, **85**, 694 (1952).
142   Giulotto, L., G. Chiarotti, and G. Cristiani: *J. Chem. Phys.*, **22**, 1143 (1954).
143   Glick, R. E., and A. A. Bothner-By: *J. Chem. Phys.*, **25**, 362 (1956).
143a   Glick, R. E., and S. J. Ehrenson: *J. Phys., Chem.* **62**, 1599 (1958).
143b   Golay, M. J. E.: *Rev. Sci. Instr.*, **29**, 313 (1958).
144   Goodman, L., R. M. Silverstein, and J. N. Shoolery: *J. Am. Chem. Soc.*, **78**, 4493 (1956).
145   Gorter, C. J.: *Physica*, **3**, 995 (1936).
146   Gouriet, G. G.: *Wireless Eng.*, **27**, 105 (1950).
147   Graham, D. M., and J. S. Waugh: *J. Chem. Phys.*, **27**, 968 (1957).
148   Griffith, J. S., and L. E. Orgel: *Trans. Faraday Soc.*, **53**, 601 (1957).
149   Gripenberg, J.: *Acta Chem. Scand.*, **10**, 487 (1956).
150   Grivet, P., M. Soutif, and M. Bugle: *Compt rend.*, **229**, 113 (1949).
151   Grossman, P.: *Z. physik. Chem.*, **109**, 305 (1924).
152   Grunwald, E., A. Loewenstein, and S. Meiboom: *J. Chem. Phys.*, **27**, 630 (1957).
153   Grunwald, E., A. Loewenstein, and S. Meiboom: *J. Chem. Phys.*, **27**, 641 (1957).
154   Gutowsky, H. S.: *Discussions Faraday Soc.*, **19**, 246 (1955).
155   Gutowsky, H. S.: *Discussions Faraday Soc.*, **19**, 247 (1955).
156   Gutowsky, H. S.: Analytical Applications of NMR, in W. G. Berl (ed.): "Physical Methods in Chemical Analysis," vol. 3, p. 303, Academic Press, Inc., New York, 1956.
157   Gutowsky, H. S., and S. Fujiwara: *J. Chem. Phys.*, **22**, 1782 (1954).
158   Gutowsky, H. S., and C. J. Hoffman: *Phys. Rev.*, **80**, 110 (1950).
159   Gutowsky, H. S., and C. J. Hoffman: *J. Chem. Phys.*, **19**, 1259 (1951).
160   Gutowsky, H. S., and C. H. Holm: *J. Chem. Phys.*, **25**, 1228 (1956).
161   Gutowsky, H. S., C. H. Holm, A. Saika, and G. A. Williams: *J. Am. Chem. Soc.*, **79**, 4596 (1957).
162   Gutowsky, H. S., and D. W. McCall: *Phys. Rev.*, **82**, 748 (1951).
163   Gutowsky, H. S., and D. W. McCall: *J. Chem. Phys.*, **22**, 162 (1954).
164   Gutowsky, H. S., D. W. McCall, B. R. McGarvey, and L. H. Meyer: *J. Am. Chem. Soc.*, **74**, 4809 (1952).
165   Gutowsky, H. S., D. W. McCall, and C. P. Slichter: *Phys. Rev.*, **84**, 589 (1951).
166   Gutowsky, H. S., D. W. McCall, and C. P. Slichter: *J. Chem. Phys.*, **21**, 279 (1953).
167   Gutowsky, H. S., and B. R. McGarvey: *J. Chem. Phys.*, **21**, 1423 (1953).
168   Gutowsky, H. S., and B. R. McGarvey: *Phys. Rev.*, **91**, 81 (1953).

169   Gutowsky, H. S., L. H. Meyer, and D. W. McCall: *J. Chem. Phys.*, **23**, 982 (1955).

170   Gutowsky, H. S., L. H. Meyer, and R. E. McClure: *Rev. Sci. Instr.*, **24**, 644 (1953).

171   Gutowsky, H. S., R. L. Rutledge, M. Tamres, and S. Searles: *J. Am. Chem. Soc.*, **76**, 4242 (1954).

172   Gutowsky, H. S., and A. Saika: *J. Chem. Phys.*, **21**, 1688 (1953).

173   Gutowsky, H. S., and D. E. Woessner: *Phys. Rev.*, **104**, 843 (1956).

174   Habgood, T., and L. Marion: *Can. J. Chem.*, **33**, 604 (1955).

175   Hahn, E. L.: *Phys. Rev.*, **77**, 297 (1950).

176   Hahn, E. L.: *Phys. Rev.*, **80**, 580 (1950).

177   Hahn, E. L., and D. E. Maxwell: *Phys. Rev.*, **84**, 1246 (1951).

178   Hahn, E. L., and D. E. Maxwell: *Phys. Rev.*, **84**, 1286 (1951).

179   Hahn, E. L., and D. E. Maxwell: *Phys. Rev.*, **88**, 1070 (1952).

180   Halbach, K.: *Helv. Phys. Acta*, **29**, 37 (1956).

181   Hammett, L. P.: "Physical Organic Chemistry," p. 186, McGraw-Hill Book Company, Inc., New York, 1940.

182   Hassel, O.: *Quart. Revs. (London)*, **7**, 221 (1953).

183   Hassel, O., and A. Pettersen: *Tidsskr. Kjemi, Bergvesen Met.*, **1**, 57 (1941).

184   Havens, G. G.: *Phys. Rev.*, **43**, 992 (1933).

185   Haworth, W. N.: "The Constitution of Sugars," p. 90, Edward Arnold & Co., London, 1929.

186   Hedberg, K., M. E. Jones, and V. Shomaker: *J. Am. Chem. Soc.*, **73**, 3538 (1951).

187   Hedberg, K., and V. Shomaker: *J. Am. Chem. Soc.*, **73**, 1482 (1951).

188   Herbstein, F. H., and G. H. J. Schmidt: *J. Chem. Soc.*, 3302 (1954).

189   Herzberg, G.: "Infrared and Raman Spectra," D. Van Nostrand Company, Inc., Princeton, N.J., 1945.

190   Hichmott, T. W., and P. W. Selwood: *J. Chem. Phys.*, **20**, 1339 (1952).

191   Hoffman, C. J., B. E. Holder, and W. L. Jolly: *J. Phys. Chem.*, **62**, 364 (1958).

192   Holder, B. E., and M. P. Klein: *J. Chem. Phys.*, **23**, 1956 (1955).

193   Holder, B. E., and M. P. Klein: *Phys. Rev.*, **98**, 265A (1955).

194   Holm, C. H.: *J. Chem. Phys.*, **26**, 707 (1957).

195   Holzman, G. R., P. C. Lauterbur, J. H. Anderson, and W. Koth: *J. Chem. Phys.*, **25**, 172 (1956).

196   Hood, G. C., O. Redlich, and C. A. Reilly: *J. Chem. Phys.*, **22**, 2067 (1954).

197   Hood, G. C., and C. A. Reilly: *J. Chem. Phys.*, **27**, 1126 (1957).

197a Hood, G. C., and C. A. Reilly: *J. Chem. Phys.*, **28**, 329 (1958).

198   Hopkins, C. Y., and H. J. Bernstein: *Can. J. Chem.*, **37**, 775 (1959).

199   Hudson, C. S.: *Advances in Carbohydrate Chem.*, **3**, 15 (1948).

200   Huggins, C. M., and G. C. Pimentel: *J. Chem. Phys.*, **23**, 896 (1955).

201   Huggins, C. M., G. C. Pimentel, and J. N. Shoolery: *J. Chem. Phys.*, **23**, 1244 (1955).

202   Huggins, C. M., G. C. Pimentel, and J. N. Shoolery: *J. Phys. Chem.*, **60**, 1311 (1956).

203   Hund, F.: *Z. Physik*, **43**, 805 (1927).

204   Ingold, C. K.: "Structure and Mechanism in Organic Chemistry," Cornell University Press, Ithaca, N.Y., 1953.

204a Isobe, T., K. Inukai, and K. Ito: *J. Chem. Phys.*, **27**, 1215 (1957).

205   Jacobson, B., W. A. Anderson, and J. T. Arnold: *Nature*, **173**, 772 (1954).

206   Jacobsohn, B. A., and R. K. Wangsness: *Phys. Rev.*, **73**, 942 (1948).

207   James, H. M., and A. S. Coolidge: *J. Chem. Phys.*, **1**, 825 (1933).
207a   Jardetzky, O., and C. D. Jardetzky: *J. Am. Chem. Soc.*, **79**, 5322 (1957).
208   Jarret, H. S., M. S. Sadler, and J. N. Shoolery: *J. Chem. Phys.*, **21**, 2092 (1953).
209   Jaynes, E. T.: *Phys. Rev.*, **98**, 1099 (1955).
210   Josien, M. L., and G. Sourisseau: *Bull. soc. chim. France*, 178 (1955).
211   Kanda, T.: *J. Phys. Soc. Japan*, **10**, 85 (1955).
211a   Kaplan, J. I.: *J. Chem. Phys.*, **27**, 1426 (1957).
212   Kaplan, J. I.: *J. Chem. Phys.*, **28**, 278 (1958).
213   Kaplan, J. I., and S. Meiboom: *Phys. Rev.*, **106**, 499 (1957).
214   Karplus, R.: *Phys. Rev.*, **73**, 1027 (1948).
214a   Karplus, M.: *J. Chem. Phys.*, **30**, 11 (1959).
215   Karplus, M., D. H. Anderson, T. C. Farrar, and H. S. Gutowsky: *J. Chem. Phys.*, **27**, 597 (1957).
215a   Karplus, M., and H. S. Gutowsky: *Abstracts, Am. Chem. Soc. Meeting*, San Francisco, 1958.
216   Kasper, J. S., C. M. Lucht, and D. Hauker: *Acta Cryst.*, **3**, 436 (1950).
217   Kelly, J., J. Ray, and R. A. Ogg: *Phys. Rev.*, **94**, 767 (1954).
218   Kende, A. S.: *Chem. & Ind. (London)*, 544 (1956).
219   Klyne, W.: "Progress in Stereochemistry I," chap. 2, Butterworth & Co. (Publishers) Ltd., London, 1954.
220   Knight, W. D.: *Phys. Rev.*, **76**, 1259 (1949).
220a   Kohlrausch, K. W. F.: "Ramanspektren," J. W. Edwards, Publisher, Inc., Ann Arbor, Mich., 1945.
221   Korinek, G., and W. G. Schneider: *Can. J. Chem.*, **35**, 1157 (1957).
222   Koske, W. S., J. J. Kaufman, and P. C. Lauterbur: *J. Am. Chem. Soc.*, **79**, 2382 (1957).
223   Krishnan, K. S.: *Nature*, **130**, 212, 698 (1932).
224   Krishnan, K. S., and S. Banerjee: *Phil. Trans. Roy. Soc. London*, **A234**, 265 (1935).
225   Krishnan, K. S., B. Guha, and S. Banerjee: *Phil. Trans. Roy. Soc. London*, **A231**, 235 (1933).
226   Kubo, R.: *J. Phys. Soc. Japan*, **9**, 935 (1954).
227   Kubo, R., and K. Tomita: *J. Phys. Soc. Japan*, **9**, 888 (1954).
228   Lamb, W. E.: *Phys. Rev.*, **60**, 817 (1941).
229   Langevin, P.: *Ann. chim. et phys.*, (8)**5**, 70 (1905).
230   Langevin, P.: *Compt. rend.*, **151**, 475 (1910).
231   Langevin, P.: *J. phys.*, **4**, 678 (1905).
232   Larmor, J.: "Aether and Matter," p. 341, Cambridge University Press, New York, 1900.
233   Lasarew, B. E., and L. W. Schubnikow: *Physik. Z. Sowjetunion*, **11**, 445 (1937).
234   Laukien, G., and J. Schlüter: *Z. Physik*, **146**, 113 (1956).
235   Lauterbur, P. C.: *Ann. N.Y. Acad. Sci.*, **70**, 841 (1958).
236   Lauterbur, P. C.: *J. Chem. Phys.*, **26**, 217 (1957).
237   Lauterbur, P. C., and J. J. Burke: *Abstracts, Am. Chem. Soc. Meeting*, San Francisco, 1958.
238   LeFevre, C. G., and R. J. W. LeFevre: *J. Chem. Soc.*, 1696 (1935).
239   LeFevre, R., and H. Welsh: *J. Chem. Soc.*, 2230 (1949).
240   Lemair, H. P., and R. L. Livingston: *J. Chem. Phys.*, **18**, 569 (1950).
241   Lemieux, R. U., R. K. Kullnig, H. J. Bernstein, and W. G. Schneider: *J. Am. Chem. Soc.*, **79**, 1005 (1957).
242   Lemieux, R. U., R. K. Kullnig, H. J. Bernstein, and W. G. Schneider: *J. Am. Chem. Soc.*, **80**, 6098 (1958).

243 Lemieux, R., R. K. Kullnig, and R. Y. Moir: *J. Am. Chem. Soc.*, **80**, 2237 (1958).

244 Lennard-Jones, J. E.: *Proc. Roy. Soc. (London)*, **A198**, 1 (1949).

244a Leto, J. R., F. A. Cotton, and J. S. Waugh: *Nature*, **180**, 978 (1957).

245 Levinthal, E. C.: *Phys. Rev.*, **78**, 204 (1950).

246 Liddel, U., and E. D. Becker: *Spectrochim. Acta*, **10**, 70 (1957).

247 Liddel, U., and N. F. Ramsey: *J. Chem. Phys.*, **19**, 1608 (1951).

248 Lindström, G.: *Phys. Rev.*, **78**, 817 (1950).

249 Lindström, G., and B. N. Bhar: *Arkiv Fysik*, **10**, 489 (1956).

250 Lipscomb, W. N.: *J. Chem. Phys.*, **22**, 985 (1954).

251 Lloyd, D., T. C. Downie, and J. C. Speakman: *Chem. & Ind. (London)*, **222**, 492 (1954).

252 Lloyd, J. P.: *Bull. Am. Phys. Soc.*, **1**, 92 (1956).

253 Loewenstein, A., and S. Meiboom: *J. Chem. Phys.*, **27**, 1067 (1957).

254 London, F.: *J. Chem. Phys.*, **5**, 837 (1937).

255 London, F.: *J. phys. radium*, **8**, 397 (1937).

256 Lonsdale, K., and K. S. Krishnan: *Proc. Roy. Soc. (London)*, **A156**, 597 (1936).

257 Lonsdale, K.: *Proc. Roy. Soc. (London)*, **A159**, 149 (1937).

258 Lonsdale, K.: *Proc. Roy. Soc. (London)*, **A171**, 541 (1939).

259 Looney, C. E., W. D. Phillips, and E. L. Reilly: *J. Am. Chem. Soc.*, **79**, 6136 (1957).

260 Lord, R. C., M. A. Lynch, W. C. Schumb, and E. J. Slowinski: *J. Am. Chem. Soc.*, **72**, 522 (1950).

261 Marion, L.: *Can. J. Research*, **B21**, 247 (1943).

262 Marion, L., and K. Sargeant: *Can. J. Chem.*, **35**, 301 (1957).

262a Marshall, T. W., and J. A. Pople: *Mol. Phys.*, **1**, 199 (1958).

263 Masuda, Y.: *J. Phys. Soc. Japan*, **11**, 670 (1956).

264 Masuda, Y., and T. Kanda: *J. Phys. Soc. Japan*, **8**, 432 (1953).

265 Masuda, Y., and T. Kanda: *J. Phys. Soc. Japan*, **9**, 82 (1954).

266 Mayot, M., G. Berthier, and B. Pullman: *J. phys. radium*, **12**, 652, 717 (1951); **13**, 15 (1952); *J. Chem. Phys.*, **50**, 176 (1953).

266a McConaghie, U. M., and H. H. Nielsen: *J. Chem. Phys.*, **21**, 1836 (1953).

267 McConnell, H. M.: *J. Chem. Phys.*, **24**, 460 (1956).

268 McConnell, H. M.: *J. Chem. Phys.*, **24**, 764 (1956).

269 McConnell, H. M.: *J. Chem. Phys.*, **27**, 226 (1957).

270 McConnell, H. M.: *J. Mol. Spectroscopy*, **1**, 11 (1957).

270a McConnell, H. M.: *J. Chem. Phys.*, **28**, 430 (1958).

271 McConnell, H. M., and S. B. Berger: *J. Chem. Phys.*, **27**, 230 (1957).

272 McConnell, H. M., and C. H. Holm: *J. Chem. Phys.*, **25**, 1289 (1956).

273 McConnell, H. M., A. D. McLean, and C. A. Reilly: *J. Chem. Phys.*, **23**, 1152 (1955).

274 McConnell, H. M., and C. A. Reilly: *J. Chem. Phys.*, **25**, 184 (1956).

275 McConnell, H. M., C. A. Reilly, and A. D. McLean: *J. Chem. Phys.*, **24**, 479 (1956).

276 McConnell, H. M., and H. E. Weaver: *J. Chem. Phys.*, **25**, 307 (1956).

277 McGarvey, B. R.: *J. Chem. Phys.*, **27**, 68 (1957).

278 McNeil, E. B., C. P. Slichter, and H. S. Gutowsky: *Phys. Rev.*, **84**, 1245 (1951).

279 McWeeny, R.: *Proc. Phys. Soc. (London)*, **64A**, 261, 291 (1951); **65A**, 839 (1952); **66A**, 714 (1953).

280 Meacham, L. A.: *Proc. IRE*, **26**, 1278 (1938).

281 Mecke, R.: *Discussions Faraday Soc.*, **9**, 161 (1950).

282 Meiboom, S., Z. Luz, and D. Gill: *J. Chem. Phys.*, **27**, 1411 (1957).

283 Meyer, K. H.: *Ann. Physik*, **380**, 212 (1911); *Ber.*, **45**, 2843 (1912).

284   Meyer, K. H., and F. G. Wilson: *Ber.*, **47**, 837 (1914).

285   Meyer, L. H., and H. S. Gutowsky: *J. Phys. Chem.*, **57**, 481 (1953).

286   Meyer, L. H., A. Saika, and H. S. Gutowsky: *J. Am. Chem. Soc.*, **75**, 4567 (1953).

287   Mitchell, A. M. J., and G. Phillips: *Brit. J. Appl. Phys.*, **7**, 67 (1956).

288   Mizushima, S.: "Structure of Molecules and Internal Rotation," Academic Press, Inc., New York, 1954.

289   Morgan, L. O., A. W. Nolle, R. L. Hull, and J. Murphy: *J. Chem. Phys.*, **25**, 206 (1956).

290   Morin, M. G., G. Paulett, and M. E. Hobbs: *J. Phys. Chem.*, **60**, 1594 (1956).

291   Muetterties, E. L., and W. D. Phillips: *J. Am. Chem. Soc.*, **79**, 322 (1957).

292   Muetterties, E. L., and W. D. Phillips: *J. Am. Chem. Soc.*, **79**, 2975 (1957).

293   Mulay, L. N.: *Rev. Sci. Instr.*, **28**, 279 (1957).

294   Muller, N., and J. Goldenson: *J. Am. Chem. Soc.*, **78**, 5182 (1956).

295   Muller, N., P. C. Lauterbur, and J. Goldenson: *J. Am. Chem. Soc.*, **78**, 3557 (1956).

296   Muller, N., P. C. Lauterbur, and G. F. Svatos: *J. Am. Chem. Soc.*, **79**, 1043 (1957).

297   Muller, N., P. C. Lauterbur, and G. F. Svatos: *J. Am. Chem. Soc.*, **79**, 1807 (1957).

298   Mulliken, R. S.: *J. Chem. Phys.*, **23**, 1833 (1955).

299   Nair, P. M., and J. D. Roberts: *J. Am. Chem. Soc.*, **79**, 4565 (1957).

300   Nederbragt, G. W., and C. A. Reilly: *J. Chem. Phys.*, **24**, 1110 (1956).

301   Newell, G. F.: *Phys. Rev.*, **80**, 476 (1950).

302   Novak, A., and E. Whalley: *Can. J. Chem.*, **36**, 1116 (1958).

303   Ogg, R. A.: *J. Chem. Phys.*, **22**, 560 (1954).

304   Ogg, R. A.: *J. Chem. Phys.*, **22**, 1933 (1954).

305   Ogg, R. A.: *Helv. Phys. Acta*, **30**, 89 (1957).

306   Ogg, R. A., and J. D. Ray: *Discussions Faraday Soc.*, **19**, 239 (1955).

307   Ogg, R. A., and J. D. Ray: *J. Chem. Phys.*, **25**, 797 (1956).

308   Ogg, R. A., and J. D. Ray: *J. Chem. Phys.*, **26**, 1339 (1957).

309   Ogg, R. A., and J. D. Ray: *J. Chem. Phys.*, **26**, 1515 (1957).

310   Overhauser, A. W.: *Phys. Rev.*, **91**, 476 (1953).

311   Pacault, A.: *Rev. sci.*, **82**, 465 (1944).

312   Pacault, A.: *Rev. sci.*, **86**, 38 (1948).

313   Pacault, A.: *Bull. soc. chim. France*, D371 (1949).

314   Pacault, A.: *Experientia*, **10**, 41 (1954).

315   Packard, M. E.: *Rev. Sci. Instr.*, **19**, 435 (1948).

316   Packard, M. E.: *Phys. Rev.*, **88**, 163 (1952).

317   Packard, M. E., and J. T. Arnold: *Phys. Rev.*, **83**, 210A (1951).

318   Pake, G. E.: *J. Chem. Phys.*, **16**, 327 (1948).

319   Pariser, R.: *J. Chem. Phys.*, **25**, 1112 (1956).

320   Parks, J. R.: *J. Am. Chem. Soc.*, **79**, 757 (1957).

321   Pascal, P.: *Ann. chim. et phys.*, **19**, 5 (1910); **25**, 289 (1912); **29**, 218 (1913).

322   Pascal, P.: "Chimie generale," Masson et Cie, Paris, 1949.

323   Pauli, W.: *Naturwiss.*, **12**, 741 (1924).

324   Pauling, L.: *J. Chem. Phys.*, **1**, 280 (1933).

325   Pauling, L.: *J. Chem. Phys.*, **4**, 673 (1936).

326   Pauling, L.: "The Nature of the Chemical Bond," 2d ed., p. 207, Cornell University Press, Ithaca, N.Y., 1942.

327   Pauling, L.: "The Nature of the Chemical Bond," 2d ed., p. 236, Cornell University Press, Ithaca, N.Y., 1942.

328   Pauling, L., and E. B. Wilson, Jr.: "Introduction to Quantum Mechanics," McGraw-Hill Book Company, Inc., New York, 1935.

329   Peter, Brother Simon: *Phys. Rev.*, **93**, 940 (1954).

330   Phillips, W. D.: *J. Chem. Phys.*, **23**, 1363 (1955).

331   Phillips, W. D.: *J. Chem. Phys.*, **25**, 949 (1956).

332   Phillips, W. D.: *Ann. N.Y. Acad. Sci.*, **70**, 817 (1958).

333   Phillips, W. D., C. E. Looney, and C. P. Spaeth: *J. Mol. Spectroscopy*, **1**, 35 (1957).

333a   Phillips, W. D., and E. L. Muetterties: *Abstracts, Am. Chem. Soc. Meeting*, San Francisco, 1958.

334   Piette, L. H., J. D. Ray, and R. A. Ogg: *J. Chem. Phys.*, **26**, 1341 (1957).

335   Piette, L. H., J. D. Ray, and R. A. Ogg: *J. Mol. Spectroscopy*, **2**, 66 (1958).

335a   Piette, L. H., and H. E. Weaver: *J. Chem. Phys.*, **28**, 735 (1958).

335b   Pimentel, G. C., and A. L. McClellan: "The Hydrogen Bond," W. H. Freeman and Co., San Francisco, 1959.

336   Pople, J. A.: *J. Chem. Phys.*, **24**, 1111 (1956).

337   Pople, J. A.: *Proc. Roy. Soc. (London)*, **A239**, 541 (1957).

338   Pople, J. A.: *Proc. Roy. Soc. (London)*, **A239**, 550 (1957).

339   Pople, J. A.: *Mol. Phys.*, **1**, 3 (1958).

340   Pople, J. A.: *Mol. Phys.*, **1**, 168 (1958).

341   Pople, J. A.: *Mol. Phys.*, **1**, 175 (1958).

341a   Pople, J. A.: *Mol. Phys.*, **1**, 216 (1958).

342   Pople, J. A., W. G. Schneider, and H. J. Bernstein: *Can. J. Chem.*, **35**, 1060 (1957).

343   Pound, R. V.: *Phys. Rev.*, **79**, 685 (1950).

344   Pound, R. V., and W. D. Knight: *Rev. Sci. Instr.*, **21**, 219 (1950).

345   Powling, J., and H. J. Bernstein: *J. Am. Chem. Soc.*, **73**, 4353 (1951).

346   Price, W. C.: *J. Chem. Phys.*, **16**, 894 (1948).

347   Price, W. C.: *J. Chem. Phys.*, **17**, 1044 (1949).

348   Primas, H. S., and Hs. H. Gunthard: *Chimia (Switz.)*, **11**, 130 (1957).

349   Primas, H. S., and Hs. H. Gunthard: *Helv. Phys. Acta*, **30**, 315 (1957).

350   Primas, H. S., and Hs. H. Gunthard: *Helv. Phys. Acta*, **30**, 331 (1957).

351   Primas, H. S., and Hs. H. Gunthard: *Rev. Sci. Instr.*, **28**, 510 (1957).

352   Proctor, W. G., and F. C. Yu: *Phys. Rev.*, **77**, 717 (1950).

353   Proctor, W. G., and F. C. Yu: *Phys. Rev.*, **78**, 471 (1950).

354   Proctor, W. G., and F. C. Yu: *Phys. Rev.*, **81**, 20 (1951).

355   Pullman, B., and A. Pullman: "Les Theories electroniques de la chimie organique," p. 193, Masson et Cie, Paris, 1952.

356   Purcell, E. M., R. V. Pound, and N. Bloembergen: *Phys. Rev.*, **70**, 986 (1946).

357   Purcell, E. M., and R. V. Pound: *Phys. Rev.*, **81**, 279 (1951).

358   Purcell, E. M., H. C. Torrey, and R. V. Pound: *Phys. Rev.*, **69**, 37 (1946).

359   Quinn, W. E., and R. M. Brown: *J. Chem. Phys.*, **21**, 1605 (1953).

360   Rabi, I. I.: *Phys. Rev.*, **51**, 652 (1937).

361   Rabi, I. I., S. Millman, P. Kusch, and J. R. Zacharias: *Phys. Rev.*, **55**, 526 (1939).

362   Raman, C. V., and K. S. Krishnan: *Proc. Roy. Soc. (London)*, **A113**, 511 (1927).

363   Ramandham, M.: *Indian J. Phys.*, **4**, 15 (1929).

364   Ramsey, N. F.: *Phys. Rev.*, **78**, 699 (1950).

365   Ramsey, N. F.: *Phys. Rev.*, **86**, 243 (1952).

366   Ramsey, N. F.: *Phys. Rev.*, **91**, 303 (1953).

367   Ramsey, N. F.: "Nuclear Moments," John Wiley & Sons, Inc., New York, 1953.

368   Ramsey, N. F., and E. M. Purcell: *Phys. Rev.*, **85**, 143 (1952).
369   Raphael, R. A.: in E. H. Rodd (ed.), "The Chemistry of Carbon Compounds," vol. 2A, p. 132, Elsevier Publishing Company, Amsterdam, 1953.
370   Ray, J. D., and R. A. Ogg: *J. Chem. Phys.*, **26**, 1452 (1957).
371   Reber, R. K., and G. F. Boeker: *J. Chem. Phys.*, **15**, 508 (1947).
372   Redlich, O., and J. Bigeleisen: *J. Am. Chem. Soc.*, **65**, 1883 (1943).
373   Reeves, L. W.: *Can. J. Chem.*, **35**, 1351 (1957).
374   Reeves, L. W., and W. G. Schneider: *Can. J. Chem.*, **35**, 251 (1957).
375   Reeves, L. W., and W. G. Schneider: *Can. J. Chem.*, **36**, 793 (1958).
376   Reeves, L. W., and W. G. Schneider: *Trans. Faraday Soc.*, **54**, 314 (1958).
377   Reeves, R. E.: *J. Am. Chem. Soc.*, **72**, 1499 (1950).
378   Reid, C.: *J. Mol. Spectroscopy*, **1**, 18 (1957).
379   Reilly, C. A.: *J. Chem. Phys.*, **25**, 604 (1956).
380   Reilly, C. A.: *Anal. Chem.*, **30**, 839 (1958).
381   Reilly, C. A., H. M. McConnell, and R. G. Meisenheimer: *Phys. Rev.*, **98**, 264A (1955).
382   Richards, R. E.: unpublished results.
383   Rinehart, K. L., W. A. Nilsson, and A. A. Whaley: *J. Am. Chem. Soc.*, **80**, 503 (1958).
384   Rivkind, A. L.: *Proc. Acad. Sci. USSR (Physics)*, **112**, 239 (1957).
385   Robertson, J. M., and H. M. M. Shearer: *Nature*, **177**, 885 (1956).
386   Roberts, J. D.: *J. Am. Chem. Soc.*, **78**, 4495 (1956).
387   Roberts, J. D., and W. T. Moreland: *J. Am. Chem. Soc.*, **75**, 2167 (1953).
388   Rollwitz, W. L.: *Proc. Natl. Electronics Conf.*, **12**, 113 (1957).
389   Roux, D. P., and G. J. Bene: *J. Chem. Phys.*, **26**, 968 (1957).
390   Royden, V.: *Phys. Rev.*, **96**, 543 (1954).
391   Sack, R. A.: *Mol. Phys.*, **1**, 163 (1958).
392   Saika, A., and H. S. Gutowsky: *J. Am. Chem. Soc.*, **78**, 4818 (1956).
393   Saika, A., and C. P. Slichter: *J. Chem. Phys.*, **22**, 26 (1954).
394   Sanford, R. L.: *Natl. Bur. Standards Circ.* 448, 1944.
395   Saunders, M., A. Wishma, and J. G. Kirkwood: *J. Am. Chem. Soc.*, **79**, 3289 (1957).
396   Shaeffer, R., J. N. Shoolery, and R. Jones: *J. Am. Chem. Soc.*, **79**, 4606 (1957).
397   Schmidlin, J., and R. Lang: *Ber.*, **43**, 2806 (1910).
398   Schmitz, H., and H. J. Schumacher: *Z. Naturforsch.*, **2a**, 363 (1947).
399   Schneider, W. G.: *J. Chem. Phys.*, **23**, 26 (1955).
400   Schneider, W. G.: *Proc. Symposium on Hydrogen Bonding, Lubliana*, Pergamon Press, Ltd., London, 1959.
401   Schneider, W. G., H. J. Bernstein, and J. A. Pople: *Can. J. Chem.*, **35**, 1487 (1957).
402   Schneider, W. G., H. J. Bernstein, and J. A. Pople: *J. Chem. Phys.*, **28**, 601 (1958).
403   Schneider, W. G., H. J. Bernstein, and J. A. Pople: *J. Am. Chem. Soc.*, **80**, 3497 (1958).
404   Schneider, W. G., H. J. Bernstein, and J. A. Pople: *Ann. N.Y. Acad. Sci.*, **70**, 806 (1958).
405   Schneider, W. G., and L. W. Reeves: *Ann. N.Y. Acad. Sci.*, **70**, 858 (1958).
406   Schnell, E., and E. G. Rochow: *J. Am. Chem. Soc.*, **78**, 4178 (1956).
407   Schwinger, J.: *Phys. Rev.*, **51**, 648 (1937).
408   Searles, S., and M. Tamres: *J. Am. Chem. Soc.*, **73**, 3704 (1951).
409   Searles, S., M. Tamres, and E. R. Lippincott: *J. Am. Chem. Soc.*, **75**, 2775 (1953).

410 Selwood, P. W.: "Magneto Chemistry," Interscience Publishers, Inc., New York, 1956, and references therein.

411 Shaney, R. C., S. L. Aggarival, and M. Singh: *J. Indian Chem. Soc.*, **23**, 335 (1946).

412 Sharts, C. M., and J. D. Roberts: *J. Am. Chem. Soc.*, **79**, 1008 (1957).

413 Shaw, T. M., and R. H. Elsken: *J. Chem. Phys.*, **18**, 1113 (1950).

414 Shaw, T. M., and R. H. Elsken: *J. Appl. Phys.*, **26**, 313 (1955).

415 Shaw, T. M., R. H. Elsken, and C. H. Kunsman: *J. Assoc. Offic. Agr. Chemists*, **36**, 1070 (1953).

416 Schiff, L. I.: "Quantum Mechanics," 2d ed., McGraw-Hill Book Company, Inc., New York, 1955.

417 Shoolery, J. N.: *J. Chem. Phys.*, **21**, 1899 (1953).

418 Shoolery, J. N.: *Varian Tech. Inform. Bull.*, **1**(3), (1955).

419 Shoolery, J. N.: *Discussions Faraday Soc.*, **19**, 215 (1955).

420 Shoolery, J. N.: *Svensk Kem. Tidskr.*, **69**, 185 (1957).

421 Shoolery, J. N., and B. Alder: *J. Chem. Phys.*, **23**, 805 (1955).

422 Shoolery, J. N., and B. Crawford: *J. Mol. Spectroscopy*, **1**, 270 (1957).

423 Shoolery, J. N., and B. P. Dailey: *J. Am. Chem. Soc.*, **77**, 3977 (1955).

424 Shoolery, J. N., and J. D. Roberts: *Rev. Sci. Instr.*, **28**, 61 (1957).

424a Shoolery, J. N., and M. T. Rogers: *J. Am. Chem. Soc.*, **80**, 5121 (1958).

425 Shoolery, J. N., and H. E. Weaver: *Ann. Rev. Phys. Chem.*, **6**, 433 (1955).

426 Silbiger, G., and S. H. Bauer: *J. Am. Chem. Soc.*, **68**, 312 (1946).

427 Smaller, B.: *Phys. Rev.*, **83**, 812 (1951).

428 Smith, D. F.: *J. Chem. Phys.*, **21**, 609 (1953).

429 Solomon, I.: *Phys. Rev.*, **99**, 559 (1955).

430 Solomon, I., and N. Bloembergen: *J. Chem. Phys.*, **25**, 261 (1956).

431 Stephen, M. J.: *Proc. Roy. Soc. (London)*, **A243**, 264 (1957).

432 Suryan, G.: *Proc. Indian Acad. Sci.*, **33A**, 107 (1951).

433 Taft, R. W.: in M. S. Newman (ed.), "Steric Effects in Organic Chemistry," chap. 13, John Wiley & Sons, Inc., New York, 1956.

434 Taft, R. W., Jr.: *J. Am. Chem. Soc.*, **79**, 1045 (1957).

435 Takeda, M., and O. Jardetzky: *J. Chem. Phys.*, **26**, 1346 (1957).

436 Takeuchi, Y., and R. Pepinsky: *Science*, **124**, 126 (1956).

437 Tamres, M., S. Searles, and R. F. Vance: *Abstracts, Am. Chem. Soc. Meeting*, Los Angeles, 1953.

438 Tarte, P.: *J. Chem. Phys.*, **20**, 1570 (1952).

439 Thomas, H. A.: *Phys. Rev.*, **80**, 901 (1950).

440 Thomas, H. A., and R. D. Huntoon: *Rev. Sci. Instr.*, **20**, 516 (1949).

441 Tiers, G. V. D.: *J. Am. Chem. Soc.*, **78**, 2914 (1956).

442 Torrey, H. C.: *Phys. Rev.*, **76**, 1059 (1949).

443 Torrey, H. C.: *Phys. Rev.*, **104**, 563 (1956).

444 Tuttle, W. N.: *Proc. IRE*, **28**, 23 (1940).

445 Van Vleck, J. H.: "Electric and Magnetic Susceptibilities," Oxford University Press, New York, 1932.

446 Van Vleck, J. H.: *Phys. Rev.*, **74**, 1168 (1948).

447 van Vloten, W., C. A. Kruissink, B. Strijk, and J. M. Bijvoet: *Acta Cryst.*, **3**, 139 (1950).

448 Van Wazer, J. R., C. F. Callis, and J. N. Shoolery: *J. Am. Chem. Soc.*, **77**, 4945 (1955).

449 Van Wazer, J. R., C. F. Callis, J. N. Shoolery, and R. C. Jones: *J. Am. Chem. Soc.*, **78**, 5715 (1956).

450 Van Wazer, J. R., and K. A. Holst: *J. Am. Chem. Soc.*, **72**, 639, 647 (1950).

451 Verbrugge, F., and R. L. Henry: *Phys. Rev.*, **83**, 211 (1951).

452 Walchli, H. E.: *Phys. Rev.*, **90**, 331 (1953).

453 Wallman, H., A. B. MacNee, and C. P. Gadsden: *Proc. IRE*, **36**, 700 (1948).

454 Wangsness, R. K., and F. Bloch: *Phys. Rev.*, **89**, 728 (1953).

455 Waring, C. E., R. H. Spencer, and R. L. Custer: *Rev. Sci. Instr.*, **23**, 497 (1952).

456 Waugh, J. S., and R. W. Fessenden: *J. Am. Chem. Soc.*, **79**, 846 (1957).

457 Weaver, H. E.: *Phys. Rev.*, **89**, 923 (1953).

458 Weaver, H. E., B. M. Tolbert, and R. C. LaForce: *J. Chem. Phys.*, **23**, 1956 (1955).

459 Weinberg, I., and J. R. Zimmerman: *J. Chem. Phys.*, **23**, 748 (1955).

460 Wertz, J. E.: *J. Chem. Phys.*, **24**, 484 (1956).

461 Wertz, J. E., P. L. Jain, and R. L. Batdorf: *Phys. Rev.*, **102**, 920 (1956).

462 Wertz, J. E., and O. Jardetzky: *J. Chem. Phys.*, **25**, 357 (1956).

463 Whittaker, A. G., D. W. Moore, J. N. Shoolery, and R. Jones: *J. Chem. Phys.*, **25**, 366 (1956).

464 Williams, G. A., and H. S. Gutowsky: *J. Chem. Phys.*, **25**, 1288 (1956).

465 Williams, G. A., and H. S. Gutowsky: *Phys. Rev.*, **104**, 278 (1956).

465a Williams, R. B.: *Ann. N.Y. Acad. Sci.*, **70**, 890 (1958).

466 Wilmshurst, J. K., and H. J. Bernstein: *Can. J. Chem.*, **35**, 734 (1957).

467 Wilson, E. B.: *J. Chem. Phys.*, **27**, 60 (1957).

468 Wilson, E. B., Jr., J. C. Decius, and P. C. Cross: "Molecular Vibrations," McGraw-Hill Book Company, Inc., New York, 1955.

469 Wimett, T. F.: *Phys. Rev.*, **91**, 476 (1953).

470 Witmer, E.: *Phys. Rev.*, **48**, 380 (1935).

471 Witmer, E.: *Phys. Rev.*, **51**, 383 (1937).

472 Young, T. F.: *Record Chem. Progr. (Kresge-Hooker Sci. Lib.)*, **12**, 81 (1951).

473 Zimmerman, J. R.: *J. Chem. Phys.*, **22**, 950 (1954).

474 Zimmerman, J. R., and M. R. Foster: *J. Phys. Chem.*, **61**, 282 (1957).

APPENDIXES

TABLE OF NUCLEAR PROPERTIES†

Isotope (* indicates radioactive)	NMR frequency in Mc for a 10-kilogauss field	Natural abundance, %	Relative sensitivity for equal number of nuclei		Magnetic moment μ, in multiples of the nuclear magneton $(eh/4\pi Mc)$	Spin I, in multiples of $h/2\pi$	Electric quadrupole moment Q, in multiples of $e \times 10^{-24}$ cm^2
			At constant field	At constant frequency			
n^1*	29.165		0.322	0.685	-1.9130	1/2	
H^1	42.577	99.9844	1.000	1.000	2.79270	1/2	
H^2	6.536	1.56×10^{-2}	9.64×10^{-3}	0.409	0.85738	1	2.77×10^{-3}
H^3*	45.414		1.21	1.07	2.9788	1/2	
He^3	32.434	10^{-5} to 10^{-7}	0.443	0.762	-2.1274	1/2	
Li^6	6.265	7.43	8.51×10^{-3}	0.392	0.82191	1	4.6×10^{-4}
Li^7	16.547	92.57	0.294	1.94	3.2560	3/2	-4.2×10^{-2}
Be^9	5.983	100.	1.39×10^{-2}	0.703	-1.1774	3/2	2×10^{-2}
B^{10}	4.575	18.83	1.99×10^{-2}	1.72	1.8006	3	0.111
B^{11}	13.660	81.17	0.165	1.60	2.6880	3/2	3.55×10^{-2}
C^{13}	10.705	1.108	1.59×10^{-2}	0.251	0.70216	1/2	
N^{14}	3.076	99.635	1.01×10^{-3}	0.193	0.40357	1	2×10^{-2}
N^{15}	4.315	0.365	1.04×10^{-3}	0.101	-0.28304	1/2	
O^{17}	5.772	3.7×10^{-2}	2.91×10^{-2}	1.58	-1.8930	5/2	-4×10^{-3}
F^{19}	40.055	100.	0.834	0.941	2.6273	1/2	
Ne^{21}		0.257				$\geqslant 3/2$	
Na^{22}*	4.434		1.81×10^{-2}	1.67	1.745	3	
Na^{23}	11.262	100.	9.27×10^{-2}	1.32	2.2161	3/2	
Mg^{25}	2.606	10.05	2.68×10^{-2}	0.714	-0.85471	5/2	0.1
Al^{27}	11.094	100.	0.207	3.04	3.6385	5/2	0.149
Si^{29}	8.460	4.70	7.85×10^{-2}	0.199	-0.55477	1/2	

Isotope						I	
P^{31}	17.235	100.	6.64×10^{-2}	0.405	1.1305	1/2	
S^{33}	3.266	0.74	2.26×10^{-3}	0.384	0.64274	3/2	-6.4×10^{-2}
S^{35}*	5.08		8.50×10^{-3}	0.599	1.00	3/2	4.5×10^{-2}
Cl^{35}	4.172	75.4	4.71×10^{-3}	0.490	0.82089	3/2	-7.97×10^{-2}
Cl^{36}*	4.893		1.21×10^{-2}	0.919	1.2838	2	-1.68×10^{-2}
Cl^{37}	3.472	24.6	2.72×10^{-3}	0.408	0.68329	3/2	-6.21×10^{-2}
K^{39}	1.987	93.08	5.08×10^{-4}	0.233	0.39094	3/2	
K^{40}*	2.470	1.19×10^{-2}	5.21×10^{-3}	1.55	−1.296	4	
K^{41}	1.092	6.91	8.39×10^{-5}	0.128	0.21453	3/2	
Ca^{43}	2.865	0.13	6.39×10^{-2}	1.41	−1.3153	7/2	
Sc^{45}	10.343	100.	0.301	5.10	4.7491	7/2	
Ti^{47}	2.400	7.75	2.10×10^{-3}	0.659	−0.78712	5/2	
Ti^{49}	2.401	5.51	3.76×10^{-3}	1.19	−1.1023	7/2	
V^{50}	4.245	0.24	5.53×10^{-2}	5.58	3.3413	6	0.3
V^{51}	11.193	~100.	0.383	5.53	5.1392	7/2	
Cr^{53}	2.406	9.54	1.0×10^{-4}	0.29	−0.4735	3/2	
Mn^{55}	10.553	100.	0.178	2.89	3.4610	5/2	0.5
Fe^{57}		2.245			≤ 0.05		
Co^{57}*	10.0		0.274	4.95	4.6	7/2	
Co^{58}*	13.3		0.25	2.5	3.5	2	
Co^{59}	10.103	100.	0.281	4.83	4.6388	7/2	0.5
Co^{60}*	4.6		5×10^{-2}	4.3	3.0	5?	
Ni^{61}		1.25			< 0.25		
Cu^{63}	11.285	69.09	9.38×10^{-2}	1.33	2.2206	3/2	−0.15
Cu^{65}	12.090	30.91	0.116	1.42	2.3790	3/2	−0.14
Zn^{67}	2.635	4.12	2.86×10^{-3}	0.730	0.8735	5/2	
Ga^{69}	10.218	60.2	6.93×10^{-2}	1.201	2.0108	3/2	0.2318
Ga^{71}	12.984	39.8	0.142	1.525	2.5549	3/2	0.1461
Ge^{73}	1.485	7.61	1.40×10^{-3}	1.15	−0.8768	9/2	−0.2
Ge^{75}							
As^{75}	7.292	100.	2.51×10^{-2}	0.856	1.4349	3/2	0.3
Se^{77}	8.131	7.50	6.97×10^{-3}	0.191	0.5333	1/2	

TABLE OF NUCLEAR PROPERTIES (Continued)

Isotope (* indicates radioactive)	NMR frequency in Mc for a 10-kilogauss field	Natural abundance, %	Relative sensitivity for equal number of nuclei		Magnetic moment μ, in multiples of the nuclear magneton $(eh/4\pi Mc)$	Spin I, in multiples of $h/2\pi$	Electric quadrupole moment Q, in multiples of $e \times 10^{-24}$ cm²
			At constant field	At constant frequency			
Se^{79}*	2.210		2.94×10^{-3}	1.12	-1.015	7/2	0.9
Br^{79}	10.667	50.57	7.86×10^{-2}	1.26	2.0990	3/2	0.33
Br^{81}	11.498	49.43	9.84×10^{-2}	1.35	2.2626	3/2	0.28
Kr^{83}	1.64	11.55	1.89×10^{-3}	1.27	-0.968	9/2	0.15
Rb^{85}	4.111	72.8	1.05×10^{-2}	1.13	1.3483	5/2	0.31
Rb^{87}	13.932	27.2	0.177	1.64	2.7415	3/2	0.15
Sr^{87}	1.845	7.02	2.69×10^{-3}	1.43	-1.0893	9/2	
Y^{89}	2.086	100.	1.17×10^{-4}	4.90×10^{-2}	-0.1368	1/2	
Zr^{91}	4.0	11.23	9.4×10^{-3}	1.04	-1.3	5/2	
Nb^{93}	10.407	100.	0.482	8.06	6.1435	9/2	-0.4 ± 0.3
Mo^{95}	2.774	15.78	3.22×10^{-3}	0.761	-0.9099	5/2	
Mo^{97}	2.833	9.60	3.42×10^{-3}	0.776	-0.9290	5/2	
Tc^{99}*	9.583		0.376	7.43	5.6572	9/2	0.3
Ru^{99}		12.81				6/2	
Ru^{101}		16.98				5/2	
Rh^{103}	1.340	100.	3.12×10^{-5}	3.15×10^{-2}	-0.0879	1/2	
Pd^{105}	1.74	22.23	7.79×10^{-4}	0.47	-0.57	5/2	
Ag^{107}	1.722	51.35	6.69×10^{-5}	4.03×10^{-2}	-0.1130	1/2	
Ag^{109}	1.981	48.65	1.01×10^{-4}	4.66×10^{-2}	-0.1299	1/2	
Cd^{111}	9.028	12.86	9.54×10^{-3}	0.212	-0.5922	1/2	
Cd^{113}	9.444	12.34	1.09×10^{-2}	0.222	-0.6195	1/2	
In^{113}	9.310	4.16	0.345	7.22	5.4960	9/2	1.144

Isotope		Abundance			Magnetic moment	Spin	
In¹¹⁵*	9.329	95.84	0.348	7.23	−5.5072	9/2	1.161
Sn¹¹⁵	13.22	0.35	3.50×10^{-2}	0.327	−0.9132	1/2	
Sn¹¹⁷	15.77	7.67	4.53×10^{-2}	0.356	−0.9949	1/2	
Sn¹¹⁹	15.87	8.68	5.18×10^{-2}	0.373	−1.0409	1/2	−0.8
Sb¹²¹	10.19	57.25	0.160	2.79	3.3417	5/2	−1.0
Sb¹²³	5.518	42.75	4.57×10^{-2}	2.72	2.5334	7/2	
Te¹²³	11.59	0.89	1.80×10^{-2}	0.262	−0.7319	1/2	
Te¹²⁵	13.45	7.03	3.16×10^{-2}	0.316	−0.8824	1/2	−0.75
I¹²⁷	8.519	100.	9.35×10^{-2}	2.33	2.7939	5/2	−0.43
I¹²⁹*	5.669		4.96×10^{-2}	2.80	2.6030	7/2	
Xe¹²⁹	11.78	26.24	2.12×10^{-2}	0.277	−0.7726	1/2	−0.12
Xe¹³¹	3.490	21.24	2.77×10^{-3}	0.410	0.6868	3/2	≤0.3
Cs¹³³	5.585	100.	4.74×10^{-2}	2.75	2.5642	7/2	
Cs¹³⁴*	5.64		6.21×10^{-2}	3.53	2.96	4	
Cs¹³⁵*	5.94		5.70×10^{-2}	2.94	2.727	7/2	
Cs¹³⁷*	6.19		6.44×10^{-2}	3.05	2.84	3/2	
Ba¹³⁵	4.25	6.59	4.99×10^{-3}	0.499	0.837	3/2	
Ba¹³⁷	4.76	11.32	6.97×10^{-3}	0.559	0.936	3/2	
La¹³⁸*	5.617	0.089	9.18×10^{-2}	2.64	3.6844	5	2.7
La¹³⁹	6.014	99.911	5.92×10^{-2}	2.97	2.7615	7/2	0.9
Ce¹⁴¹*	0.35		1.1×10^{-5}	0.17	0.16	5/2	
Pr¹⁴¹	11.3	100.	0.234	3.18	3.8	7/2	-5.4×10^{-2}
Nd¹⁴³	2.2	12.20	2.81×10^{-3}	1.07	−1.1	7/2	≤1.2
Nd¹⁴⁵	1.4	8.30	6.70×10^{-4}	0.666	−0.69	7/2	≤1.2
Sm¹⁴⁷	1.47	15.07	8.8×10^{-4}	0.725	−0.68	7/2	0.72
Sm¹⁴⁹	1.19	13.84	4.7×10^{-4}	0.591	−0.55	7/2	0.72
Eu¹⁵¹	10.	47.77	0.168	2.84	3.4	5/2	~1.2
Eu¹⁵³	4.6	52.23	1.45×10^{-2}	1.25	1.5	5/2	~2.5
Gd¹⁵⁵		14.68			−0.19	(7/2)	
Gd¹⁵⁷		15.64			−0.33	(7/2)	
Tb¹⁵⁹		100.				3/2	

TABLE OF NUCLEAR PROPERTIES (Continued)

Isotope (* indicates radioactive)	NMR frequency in Mc for a 10-kilogauss field	Natural abundance, %	Relative sensitivity for equal number of nuclei		Magnetic moment μ, in multiples of the nuclear magneton $(eh/4\pi Mc)$	Spin I, in multiples of $h/2\pi$	Electric quadrupole moment Q, in multiples of $e \times 10^{-24}$ cm²
			At constant field	At constant frequency			
Dy^{161}		18.73				7/2	
Dy^{163}		24.97				7/2	
Ho^{165}		100.				7/2	~10
Er^{167}		22.82				7/2	
Tm^{169}		100.					
Yb^{171}	6.9	14.27	4.19×10^{-3}	0.161	0.45	1/2	
Yb^{173}	1.98	16.08	1.18×10^{-3}	0.543	−0.65	1/2	3.9
Lu^{175}	5.7	97.40	4.94×10^{-2}	2.79	2.6	5/2	5.9
Lu^{176*}		2.60			4.2	>7	6–8
Hf^{177}		18.39				1/2 or 3/2	
Hf^{179}		13.78				1/2 or 3/2	
Ta^{181}	4.6	100.	2.60×10^{-2}	2.26	2.1	7/2	6.5
W^{183}	1.75	14.28	6.98×10^{-5}	4.12	0.115	1/2	
Re^{185}	9.586	37.07	0.133	2.63	3.1437	5/2	2.8
Re^{187}	9.684	62.93	0.137	2.65	3.1760	5/2	2.6
Os^{189}	3.307	16.1	2.24×10^{-3}	0.385	0.6507	3/2	2.0
Ir^{191}	0.81	38.5	3.5×10^{-5}	9.5×10^{-2}	0.16	3/2	~1.2
Ir^{193}	0.86	61.5	4.2×10^{-5}	0.104	0.17	3/2	~1.0
Pt^{195}	9.153	33.7	9.94×10^{-3}	0.215	0.6004	1/2	
Au^{197}	0.691	100.	2.14×10^{-5}	8.1×10^{-2}	0.136	3/2	0.56
Hg^{199}	7.612	16.86	5.72×10^{-3}	0.179	0.4993	1/2	
Hg^{201}	3.08	13.24	1.90×10^{-3}	0.362	−0.607	3/2	0.5

						Spin	
Tl^{203}	24.33	29.52	0.187	0.571	1.5960	1/2	
Tl^{205}	24.57	70.48	0.192	0.577	1.6114	1/2	
Pb^{207}	8.899	21.11	9.13×10^{-3}	0.209	0.5837	1/2	
Bi^{209}	6.842	100.	0.137	5.30	4.0389	9/2	−0.4
U^{235}*	~20	0.71	1.0	5.0	6 ± 2.5	5/2	
Np^{237}*	6.1		2.9×10^{-3}	0.14	0.4	5/2	
Pu^{239}*	4.3		1.2×10^{-2}	1.2	1.4	1/2	
Pu^{241}*			2.85×10^{8}	658		5/2	
Free electron	27,994				−1836	1/2	

† Reproduced by permission of Varian Associates.

485

TRANSITIONS DUE TO RANDOM FIELDS

Here we give the quantum-mechanical theory of the transition probability between two states due to a perturbing field fluctuating in a random
stochastic manner. This is required in connection with the theory of the
various processes leading to spin-lattice relaxation described in Chap. 9.
Suppose the Hamiltonian determining the motion is

$$\mathfrak{IC}_0 + \mathfrak{IC}'(t) \tag{B-1}$$

where $\mathfrak{IC}'(t)$ is the random perturbation. Then we may calculate the
transition probability between two eigenstates of $\mathfrak{IC}_0$ (states 1 and 2) as
follows: The probability of the system having made a transition from 1 to
2 in time T is

$$P(1,2) = \hbar^{-2} \left| \int_0^T e^{i(E_2 - E_1)t'/\hbar}[2|\mathfrak{IC}'(t')|1] \, dt' \right|^2 \tag{B-2}$$

where E_1 and E_2 are the energies of the two states (eigenvalues of $\mathfrak{IC}_0$)
and $[2|\mathfrak{IC}'(t)|1]$ is the matrix element of the perturbing Hamiltonian
between the stationary-state wave functions. Since $\mathfrak{IC}'(t)$ is a function of
time, this matrix element will fluctuate, and the integral appearing in
(B-2) is effectively picking out the appropriate Fourier component of
these fluctuations for the transition.

To simplify the notation, we shall write

$$\omega = \frac{E_2 - E_1}{\hbar} \tag{B-3}$$

for the angular frequency of the transition. Further, we shall suppose
that the mean value (averaged over time) of the matrix element $[2|\mathfrak{IC}'(t)|1]$
is zero and write

$$[2|\mathfrak{IC}'(t)|1] = [|\overline{(2|\mathfrak{IC}'|1)|^2}]^{1/2}u(t) \tag{B-4}$$

where $u(t)$ is the reduced random function with mean-square modulus
value unity. The transition probability $P(1,2)$ can then be written

$$P(1,2) = \hbar^{-2}\overline{|(2|\mathfrak{IC}'|1)|^2} \int_0^T \int_0^T e^{i\omega(t'-t'')}u^*(t'')u(t') \, dt' \, dt'' \tag{B-5}$$

486

The next step is to average $P(1,2)$ over many realizations of the random function $u(t')$. The average of $u^*(t'')u(t')$ taken in this way is the *autocorrelation* function of the fluctuating matrix element $[2|\mathfrak{IC}'(t)|1]$. It will be a function only of the difference $t'' - t'$ and will be written $\rho(t'' - t')$. Then, putting $t'' = t' + t$ and treating t' and t as new variables, the mean probability takes the form

$$\overline{P(1,2)} = \hbar^{-2}\overline{|(2|\mathfrak{IC}'|1)|^2} \int_0^T \left[\int_{-t'}^{T-t'} e^{i\omega t}\rho(t)\, dt \right] dt' \qquad \text{(B-6)}$$

If T is long enough, this is proportional to T and we have the transition probability per unit time

$$P_{1\to2} = \frac{\overline{P(1,2)}}{T} = \hbar^{-2}\overline{|(2|\mathfrak{IC}'|1)|^2} \int_{-\infty}^{\infty} e^{i\omega t}\rho(t)\, dt \qquad \text{(B-7)}$$

This is the required general formula.

If it is assumed that the fluctuations of $\mathfrak{IC}'(t)$ are such that the auto-correlation function $\rho(t)$ decays exponentially, the integration can be carried out. This type of autocorrelation function follows from the assumptions made in the theory of Brownian motion. We may then write

$$\rho(t) = e^{-t/\tau_c} \qquad \text{(B-8)}$$

where τ_c is a *correlation time* characteristic of the fluctuations of $\mathfrak{IC}'(t)$. Substituting in (B-7), we obtain for the transition probability per unit time

$$P_{1\to2} = \hbar^{-2}\overline{|(2|\mathfrak{IC}'|1)|^2} \frac{2\tau_c}{1 + \omega^2\tau_c^2} \qquad \text{(B-9)}$$

Regarded as a function of the correlation time τ_c, this has a maximum when $\tau_c = \omega^{-1}$.

VOLUME DIAMAGNETIC SUSCEPTIBILITIES OF SOME CHEMICAL COMPOUNDS*

Compound	Volume susceptibility $-\chi_v \times 10^6$	Compound	Volume susceptibility $-\chi_v \times 10^6$
Acetaldehyde	0.393	Ethyl ether	0.547
Acetic acid	0.552	Ethyl formate	0.537
Acetone	0.460	Ethylene, 1,2-dibromo-	0.877
Aniline	0.707	Ethylene, 1,2-dichloro-	0.664
Benzaldehyde	0.602	Ethylene, 1,1-diphenyl-	0.669
Benzene	0.626	Formamide	0.551
Benzene, bromo-	0.771	Formic acid	0.530
Benzene, chloro-	0.707	Glycerol	0.678
Benzene, fluoro-	0.623	Glycol	0.696
Benzene, iodo-	0.863	n-Hexane	0.586
Benzene, nitro-	0.598	Isobutyl alcohol	0.652
Benzonitrile	0.658	Isobutylamine	0.620
Benzyl alcohol	0.741	Isobutyric acid	0.613
Benzyl chloride	0.767	Methane (liquid at $-164°C$)	1.037
Bromoform	0.913	Methyl acetate	0.547
n-Butyl alcohol	0.602	Methyl alcohol	0.515
t-Butyl alcohol	0.631	Methyl bromide	1.044
Butyraldehyde	0.519	Methyl formate	0.505
n-Butyric acid	0.606	Methyl iodide	0.918
Carbon disulfide	0.681	Methylene bromide	0.946
Carbon tetrachloride	0.684	Methylene chloride	0.733
Chloroform	0.735	Methylene iodide	1.160
Cyclohexane	0.631	Nitric acid	0.701
Cyclohexanone	0.614	Piperidine	0.651
Cyclohexene	0.576	n-Propyl alcohol	0.616
Diethylamine	0.594	Pyridine	0.612
Dimethyl sulfate	0.657	Quinoline	0.725
Dioxane	0.589	p-Quinone	0.503
Ethane, bromo-	0.699	Styrene	0.594
Ethane, 1,2-dibromo-	0.916	Sulfuric acid	0.808
Ethane, 1,1-dichloro-	0.681	Toluene	0.631
Ethane, 1,2-dichloro-	0.757	Water	0.721
Ethyl acetate	0.547	m-Xylene	0.642
Ethyl alcohol	0.594	o-Xylene	0.579

* Data derived from "International Critical Tables," vol. 6, McGraw-Hill Book Company, Inc., New York, 1929, for liquids at 20°C.

NAME INDEX

SUBJECT INDEX

Absorption signal, 31
  integrated intensity of, 39, 458
    measurement of, 458
  peak voltage of, 39
    measurement of, 458
Acepleiadylene, 193
Acetaldehyde, 276, 307
Acetic acid, 91, 207, 307, 309, 316, 416, 439
Acetone, 91, 307, 316, 423
Acetonitrile, 91, 276
Acetophenone, 276
Acetylacetone, 433, 440
Acetylene, 90, 163, 179, 193, 247, 403
Activation energy, for fluorine exchange,
  339, 341
  for internal rotation, 367, 368, 376
  for proton exchange, 421
Aldoximes, 374
Alkaloids, 280
Alkyl nitrites, 371
Amides, 366
Ammonia, 90, 101, 180, 196, 227, 313,
  403, 452
Ammonium hydroxide, 313
Ammonium ion, 101, 313, 452
Analysis of NMR spectra, 103
  first-order, 91, 115, 116, 131
  moment method of, 156
  notation, 98
  perturbation method of, 151
  rules for, 91, 113
    type AB, 111, 119
      AB_2, 123
      AB_3, 128
      ABC, 131
      ABX, 132
      A_2B_2, 138, 142
      A_2B_3, 154
      A_2X_2, 140
  (*See also* Quantitative analysis by
    NMR)
Anilines, 258, 259
Anisotropy, of diamagnetic susceptibility,
  13, 19
  of nuclear screening, 167

Anisotropy, of nuclear screening, effect
  of neighboring atoms, 176
Anthracene, 248
Antimony pentafluoride, 318, 341
Aqueous electrolytes (*see* Electrolytes)
Azulene, 193, 254, 431

Benzaldehyde, 259
Benzene, 89, 90, 182, 193, 196, 207, 248,
  306, 309, 425, 428
Benzoic acid, 259
Benzotrifluoride, 424
Bloch equations, 31
  for nuclear exchange, 219
  for rotating axes, 34
  solution of, 35
  for transient effects, 43
Bloch susceptibilities, 36
Boron hydrides, 196, 298
Boron (B^{11}) resonance measurements, 298
  spin coupling constants (table), 305
Boron trifluoride, 318, 344
Bridge method, the, 52
Bromine (Br^{79}, Br^{81}) resonance measure-
  ments, 361
Bromobenzenes, 259
Bromoethanes, 149, 380
Bromoform, 196, 279, 306, 311, 423
Bulk susceptibility corrections, 80
  application of, 81
  for cylinders, 81
Butanes, 235, 236
Butenes, 241, 366

Carbon disulfide, 91, 307
Carbon (C^{13}) resonance measurements,
  307
  chemical shifts (table), 306
  spin coupling constants (table), 306
Carbon tetrachloride, 91, 306
Carbon tetrafluoride, 91, 306, 318
Carboxylic acids, 285, 415
Cesium (Cs^{133}) resonance measurements,
  362